Introduction to

MECHANICS, MATTER, AND WAVES

Introduction to
MECHANICS,
MATTER, AND WAVES

by

UNO INGARD

and

WILLIAM L. KRAUSHAAR

Department of Physics
Massachusetts Institute of Technology

ADDISON-WESLEY PUBLISHING COMPANY, INC.

READING, MASSACHUSETTS, U.S.A.

LONDON, ENGLAND

PREFACE

This book has grown out of the authors' experience in teaching one year of a two-year sequence of courses in general physics at the Massachusetts Institute of Technology. More material than we have covered in any one year has been included, and it is anticipated that the book may find some use as a text for a second course in mechanics and the related subjects.

Mechanics can be and frequently is taught as a highly deductive subject. The foundations laid down by Galileo and Newton 300 years ago can be taken as postulates and the subject can be developed logically from there into a concise mathematical scheme. A presentation of this kind, although valuable and essential at some point in a student's education, tends to obscure the importance of experiments and can give the beginning student a distorted picture of physics as it really is. A totally analytic approach often overemphasizes the "given the forces—find the motion" situation at the expense of the "given the motion or behavior— what are the model and forces from which the phenomena can be understood" type of situation. We have in the present approach emphasized the study of interactions through observations of motion and have emphasized further that mechanics deals with motion as influenced by *all* the different types of interactions in nature: electric, magnetic, nuclear, etc. as well as the traditional contact, spring, and gravitational forces.

We are led naturally to first investigate two-body collisions* and so can begin the course with inertial mass, momentum and its conservation, and center-of-mass motion—all fundamental and interesting aspects of the physics of motion which require no calculus. The concept of force then emerges as the rate of momentum transfer from one body to another during an interaction and, by this time, the calculus course which the students take concurrently is well into differentiation.

The conservation laws—conservation of mass, momentum, energy, and angular momentum—have been given more than the usual emphasis. In

---

* The apparatus for the crucial collision experiments as described in the text is relatively simple, and we have found that *quantitative* lecture experiments are well worth the effort and class time expended. Stroboscopic flash pictures have been taken with a Land camera, developed, and then projected and analyzed in front of the students.

vii

fact, collision experiments and momentum conservation not only serve as the starting point but as a central theme through much of the book.

Chapters 5, 8, 10, 12, and 13 discuss, as their titles indicate, special important examples of forces and motion, and have been chosen and placed so as to illustrate the basic concepts as they are developed. Chapter 8, for example, which is on oscillations, follows directly the introduction of potential energy, and Chapter 10 which is on orbits in the gravitational field and alpha-particle scattering follows the introductory chapter on angular momentum. The discussion of planetary motion and the formulation of the universal law of gravitation from Kepler's laws are quite thorough.

The chapter on moving coordinate systems and inertial forces serves both as a summary and as a re-examination of the discussion of the basic laws of motion in the first part of the book. Here we have brought out the important role that the coordinate system plays in the description of motion, and the distinction between interaction forces and inertial forces is emphasized. There *is* a force tending to push passengers toward the rear of an accelerating car, and there *is* such a thing as a centrifugal force. We feel the time is well spent in having a student see why and from what viewpoint his preconceived notions are right.

The transition from the study of the gross motion of bodies to the internal motion in matter and the associated macroscopic properties of matter is accomplished in a chapter on the temperature concept and thermal interactions and a chapter on the elementary theory of the atomic structure of matter. The following chapters on kinetic theory, thermodynamics, and properties of matter have been woven together, and the atomic-molecular interpretation of concepts such as internal energy and entropy and properties of matter have been kept in the foreground.

The discussion of the kinetic theory of gases is comparatively extensive both in terms of basic concepts and discussion of experiments. In the analysis of specific heat the failure of the classical theory is emphasized and a qualitative quantum-mechanical interpretation of experimental results is given.

The role of intermolecular forces in the interpretation of the equation of state of real gases is studied in some detail, together with molecular interpretations of other gross mechanical properties of gases and liquids.

The mechanics of deformable bodies and waves is introduced through a study of what happens when a deformable body is given an impulse by an external force. Through a combination of experiments and application of conservation of momentum we obtain quickly the behavior of wave pulses, their wavespeed and energy content, and examples are given involving both transverse and longitudinal waves in different media. From the principle of superposition, waves of arbitrary shape are then constructed and the properties of harmonic waves are studied. Similarly, the problem of the reflection of waves at the interface between two elastic media is first solved for a wave pulse by application of the conservation laws.

The authors wish to acknowledge with thanks the helpful criticism of many of their students and colleagues. Our wives, Doris Ingard and Margaret Kraushaar, have contributed to the book and its completion in many ways, including heroic displays of patience.

U.I.
W.K.

June 1960

CONTENTS

vitational, electromagnetic, and nuclear forces are perhaps the most
ar interaction forces, and a great variety of experimental techniques
een developed for their study. In the case of gravitational inter-
the sky has been the best laboratory, and the motion of the planets
the sun has provided the best clue to the basic properties of this
of interaction. The study of electromagnetic interactions, on the
hand, can be carried out in the laboratory with relatively simple
mental arrangements. However, as we probe into the forces between
rticles in the nucleus of an atom, experimental techniques and ap-
s of great complexity (and size) are required, as exemplified by the
nergy accelerators in which particles are hurled against each other
eds which often are close to the speed of light.
problem of interaction forces is considered solved when laws of
(or preferably a single law of motion) can be formulated which
plain the experimental observations and from which the outcome of
periments can be predicted. It is clear that such a law must involve
made) concepts which cannot be defined or explained but must be
ed as basic building blocks in the theory. Such quantities and con-
re, for example, length, time, and electric charge, about which ques-
ke "what is time," "what is length," and "what is electric charge"
answerable in terms of more fundamental quantities.
s matter, or matter in bulk, we now know is made up of atoms and
les. The basic problem here is to try to determine the bulk proper-
matter in terms of the fundamental forces between the atoms and
les. For example: How can the thermal expansion of a body be
ed and calculated in terms of the intermolecular forces? How are
ermolecular forces related to the speed of sound in matter? What is
roscopic nature of the electrical resistance of a body and what prop-
f the molecules and their arrangement make the difference between
rical conductor and an insulator? There is an endless number of
ns of this type which we wish to answer and understand in terms
cular motion and forces. Although great advances have been made
field in the past few decades, our understanding of matter is far
mplete. Therefore in many cases one has to be satisfied with
nenological" descriptions of the behavior of matter in bulk. These
ions, which involve such concepts as electrical resistance, modulus
city, thermal conductivity, reflectivity, etc., are of great practical
nce in engineering applications.
cs is very much concerned with motion. Motion is evident all
s. We move, airplanes move, trees move, clouds move, waves in
ove. But these motions are often complicated and, as we shall see
y, one of our first tasks in physics is to explore the simple motion
e bodies. Then we shall investigate the manner in which the

CONTENTS

CHAPTER 1

INTRODUCTION

Summary. Physics is vitally concerned wit
causes. In this chapter some of the early ideas
development of physics are discussed. There f
the basic concepts of length and time and
measurement, and a brief discussion of the mat
tion of motion.

1–1 The scope of physics. The scope of physic
so broad, in fact, that we cannot say precisely w
If we regard geology as the study of the planet
study of life, we must regard physics as somethin
ter, motion, and energy. But this is not very hel
daries of physics, because matter, motion, and
little. What in all of science and technology is
cerned with one or more of these three very gen

The very early investigators of nature were ca
and they were concerned with such diverse mat
heavenly bodies, navigation, projectile motion
matter and space, strength of construction ma
veying, respiration of animal and plant life, and
ogy. Natural philosophy, in other words, was
and it included the applied aspects as well as
about life, matter, and motion and its causes.

Progress in science, if measured in discoverie
ideas, became marked during and after the 17t
philosophers tended to specialize and the vari
biology, chemistry, physics, meteorology, as
being. As specific aspects of applied science be
and the number of specialists in these fields incr
were established. But physics, astronomy,
tained positions that corresponded most closely
phy. These are the sciences upon which the ot
ing applications are based.

Present-day physicists are concerned with tv
lems. The first type, which might be called
concerns the nature of the interactions or for
constituents of matter. The second type con
matter in bulk.

1

2

Gr
famil
has b
action
about
type
other
experi
the p
parat
high-e
at spe

The
motio
can ex
new ex
(man-
accept
cepts
tions l
are no

Gros
molecu
ties of
molecu
explain
the int
the mi
erties o
an elec
questio
of mole
in this
from c
"phenol
descript
of elasti
importa

Physi
about u
water m
presentl
of simp

motions of bodies change—how the presence of one body may affect the motion of another. There is also "hidden" motion. Upon closer examination we shall find that even if a body as a whole is at rest, its constituents are in constant (thermal) motion. The molecules in a gas fly back and forth and collide with one another and with the surrounding walls, and the molecules in a solid vibrate about their equilibrium positions. On an even smaller scale we find "motion" of the electrons in an atom and of neutrons and protons in the nucleus. In this sense it can freely be said that the world is "rest-less,"* and it is therefore natural that the study of physics should start with the study of motion. Most properties of matter can be related to motion, at least on an atomic or subatomic scale. Heat and temperature can be directly described in terms of molecular motion, and electromagnetic waves (radio, heat, and light waves, and x-rays and γ-rays) can be related to the motion of charged particles. Traditionally, the study of motion and its causes has come to be called "mechanics"; other branches of physics are electromagnetism, optics, atomic physics, nuclear physics, etc. All these aspects of physics are concerned with motion too, but what sets mechanics apart from the rest is that mechanics is concerned with motion and its causes *per se*, and with the formulation of general laws and properties of motion that are independent of the type of inter-action (gravitational, electromagnetic, nuclear, etc.) involved.

1–2 Motion: brief historical introduction. The ideas about the motion of bodies that come naturally to a casual observer are for the most part the same as the views recorded by Aristotle (384–322 B.C.). Stripped of the philosophical system of which they were a part, the Aristotelian views of motion were as follows: All accessible matter is composed of Earth, Water, Fire, and Air, and these four elements have natural states—Fire and Air above Earth and Water. From this it follows that smoke and steam rise, and stones and water fall. Since big objects contain more Earth than small objects, big objects fall faster than small ones. The time of free fall is inversely proportional to weight. The natural state of bodies is one of rest, so it is necessary to do something to a body to make it move or to keep it moving. The heavenly bodies are not within the scheme and are not subject to the ordinary laws of physics. They, including the sun and the moon, revolve about the earth in circular paths, and the earth does not move.

These are not unreasonable ideas. The "deductions" and statements are in accord with qualitative observation. It should be pointed out that the Aristotelian views of motion were a part of a much larger whole—a

---

* For a lucid survey of physics, see Max Born, *The Restless Universe*, Dover Publications, Inc., New York, 1951.

philosophy which engulfed religion as well as nature, and in which the completeness, beauty, and symmetry of the philosophy itself took precedence over "minor" discrepancies.

The authority of the Aristotelian doctrine became firmly established and was not seriously questioned for many centuries. There were some grumblings, to be sure, but not until the European Renaissance did anyone offer contrary arguments and compelling contrary evidence. One point of controversy concerned celestial motion, the apparent motion of the sun, moon, planets, and stars; another concerned the motion of bodies on the earth.

Celestial motion. Less than a century after Aristotle, Aristarchus put forth the suggestion that the stars were fixed and that the earth and planets rotated about the sun. There was apparently no general acceptance of his idea. It did offer a reasonable explanation for the variations in the brightness of the planets (the earth-planet distances would of course vary) but it seemed to have no other advantage over the Aristotelian geocentric view. According to the heliocentric view, there should be an annual parallax, i.e., a variation in the apparent position of a star as the earth circled the sun. This parallax went unobserved, and the heliocentric idea found little favor among the astronomers of the time, especially since it contradicted Aristotle's teachings.

The geocentric view was greatly refined by Ptolemy (70–147 A.D.). By this time astronomical observations of the planets, sun, moon, and fixed stars were sufficiently accurate and complete to indicate that not all celestial objects could be circling the earth in perfectly circular earth-centered paths. The rigid geocentric assumptions were therefore relaxed somewhat. The earth was kept at rest at the center of the celestial sphere and the sun, moon, planets, and stars still moved around the earth. The motions, however, were not along perfectly circular earth-centered paths. Ptolemy found it necessary to invoke an increasingly complicated set of additional assumptions. First there were epicycles, shown in Fig. 1–2. These were needed to account for the retrograde motion or apparent reversals in the paths of planets. Then the earth was placed slightly off the center of rotation, as shown in Fig. 1–3. This was needed to explain the observed changes in the brightness of planets. Finally, it was found necessary to assume that while the point P, shown in Figs. 1–2 and 1–3, moved in a circular path about some point O (not the earth), it moved with a varying angular velocity about that point. The angular velocity was constant about some other point in space, say A in Fig. 1–3. With this elaborate mechanism, Ptolemy successfully explained most of the features of celestial motion. It was a gigantic and skillful accomplishment, and for the first time the positions of celestial bodies could be predicted in advance with reasonable accuracy.

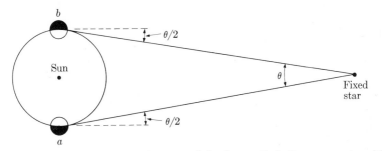

Fig. 1–1. As the earth moves from a to b (in six months), the apparent position of the fixed star on the celestial sphere changes. The angle θ depends upon how far the star is from the solar system.

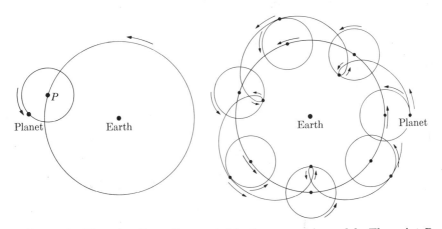

Fig. 1–2. The epicyclic motion needed in the geocentric model. The point P moves with uniform angular velocity about the earth, and the planet moves with uniform angular velocity about P.

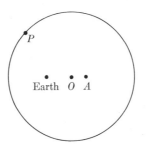

Fig. 1–3. The point P rotates about O with uniform angular velocity, but the earth is not at O.

The Ptolemaic geocentric system survived for about 1400 years. Even then it did not die suddenly or peacefully. In fact, the geocentric system is still used for some navigational purposes, and we still speak of the rising and setting of the various celestial bodies. The idea of a heliocentric system was revived by Nicolaus Copernicus (1473–1543). Copernicus was evidently disturbed by the complexities of the Ptolemaic system and found the nonuniform rotations about the center (O in Fig. 1–3) particularly distasteful. The heliocentric system which Copernicus put forth was similar to that of Aristarchus, but the Copernican scheme was quantitative. Not only were the motions of the planets and the earth about the sun relatively simple, but also the known planets were placed in their correct relative positions and the periods of rotation about the sun were specified. Copernicus pointed out that the planets farther from the sun had longer periods than those close to the sun. So far as parallax was concerned, Copernicus simply stated that it must be that the fixed stars were too far away for the effect to be measurable.

The Copernican system was welcomed by almost no one. The geocentric system was established doctrine both in religion and in natural philosophy. The distances necessary to explain the lack of parallax of the fixed stars were considered absurd. Both the geocentric and heliocentric systems explained the astronomical observations, and while the heliocentric system offered some desirable simplicity, its acceptance would have necessitated the heretical assumption that ours was not an earth-centered universe.

The next important development in the heliocentric *vs.* geocentric controversy emerged from the work of Galileo Galilei (1564–1642). His accomplishments and contributions were many and we shall hear more of him in the next section. He realized that insofar as pure description was concerned, the heliocentric and geocentric systems were equivalent and the question was one of choosing a frame of reference (coordinate system). But because of its simplicity, and because of his own telescopic observations (he evidently was the first man to observe the sky with a telescope), he held to the Copernican heliocentric system with considerable enthusiasm. Among the evidences in its favor which Galileo offered were the discovery of the phases of the planet Venus and the discovery of four of the moons of Jupiter. These moons, he found, moved around Jupiter in just the way he supposed the planets must move around the sun. Further, the moons farthest from Jupiter had the longest periods. To Galileo, his observations of Jupiter and her moons were equivalent to the direct observation of a small solar system and the correctness of the Copernican view was obvious. To most of his contemporaries, on the other hand, the geocentric system was obviously correct and not even a topic for discussion.

Galileo's views and the evidence he offered brought him into direct conflict with church dogma. His *Dialogue Concerning the Two Chief World*

Systems finally brought him before the Inquisition. In 1631 he was questioned, made to sign a renunciation of his pro-Copernican views, and put under technical imprisonment* for the remaining eleven years of his life.

The development of the views of celestial motion was a truly international endeavor. Aristotle and Aristarchus were Greek. Ptolemy's work in astronomy and mathematics was done in Alexandria. Copernicus was Polish, but studied in Italy, and Galileo was Italian. The next three important figures we shall mention are Brahe, Kepler, and Newton. Brahe was Danish, Kepler was German, and Newton was English.

Tycho Brahe (1546–1601) was a superb astronomer. The astronomical data available before his time were not particularly reliable and were certainly not very precise. Tycho constructed a new observatory at Copenhagen, and had massive precise observation equipment built. Galileo's astronomical telescope had not yet been developed, and all of Tycho's observations were made with the unaided eye. His angle measurements were accurate to less than half a minute of arc. One of Tycho's purposes was to find and measure the parallax of the fixed stars. In this he did not succeed, and evidently believing that there was no parallax, he developed a novel geocentric system of his own. In Tycho's system the earth was stationary. Mercury and Venus circled the sun, and the sun in turn circled the earth. Tycho's significant contribution, however, was not his geocentric system but the amazingly accurate astronomical data which he left to his successor, Johannes Kepler.

Johannes Kepler (1571–1630), a one-time student of Tycho, was a convinced Copernican. He was somehow certain that amid all the complexity there was an underlying simplicity that could be expressed in the terms of geometry and mathematics. Tycho's data, it should be emphasized, were left in a relatively undigested state. There were voluminous records of the time of passage and angular positions of the various members of the solar system, but for their interpretation all these data had to be reduced. Kepler attempted to fit the Copernican system to Tycho's data, and found, particularly in the case of Mars, that assumptions fully as complicated as those used in the Ptolemaic system were necessary. Later he was led to drop the assumption of circular motion and found that the planets moved in elliptic paths about the sun. Each ellipse had one of its foci at the sun. This is the first of what have come to be known as Kepler's three laws of planetary motion.

---

* The technical imprisonment involved his seclusion and the suppression of his works. He was not actually confined to prison. A somewhat earlier proponent of the Copernican system, Giordano Bruno (1548–1600), was brought before the Inquisition and eventually burned at the stake.

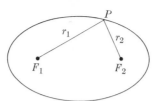

FIG. 1-4. An ellipse. The distance $r_1 + r_2$ is constant for any point P on the curve.

An ellipse is one of the conic sections, and has the property that the distance from one of the focal points to any point on the curve plus the distance from the other focal point to that same point on the curve is constant. When the focal points are widely separated, the curve is elongated. As the focal points move close together, the curve approaches a circle.

The second of Kepler's experimental laws states that as a planet moves around the sun, the area swept out per unit time by the sun-planet line remains constant. This is often referred to as the law of equal areas.

The third law is a quantitative statement of a fact noticed by Copernicus and discussed by Galileo in connection with the motion of Jupiter's moons. Those planets farthest from the sun have the longest periods. Kepler's quantitative third law states that

$$T^2 = CR^3, \qquad (1\text{--}1)$$

where T is the time for one revolution about the sun (one year for the earth) and R is the mean distance from the sun to the planet. The constant C is the same for all planets.

Here indeed was simplicity at last. Kepler had successfully found a concise mathematical description of the motion of the planets. His accomplishment was remarkable for several reasons. First and most obvious

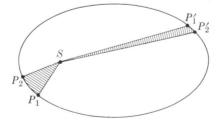

FIG. 1-5. As the planet moves about the sun, the line which connects the sun and the planet sweeps out equal areas in equal times. In the figure, the area of SP_1P_2 is the same as the area $SP_1'P_2'$, and so the time taken for the planet to move from P_1 to P_2 must have been the same as the time taken for it to move from P_1' to P_2'.

was the pure enormity of the task. Kepler was a skilled mathematician, yet he spent 17 years in the work that culminated in his three laws. Second, Kepler's work, together with that of Galileo, marked the beginning of the era of successful applications of mathematical reasoning in the description and interpretation of nature. Third, Kepler's concise and beautiful mathematical description of planetary motion was the basis for the even more spectacular developments of Isaac Newton, who, nearly 80 years after Kepler, formulated the general laws of mechanics.

Isaac Newton (1642–1727) was a natural philosopher in the very broadest sense. He made profound contributions to mathematics, mechanics, heat, astronomy, and optics, and his work in any one of these fields would have established him as one of the world's greatest thinkers. While a student at Cambridge University, Newton discovered the binomial theorem, the methods of infinite series, and "fluxions" or the differential calculus. By the time he was 24 he had formulated the first clear definition of force and had shown that a single set of assumptions (his laws of motion and his universal law of gravitation) explained and summarized planetary motion as well as the motion of bodies on the surface of the earth. Elementary mechanics, the mechanics presented in this book for example, is for the most part the subject as left by Newton. Newton was a complicated person. He was frail and modest, a devoted student and author of theology, and yet a bold intellectual adventurer frequently in heated debate with his contemporaries over priority of invention and discovery.

Motion on the earth's surface. Galileo Galilei was born in Pisa in 1564. He was evidently an extraordinarily gifted person. His father, Vincenzio Galilei, arranged for him to study medicine and this he did for a while, but his attention soon turned to mathematics and science. As has been the case with most of the world's especially creative persons, his genius became evident early in life and in 1592, at age 28, he was appointed to the chair of mathematics at Padua. He had already been a lecturer at Pisa for two years but he was not particularly tactful in the expression of his views and this finally necessitated his departure. At Padua, however, his lectures were popular, and his fame grew. By 1610 his work had become known throughout Europe and he was invited to return to Pisa as Mathematician and Philosopher to the Grand Duke of Tuscany. A year or so later Galileo's difficulties, which arose from his pro-Copernican views, started. The story of his life, his renunciation of his Copernican views, and his trial before the Inquisition make most interesting and informative reading and are highly recommended.*

---

* See, for example, J. J. Fahie, *Galileo: His Life and Work*, James Pott and Co., New York, 1903.

Galileo's contributions to physics are delightfully presented in his two Dialogues, *Dialogues Concerning the Two Chief World Systems* (1630) and *Dialogues Concerning Two New Sciences* (1638). The Dialogues are written in the form of conversations among Simplicio, who represents the Aristotelian point of view; Salviati, who presents and discusses Galileo's points of view; and Sagredo, in whose home the three meet.

Recall now one of the Aristotelian views that we mentioned earlier. The natural state of bodies is at rest, so it is necessary to do something to a body to make it move or to keep it moving. This idea is completely reasonable. Even on the slickest ice a skidding object will eventually slow down and stop. If we want the object to keep moving, we must do something to it—blow on it, pull it, etc. Even a body moving on wheels on the best conceivable ball bearings would, if we did nothing to help keep it moving, eventually slow down and stop. The Aristotelian view of this matter was not wrong. It was, however, unproductive.

Galileo, on the other hand, adopted quite another point of view. Since it is an idealization, it is perhaps less obviously correct, but it was productive. It was a point of view from which a quantitative development of the subject could and did develop. Galileo said, in effect, that bodies at rest tend to stay at rest, bodies in motion tend to stay in motion, and something must be done to a body to change its state of motion. Let us see how he presented his case in *Dialogues Concerning the Two Chief World Systems.* * Salviati has been discussing with Simplicio the motion of a hard sphere on an inclined plane. Simplicio has been convinced that a sphere moving *up* the plane has its motion retarded, i.e., it slows down (decelerates), while a sphere moving down the plane has its motion increased (accelerates). Then Salviati continues:

Now tell me what would happen to the same movable body placed upon a surface with no slope upward or downward.

Simplicio: Here I must think a moment about my reply. There being no downward slope, there can be no natural tendency toward motion; and there being no upward slope, there can be no resistance to being moved, so there would be indifference between the propensity and the resistance to motion. Therefore it seems to me that it ought naturally to remain stable. But I forgot; it was not so very long ago that Sagredo gave me to understand that this is what would happen.

Salviati: I believe it would do so if one set the ball down firmly. But what would happen if it were given an impetus in any direction?

Simplicio: It must follow that it would move in that direction.

---

* From the translation by Stillman Drake, University of California Press, Berkeley and Los Angeles, 1953.

Salviati: But with what sort of movement? One continually accelerated, as on the downward plane, or increasingly retarded as on the upward one?

Simplicio: I cannot see any cause for acceleration or deceleration, there being no slope upward or downward.

Salviati: Exactly so. But if there is no cause for the ball's retardation, there ought to be still less for its coming to rest; so how far would you have the ball continue to move?

Simplicio: As far as the extension of the surface continued without rising or falling.

Salviati: Then if such a space were unbounded, the motion on it would likewise be boundless? That is, perpetual?

Simplicio: It seems so to me, if the movable body were of durable material.

Salviati: That is of course assumed, since we said that all external and accidental impediments were to be removed, and any fragility on the part of the moving body would in this case be one of the accidental impediments.

Here Galileo has made use of an idealized thought-experiment to make plausible his assertion that if all "external and accidental impediments were to be removed" a body moving along a horizontal plane would do so perpetually. He has not denied the fact that the conditions prescribed for his experiment are impossible to realize. Air resistance, friction, imperfections in the ball, a slight roughness of the plane, the finite size of the earth—all these things would in practice affect the motion of the ball. But Galileo's approach to the matter—the only approach upon which further developments have been successfully based—involved the reasonable (but not obvious) idea that the natural or uninfluenced state of motion of a body is the state in which the body moves with constant velocity. In short, something must be done to a body to cause a change in its velocity. This was the big idea, the break-through, in mechanics. Like most really good ideas in physics, *post hoc* it seems, and is, very simple. It is usually referred to as the first of Newton's three laws of motion.

In *Dialogues Concerning Two New Sciences*, Galileo discussed many other aspects of motion. Particularly interesting is the presentation of his ideas and experiments on falling bodies and projectile motion. His arguments and deductions are clever and tightly knit. His experiments are ingeniously simple, being designed to emphasize as vividly as possible the point he wishes to make. Let us see how Galileo presented his case regarding the motion of falling bodies of different weights.* Recall Aristotle's claim that the time of free fall is inversely proportional to weight.

---

* From the translation by Henry Crew and Alfonso de Salvio. Dover Publications, Inc., New York, 1952.

Salviati: . . . I greatly doubt that Aristotle ever tested by experiment whether it be true that two stones, one weighing ten times as much as the other, if allowed to fall, at the same instant, from a height of, say, 100 cubits, would so differ in speed that when the heavier had reached the ground, the other would not have fallen more than 10 cubits.

Simplicio: His language would seem to indicate that he had tried the experiment, because he says: *We see the heavier;* now the word *see* shows that he had made the experiment.

Sagredo: But I, Simplicio, who have made the test can assure you that a cannon ball weighing one or two hundred pounds, or even more, will not reach the ground by as much as a span ahead of a musket ball weighing only half a pound, provided both are dropped from a height of 200 cubits.

Salviati: But, even without further experiment, it is possible to prove clearly, by means of a short and conclusive argument, that a heavier body does not move more rapidly than a lighter one provided both bodies are of the same material and in short such as those mentioned by Aristotle. But tell me, Simplicio, whether you admit that each falling body acquires a definite speed fixed by nature, a velocity which cannot be increased or diminished except by the use of force [violenza] or resistance.

Simplicio: There can be no doubt but that one and the same body moving in a single medium has a fixed velocity which is determined by nature and which cannot be increased except by the addition of momentum [impeto] or diminished except by some resistance which retards it.

Salviati: If then we take two bodies whose natural speeds are different, it is clear that on uniting the two, the more rapid one will be partly retarded by the slower, and the slower will be somewhat hastened by the swifter. Do you not agree with me in this opinion?

Simplicio: You are unquestionably right.

Salviati: But if this is true, and if a large stone moves with a speed of, say, eight while a smaller moves with a speed of four, then when they are united, the system will move with a speed less than eight; but the two stones when tied together make a stone larger than that which before moved with a speed of eight. Hence the heavier body moves with less speed than the lighter; an effect which is contrary to your supposition. Thus you see how, from your assumption that the heavier body moves more rapidly than the lighter one, I infer that the heavier body moves more slowly.*

After some further discussion, they continue:

Simplicio: Your discussion is really admirable; yet I do not find it easy to believe that a bird-shot falls as swiftly as a cannon ball.

Salviati: Why not say a grain of sand as rapidly as a grindstone? But, Simplicio, I trust you will not follow the example of many others who divert the discussion from its main intent and fasten upon some statement of mine which lacks a hair's-breadth of the truth and, under this hair, hide the fault of another which is as big as a ship's cable. Aristotle says that "an iron ball of one hundred pounds falling from a height of one hundred cubits reaches the

---

* Does this argument seem perfectly consistent to you?

ground before a one-pound ball has fallen a single cubit." I say that they arrive at the same time. You find, on making the experiment, that the larger outstrips the smaller by two finger-breadths, that is, when the larger has reached the ground, the other is short of it by two finger-breadths; now you would not hide behind these two fingers the ninety-nine cubits of Aristotle, nor would you mention my small error and at the same time pass over in silence his very large one.

. . . .

Simplicio: Perhaps the result would be different if the fall took place not from a few cubits but from some thousands of cubits.

Salviati: If this were what Aristotle meant you would burden him with another error which would amount to a falsehood; because, since there is no such sheer height available on earth, it is clear that Aristotle could not have made the experiment; yet he wishes to give us the impression of his having performed it when he speaks of such an effect as one which we see.

In further discussions, Galileo points out that bodies of different materials when dropped at the same time from the same height also reach the ground at the same (or very nearly the same) time. He correctly attributes the slight differences in the time of fall to differences in the drag of the air on bodies of different shapes and sizes, and asserts his belief that all bodies when dropped in vacuum would reach the bottom at the same time.

Galileo's contributions to mechanics cannot be adequately summarized concisely. He not only practiced the experimental approach in physics but also, together with Kepler, introduced and proved the usefulness of mathematical reasoning in the discussion of physical phenomena. He provided the strength and impetus for the final break from the Aristotelian authority. In a more technical sense, he provided the real basis for Newton's further developments, since it was Galileo who introduced the idea that pushes and pulls (forces) serve to change the state of motion of a body. It was Galileo to whom Newton referred when he said that if he (Newton) had accomplished more than other men it was because he rested on the shoulders of giants.

As we mentioned in the previous section, Isaac Newton brought celestial and local motion together and in one grand gesture showed that the same set of laws led to a correct description of both types of phenomena.

Newton and his contemporaries and predecessors were concerned for the most part with pushes and pulls of the "contact" and gravitational types. A body falls because of the pull of the earth (gravitational force), and when it hits the floor it stops because of a "contact" force. After Newton's time, during the 18th and 19th centuries, electrostatic and electromagnetic forces were investigated in detail. Coulomb and Cavendish were responsible for most of the developments in electrostatics, and Faraday and Henry contributed most to the developments in magnetism.

James Clerk Maxwell (1831–1879) brought magnetic and electrostatic phenomena together under one general theory, and from this theory emerged our understanding of electromagnetic waves and electromagnetic forces. During the 20th century our understanding of all these forces, gravitational, electromagnetic, and contact (ultimately interatomic), has increased, and of course nuclear forces are still under intensive study.

1–3 Length and time. Length and time are the basic ingredients in the discussion of motion. If we were to attempt to formulate an operational definition, i.e., a description of these quantities in terms of the method of measurement, we would find that there is nothing much more profound that we can say in principle than "length is the thing that we measure with a meter stick or an instrument based thereupon" and "time is the thing we measure with a clock." Further explanation involves a description of the properties of length-measuring devices and clocks. In the development of the (nonrelativistic) theory of motion we shall assume that these properties are those familiar from everyday experience. For example, we shall assume that lengths and times, as measured by observers who move relative to each other, are not influenced by the motion. This assumption is well established experimentally at the speeds encountered in everyday life. However, at speeds close to that of light, it turns out that a self-consistent description of experimental observations on motion is not possible on this basis. Instead, it must be assumed that measurements of length and time by observers in motion with respect to each other indeed depend on their motion. This subject, special relativity (Einstein), is very important in the study of the motion of atomic and subatomic particles, which often have speeds close to that of light.

Units. A measurement of length inherently involves a comparison with a standard chosen as a unit of length, and the unit may be divided into fractions of its length. Meter sticks, for example, are marked off in 1/100's (centimeters) and 1/1000's (millimeters). The primary unit of length (the meter) is the distance between two scratches on a platinum-iridium bar kept at Sèvres, France. The distance between these two scratches, which defines the meter, was chosen arbitrarily. Secondary standards have been carefully prepared and are available in many places throughout the world. The General Conference on Weights and Measures, an international body, has considered the possibility of defining the meter in terms of a certain number of wavelengths of the light of a particular atomic spectral line. The definition would still be arbitrary, but such a definition has the advantage that the primary standard of length would be independent of the environment and available to anyone who wished to set up the necessary apparatus.

The first basis for the time concept is our subjective experiences. Our pulse rate, our breathing rate, growth, aging—all these and, in addition, the passage of days and seasons, establish our notion of time. Before the 17th century and the invention of accurate timepieces,* the unit of time was based on the solar day, the solar day being effectively the time between two successive noons. It was found, however, that the length of the solar day varied, the variation being due to the fact that the earth travels about the sun in an elliptic path, and that the plane of the ellipse does not coincide with the plane of the earth's equator. The mean solar day, defined as the length of the solar day averaged over a year, was therefore adopted. [The second, of course, is $1/(24 \cdot 3600)$ of a day.] This time standard survived until recently, when it was found that the period of the earth's rotation, as reckoned from the apparent motion of the stars, varied by about 0.03 second a year. This variation, to be sure, is of no consequence in civil affairs, but it is much larger than the uncertainty in some laboratory "atomic clock" time measurements. It is interesting to note how far science has departed from the Aristotelian view, which no doubt would have claimed that there could be no more perfect timekeeper than the earth itself.

Measurement and range of time and length. Length and time and their methods of measurement as we know them from everyday experience are used in physics both on very small and very large-scale phenomena. We certainly cannot discuss here all the different types of measurements of length and time. Such a discussion would carry us through most of science and all of physics. Certainly "direct" measurements—measurements of length with steel tapes, meter sticks, or micrometers, and measurements of time with clocks and stopwatches—do not carry us far into the domains in which the measurements can be and are made. We must resort to indirect measurements.

Just below the range of micrometers (10^{-3} cm), microscopes, both optical and electron, make possible observation and measurement of microorganisms and the very large organic molecules. With optical microscopes these measurements have a lower limit of a few wavelengths of light, or about 10,000 A. (One angstrom unit, A, is 10^{-8} cm.) Electron microscopes, on the other hand, permit the study of details in the 100 A region, and measurements can be made to perhaps 10 A. Inorganic molecules are a few angstroms and atoms are about one angstrom in size. Nuclei, the heavy cores of atoms, are 10^{-12} or 10^{-13} cm in diameter.

Just as light has a wavelength, so also do the particles of which matter is made. The faster a particle moves, the smaller its wavelength be-

---

* For the fascinating story of the importance and development of good clocks for navigation, see "The Longitude" by Lloyd A. Brown in *The World of Mathematics*, Vol. 2, edited by J. R. Newman. Simon and Schuster, New York, 1956.

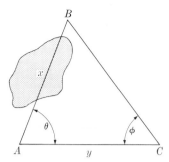

FIG. 1–6. The distance x, not measurable by direct means, can be found from the distance y and the angles θ and ϕ.

comes. The wavelengths of some particles, notably those accelerated in cyclotrons, synchrotrons, etc., are as small as 10^{-15} cm. The smallest particle wavelengths, 10^{-23} cm, are those of the most energetic cosmic-ray particles.

Triangulation is a familiar type of indirect measurement. Suppose we wish to know the distance x between points A and B, which, for some reason, is not accessible to direct measurement. Then, as shown in Fig. 1–6, the distance x can be determined if the two angles θ and ϕ and the distance y are known.

We have discussed the triangulation type of length or distance measurement before, in connection with the geocentric-heliocentric controversy. Not until 1838 was stellar parallax measured and the distance to a star found (indirectly) by triangulation. The star nearest the solar system is 4.3 light-years away, and has a parallax of less than one second of arc. Most of the stars and galaxies are far too distant for meaningful parallax measurements. As an example of even less direct measurements we shall discuss briefly one of the ways in which these huge distances are measured.

There exists a type of stars, known as the Cepheid variables, which have light intensities or brightnesses that oscillate in time. Typically, a Cepheid-variable star may appear bright, become dim, then become bright again with a period of, say, five days. Several of these special stars were discovered in the Smaller Magellanic Cloud, the galaxy nearest our galaxy, the Milky Way. Aside from angular position, two things about a Cepheid variable are readily measured, its apparent brightness (magnitude) and its period. If a diagram is made on which period is plotted against magnitude (or apparent brightness) and if each Cepheid star in the Smaller Magellanic Cloud is indicated by a point, we find that the points are not scattered at random on the diagram but lie along a smooth curve. This means that the period of a Cepheid-variable star depends somehow on its brightness. Now the brightness of a star depends upon the total light emitted and on how far away the star is. When diagrams for other galaxies are prepared, we find that the Cepheid-variable stars lie along smooth curves, but these curves are displaced from the one for the Smaller Magellanic Cloud. Hence if we assume that the total light emitted by a Cepheid-variable star of a given period is the same no matter what galaxy the star is in, the displacement of these curves gives us a relative measure of how far these other galaxies are from us. This is one of the ways that the immense distances in our universe are measured by astronomers. One can certainly point out possible sources of error in such an indirect measurement. Indeed, it is important that these possible sources of error be made explicit and kept in mind.

The diameter of the earth is $1.3 \cdot 10^7$ meters, while its orbit about the sun is $3 \cdot 10^{11}$ meters in diameter. The nearest star, alpha Centauri, is 4.3 light-years or about $4 \cdot 10^{16}$ meters away, and our galaxy is 100,000 light-years or 10^{21} meters in diameter. The Magellanic Clouds are a few galactic diameters away, and other galaxies are found in space as far as we can probe. At present this probing of distance is limited to about a billion light-years, or 10^{25} meters.

Time measurements, like those of length, extend many orders of magnitude to either side of everyday experience. Photographic techniques such as the multiflash photography we shall discuss later in this chapter are useful in timing subsequent events more than 10^{-4} second apart. In 10^{-4} second a bullet or sound wave travels a few centimeters and light and radio waves travel almost 20 miles. It takes 10^{-8} second for an excited atom to emit light, and about 10^{-9} second for the light to leave this page and reach your eyes. Some of the recently discovered particles of high-energy physics have average lifetimes of only 10^{-13} second, and it takes about 10^{-22} second for light to travel a nuclear diameter. We would be carried rather far afield were we to describe how some of these very short times are measured or estimated. Needless to say, the methods are indirect and only loosely connected with the familiar phenomena that suggested the time concept to us in the first place.

In the realm of long times, measurements are no less challenging and perhaps even less direct. Man as he exists today has occupied the earth for perhaps 100,000 years, a very small part of the estimated age of the earth (several billion years), and recorded history goes back only some 5000 years. The combined talents of people in all the sciences have contributed to the attempted reconstruction of the history of man, the earth, and the universe. When we look at a star, alpha Centauri for example, we see light that was emitted 4.3 years ago and so we are, in a sense, seeing history. And of course it follows that we have to wait 4.3 years to see light that was emitted today.

One sometimes sees the age of the universe referred to as about 10 billion years. What does this mean? As we have mentioned before in this section, galaxies have been observed all the way out to about a billion light-years away. Strangely, the general motion of these galaxies is such that they have velocities (directed away from us) proportional to their distances from us. This has been interpreted to mean that all galaxies are getting farther and farther from each other and that an observer in any galaxy would see the same general motion of other galaxies that we see. If we assume that all the galaxies we see have always existed, and if their velocities have always been proportional to their distances away, at one time they must all have been in a very condensed state and this condensed state must have existed about 10 billion years ago. This estimate is controversial and there are other interpretations of the data. Interestingly, the age of the earth as found from geological and radioactive evidence is also estimated to be several billion years.

1–4 Velocity and acceleration. In this section we shall review the quantities *velocity* and *acceleration* and shall take the opportunity to introduce the technique of multiflash photography for the study of motion.

Velocity. The object whose motion we wish to study is illuminated by a light that flashes at a regular rate. A camera, with its shutter left open, is focused on the object. The duration of the light flash is very short, so that if the object is not moving too fast each flash results in a single sharp image of the object on the photograph. Figure 1–7 is a multiflash photograph of a white billiard ball rolling along a smooth horizontal surface. From this photograph we can determine the position of the ball at each instant the light flashed. The data can be plotted on a graph, position x vs. time t. In the graph of Fig. 1–8 we have chosen the leftmost image of the ball to be at the point $x = 0$. The points lie along a straight line, and in drawing the line we have assumed that had there been more light flashes per second, the additional points would have fallen on this same straight line. In this particular case, the distance traveled is proportional to the elapsed time. The proportionality constant which tells us the distance traveled per unit time is called the velocity v, and we have

$$x = vt.$$

If we were to make a graph of the algebraic equation $y = bx$, we would obtain a straight line with slope b. If θ were the angle between the line and the x-axis, b and θ would be related according to the expression $b = \tan \theta$. Clearly, velocity is related to the slope of the x vs. t graph, for it appears in $x = vt$ just as b appears in $y = bx$. Only infrequently, however, does it happen that graphs are plotted with unit time and unit distances represented by equal lengths on the t- and x-axes. Therefore we cannot ordinarily say that v is $\tan \phi$, where ϕ is the angle between the line through the plotted points and the t-axis. Even so, we shall often refer to velocity as

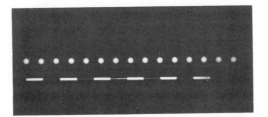

FIG. 1–7. Multiflash photograph of a billiard ball rolling to the right along a smooth horizontal surface. Note that the ball has moved equal distances between successive flashes. (The white stripes on the bar are 10 cm long.)

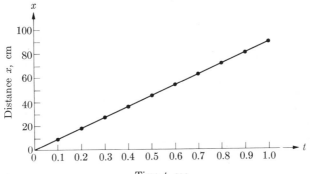

FIG. 1–8. Observed data, position x vs. time t. The velocity is constant.

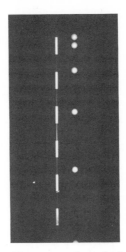

FIG. 1–9. Free fall. The object was released at the instant of the first light flash, and subsequent flashes were 0.1 sec apart.

the slope of the x vs. t graph, and by this we mean $v = \Delta x/\Delta t$, where Δx is the distance traveled during the time interval Δt.

Now let us use the multiflash technique to investigate the velocity of a freely falling body. In Fig. 1–9 the first flash occurred at the instant the ball was released, and subsequent flashes were 0.1 sec apart. Distances can be scaled from the figure, and the position *vs.* time graph is shown in Fig. 1–10. A smooth curve has been drawn through the experimental points. Clearly, the velocity increases with time, for the distance traveled in a given time, $\Delta t = 0.1$ sec, say, steadily increases. If we compute the velocity in accordance with $v = \Delta x/\Delta t = (x_2 - x_1)/(t_2 - t_1)$, we see that this must now be interpreted as the *average* velocity of the body between times t_1 and t_2, for the velocity is steadily changing. We shall therefore take $\Delta x/\Delta t$ as our definition of average velocity.*

$$\bar{v} = \frac{x_2 - x_1}{t_2 - t_1} = \frac{\Delta x}{\Delta t}. \qquad (1\text{--}2)$$

This average velocity $\bar{v}$ may be interpreted as the slope of the secant drawn through the two points (t_1, x_1) and (t_2, x_2), as indicated in Fig. 1–11(a). The x vs. t curve which represents the motion of any real body is always smooth. Therefore, if we let t_2 approach t_1 (that is, let the time interval, $\Delta t = t_2 - t_1$, approach zero) the secant referred to above will have a slope which approaches the slope of the tangent to the x vs. t curve at time t_1. The slope of the tangent to the x vs. t curve at a time t_1 we shall take as the instantaneous velocity at t_1:

$$v = \lim_{\Delta t=0} \frac{\Delta x}{\Delta t} = \frac{dx}{dt}, \qquad (1\text{--}3)$$

where, in the notation of calculus, dx/dt is the derivative of x with respect to time. The velocity not only can be found from the geometrical procedure described above, but also can be found analytically if x is known as an algebraic function of the time. However, for the present we shall make use of only the geometric interpretation of the derivative. Since we shall always consider Δt a positive quantity, the definitions (1–2) and (1–3) indicate that a positive velocity (i.e., a positive Δx) corresponds to motion in the direction of increasing x, and a negative velocity corresponds to motion in the direction of decreasing x. The magnitude of the velocity is called the *speed*. It indicates only how fast the body is moving, and says nothing about the direction.

Let us now return to the free-fall motion in Fig. 1–10. The position of the falling body is measured from the point of release and the corresponding

---

* Hereafter a bar over a quantity will indicate the time average of that quantity.

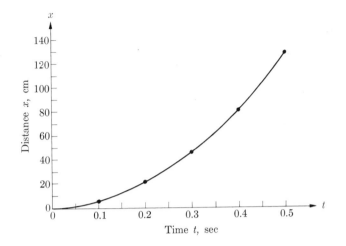

Fig. 1–10. Distance fallen x vs. time t for the free fall shown in Fig. 1–9.

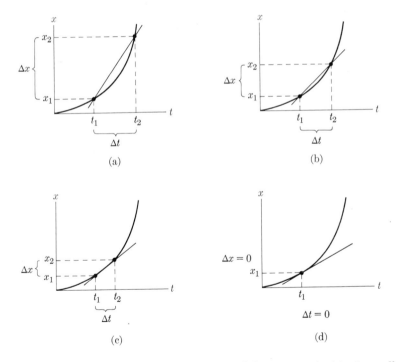

Fig. 1–11. The average velocity is the slope of the secant. As Δt gets smaller and smaller, the slope of the secant approaches the slope of the tangent.

x-coordinate increases *downward*. With this choice of the direction of x the velocity of the body is positive and, as we have just discussed, it increases steadily.

Acceleration. Just as velocity is a measure of how fast the position changes with time, acceleration is a measure of how fast the velocity changes with time, and just as velocity can be interpreted as the slope of the x vs. t curve, the acceleration can be interpreted as the slope of the v vs. t curve.

The velocity in the free-fall motion, determined from the slope of the x vs. t curve in Fig. 1–10, is plotted as a function of time in Fig. 1–12. We see that the velocity increases linearly with time, i.e., the acceleration a is constant, and we have

$$v = at.$$

In this case we find from the experimental results the value $a \approx 980$ cm/sec^2 or 9.8 m/sec^2. [The acceleration of gravity has been measured many ways and in many places. Its value varies with height above the earth's surface, and varies as well with location, being about 1/2 percent larger at the geographic poles than at the equator.] In general the slope of the v vs. t curve is not constant and we shall define the (instantaneous) acceleration at a time t_1 as the slope at that point. This slope can be approximated to any desired degree of accuracy by the ratio $\Delta v/\Delta t = (v_2 - v_1)/(t_2 - t_1)$ by taking Δt sufficiently small. The quantity

$$\bar{a} = \frac{v_2 - v_1}{t_2 - t_1} = \frac{\Delta v}{\Delta t} \qquad (1\text{–}4)$$

is called the *average* acceleration in the time interval Δt. The instantaneous acceleration, in complete analogy with the instantaneous velocity, is

$$a = \lim_{\Delta t = 0} \frac{\Delta v}{\Delta t} = \frac{dv}{dt}. \qquad (1\text{–}5)$$

Position vs. time. Suppose we have the v vs. t graph for a moving body. How can we find its position as a function of time? Let us look at a simple example first. In Fig. 1–13 the velocity is 10 m/sec for 5 sec and then 7 m/sec for 10 sec. How far has the object moved at the end of 15 sec? The distance traveled is the sum of 50 m (10 m/sec for 5 sec) plus 70 m (7 m/sec for 10 sec) or 120 m. The distance traveled is represented by the area under the velocity curve as shown in the figure. Actually, the distance traveled is proportional to this area. The constant of proportionality, of course, depends upon the scales of the v- and t-axes. In the future we shall always assume that this problem of scale factors has been considered when the area under a curve is used to represent a physical quantity.

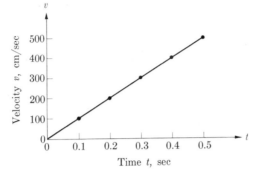

FIG. 1–12. Velocity as a function of time for free-fall motion. The velocity increases linearly with time.

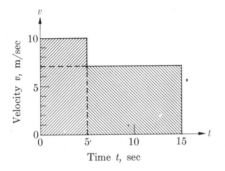

FIG. 1–13. Velocity *vs.* time graph. The total distance traveled is 120 m, and is represented by the crosshatched area.

The situation is entirely similar when the velocity changes continuously with time. Approximating the motion by a succession of constant-speed motions we again find that the distance traveled is represented by the area under the curve, as shown in Fig. 1–13. In Fig. 1–14(a) is illustrated the special case where the velocity increases uniformly from 0 to v in a time t. The average velocity is then $v/2$, and so the distance traveled is $vt/2$, or the area under the v vs. t line. Since in uniformly accelerated motion the velocity is simply $v = at$, the distance traveled is

$$x = \frac{vt}{2} = \tfrac{1}{2}at^2.$$

If a body has an initial velocity v_0 and moves thereafter with uniformly accelerated motion, its v vs. t curve might be as shown in Fig. 1–14, and given algebraically by

$$v = v_0 + at. \tag{1-6}$$

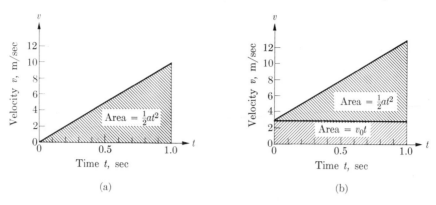

Fig. 1–14. In (a), the velocity increases uniformly from 0 to 10 m/sec in 1.0 sec. The acceleration is 10 m/sec² and the distance traveled is 5 m. In (b), the acceleration is the same as in (a), but the initial velocity is $v_0 = 3$ m/sec. The distance traveled is 8 m.

The distance traveled is again the product of the average velocity and the elapsed time (the area under the v vs. t curve):

$$x = v_0 t + \tfrac{1}{2} a t^2. \tag{1–7}$$

Frequently, in connection with falling bodies, it is convenient to use a position coordinate y which increases upward. Then the expressions we have developed for freely falling bodies, with $a = -g$, $y = y_0$ at $t = 0$, take the forms:

$$v = v_0 - gt, \qquad y = y_0 + v_0 t - \tfrac{1}{2} g t^2, \tag{1–8}$$

where velocities are now positive in the upward direction and g is the acceleration of gravity, nominally 9.8 m/sec² or 980 cm/sec². We shall present a more complete discussion of this motion in Chapter 5.

Vectors. Physical quantities such as mass, density, temperature, speed, etc., called *scalar* quantities, have one property in common: they require only one number for their specification. When we speak of the mass of a car, it is sufficient to say 1000 kgm, for example. A unique description of the velocity or displacement of a car, on the other hand, requires information not only of the magnitude of the velocity or of the displacement but also knowledge of the direction of travel. Quantities such as displacement and velocity which need both magnitude and direction, or more than one number, for their description are called *vectors*. Since the displacement vector is particularly easy to visualize we shall use it in discussing some of the basic properties of vectors. The results obtained for the displacement vector are directly applicable to other vector quantities.

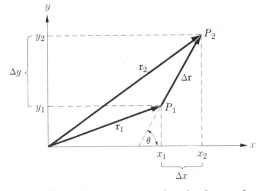

Fɪɢ. 1–15. P_1 and P_2 are two points in the xy-plane.

Consider two points P_1 and P_2 in the xy-plane of a coordinate system, as shown in Fig. 1–15. The coordinates of the two points are x_1,y_1 and x_2,y_2. The displacement from P_1 to P_2 is defined by the components

$$\Delta x = x_2 - x_1, \qquad \Delta y = y_2 - y_1.$$

The magnitude of the displacement, defined as the distance P_1P_2, is then

$$\Delta r = \sqrt{(\Delta x)^2 + (\Delta y)^2} = \sqrt{(x_2 - x_1)^2 + (y_2 - y_1)^2}, \qquad (1\text{–}9)$$

and the direction of the displacement specified by the angle θ between P_1P_2 and the x-axis is given by

$$\tan \theta = \frac{\Delta y}{\Delta x} = \frac{y_2 - y_1}{x_2 - x_1}. \qquad (1\text{–}10)$$

Conversely, if we know the magnitude and the direction of the displacement the components of the displacement are obtained from the relations

$$\Delta x = \Delta r \cos \theta, \qquad \Delta y = \Delta r \sin \theta. \qquad (1\text{–}11)$$

As a shorthand notation for the two numbers $(\Delta x,\Delta y)$ or $(\Delta r,\theta)$ defining the displacement from P_1 to P_2, it is convenient to use the single symbol $\mathbf{\Delta r}$, called the vector representation of the displacement. The magnitude of the displacement which we have denoted by Δr above is also written as $|\mathbf{\Delta r}|$.

In connection with the definition of the vector $\mathbf{\Delta r}$ the following additional comment is important. Two displacement vectors are considered to be the same so long as their components Δx and Δy are the same. In other words, two displacements starting from *different* points but having the same magnitudes and directions are described by the *same* vector. Because of this property of the displacement vector it is sometimes called

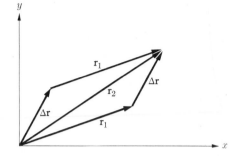

Fig. 1–16. Vector $r_2 = r_1 + \Delta r$ or $r_2 = \Delta r + r_1$.

a "free" vector. The displacement vector from the origin of the coordinate system to the point P_1 is called the *position vector* of P_1 and is denoted by r_1, which has the components x_1 and y_1. Similarly, the position vector of P_2 is denoted by r_2 and its components are

$$x_2 = x_1 + \Delta x, \qquad y_2 = y_1 + \Delta y, \tag{1–12}$$

where Δx and Δy are the components of the displacement vector Δr, corresponding to the displacement from P_1 to P_2, as shown in Fig. 1–15.

Vector addition. Since a vector r represents the two components x,y, we can interpret Eq. (1–12) as a relation among the vectors r_1, r_2, and Δr, and as a shorthand method of writing the two relations (1–12), we shall use the vector equation

$$r_2 = r_1 + \Delta r. \tag{1–13}$$

The vector r_2 is then called the *vector sum* of the two vectors r_1 and Δr. The geometrical meaning of vector addition is illustrated in Fig. 1–16. The sum of the vectors r_1 and Δr can be described as the diagonal drawn from the beginning of r_1 to the end of Δr in the parallelogram defined by these vectors. It is important to note that the magnitude of the vector r_2 is *not* the sum of the magnitudes of the vectors r_1 and Δr unless these vectors have the same direction. Rather, the magnitude of r_2 is obtained from the relation

$$r_2 = |r_2| = \sqrt{(x_1 + \Delta x)^2 + (y_1 + \Delta y)^2}\ ; \tag{1–14}$$

and the direction of r_2 is obtained from

$$\tan \theta = \frac{y_2}{x_2} = \frac{y_1 + \Delta y}{x_1 + \Delta x}. \tag{1–15}$$

It follows from Fig. 1–16 that the order of the vectors in vector addition is immaterial, i.e., we have

$$r_1 + \Delta r = \Delta r + r_1. \tag{1–16}$$

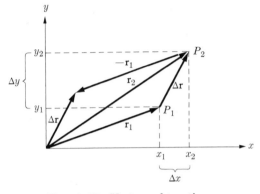

FIG. 1-17. Vector subtraction.

The negative of a vector **r** is defined as the vector which, when added to **r**, gives zero. This vector clearly has the components $-x$ and $-y$ and it is denoted by $-\mathbf{r}$. The difference between two vectors $\mathbf{r}_2$ and $\mathbf{r}_1$ is then defined as the vector $\Delta\mathbf{r} = \mathbf{r}_2 + (-\mathbf{r}_1)$, which we write as

$$\Delta\mathbf{r} = \mathbf{r}_2 - \mathbf{r}_1. \tag{1-17}$$

This defines the operation of subtraction of vectors. The components of the difference vector $\Delta\mathbf{r}$ are

$$\Delta x = x_2 - x_1, \qquad \Delta y = y_2 - y_1,$$

which is illustrated graphically in Fig. 1-17. When two vectors are drawn from the same point, the vector difference $\mathbf{r}_2 - \mathbf{r}_1$ is represented by the arrow drawn from the tip of $\mathbf{r}_1$ to the tip of $\mathbf{r}_2$.

The addition and subtraction of vectors can be applied to an arbitrary number of vectors. Some examples are illustrated in Fig. 1-18.

In the discussion above we have considered only two-dimensional vectors, i.e., vectors in a plane. However, the results easily can be extended to three-dimensional vectors. If the point P does not lie in the xy-plane the displacement vector also has a z-component. The magnitude of the displacement vector becomes

$$r = \sqrt{x^2 + y^2 + z^2} \tag{1-18}$$

and the direction is determined by the "direction cosines,"

$$\cos\theta_x = \frac{x}{r}, \qquad \cos\theta_y = \frac{y}{r}, \qquad \cos\theta_z = \frac{z}{r}, \tag{1-19}$$

where θ_x, θ_y, θ_z are the angles between the displacement and the three coordinate axes.

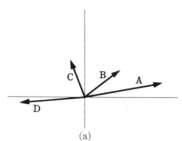
(a)

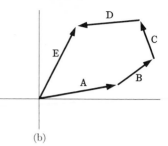
(b)

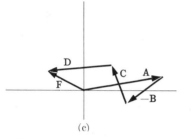
(c)

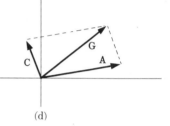
(d)

FIG. 1–18. The vectors **A**, **B**, **C**, and **D** in (a) are added in (b) to form **E** = **A** + **B** + **C** + **D**. In (c), **F** = **A** − **B** + **C** + **D**, and in (d), **G** = **A** + **C**.

Velocity, a vector. Velocity is the time rate of displacement. We have seen that the magnitude of the displacement in a plane is $\Delta r = |\Delta \mathbf{r}| = \sqrt{(\Delta x)^2 + (\Delta y)^2}$ and if this displacement is made in the time Δt the magnitude of the *average* velocity in this time interval (the average speed) is

$$\bar{v} = \frac{\Delta r}{\Delta t} = \sqrt{(\Delta x/\Delta t)^2 + (\Delta y/\Delta t)^2} = \sqrt{\bar{v}_x^2 + \bar{v}_y^2}. \qquad (1\text{–}20)$$

The magnitude of the instantaneous velocity is obtained in complete analogy with the one-dimensional discussion, and we have

$$v = \sqrt{v_x^2 + v_y^2} \quad \left(v_x = \frac{dx}{dt}, \quad v_y = \frac{dy}{dt} \right), \qquad (1\text{–}21)$$

where v_x and v_y are the velocity components along the x- and y-axes. The direction of the velocity is the same as the direction of the displacement and is given by

$$\tan \theta = \frac{dy/dt}{dx/dt} = \frac{v_y}{v_x}. \qquad (1\text{–}22)$$

Average velocity differs from displacement merely by a time factor and it follows that velocity, like displacement, can be described by a vector. The average velocity vector in the time interval Δt is then

$$\bar{\mathbf{v}} = \frac{\Delta \mathbf{r}}{\Delta t} = \frac{\mathbf{r}_2 - \mathbf{r}_1}{t_2 - t_1} \qquad (1\text{-}23)$$

with the components

$$\bar{v}_x = \frac{x_2 - x_1}{t_2 - t_1}, \qquad \bar{v}_y = \frac{y_2 - y_1}{t_2 - t_1}.$$

Similarly, the instantaneous velocity vector is a vector with components dx/dt and dy/dt and we can express it as the time rate of change of the position vector $\mathbf{r}$. Symbolically,

$$\mathbf{v} = \frac{d\mathbf{r}}{dt} \qquad \left(v_x = \frac{dx}{dt}, \quad v_y = \frac{dy}{dt} \right). \qquad (1\text{-}24)$$

When we deal with displacements, the meanings of vector addition and subtraction and the need for using these operations are quite obvious. However, the use of addition or subtraction of velocities is perhaps not so apparent. For example, the sum of the velocities of two different particles has no obvious physical significance. Actually, addition of velocities has meaning only when both the particle and the reference point of the particle-displacement vector are moving. For example, if the coordinate system is attached to a moving platform the total velocity (with respect to the ground) of a particle moving on the platform is the vector sum of the velocity of the platform and the velocity of the body with respect to the platform. Another situation arises when in a fixed coordinate system we study the velocity of one moving body with respect to another moving body. If, for example, the two points P_1 and P_2 in Fig. 1–15 are both moving, the separation between these points described by the vector $\Delta \mathbf{r} = \mathbf{r}_2 - \mathbf{r}_1$ will change with time. The rate of change of this vector is called the *relative velocity* of P_2 with respect to P_1. The average value of the relative velocity in the time interval Δt is then

$$\bar{\mathbf{v}}_r = \frac{\Delta \mathbf{r}}{\Delta t} = \frac{\Delta (\mathbf{r}_2 - \mathbf{r}_1)}{\Delta t} = \frac{\Delta \mathbf{r}_2}{\Delta t} - \frac{\Delta \mathbf{r}_1}{\Delta t} = \bar{\mathbf{v}}_2 - \bar{\mathbf{v}}_1 \qquad (1\text{-}25)$$

i.e., the vector difference between the average velocities of the two points. Similarly, the instantaneous value of the relative velocity of P_2 with respect to P_1 is the vector difference between the instantaneous velocities

$$\mathbf{v}_r = \mathbf{v}_2 - \mathbf{v}_1. \qquad (1\text{-}26)$$

EXAMPLE. A body B_1 moves along a straight line making an angle of $30°$ with the x-axis and another body B_2 moves along a straight line making an angle of $45°$ with the x-axis. They both start from the origin of the coordinate system at $t = 0$ and move with constant speeds $v_1 = 10$ m/sec and $v_2 = 20$ m/sec. The relative velocity vector of B_2 with respect to B_1 is then

$$\mathbf{v}_r = \mathbf{v}_2 - \mathbf{v}_1 = \frac{d(\mathbf{r}_2 - \mathbf{r}_1)}{dt},$$

with the components

$$v_{rx} = 20 \cos 45° - 10 \cos 30° \simeq 5.4 \text{ m/sec},$$

$$v_{ry} = 20 \sin 45° - 10 \sin 30° \simeq 9.1 \text{ m/sec}.$$

The magnitude of the relative velocity is then

$$v_r = \sqrt{5.4^2 + 9.1^2} \simeq 10.6 \text{ m/sec}.$$

The distance $|\mathbf{r}_2 - \mathbf{r}_1|$ between B_1 and B_2 increases with time as $v_r t$.

There is a subtle difference between the situation discussed above in which we, as observers at rest, calculate the relative velocities of two moving objects, and the situation in which an observer is moving with the object B_1 from which he measures the relative velocity of the object B_2. We have indicated in Sec. 1–3 that the results of length and time measurements made by observers in relative motion with respect to each other depend noticeably upon the relative speeds of the observers when their velocities approach the velocity of light. Under such conditions Eq. (1–26), the simple addition law of velocities, does not apply. If, for example, B_1 and B_2 move along the same straight line in the same direction, and the velocity of B_2 as measured from B_1 is $v_2' = c$ (c = speed of light), and the velocity of B_1 as measured from the ground is $v_1 = 0.5c$, Eq. (1–26) says that the velocity of B_2 with respect to the ground is $v_2 = v_1 + v_2' = 0.5c + c = 1.5c$. According to the famous Michelson-Morley experiments and the Einstein theory of relativity, the speed of light in vacuum is the same in all coordinate systems (moving or not) and consequently the simple addition formula (1–26) for velocities, leading to the result $1.5c$ in this example, cannot be used. This formula should then be replaced by the relativistically correct relation:*

$$v_2 = \frac{v_1 + v_2'}{1 + (v_1 v_2'/c^2)}. \qquad (1\text{–}27)$$

With $v_1 = 0.5c$ and $v_2' = c$, this formula gives the velocity of B_2,

$$v_2 = \frac{v_1 + c}{1 + (v_1 c/c^2)} = c,$$

---

* The mathematical aspects of the special theory of relativity are not difficult. A good book to study is Max Born, *Einstein's Theory of Relativity*, Methuen, London, 1924.

which is again the speed of light, the same for the observer on the ground as for the observer on B_1. This is consistent with the postulate of relativity theory. Note that the relativistic addition formula (1–27) reduces to the familiar relation $v_2 = v_1 + v_2'$ when the velocities of the bodies are small compared with c_1.

Acceleration, a vector. The acceleration is related to the velocity vector in the same way as the velocity vector is related to the position vector. Just as the average velocity in the time interval Δt is $\Delta r/\Delta t = (r_2 - r_1)/(t_2 - t_1)$, the average acceleration in the same interval is

$$\bar{a} = \frac{v_2 - v_1}{t_2 - t_1} = \frac{\Delta v}{\Delta t} \qquad (1\text{--}28)$$

with the components

$$\bar{a}_x = \frac{v_{2x} - v_{1x}}{t_2 - t_1}, \qquad \bar{a}_y = \frac{v_{2y} - v_{1y}}{t_2 - t_1}.$$

Similarly, the instantaneous acceleration is the vector with components dv_x/dt and dv_y/dt. Symbolically this vector is denoted by

$$a = \frac{dv}{dt}. \qquad (1\text{--}29)$$

EXAMPLE. A body slides over a smooth ice surface with a speed of 5 m/sec in a direction making an angle of 60° with an x-axis. A wind gust lasting 0.5 sec causes the body to change its motion so that it travels with a speed of 3 m/sec along a line making an angle of 150° with the x-axis. Determine the average acceleration during the gust. We have:

$$\bar{a}_x = \frac{3\cos 150° - 5\cos 60°}{0.5} \simeq -\frac{5.1}{0.5} = -10.2 \text{ m/sec}^2,$$

$$\bar{a}_y = \frac{3\sin 150° - 5\sin 60°}{0.5} \simeq -\frac{2.8}{0.5} = -5.6 \text{ m/sec}^2.$$

The magnitude of the acceleration is then

$$\bar{a} = \sqrt{\bar{a}_x^2 + \bar{a}_y^2} \simeq 11.6 \text{ m/sec}^2$$

and the direction is given by

$$\tan \theta = \frac{\bar{a}_y}{\bar{a}_x} = 0.55, \qquad \theta \simeq 209°.$$

The scalar product. Many of our forthcoming discussions can be expressed concisely in terms of vector symbols and vector algebra. However, when it comes to numerical calculations we usually have to refer to the components of the vectors and use the expressions for magnitude

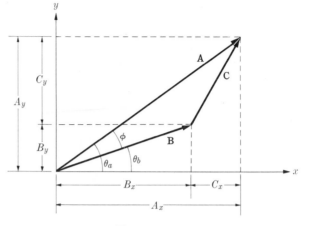

FIGURE 1–19

and direction of a vector as given by Eqs. (1–14) and (1–15). To illustrate this point, let us consider the familiar geometrical problem of determining the length of one side of a triangle when the lengths of the other sides are given. Let the three sides of the triangle be described by the displacement vectors **A**, **B**, and **C**, of which **A** and **B** are known. Using vector symbolism and vector algebra it follows directly from Fig. 1–19 that the unknown side of the triangle can be expressed as

$$\mathbf{C} = \mathbf{A} - \mathbf{B}. \tag{1–30}$$

To find the magnitude of **C**, that is, the length of the third side, we have to use the component form,

$$C^2 = (A_x - B_x)^2 + (A_y - B_y)^2 = A^2 + B^2 - 2(A_x B_x + A_y B_y), \tag{1–31}$$

which is the well-known cosine theorem in elementary plane geometry, since the quantity $A_x B_x + A_y B_y$ can be expressed as

$$A_x B_x + A_y B_y = (A \cos \theta_a)(B \cos \theta_b) + (A \sin \theta_a)(B \sin \theta_b)$$
$$= AB \cos (\theta_a - \theta_b) = AB \cos \phi, \tag{1–32}$$

where ϕ is the angle between the vectors **A** and **B**. Since the quantity $AB \cos \phi = A_x B_x + A_y B_y$ occurs quite often in many geometrical as well as physical problems, it is convenient to introduce a shorthand notation for it in terms of vectors **A** and **B**. This notation is $\mathbf{A} \cdot \mathbf{B}$ so that, by definition

$$\mathbf{A} \cdot \mathbf{B} = AB \cos \phi = A_x B_x + A_y B_y, \tag{1–33}$$

and $\mathbf{A} \cdot \mathbf{B}$ is called the scalar product of the vectors $\mathbf{A}$ and $\mathbf{B}$. The scalar product of a vector with itself is clearly $\mathbf{C} \cdot \mathbf{C} = C^2$, that is, the squared magnitude of the vector. Using the scalar-product notation, we then have

$$C^2 = (\mathbf{A} - \mathbf{B}) \cdot (\mathbf{A} - \mathbf{B}) = A^2 + B^2 - 2\mathbf{A} \cdot \mathbf{B},$$

which again is just the law of cosines, since $\mathbf{A} \cdot \mathbf{B}$ is $AB \cos \phi$.

When vectors have components in all three directions in space, the scalar product is

$$\mathbf{A} \cdot \mathbf{B} = AB \cos \phi = A_x B_x + A_y B_y + A_z B_z, \qquad (1\text{--}34)$$

where A and B are given by

$$A = \sqrt{A_x^2 + A_y^2 + A_z^2} \quad \text{and} \quad B = \sqrt{B_x^2 + B_y^2 + B_z^2}.$$

Problems

1-1. (a) Plot on a graph the position vs. time of a body dropped at $t = 0$ from a platform 100 ft high. Let the point $y = 0$ be at the surface of the earth. (b) What is the average velocity in the interval between $t = 1$ and $t = 2$ sec? Between $t = 1$ and $t = 1.5$ sec? Between $t = 1$ and $t = 1.1$ sec? Between $t = 1$ and $t = 1.01$ sec? (c) What is the instantaneous velocity at $t = 1$ sec?

1-2. A body starts at $t = 0$ from $x = 0$ with a velocity of 10 m/sec. The acceleration is constant, directed toward the left, and has a value of 2 m/sec^2. (a) What is the velocity at $t = 2$ sec? (b) Where is the body at this time? (c) When does the body return to its starting point, and what then is its velocity?

1-3. A body moves so that its velocity is given by $v = 3t^2$, where v is measured in cm/sec and t in seconds. (a) Plot a graph of v vs. t. (b) How far does the body move between $t = 1$ and $t = 2$ sec? (c) Compare the average velocity in the interval $t = 1$ to $t = 2$ sec with the instantaneous velocity at $t = 1$, 1.5, and 2 sec.

1-4. A man can jump about 3 feet high from a standing position. What is his velocity just as he leaves the ground?

1-5. What acceleration in ft/sec^2 (four significant figures) corresponds to 980.0 cm/sec^2? What acceleration in m/sec^2 (four significant figures) corresponds to 32.00 ft/sec^2?

1-6. If a body starts with velocity v_0 and has uniform acceleration a, what is its velocity after a distance s has been traversed? Examine your relation for $s = 0$ and for negative values of s.

1-7. A man walks 2 mi north, 3 mi east, then an unknown distance in an unknown direction (displacement vector $\mathbf{X}$) and finds himself 10 mi south of where he started. Find the components of the vector $\mathbf{X}$, and its magnitude and direction.

1-8. Choose a suitable scale, and solve the above problem graphically.

1-9. What are the properties of two vectors $\mathbf{A}$ and $\mathbf{B}$ such that: (a) $\mathbf{A} + \mathbf{B} = \mathbf{C}$ and $A + B = C$? (b) $\mathbf{A} + \mathbf{B} = \mathbf{A} - \mathbf{B}$? (c) $\mathbf{A} + \mathbf{B} = \mathbf{C}$ and $A^2 + B^2 = C^2$? (d) $\mathbf{A} - \mathbf{B} = \mathbf{C}$ and $A + B = C$?

1-10. Vector **A** has a magnitude of 30 m and makes an angle of 30° with the x-axis. Vector **C**, the resultant of **A** and **B** (**A** + **B** = **C**), makes an angle of 60° with the x-axis and has a magnitude of $30\sqrt{3}$ m. Find vector **B**.

1-11. A girl can paddle a canoe with a speed of 5 mi/hr relative to the water. She wishes to cross a canal one mile wide, in which the speed of the water is 3 mi/hr. (a) In what direction should she paddle to reach the other side as quickly as possible? (b) In what direction should she paddle if she wishes to land directly across the canal? How long will this trip take?

1-12. A car and a motorcycle travel 30 and 40 mi/hr, respectively. They start from the same place and one hour later are 50 mi apart. (a) In what (relative) directions did they travel? (b) Indicate on a vector diagram the velocity of the car, the velocity of the motorcycle, and the velocity of the car relative to the motorcycle.

1-13. What is the relativistically correct value for the velocity of a boy relative to the ground if his velocity relative to a train moving with a velocity of 88 ft/sec is 5 ft/sec in the direction of forward motion of the train?

1-14. Convince yourself that, according to the relativistically correct formula (1–27), the velocity of the front of a light beam relative to the ground is c even when the source of the light has a velocity v.

1-15. If an atomic particle A moves to the right with velocity $0.95c$, and another atomic particle B moves to the left with velocity $0.90c$, what is the velocity of A relative to B? What is the velocity of B relative to A?

1-16. Using the scalar product, find the angle between the vectors **A** and **B** where $A_x = 1$, $A_y = 2$, $A_z = 3$, $B_x = 3$, $B_y = -1$, $B_z = 2$, all measured in cm.

1-17. Consider as vectors the lines AB and AC in the parallelepiped in Fig. 1–20. The lines AB and AC are drawn from A to the midpoints of two surfaces of the parallelepiped. The side lengths are 1, 2, and 3 ft. Determine the angle between AB and AC.

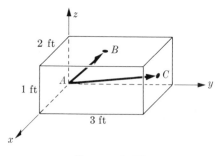

FIGURE 1–20

CHAPTER 2

INERTIAL MASS

Summary. This chapter starts with a qualitative discussion of inertia, the inherent property of matter that is responsible for the resistance of matter to changes in its state of motion. Several experiments illustrating inertial effects are presented, and one of them, a collision experiment, is chosen for the *operational definition of inertial mass.* The *conservation* of mass then follows from experiments. The concept of weight is introduced, and experimental evidence for the proportionality of mass and weight is presented. Finally, the unit of mass and a review of the range of masses encountered in nature are discussed.

In the first chapter we have discussed, among other matters, the concepts of length and time. Length and time, together with mass, the subject of this chapter, are the three quantities at the very heart of mechanics. While measurements of length and time are very much a part of our everyday experience, the measurement of inertial mass is somewhat more delicate.

Qualitatively, the everyday meaning of the word *inertia* carries with it the essence of the (inertial) mass concept. Recall Galileo's contention that the natural or uninfluenced state of motion of a body is the state in which the body moves with constant velocity. Inertial mass is a measure of the perseverance with which a body retains this state of constant velocity. We often say that a person has a lot of inertia if we (or he) find it difficult to change his ways. Correspondingly, we say that a body has a lot of inertia when we must do something relatively violent to change its state of motion. It is evident, then, that the inertial mass of a body will influence its motion, or changes of motion, as it interacts with other bodies. Therefore, it is important that we have a precise definition of and means for the measurement of inertial mass when we start a quantitative analysis of interactions and motion. Much of this chapter is devoted to this end.

2–1 Exploratory experiments. Consider two baseball-size balls, one of wood and the other of lead, moving along the same path with the same speed. Although the velocities of the balls may be identical, we certainly realize that their motions have different properties when we compare how it feels to try to stop these balls. Although the wooden ball can be caught with comparative ease, the lead ball would "send one spinning." We say that the lead ball has larger inertia than the wooden ball, in other words, a greater desire to remain in its original state of motion. Similarly, when we try to set the two balls in motion from rest, we again find that the lead ball offers the greater resistance to a change in its state of motion.

Alternatively, consider a collision between two balls. If we roll two identical wooden balls against each other with the same speeds along the same straight line, the balls will fly apart with equal speeds after the collision. However, if we repeat this experiment with one wooden and one lead ball we find that the velocity of the lead ball is changed but little. The property of the lead ball to tend to remain in motion is evidently greater than that of the wooden ball.

We can proceed to do a number of other experiments with the two balls. Imagine an experiment in which the balls are pulled one after the other over a smooth table with equal "forces" for a certain time, after which the balls are released. To assure constant "force" we could pull the ball with a spring stretched to an unchanging length during the pull. After completion of the pull, we find that the wooden ball has acquired a much greater velocity than the lead ball. Clearly, again the lead ball resists change in velocity more than the wooden ball—the inertia of the lead ball is larger.

An even more illuminating experiment of inertia is shown in Fig. 2–1. This experiment demonstrates an effect similar to that which is experienced by a passenger in an accelerating or decelerating car. Two balls are attached to the ends of a thin uniform bar that is free to rotate about a vertical axis. This system is mounted on a car, as shown. Suppose we start with two identical lead balls. As the car is pushed forward, starting from rest, we find that the bar remains in its original location, that is, perpendicular to the direction of motion. Next, we replace one of the lead

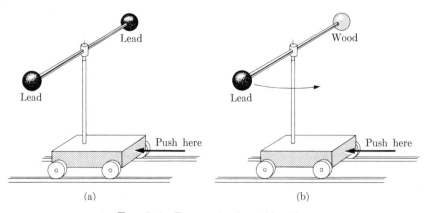

Fig. 2–1. Demonstration of inertia.

balls with a wooden one of equal size. Now, when the car is pushed from rest, we find that the bar turns, the lead ball moves backward, and the wooden ball forward. This again indicates that the inertia of the lead ball is larger than that of the wooden ball. Similarly, if the car is initially in motion at a constant speed, with the bar pointing in a fixed direction, the lead ball will move forward when the car is brought to a stop.

2–2 Measurement of inertial mass. In order to be able to measure inertia, we have to select an experiment which will serve as an operational definition. The quantity measured in such a way will be called *inertial mass*, or simply the *mass* of the body. In principle, we can choose any one of the experiments described above or another similar experiment for this operational definition of mass. Whatever choice is made, we shall have to select some measurable quantity in the experiment and define inertial mass in terms of it. It is conceivable, of course, that different ways of defining mass will not be consistent. Under these conditions we should choose the definition in terms of which the description of motion becomes the simplest. We shall select the *collision experiment* described briefly above as the basis for the operational definition of inertial mass.

In Fig. 2–2 are shown two cars A and B on a horizontal track. The cars are originally at rest and are held together by a string. A compressed spring is between the cars, and when the string is burned, the cars fly apart under the influence of the spring. (We shall often call this type of event an explosive collision.)

If the speeds of cars A and B after the "explosion" are found to be $|v_a|$ and $|v_b|$, respectively, we shall define the ratio between their inertial masses as $m_b/m_a = |v_a|/|v_b|$, where m is the symbol chosen for the *inertial mass*.

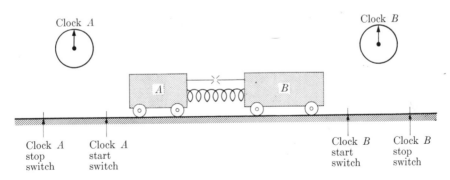

Fig. 2–2. The measuring device used in the operational definition of inertial mass. A spring is held in compression by a string between the two cars A and B. The spring is then released (by burning the string), and the two cars move apart. Using body A as a reference, we can measure the inertial mass of B in terms of the ratio of the velocities of A and B. We have $m_b = -m_a(v_a/v_b)$.

Or, if we describe the result in terms of the *velocities* rather than the speeds, the ratio of the inertial masses of B and A is defined by

$$\frac{m_b}{m_a} = -\frac{v_a}{v_b}, \tag{2-1}$$

where the minus sign accounts for the different directions of motion of A and B. If the speed of B is the same as that of A after the explosion, the inertial masses of B and A are the same, by definition.

Suppose now that from such experiments we have found that two cars B and C each have an inertial mass equal to that of A; that is, $m_b = m_c = m_a$. (Cars A, B, and C, of course, need not have the same shapes or compositions.) We then combine B and C into a unit and measure the combined inertial mass of $B + C$ in relation to A. In the corresponding explosive collision we then have bodies B and C each with an inertial mass m_a on one side, and the single mass m_a of A on the other. The result of the experiment is that $B + C$ acquires a speed only half that of A, and this means that the combined inertial mass of $B + C$ is $2m_a$. Similarly, if we measure the inertial mass of a collection of n bodies, each with an inertial mass m_a, we find that the combined inertial mass of the system is $n \cdot m_a$. In other words, the total inertial mass of a system of bodies is the *sum of the inertial masses* of the individual bodies in the system.

The above definition of mass would not be very satisfactory if the ratio between the masses of two bodies B and C, measured in collision experiments with reference to a body A, was found to depend upon the choice of the reference body. However, experiments show that such a dependence does not exist. Furthermore, if B and C have equal masses, that is, $m_b = m_c$, determined by comparison with A, it is found that $|v_b| = |v_c|$ in an explosive-collision experiment involving B and C.

Conservation of mass. One of the most important properties of mass is its conservation. Now that we have available an experimental method for comparing masses, we can discuss experiments one might conduct to make the law of the conservation of mass convincing.

Suppose two similar steel balls have been found to have equal masses. Let one of the balls be preserved as a standard for comparison, and let the other be cut into pieces or ground into a fine powder. If all the pieces or all the powder is accounted for, it can be found by experiment that the mass is unchanged. Separating a steel ball or any other body into many parts does not change the mass.

What about chemical reactions? What happens to the mass of an object when its atoms enter into chemical combinations? Here we must be a little careful. If lead is oxidized by heating it in air, litharge (lead monoxide, PbO) is formed. We are not finding out anything about conservation of mass if we collect the litharge powder and remeasure its mass, for oxygen has combined with the lead. Rather, if we wish to perform this experiment, we must put oxygen and lead in a closed container, heat the container, and compare the masses before and after heating. Then we are investigating the effect of chemical combination on mass, and we do find that the mass is unchanged.

Similar experiments are possible in which temperature is changed, or bodies change state from liquid to gas or from solid to liquid. The result is always the same: mass is conserved.

We must qualify the conservation of mass concept in one important way. We have not yet discussed energy, but it suffices to note that a body increases its energy content when it gets hotter, and similarly, can have energy by virtue of its motion or position. There is energy even in a light wave or a radio wave. According to the special theory of relativity, mass and energy are equivalent. Associated with a mass m there is an amount of energy $E = mc^2$, where c is the speed of light, and associated with an energy E there is an amount of mass $m = E/c^2$. This means, for example, that when an atom of carbon and a molecule of oxygen combine to form carbon dioxide, we would expect the mass of the carbon-dioxide molecule to be somewhat less than the combined masses of the carbon atom and oxygen molecule. This is because some heat (energy) is given off in the chemical reaction and associated with this energy is mass. Actually, the mass associated with the energy of chemical reactions is typically only one part in 10^{10} of the mass of the combining elements, and has never been measured. In nuclear fusion, on the other hand, this fraction is not one part in 10^{10}, but is near one part in 10^3 and is readily measured.

A related aspect of the special theory of relativity concerns the increase in the mass of a body that accompanies an increase in the speed of the body. In fact, the mass of a body which moves with a speed v is

$$m = \frac{m_0}{\sqrt{1 - v^2/c^2}},   \tag{2–2}$$

where m_0 is the mass when the body is at rest and c is the speed of light. This means, for example, that the mass of a container of gas increases when the gas is heated, for when the gas is heated its molecules move faster. From the viewpoint of conservation of mass, we must note that, associated with the heat (energy) used to increase the speed of the gas molecules was a mass, and this mass plus the initial mass of the gas remains constant.

In summary, then, conservation of mass is a strictly correct conservation law only if the mass associated with energy is included.

Weight. There is (evidently) a close relation between the inertial mass of a body, for example the mass measured in an explosive-collision experiment, and the weight (earth's attraction) as measured by a calibrated spring scale or pan balance. The distinction between mass and weight is rather well demonstrated by the "pan balance" shown in Fig. 2–1(b). In the experiment described by this figure, the inequality of the *inertial masses* of the balls caused the bar to turn as the car on which the balance was mounted was set in motion. However, if we remove the bar with balls from the car and place it in a plane so that the axis of rotation is horizontal, the bar will turn as a result of the difference in *weight* of the balls.

Careful measurements (R. Eötvös, 1909) have shown that the inertial mass of a body is proportional to its weight, and that the proportionality constant to within one part in 10^8 is the same for all bodies regardless of their chemical compositions. As we shall discuss in more detail later, the ratio between the weight and the mass of a body is the free-fall acceleration of the body. The very fact that all bodies are found to fall in vacuum with the same acceleration, regardless of composition or shape, is one of the experimental results that demonstrates the proportionality between weight and mass. Similarly, the period of a simple pendulum, we shall see, depends upon the ratio between the weight and the mass of the pendulum bob. The fact that the period of the pendulum is found to be the same, regardless of the mass or the composition of the bob, again demonstrates the proportionality between weight and mass. As a result of this proportionality, we need not always resort to collision experiments for comparing or determining inertial masses. A determination of the weights of two bodies by means of pan balances or calibrated spring scales is sufficient.

The weight of a body varies with its position; its mass does not. In free space, outside the range of any significant gravitational pull, the weight of a body would be practically zero, and a weight comparison of inertial masses would not be possible. On the other hand, collision experiments, at least in principle, can be performed anywhere. A pendulum is one type of oscillator. A mass attached to the end of a spring is another type, and here the oscillation period depends upon the mass and certain properties of the spring, but not on the weight of the mass. As a consequence, an old-fashioned pendulum clock would run slow on the moon where all bodies weigh less, but a spring wind-up clock would keep good time.

Variation in the weight of a body with the change of location on the earth's surface is rather small. At a given elevation, say sea level, the weight of a body is maximum at the geographic poles and is minimum at the equator; the variation is about $\frac{1}{2}\%$. At a given latitude, weight decreases with elevation, and, for example, this variation is about $\frac{1}{3}\%$ from sea level to the top of Mt. Everest.

Measurements of the variation of gravity with location on the earth's surface can be made by comparing the periods of pendulums placed at different positions. Measurements of this type can be made with great accuracy, for example, by counting the number of periods between two or more "coincidences" of the pendulums. In 1898, pendulum measurements were reported in which the weight variation over a difference in height of only two meters was determined.

2–3 The unit of mass. If a standard body is chosen as the unit inertial mass, clearly one can measure the inertial masses of other bodies with the method indicated in the previous section. The mass unit in the metric system is *one kilogram.* The international standard of one kilogram is a piece of platinum kept at the International Bureau of Weights and Measures, Sèvres, France. A kilogram weighs about 2.2 pounds, about the same as a liter of water. A gram is 1/1000 of a kilogram and is approximately the mass of one cubic centimeter of water. In the English gravitational system of units, the unit of mass is the *slug.* A slug, which weighs about 32 pounds, has a mass of 14.6 kilograms. In this system there does not exist a standard mass; rather, the system is based on a standard weight (or force) of one pound.

Measurement and range of mass. Mass measurements like those of time and length have been extended to cover a very wide range. A comparison of weight is equivalent, we have seen, to a comparison of mass, and this is perhaps the type of mass measurement most familiar to us. Scales marked "honest weight, no springs" are really devices for weight comparison, and they are used in appropriately modified forms for things as heavy as locomotives (weight about 200 tons) and as light as a millimeter length or so of human hair (mass about 10^{-7} gram). Masses less than 10^{-7} or 10^{-8} are determined by various indirect means. Perhaps the most common method involves the determination of the number of identical pieces that compose a sample large enough for conventional weighing. Two grams of hydrogen gas, for example, comprise one mole and so contain about $6 \cdot 10^{23}$ molecules. A hydrogen molecule, therefore, has a mass of about $3 \cdot 10^{-24}$ gram. The comparison of atomic and subatomic masses has become almost a routine laboratory procedure in recent years. Some of the bases for these types of comparison will be taken up in the following chapter. Of all bodies known, the electron has the smallest mass, $0.91 \cdot 10^{-27}$ gram.

Of course, no one attempts literally to weigh things like mountains or oceans, yet the masses of these are known with considerable accuracy. One method is to use the common-sense approach of measuring the volume, and multiplying it by the estimated average mass per unit volume, or average density. Such estimated masses are particularly accurate in the case of water because the density of water varies so little. Rock and earth, on the other hand, have widely varying densities and an average must be obtained from a large number of samples taken at various depths and places. Alternatively, pendulum methods similar to those discussed in connection with weight variation may be used to estimate the mass of large nearby objects such as mountains or mineral deposits.

The determination of the masses of astronomical bodies presents quite a different problem. Even if the volume can be found, the density is usually quite uncertain. The masses of astronomical bodies are therefore measured by investigating their motion and the motion of associated bodies. The mass of the earth, for example, can be determined from a study of the motion of the moon, and the mass turns out to be about $6 \cdot 10^{24}$ kilograms. The mass of the sun as revealed by the motion of the planets is about 330,000 times that of the earth. Some stars have masses hundreds of times that of our sun, and our galaxy (the Milky Way) has a mass of about 10^{11} suns.

PROBLEMS

2–1. A 1-kgm mass is placed on one of two cars of unknown but equal inertial masses. The cars, which are initially at rest, interact explosively with each other, and attain velocities of 2 and -3 m/sec, respectively. (a) What are the masses of the cars? (b) The experiment is repeated but now, rather than the 1-kgm mass, an object of unknown mass is placed on one of the cars. The observed velocities are 1.8 m/sec and -4 m/sec. What is the mass of the object?

2–2. In the operational procedure for the measurement of inertial mass as described in the text, a meter stick and a clock were required. Try to invent a modification of this procedure in which a clock is not necessary but where a meter stick is the only measuring instrument required.

2–3. Propose an operational definition of inertial mass based on the experiment described in Fig. 2–1. Describe how you can construct a mass scale on the basis of your definition. Similarly, propose a mass definition on the basis of the experiment described in the text in which bodies are pulled equal lengths of time by a spring stretched to a certain constant value.

2–4. In his *Principia*, Book III, Proposition 6, Newton described an experiment in which he used two pendulums. Each consisted of a wooden box suspended on an 11-ft length of string. He filled one of the boxes with wood, and at the center of the other box he placed a piece of gold of a size such that the weights of the two pendulums were the same. The pendulums were set in oscillation and were found to follow each other in synchronism for a long time. He repeated the experiment, now comparing the pendulum filled with wood with other pendulums containing such substances as silver, lead, glass, sand, common salt, water, and wheat. For what purpose do you think Newton made these experiments, and what conclusion could he draw from them?

2–5. It was mentioned in the text that a pendulum will have a longer period on the moon than on the earth, and consequently a pendulum clock would be "slow" on the moon. Would the same hold true for your wrist watch? Explain.

2–6. Do you think a tuning fork would vibrate with the same frequency on the moon as on the earth? Explain.

CHAPTER 3

MOMENTUM AND FORCE — I

Summary. The concept of momentum. One-dimensional collision experiments lead to the important law of conservation of momentum of an isolated system of interacting particles. Perfectly inelastic and perfectly elastic collisions. The conservation of momentum is interpreted in terms of the center-of-mass motion. The study of momentum transfer *during* a collision leads to the force concept (Newton's second law), and it follows from experiments that the force exerted on a body B by a body A is equal and opposite to the force exerted on A by B (Newton's third law). The properties of the gravitational force and the spring force are discussed, and experiments involving these forces lead to the important property of force, the principle of superposition. The meaning of a "system" of particles and of "internal" and "external" forces is discussed, and the center-of-mass motion of a system is treated in terms of the external forces. Finally, the momentum transfer by a stream of particles and the corresponding force are given and illustrated in terms of. rocket motion.

We are now ready to take up seriously our study of interactions and motion. Just as in any other investigation, an important part of the study is to formulate and ask the "right" questions. The subject we are pursuing is very broad, and there are many questions that we can ask about many types of motion. In selecting the first experiment on motion, we shall avoid such complicated and very specialized types of motion as the (irregular) fall of a piece of paper in air or the waves produced by a speedboat, since these motions depend on many factors or parameters and are difficult to analyze. Instead, initial studies will deal with simpler and cleaner types of motion in terms of which more complicated ones can be understood. The free fall of a body in vacuum, the motion of a body pulled by a spring over a smooth horizontal surface, and planetary motion can all be considered as examples of such motions. If we accept the general idea that the motion of a body changes only as a result of interaction with one or more other bodies, the simplest experiment should be a two-body collision. Experiments of this type are comparatively easy to perform and to analyze and so will be selected as our starting point here.

A complete study of motion should, of course, involve experiments with and analysis of all the different types of interaction. Such an extensive program would carry us through most of physics and would be too extensive for discussion here. We shall therefore limit our introductory collision experiments to simple cases that involve contact and elastic interactions and, to a lesser extent, magnetic interactions. From these experiments we shall show how one of the most important basic laws of physics, the *conservation of momentum*, will emerge.

3–1 Exploratory collision experiments. How can we design an experiment that involves the interaction of only *two* bodies? This is not as easy as it might appear at first glance. For one thing, motion of a body through air is always affected by collisions with the 10^{19} or so particles per cubic centimeter of which air is composed. Furthermore, the motion of a body on the earth's surface is affected by its interactions with the earth—the gravitational pull as well as contact interactions.

The effect of gravitational pull on the motion can be eliminated if we arrange to have the two bodies under consideration move on a horizontal track or plane. Although the effect of "friction" with the track remains, even that effect can be made small enough (as will be shown in more detail later) so that a body when left alone on the track or plane will move along the track with almost constant velocity for a considerable time. The state of motion of the body is then changed only by interactions with other bodies moving on the track. It is thus possible to obtain a reasonably good approximation of the idealized *two-body interaction*, as further described below.

Experimental arrangement. The experimental arrangement with which we shall start is illustrated in Fig. 3–1. The apparatus consists of two cars free to move on a four-meter length of track. The wheels of the cars have

Fig. 3–1. Arrangement for one-dimensional collision experiments. The clocks are started and stopped electrically by switches triggered by the cars.

roller bearings, and when a car moves alone along the horizontal track, its velocity remains very nearly constant. The velocity is determined by measuring the elapsed time as the car traverses a fixed distance. Time measurements are made with clocks that are started and stopped by electrical switches mounted along the track and triggered by the cars as they pass. In the study of a collision between two cars on the track, it is usually necessary to make four velocity measurements, and this requires four clocks and four pairs of switches.

Collisions. We start with two cars free to move on the track; the task is to investigate how they affect each other's motion. The cars will not ordinarily affect each other until they come in direct contact. However, with appropriately mounted magnets, the cars will affect each other noticeably even without actual contact. In either case, when the cars are far apart they move with constant velocity, but when they come within each other's interaction or "force" range (and as a result change their velocities) they experience what we shall refer to as a *collision*, whether or not the bodies come into physical contact.

We shall consider first the velocities of the two interacting bodies *before* and *after* the collision. Later we shall investigate what happens *during* the (often comparatively short) period of collision. By varying the experimental conditions, e.g., the sizes and masses of the cars, the nature of the contact surfaces between the cars, the material of which they are made, the initial speeds, etc., we shall investigate what the important variables are and how the "outcome" of the collision depends upon these variables.

Exploratory collision experiments indicate that the relation between the final and initial velocities of the bodies seems to depend on the size and material of the bodies and the nature of the contact surfaces between them. In order to try to bring order into these observations, we shall vary one parameter at a time, starting with the simplest possible initial conditions. It is evident from the very start that the *inertial mass* of the bodies, as discussed in the previous chapter, will play an important role in the collisions, since it is this property which expresses the resistance of the bodies to changes in their states of motion.

3–2 Momentum. In Chapter 2 we used an "explosive" interaction for the operational definition of inertial mass. With this definition of mass, we have for the explosive interaction

$$m_a v_a = -m_b v_b,$$

where the minus sign signifies that v_a and v_b are oppositely directed and the subscripts identify the bodies. The product mv proves to be an important quantity and is given a special name, *momentum*, and a special symbol, p. A body of small mass but with large velocity can have just as much momentum as a massive body with small velocity. Momentum, like velocity, is taken as positive when the body moves in the positive x-direction and as negative in the opposite direction.

The expression above can be written as

$$m_a v_a + m_b v_b = 0, \qquad \text{or} \qquad p_a + p_b = 0.$$

That is, since the total momentum was zero before the cars flew apart (the velocity and hence the momentum of both cars were zero), we can say that the total momentum was unchanged or *conserved* (it remained zero) as a result of the explosion.

Conservation of momentum in this first example follows from the definitions of mass and momentum. We proceed now to discuss collision experiments with more general initial conditions in order to investigate further the exchanges of momentum and possible conservation of the total momentum of interacting bodies.

3–3 Conservation of momentum. As in our first experiment, we shall continue to let the cars interact by means of a spring attached to one of them. The experimental arrangement is shown schematically in Fig. 3–2 (see also Fig. 3–1). Both the initial conditions and the masses of the colliding bodies will be varied, and the velocities before and after collisions will be measured. In all cases the mass of the spring will be negligible.

We start with two cars of equal mass. If body A collides with body B, which is initially at rest, we find that the collision brings A to rest and that

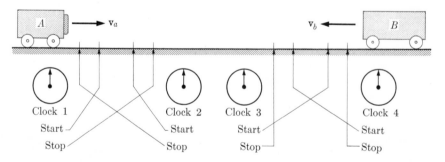

Fig. 3–2. Apparatus for studying the collision of cars A and B. Clocks 1 and 3 measure the time for A and B to travel a fixed distance before they collide, and so one can obtain v_a and v_b. Clocks 2 and 4 measure the time for the cars to travel a fixed distance after the collision, and so one can obtain v_a' and v_b'. A system of electric relays prevents clock 2 from starting until car A has passed over the clock 1 stop switch. Regardless of the form of interaction and mass of the cars, one always finds that $m_a v_a + m_b v_b = m_a v_a' + m_b v_b'$. (See also Fig. 3–1.)

B takes up the velocity that A had before the collision; i.e., we find that $v_b' = v_a$. (Hereafter, unprimed quantities will refer to conditions before a collision, and primed quantities will refer to those after a collision.)

Suppose now that we take cars of unequal mass but continue to use the spring as an insert between the bodies and continue to let body B be initially at rest. Qualitatively, we make the following observations. When A is more massive than B, both A and B have a forward motion after the collision. When A is less massive than B, body A reverses its motion and B goes forward after the collision. It is by no means true now that the velocity lost by A is transferred to B. But one regularity does persist in our observations. No matter what the masses of A and B may be, the *momentum* lost by A as a result of the collision is transferred to B. In other words, the total momentum, that of car A plus that of car B, is the same before and after the collision,

$$m_a v_a = m_a v_a' + m_b v_b'.$$

As a final collision experiment with our spring-cushioned cars, we let both cars have initial velocities. The experimental results now involve four velocities, and it becomes difficult to guess the outcomes of the various possible experiments involving different masses and velocities. A regularity again persists in our results, however, and this is a quite natural extension of our previous findings. The total momentum before and after the collision is the same:

$$m_a v_a + m_b v_b = m_a v_a' + m_b v_b', \quad \text{or} \quad p_a + p_b = p_a' + p_b'. \quad (3\text{--}1)$$

That is, the momentum change of body A is equal but opposite to the momentum change of body B. In these collisions, momentum can be transferred from one body to another, but the total momentum remains constant.

In Table 3–1 is shown an example of experimental data obtained in a spring-type collision between two identical cars running against each other on the track with different speeds. The electrical switches on the track are set apart a distance of 50 cm. The hands of the clocks (see Fig. 3–1) make one complete revolution per second and can be read to an accuracy of about 3% when the time is of the order of 0.5 sec or longer.

We see that this result is consistent with the law of conservation of momentum within the accuracy of the experiment.

Next we shall investigate the conservation of momentum for other than the spring-type interaction. If we put a piece of putty on an end of one of the cars, they will stick together after colliding. This is certainly a very different type of interaction. The results of such an experiment are shown in Table 3–2. Note that since the cars stick together after the collision, we

Table 3–1. Collision between two cars A and B of equal masses
($m_a = m_b = 6.6$ kgm). Distance between switches: 0.50 m.

	Time Δt, sec	Velocity v, m/sec	Momentum p, kgm·m/sec
Before collision			
Car A	$\Delta t_a = 0.82$	$v_a = 0.61$	$p_a = m_a \cdot 0.61$
Car B	$\Delta t_b = 0.54$	$v_b = -0.93$	$p_b = -m_a \cdot 0.93$
After collision			
Car A	$\Delta t'_a = 0.57$	$v'_a = -0.88$	$p'_a = -m_a \cdot 0.88$
Car B	$\Delta t'_b = 0.88$	$v'_b = 0.57$	$p'_b = m_a \cdot 0.57$

Total momentum before collision: $p = p_a + p_b = -0.32 m_a$
Total momentum after collision: $p' = p'_a + p'_b = -0.31 m_a$

Table 3–2. Collision between two cars A and B with $m_a = 2m_b = 2m$.
Distance between switches: 0.50 m.

	Time Δt, sec	Velocity v, m/sec	Momentum p, kgm·m/sec
Before collision			
Car A	0.60	$v_a = 0.83$	$p_a = 2m \cdot 0.83$
Car B	—	$v_b = 0$	$p_b = 0$
After collision			
Car A	0.91	$v'_a = v'_b = 0.55$	$p'_a = 2m \cdot 0.55$
Car B			$p'_b = m \cdot 0.55$

Total momentum before collision: $p = p_a + p_b = 1.6(6)m$
Total momentum after collision: $p' = p'_a + p'_b = 3m \cdot 0.55 = 1.6(5)m$

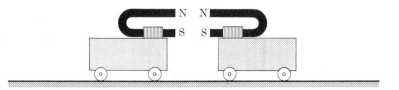

FIG. 3–3. Collision experiment involving magnetic interaction.

have $v'_a = v'_b$. Although the details of the motion in this collision are entirely different from those in the spring-type collision, we again find that within the experimental errors, the total momentum of the bodies is the same both before and after the collision.

The experiments with the spring and the putty both offered examples of contact interactions. Appropriately mounted magnets will permit the cars to interact without actually contacting each other (Fig. 3–3). Here again detailed experiments show results that are in accordance with the law of conservation of momentum.

We could go on trying all the types of interactions that come to mind, but we have tried a small but varied sample and shall now consider the law of conservation of momentum as established. The strongest evidence for this law, of course, is that it has proved useful in widely different situations encountered in the study of motion throughout the development of science, and we shall consider it one of the basic laws of physics.

EXAMPLE. A rifle is attached securely to a car that is free to roll on a level track. The total mass of the rifle and the car is $m_1 = 10$ kgm. A bullet of mass $m_2 = 0.005$ kgm (5 gm) is shot horizontally to the right and is observed to have traveled a distance $l_2 = 50$ m from the starting point in $\tau = 0.2$ sec. How far and in what direction has the car (plus the attached rifle) moved during this time?

The system (car, rifle, and bullet) had no momentum before the explosion and so must have no momentum after the explosion:

$$m_1 v'_1 + m_2 v'_2 = 0.$$

If we can find the car's velocity v'_1, we can also find the distance the car will travel in time τ.

$$v'_1 = -\frac{m_2}{m_1} v'_2,$$

$$l_1 = v'_1 \tau = -\frac{m_2}{m_1} v'_2 \tau.$$

The bullet's velocity was $v'_2 = l_2/\tau$, and so we have

$$l_1 = -\frac{m_2}{m_1} l_2 = -\frac{0.005}{10} \cdot 50 = -0.025 \text{ m} = -2.5 \text{ cm}.$$

(The minus sign indicates that the car moved to the left.)

EXAMPLE. A body of mass M moves in outer space with velocity V. It is desired to break the body into two parts so that the mass of one part is one-tenth of the total mass. The explosive separation should be such that after the explosion the heavier part comes to rest, while the lighter part continues in the original direction of motion. (This is similar to the separation of an artificial satellite from its rocket.) With what velocity does the small part continue?

We can consider the bodies to be interacting only between themselves, so that the influence of other bodies can be neglected. Hence total momentum is conserved. The total momentum before the explosion is MV. It must have the same value after the collision ($m_a = 0.9M$, $m_b = 0.1M$).

	Momentum before	Momentum after
Body A	$0.9MV$	0
Body B	$0.1MV$	$0.1Mv'_b$
Total momentum	$p = MV$	$p' = 0.1Mv'_b$

Therefore, with $p = p'$,

$$MV = 0.1Mv'_b,$$

$$v'_b = 10V.$$

3–4 Perfectly elastic and perfectly inelastic collisions. Although conservation of momentum applies to all interactions, it should be clear that the velocities of the bodies after a collision are usually different for different interactions, even if the initial velocities are the same. In spring-type collisions, we note from Table 3–1 that the magnitude of the *relative* velocity of the two bodies, i.e., the difference between the velocities of A and B, is not much different before and after the collision. From Table 3–1 these relative velocities are found to be $v_a - v_b = 0.61 - (-0.93) = 1.54$ m/sec and $v'_a - v'_b = -0.88 - 0.57 = -1.45$ m/sec. In the "clay-type" collision described in Table 3–2, we note that the relative velocity of the bodies is *zero* after the collision.

The change of relative velocity between colliding bodies is often used as a crude means of classifying interactions. It is customary to call a collision *perfectly elastic* if the relative velocity of the colliding bodies after the collision is the same as before except for a change in sign:

$$v'_a - v'_b = -(v_a - v_b) \quad \text{(perfectly elastic, one dimension).} \quad (3\text{--}2)$$

Other collisions are called inelastic, and collisions in which the relative velocity is zero after the collision are called *perfectly inelastic*:

$$v'_a - v'_b = 0 \quad \text{(perfectly inelastic, one dimension).} \quad (3\text{--}3)$$

In the original explosive-type experiment used in the definition of inertial mass as discussed in Sec. 2–2, the relative velocity was zero before we burned the string that held the cars together, and it was certainly different from zero afterwards. With a little imagination one can think of other examples of this nature, e.g., interactions or collisions in which the magnitude of the relative velocity increases as a result of the interaction or collision. So far as anyone knows, interactions of this type (and we shall for now call them explosive-type interactions) all have one feature in common: there is some definite physical change associated with the interaction. In our first experiment, for example, the spring changed from the state of being cocked to the state of being uncocked. A firecracker placed between two cars and arranged to go off at the instant of collision would be another example of an explosive-type collision. Upon exploding, the firecracker certainly has undergone a change in its physical state. Perfectly elastic collisions, on the other hand, characteristically do not involve physical changes of the colliding bodies. In spring-cushioned collisions, which we found to be almost perfectly elastic, the spring was in its natural relaxed state both before and after the interaction.

We shall see eventually that there is deep significance in the fact that the magnitude of the relative velocity does not ordinarily increase in collisions. If there were collisions in which the magnitude of the relative velocity increased, and in which there were no physical changes of the bodies taking part, one could construct so-called *perpetual-motion machines*. We suggest that the reader speculate about the nature of such machines. For example, a ball between two rigid parallel walls would gain speed each time it collided with a wall if, in the interaction between the ball and the walls, the relative velocity always increased. However, such interactions have not been found. We shall later discuss the absence of such interactions and make this observation a "law" of nature. Most collisions, we have seen, involve a decrease in the relative velocities of the bodies, and here too, if one looks hard enough, some change in the physical state of the bodies can always be found. It turns out that these matters are much better discussed in terms of (*kinetic*) *energy*, a concept which will be introduced a little later.

EXAMPLE. In a perfectly elastic collision between two cars on a track, the velocities of the bodies are $v_a = 3$ m/sec and $v_b = -2$ m/sec. The masses of the bodies are $m_a = 1$ kgm and $m_b = 2$ kgm. What are the velocities of the bodies after the collision?

Let the velocities of the bodies after the collision be v'_a and v'_b. Conservation of momentum gives

$$m_a v_a + m_b v_b = m_a v'_a + m_b v'_b.$$

Since the collision is elastic,

$$v'_a - v'_b = -(v_a - v_b).$$

Eliminating v_b' between these equations, we get for the velocity v_a',

$$v_a' = \frac{(m_a - m_b)v_a + 2m_b v_b}{m_a + m_b},$$

and, similarly, for v_b',

$$v_b' = \frac{(m_b - m_a)v_b + 2m_a v_a}{m_a + m_b}.$$

In this particular example we get

$$v_a' = \frac{(1 - 2)3 + 2 \cdot 2(-2)}{1 + 2} = -\tfrac{11}{3} \text{ m/sec,}$$

$$v_b' = \frac{(2 - 1)(-2) + 2 \cdot 1 \cdot 3}{3} = \frac{-2 + 6}{3} = \tfrac{4}{3} \text{ m/sec.}$$

3–5 Center of mass. Nothing new in principle will be introduced in this section. We shall merely indicate, by introducing the concept of the *center of mass* of the interacting bodies, how the law of conservation of momentum can be interpreted in a simple, useful, and interesting way.

Let the coordinates of two interacting bodies be x_a and x_b as measured from an arbitrary origin of a *fixed coordinate system*. For the time being, a fixed coordinate system will be defined as a system that is connected to the earth. This coordinate system we shall often refer to as the *laboratory system*. All of our experimental results and the ensuing laws of motion will refer to this fixed "laboratory" coordinate system. In a later chapter we shall discuss the influence of the motion of the coordinate system.

The location of the center of mass of the two bodies in the fixed coordinate system is defined as

$$X = \frac{m_a x_a + m_b x_b}{m_a + m_b}. \qquad (3\text{–}4)$$

This point divides the distance between the bodies into parts d_a and d_b, as in Fig. 3–4, so that $m_a d_a = m_b d_b$. The reader should convince himself that this result follows directly from the definition in Eq. (3–4). If the

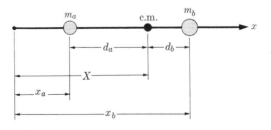

Fɪɢ. 3–4. Center of mass.

masses of the bodies are equal, the center of mass lies midway between the bodies. Clearly, the center of mass moves with the bodies, and this motion has some simple and very useful properties. This, of course, is the reason for introducing and using this concept.

When the two bodies are displaced distances Δx_a and Δx_b in time Δt, the corresponding displacement of the center of mass is $\Delta X = (m_a \Delta x_a + m_b \Delta x_b)/(m_a + m_b)$, and by dividing by Δt we obtain the velocity of the center of mass:

$$V = \frac{m_a v_a + m_b v_b}{m_a + m_b} = \frac{p_a + p_b}{m_a + m_b}. \tag{3-5}$$

Since $p = m_a v_a + m_b v_b = p_a + p_b$ remains constant according to the law of conservation of momentum, it follows that the *velocity of the center of mass is the same before and after a collision.* Furthermore, one may express the total momentum of the system as the product of the total mass of the system and the velocity of the center of mass:

$$p = p_a + p_b = (m_a + m_b)V.$$

If the total momentum is zero, the center of mass has zero velocity and so remains stationary.

EXAMPLE. Two boys of masses 40 and 60 kgm stand on a frictionless ice surface holding a straight bar of length 12 m between them. Starting from the ends of the bar, the boys pull themselves along the bar until they meet. How far has each boy moved on the ice? Neglect the mass of the bar.

The center of mass is originally at rest, and since the boys interact only with each other, the center of mass will remain at rest. Therefore, the boys must meet at the center of mass. The distance to the center of mass from boy A, of mass 40 kgm, is

$$X = \frac{m_b x_b}{m_a + m_b} = \frac{60}{40 + 60} \cdot 12 = 7.2 \text{ m}.$$

Therefore A moves 7.2 m and B moves 4.8 m.

Three or more interacting bodies. The total momentum of three or more bodies which can interact only among themselves is constant, just as the total momentum of two bodies is constant. In the most general case, in which three or more bodies interact *simultaneously*, we must appeal to experiment to show that the momentum is conserved. We shall not pursue the details of this type of experiment here. But we can see how reasonable the law of conservation of momentum is in the case of three (or more) bodies from the following simple thought experiment.

Imagine three bodies A, B, and C with momenta p_a, p_b, and p_c. The initial total momentum is therefore $p_a + p_b + p_c$. Now let A and B

collide, and then somewhat later let B and C collide. The combined
momentum of A and B, that is, $p_a + p_b$, does not change when A and B
collide, and of course the momentum p_c of C does not change either, because C did not participate. Therefore the total momentum $p_a + p_b + p_c$
does not change as a result of a collision between A and B. The same
argument can also show that the total momentum will not change as a
result of a collision between any two members of an even larger group.
This argument does not demonstrate that momentum will be conserved
when three or more bodies interact simultaneously, but experiments do
bear out our contention. We have

$$p_a + p_b + p_c + \cdots = p_a' + p_b' + p_c' + \cdots . \qquad (3\text{–}6)$$

The center of mass of a group of many bodies (or many particles) is
defined by

$$X = \frac{m_a x_a + m_b x_b + m_c x_c + \cdots}{m_a + m_b + m_c + \cdots}, \qquad (3\text{–}7)$$

and the corresponding velocity of the center of mass is

$$V = \frac{m_a v_a + m_b v_b + m_c v_c + \cdots}{m_a + m_b + m_c + \cdots}. \qquad (3\text{–}8)$$

If the various bodies can interact only among themselves, their total
momentum is constant, and it follows from Eq. (3–8) that the velocity
of their center of mass is constant.

All objects have a point which is their center of mass. Matter is composed of atoms, and to find the center of mass of an object, we can imagine
a straightforward (but hopelessly tedious) application of expression (3–7)
wherein the atoms are labeled A, B, C, etc., to find X. For many bodies
(cubes, spheres, spherical shells, uniform straight bars, etc.) the symmetry
is such that the center of mass can be found by inspection. Note that the
center of mass need not be actually within the material of a body; for
instance, the center of mass of a horseshoe is a mathematical point in
space.

3–6 Conservation of momentum during a collision. The law of conservation of momentum, obtained from the experiments we have discussed,
refers to conditions before and after collisions. Although it is reasonable
to assume that conservation of momentum also applies *during* a collision,
clearly it is difficult in most cases to study the motion of the colliding
bodies during the comparatively short collision periods. However, we can
design an experiment in which the interaction period is comparatively
long, so that velocity measurements are possible. Such an experiment
is shown in Fig. 3–5. Two pucks connected by a rubber string are pulled

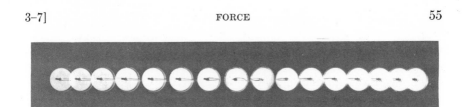

FIG. 3–5. Motion in a plane of two air-suspended pucks connected by a spring.

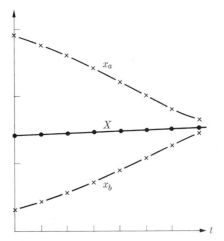

FIG. 3–6. The center of mass of the two interacting bodies in Fig. 3–5 moves with constant speed (the masses of the pucks, $m_a = 1.5$ kgm and $m_b = 2$ kgm). Total momentum is conserved during interaction.

apart, released, and photographed under stroboscopic illumination as they travel toward each other. If momentum is conserved during the interaction, the center of mass of the bodies should move with constant speed, since their total momentum can be expressed as the product of their total mass and the velocity of the center of mass. In Fig. 3–6 are shown the x-coordinates of the two pucks, plotted as functions of elapsed time. Also shown is the location of the center of mass, and since this x vs. t plot is a straight line, we conclude that the center-of-mass velocity is constant. Therefore the total momentum is also constant, and in this case we conclude that conservation of momentum is valid even during interactions. We shall take this to be true always.

3–7 Force. In our study of interactions so far, we have been concerned mainly with the total momentum of a system of interacting bodies. However, in many situations with which we deal in practice, we are interested in the motion of only one body of a system. In the case of a stone falling toward the earth in vacuum, for example, there is interaction between the stone and the earth, and according to the law of conservation of momentum, the momentum gain by the stone is counterbalanced by an equal but opposite momentum gain by the earth. Their center of mass stays at rest. But we are interested in and able to observe only the motion of the stone, and here the law of conservation of momentum does not help us very much.

Furthermore, the conservation of total momentum does not differentiate between one type of interaction or collision and another, and if we wish to introduce a measure of the "strength" of the interaction, we must consider the change of momentum of *one* of the interacting bodies. We realize, of course, that the *net* momentum change of a body can be the same in different interactions. For example, a body made to bounce against a long, soft spring can undergo the same momentum change as when a short, stiff spring is used. In other words, a body can be given the same final velocity or momentum by a "hard" push for a short time or by a weak push which lasts for a relatively long time. Therefore, in order to distinguish interactions from each other in terms of momentum transfers, it is not sufficient to specify net momentum transfers. We must also introduce and use a quantity that has to do with the rates of momentum transfer.

Let us now refer to one of the previous collision experiments and discuss it in more detail. Consider the case in which both A and B move in the positive x-direction, with $v_b > v_a$. As a result of the collision, A speeds up and B slows down, as illustrated graphically in Fig. 3–7. During collision, the momentum of A increases by the amount $\Delta p_a = p_a' - p_a$. Clearly, the details of this momentum change during the collision will be different for different interactions. A long, soft spring will cause the mo-

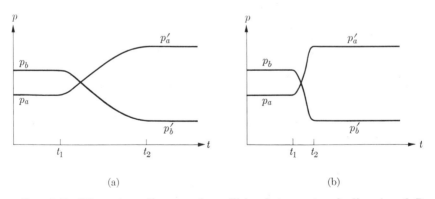

Fig. 3–7. Momentum diagram of a collision between two bodies A and B. The collision starts at $t = t_1$ and ends at $t = t_2$. During the collision, A speeds up and B slows down. In (a) the momentum changes take place slowly and the interaction is weak. In (b) the momentum changes take place more quickly and the interaction is stronger.

mentum to change slowly over a relatively long period of time, whereas a short, stiff spring will produce the same momentum change in a very short time. The time rate of change of the momentum of the body will be used as a measure of the "strength" of the interaction, and will be called the *force* on the body.

Even when the details of the momentum *vs.* time curve are not known, an average rate of change of momentum can be determined. If the collision starts at time t_1 and ends at time t_2, the average rate of momentum change is $(p_a' - p_a)/(t_2 - t_1) = \Delta p_a/\Delta t$. The (time) *average force* on body A (written $\overline{F}_a$) in the interval Δt is then, by definition,

$$\overline{F}_a = \frac{\Delta p_a}{\Delta t} = \frac{p_a' - p_a}{t_2 - t_1}. \tag{3–9}$$

Since conservation of momentum requires that $\Delta p_a = -\Delta p_b$, it follows that the forces on A and B, $\overline{F}_a = \Delta p_a/\Delta t$ and $\overline{F}_b = \Delta p_b/\Delta t$, respectively, are equal in magnitude but opposite in sign, i.e.,

$$\overline{F}_a = \frac{\Delta p_a}{\Delta t} = -\frac{\Delta p_b}{\Delta t} = -\overline{F}_b. \tag{3–10}$$

Units of force. The unit of force is a unit change of momentum per unit of time. If we choose the units of length, mass, and time to be meter, kilogram, and second, respectively, the unit of momentum is one kgm·m/sec, and the corresponding unit of force becomes one kgm·m/sec^2. This unit of force is called *one newton*, n, and the system of units based on the meter-kilogram-second is called the *mks system*.

In the *cgs system* the units of length, mass, and time are the centimeter (10^{-2} m), the gram (10^{-3} kgm), and the second. The corresponding unit of force, one gm·cm/sec^2, is called *one dyne* (10^{-5} n).

Finally, in the English system, the foot is the unit of length ($\simeq 30.5$ cm), the slug is the unit of mass ($\simeq 14.7$ kgm), and the second is the unit of time. The unit of force, one slug·ft/sec^2, is called *one pound* (4.27 n).

EXAMPLE. A baseball is pitched with a speed of 80 ft/sec and comes in toward the plate practically along a horizontal line. Assume that the batter hits the ball and that the ball leaves the bat along the same horizontal line with a speed of 160 ft/sec. The baseball weighs 5/16 lb and so, as we shall discuss presently, has a mass of $(5/16) \cdot (1/32)$ slug. What is the average force on the bat if the contact time between the ball and the bat is 0.01 sec?

The magnitudes of the momenta before and after the collision are

$$|p_1| = M \cdot 80 = \frac{5}{16} \cdot \frac{80}{32} \simeq 0.78 \text{ slug·ft/sec} = 0.78 \text{ lb·sec}$$

and

$$|p_2| = M \cdot 160 = \frac{5}{16} \cdot \frac{160}{32} \simeq 1.56 \text{ slug·ft/sec} = 1.56 \text{ lb·sec}.$$

The magnitude of the momentum transfer is then 2.34 lb·sec and the average force is

$$|\overline{F}| = \left|\frac{\Delta p}{\Delta t}\right| = \frac{2.34}{0.01} \simeq 234 \text{ lb.}$$

Instantaneous force. We have so far considered only the average force on a body in a finite time interval Δt. In order to describe the interaction in more detail, we shall introduce the *instantaneous force*. In Chapter 1, we discussed the meaning of instantaneous velocity v, and we shall assume that the reader is familiar with this concept. Now suppose that we determine the instantaneous momentum $p_a = mv_a$ of a body A during a collision and plot it as a function of time, as indicated in Fig. 3–8. In this example the collision starts at $t = 0.2$ sec and ends at $t = 0.5$ sec. The total momentum change is $40 - 10 = 30$ kgm·m/sec, and the average force is then $\overline{F}_a = 30/0.3 = 100$ n. The *instantaneous force*, or the instantaneous rate of change of momentum at a certain time t, is defined

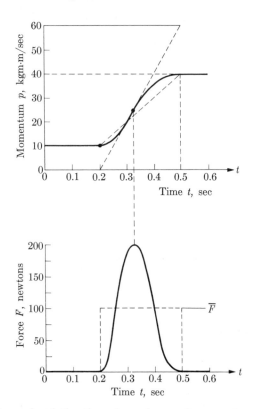

FIG. 3–8. Example of the time dependence of momentum and force in a collision. The force is determined by the slope of the momentum curve.

by the "slope" of the geometrical tangent to the momentum curve $p = p(t)$ at time t. (If the units of momentum and time are not represented by equal lengths on the p- and t-scales, we must, of course, account for the corresponding scale factors in determining the force from the slope of the tangent.) The maximum slope of the curve in Fig. 3–8 and the maximum force are $60/0.3 = 200$ n. By measuring the slope of the momentum curve as a function of time, we obtain a force curve, as shown in the figure.

The geometrical interpretation and definition of force given above are equivalent to the analytical definition which says that force is the *time derivative* of the momentum. Thus, mathematically, the instantaneous force on a body A is denoted by

$$F_a = \frac{dp_a}{dt} = m_a \frac{dv_a}{dt}, \tag{3–11}$$

where, of course, dv_a/dt is the acceleration of the body A.

It does not matter which of two interacting bodies we use to evaluate the momentum transfer, since the momentum gained by one body is lost by the other. Therefore, if the rate of change of momentum of body A is denoted by dp_a/dt, the rate of change, dp_b/dt, of the momentum of body B must be the same except for sign, that is,

$$\frac{dp_a}{dt} = -\frac{dp_b}{dt}.$$

Consequently, as a result of the law of conservation of momentum, the forces on the interacting bodies A and B are always equal in magnitude but opposite in sign:

$$F_a = -F_b. \tag{3–12}$$

This relation is called *Newton's third law*. The *second law of Newton* is the definition of force in terms of momentum as given in Eq. (3–11), and the *first law* expresses the original contention that an isolated body which does not interact with any other body moves with constant velocity.

One might wonder why we did not introduce the spatial rate of momentum transfer dp/dx rather than dp/dt. In principle, we certainly could have introduced this rate of transfer also, but we would have soon realized that dp/dx is not a very useful quantity. First of all, the rates dp/dx for A and for B do not have the same magnitude since for a given momentum change $\Delta p_a = -\Delta p_b$, the bodies usually do not move equal distances. Another important reason why dp/dx is less suitable for the description of interactions has to do with the very important *principle of superposition of forces* which holds for the dp/dt but not for a dp/dx definition of force.

To determine a force, we must know the momentum as a function of time, and it is only after first studying the motion of a body that we can find the force acting upon it. Historically, the most famous result of an analysis of motion leading to a force law is perhaps Newton's gravitational force law, derived from the study of planetary motion (see Chapter 10).

From the accumulated experience and knowledge of motion under various conditions, the situation is often, as in many engineering and scientific problems, such that the *forces are known*, and the problem is to find the motion corresponding to the given force. Knowledge of the force law means, of course, that we know the quantities the force depends upon and also the nature of this dependence. Gravitational and electrostatic forces *depend upon the distance between the interacting bodies.* Electromagnetic, nuclear, and contact forces, in general, depend upon the relative velocities of the bodies as well as the distances between them. The basic differences among forces, aside from the dependencies mentioned above, are the inherent properties of matter responsible for the existence of the forces. Electric charge determines the electrostatic force, gravitational mass determines the gravitational force, and electric currents determine the electromagnetic force.

3–8 Gravitational force. The most apparent and familiar force is perhaps local gravitational force, the pull toward earth experienced by all bodies at the surface of the earth. As indicated in Chapter 1, early experimental studies of free fall established the important property of this motion that *all* bodies regardless of their masses or initial velocities fall with the same constant acceleration in vacuum, $g \simeq 9.81$ m/sec^2. What does this result tell us about the property of the gravitational force? The force is given by $F = ma$, where a is the acceleration. The fact that the acceleration, $a = F/m$, remains constant ($a = g$) when m is varied by choosing different bodies in the free-fall experiment, shows that the force must be proportional to the inertial mass, m. In other words, if we were to introduce a property of matter which we consider responsible for the gravitational pull, this property would grow in proportion to the inertial mass. A detailed analysis of the gravitational force will be given in Chapter 10, and at present it will be sufficient merely to summarize some of the basic properties.

For the description of interactions in general, we need to know (1) how the interaction force between the bodies depends upon such quantities as the separation of the bodies and their relative speeds, and (2) which *inherent property* of the bodies is responsible for the force. For example, the electric charge responsible for electric forces is such an inherent property. The property of matter considered responsible for gravitational force is called *gravitational mass*. By definition, the ratio between the gravitational masses of two bodies A and B is measured by the ratio between the forces exerted by the earth at the same location. If these forces are measured by acceleration studies and found to be F_a and F_b, the ratio between the gravitational masses M_a and M_b is then

$$\frac{M_a}{M_b} = \frac{F_a}{F_b}.$$

From the free-fall experiments we have $F_a = m_a g$ and $F_b = m_b g$, so that

$$\frac{F_a}{F_b} = \frac{m_a}{m_b} \qquad (m = \text{inertial mass}).$$

By comparison, then, we see that the ratio between the gravitational masses of two bodies must equal the ratio between the inertial masses. In other words, the gravitational mass is proportional to the inertial mass, $M = (\text{const})\, m$. If the unit of gravitational mass is chosen equal to the unit of inertial mass, we get $M = m$.

Because of this experimentally found proportionality between the gravitational and inertial masses and the choice of the same units, the magnitudes of these quantities are always described by the same number and the distinction between them becomes obscured. In everyday practice one generally does not distinguish between the two mass concepts, both are referred to simply as "mass." We should remember, though, that the inertial mass and the gravitational mass of a body stand for two different properties of matter, the resistance to changes in motion and the property responsible for gravitational attraction.

The gravitational force, then, is ascribed to a property of matter, the gravitational mass, which is possessed by all material bodies. Gravitational interaction is always an attractive force. In Chapter 1, it was mentioned that the basis for Newton's quantitative description of gravitational interaction was Kepler's three laws of motion, which described some features of the motion of the planets about the sun and hence expressed some properties of the interaction between the sun and its planets. By introducing the concept of force, Newton showed how the interaction could be described in a concise way, and he was able to formulate the gravitational force law (see Chapter 10 for details),

$$F = G\,\frac{M_1 M_2}{r^2}. \tag{3–13}$$

The quantities M_1 and M_2 are the gravitational masses of the interacting particles and r is the distance between them. It is implied that the dimensions of the particles are small as compared with the distance between them. It will be shown in an appendix that in the special case of a sphere, the gravitational force produced by it is the same as that of a mass point of equal mass at the center of the sphere.

Newton proposed that this law be generally valid for any two interacting material particles which are small compared with the distance between them. He also proposed that G be a universal constant, the same for all bodies, independent of their chemical or physical constitution. The value of this universal constant depends, of course, upon the choice of unit of the gravitational mass, M. With the unit of gravitational mass chosen to be the same as the inertial mass, say one kilogram, and with the distance expressed in meters, the universal gravitational constant G becomes

$$G \simeq 6.67 \cdot 10^{-11} \, \text{n·m}^2/\text{kgm}^2.$$

The universal law of gravitation has been verified experimentally in the laboratory by the famous Cavendish experiment (1797).

If we apply Eq. (3–13) to the interaction between the earth and a body at the earth's surface, we have $r = R$, where R is the radius of the earth; if we denote the mass of the body by m and the mass of the earth by M, we get $F = m(GM/R^2)$. Since we also have $F = mg$, the local constant free-fall acceleration is related to the mass and the radius of the earth by the equation

$$g = \frac{GM}{R^2}. \tag{3–14}$$

As indicated in Chapter 2, the gravitational force mg on a body is called the *weight* of the body. The weight, then, in contrast to the inertial mass, is not an inherent or invariant property of the body, since it depends upon the properties of the earth and the distance from the earth. Actually, in addition to the dependence upon distance, there is also a slight variation in the weight of a body owing to its location on the earth; weight gradually increases from the equator to the poles. However, the variation is less than about 1%. This variation will be discussed in Chapter 11.

EXAMPLE. We have seen that the acceleration of a body in free fall at the surface of the earth is constant and equal to $g = 9.8 \, \text{m/sec}^2 \simeq 32 \, \text{ft/sec}^2$. (a) What is the weight of a body with a mass $M = 1$ kgm, 1 slug, 1 gm? The weights are $Mg = 9.81$ n, 32 lb, and 981 dynes, respectively. What mass has a weight of one pound? This mass is clearly such that $Mg = 1$ lb, that is, $M = 1/g = 1/32$ slug. (b) The gravitational force from the earth varies with the inverse square of the distance from the earth's center. The earth's radius is $6.4 \cdot 10^6$ m. How high above the earth's surface must a 160-lb body go in order that its weight be decreased by 40 lb?

If the earth's radius is denoted by R and the height above the earth's surface by h, we have

$$\frac{160}{160-40} = \frac{(R+h)^2}{R^2},$$

$$1+\frac{h}{R} = \sqrt{\frac{16}{12}} = \sqrt{\frac{4}{3}},$$

$$\frac{h}{R} = \sqrt{\frac{4}{3}} - 1 \simeq 0.155,$$

that is, $h \simeq 10^6$ m. We should remember, however, that although a body *loses weight as it ascends, its inertial mass remains constant.*

Motion along a vertical line. Consider now the motion of a body along a vertical line. We shall describe the motion with respect to a coordinate axis y with $y = 0$ at the ground and with the positive y-direction pointing upward. If the mass of the body is m, the force on it is then $F_y = -mg$. If the body is projected upward from the ground with the velocity v_0 at $t = 0$, we obtain from $m(dv_y/dt) = -mg$ the following expression for the velocity v_y at a later time t:

$$v_y = v_0 - gt. \tag{3-15}$$

Similarly, for the location we find (see Chapter 1)

$$y = v_0t - \frac{gt^2}{2}. \tag{3-16}$$

These relations are shown graphically in Fig. 3-9. The velocity becomes zero at the time t_0 (given by $t_0 = v_0/g$) which corresponds to a location $y_{max} = h$, given by

$$h = \frac{v_0^2}{g} - g\frac{v_0^2}{2g^2} = \frac{v_0^2}{2g}.$$

The location y is obviously zero at the starting time $t = 0$, but it also becomes zero when $t = 2v_0/g = 2t_0$, which represents the time when the body hits the ground after its flight up and down. Since the time for the trip up is t_0 and the total round-trip time is $2t_0$, the time for the trip down is also t_0, as expected.

If the motion is started at a position $y = y_0$ at a time $t = t_0$ rather than from the ground, $y = 0$, at $t = 0$, the expressions for the velocity and position are obtained from Eqs. (3-15) and (3-16) simply by replacing t with $t - t_0$ and y with $y - y_0$. Note that in this general case v_0 can be both positive and negative.

EXAMPLE. A body A of mass 2 kgm is projected upward from the surface of the ground at $t = 0$ with a velocity of 20 m/sec. One second later body B,

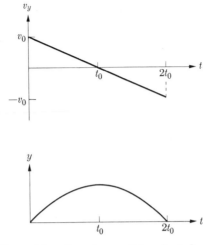

FIG. 3–9. Velocity and location of a particle, ejected upward with velocity v_0 from the ground, $y = 0$, plotted as functions of time.

also with a mass 2 kgm, is dropped from a height of 20 m. When and where do the bodies collide? (Use $g \simeq 10$ m/sec^2.)

The positions of A and B are given by the equations

$$y_a = 20t - 10t^2/2 = 20t - 5t^2$$

and

$$y_b = 20 - 10(t - 1)^2/2 = 20 - 5(t - 1)^2.$$

By setting $y_a = y_b$, we obtain $t = 3/2$ sec as the time of the collision and $18\frac{3}{4}$ m as the height at which the collision takes place. Furthermore, just before the collision the velocity of A is $20 - 10(3/2) = 5$ m/sec and the velocity of B is $0 - 10 \cdot 0.5 = -5$ m/sec.

Gravitational force is perhaps the most familiar cause of uniformly accelerated motion, but there are others too. Whenever the force on a body is constant, the acceleration is also constant and equal to $a = F/m$. In the case of gravitational force illustrated in Fig. 3–9, the acceleration is $a = -g$, where the minus sign arises because we chose the position coordinate y to increase *upward*, whereas the force F and the acceleration are directed *downward*. The kinematic equations for uniformly accelerated motion follow directly from the arguments given in arriving at Eqs. (3–15) and (3–16), and we have

$$v_x = v_0 + at, \tag{3–17}$$

$$x = x_0 + v_0t + \frac{at^2}{2}, \tag{3–18}$$

for a body with an acceleration a in the x-direction, with an initial position x_0, and with an initial velocity v_0 at $t = 0$. Note carefully that these expressions refer to uniformly accelerated motion and are *not* valid when the acceleration is not constant.

EXAMPLE. A car starts from rest with a constant acceleration $a_1 = 10$ ft/sec^2, which it maintains for a time $t_1 = 3$ sec. Thereafter, what should be the acceleration (assumed constant) to bring it to rest a distance $L = 100$ ft from the initial point?

During the first 3 sec, the car reaches the position

$$x_1 = \frac{a_1 t_1^2}{2} = 10 \cdot \frac{9}{2} = 45 \text{ ft}$$

from the starting point. The velocity is

$$v_1 = at = 30 \text{ ft/sec.}$$

The acceleration thereafter is denoted by a_2. The time required to stop is t_2. Then

$$55 = v_1 t_2 + a_2 \frac{t_2^2}{2},$$

$$v_2 = v_1 + a_2 t_2 = 0,$$

which gives $t_2 = -v_1/a_2$ and $55 = -v_1^2/a_2 + v_1^2/2a_2 = -v_1^2/2a_2$ or $a_2 = -900/(2 \cdot 55)$ ft/sec$^2 \simeq -8.17$ ft/sec^2.

3–9 The spring force. In complete analogy with the study of the gravitational force, we can now proceed to investigate the properties of other interactions by measuring, for example, the force as a function of the separation and the relative velocity of the interacting bodies. We can also vary the properties of the bodies themselves and investigate the corresponding effects on the force. At present this kind of investigation will be limited to the simple case of a spring-type force, but we shall return in later sections to other types of interactions.

To measure the force on a body in contact with a spring as a function of the compression of the spring, we measure the acceleration of the body as it moves under the influence of the spring. For simplicity, consider one end of the spring to be held fixed, as shown in Fig. 3–10. Such experiments show that the acceleration given to the body by the spring when it is released from rest will be proportional to the compression or the extension of the spring from its equilibrium length. In other words, if we account for the fact that the acceleration will be in the opposite direction to the displacement of the body, we have

$$F_x = -Kx, \tag{3–19}$$

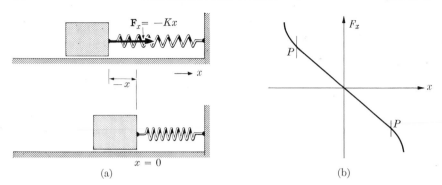

FIG. 3–10.   The spring force on a body can be expressed as $F_x = -Kx$, where K is the spring constant.

where K is a constant, called the spring constant, which depends on the nature of the spring. This simple linear relationship, illustrated in Fig. 3–10, applies to most springs, at least so long as the displacement x is sufficiently small.   At larger displacements x, the springs eventually become "nonlinear," as illustrated in Fig. 3–10(b), where the points marked P on the curve indicate the onset of nonlinearity.

Further experiments of this kind show that the force on the body at a certain compression x does not, in general, depend markedly on the speed of the body or on the direction of motion. Furthermore, the force is found to be the same on any body placed at the end of the spring, regardless of its mass. Thus, according to such measurements, the force produced by the spring on a body in contact with it is uniquely determined by the compression or extension, x, of the spring from its equilibrium length, as given by Eq. (3–19).

EXAMPLE. A spring with a relaxed length of 0.50 m is held fixed at one end. A force of 200 n is applied at the other end, increasing the length of the spring to 0.75 m. The increase of the length of the spring is then 0.25 m, and the spring constant is $K = 200/0.25 = 800$ n/m.

3–10 The principle of superposition of forces.   We have considered in detail only two-body interactions. Body A interacts with body B, the total momentum $p_a + p_b$ remains constant, and the force on body A is equal in magnitude but oppositely directed to the force on body B. This is the essence of our story so far. The real value of the force concept will become apparent when we consider the interaction of three or more bodies or the motion of a body under the influences of more than one force, for it turns out that the forces on a body may be added to give a *net (resultant) force* that determines the motion of the body. This is the principle of superposition.

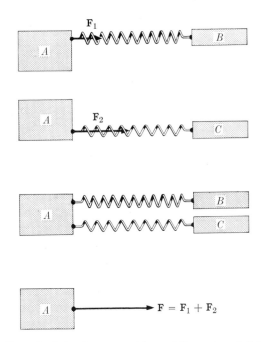

Fig. 3–11. The principle of superposition. When A and B interact alone, a force F_1 is exerted on A. When A and C interact alone, a force F_2 is exerted on A. When both B and C interact with A, body A moves as though under the influence of a single force $F = F_1 + F_2$, called the resultant or net force.

Imagine a body A which moves under the influence of one other body B. Body B may be free to move or it may be tied rigidly to the earth (Fig. 3–11). The force may arise from a spring tied between A and B, or it may be some other type of force, say magnetic or gravitational. We can certainly investigate this force and find, for example, how it depends on position, relative velocity, etc. Now let us take B away and introduce a new body C with which A can interact. Again we can investigate the force and find how it depends on position, relative velocity, etc. Now let us allow both bodies B and C to interact with A at the same time. How will A react to this new situation? What will be its motion?

We can answer these queries only by experiments, and the experimental answer is that A reacts or moves as though under the influence of a single force equal to the *sum* (or superposition) of the two previously investigated forces F_{ab} and F_{ac} from B and C, respectively. The effective force on a body is the sum of all the individual forces acting upon it, and this effective force is sometimes called the net or resultant force. This is the principle of superposition, and it is experimentally valid not for just three interacting bodies but for any number. That is, we have

$$\frac{dp}{dt} = F_1 + F_2 + F_3 + \cdots = F,$$

where F_1, F_2, F_3, etc., are individual forces on the body as found from experiments which involve the body in question and just one of the others.*

EXAMPLE. A car of mass 5 kgm is pulled along a horizontal track, by a horizontal coil-spring, with a constant acceleration of 4 m/sec². The force on the body is then $5 \cdot 4 = 20$ n. The spring is observed to be stretched by a length of 10 cm during this motion, so that the spring constant is $K = 200$ n/m. The acceleration is produced only by the influence of the spring force.

The car and the spring are now removed from the track. The spring is held vertical with its upper end fixed and with the car attached to the other end. The spring is again stretched 10 cm, and the car is released from this position. What, now, is the initial acceleration of the car?

When the car is under the influence of gravitation alone, the force on it is directed downward and has the magnitude $mg = 5 \cdot 9.8$ n. When the spring and gravitational forces are acting simultaneously on the car, according to the superposition principle the acceleration of the car is obtained from the resultant of these forces. Gravity provides a force of $5 \cdot 9.8$ n downward, and the spring force is 20 n pulling upward, so that the net force is $5 \cdot 9.8 - 20 \simeq 29$ n downward. The corresponding initial acceleration is then $29/5 \simeq 5.8$ m/sec².

On the basis of the principle of superposition, we note that one force on a body can be canceled by another which is equal but opposite in direction. In other words, if we use a spring calibrated in terms of force from direct acceleration experiments such as those described in the previous section, and extend it until the force on a mass m becomes $Kx = mg$, the mass will be given an acceleration g when it is released if no other forces are acting on m. However, when the spring is vertical and the body is under the influence of *both* the spring which produces an acceleration g

---

* There are some real and some only apparent exceptions to the principle of superposition of forces. The real exceptions arise in connection with atomic and nuclear forces. Here it is sometimes the case that the force between, say, two atoms, depends upon whether a third atom is nearby.

There are many apparent exceptions. For example, the electrostatic force between two electrically charged bodies is a result of a large number of particles (electrons) in the bodies. Although the elementary forces between the various elementary charges superpose, as described above, the net force between the bodies depends on the distribution of the charges in the bodies. This distribution, and consequently the force between the bodies, is generally changed when other charged bodies are introduced. However, the disturbance on the initial interaction force by a third body is only an apparent violation of the principle of superposition, because the force between two bodies would not change if we somehow managed to keep the charge distribution fixed.

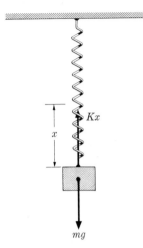

FIG. 3–12. Equilibrium when $Kx = mg$.

upward *and* the gravitational force which produces an acceleration g downward, the body will be in equilibrium at the end of the spring when the spring is stretched a distance $x = mg/K$, as illustrated in Fig. 3–12. This method of balancing two forces against each other enables the measurement of an unknown force in terms of a known one. For example, a spring balance can be calibrated in terms of the known force of gravity by measuring the equilibrium extension x produced by known weights. With zero marked on the force scale at the unstretched position of the end of the spring, the scale should be marked 9.81 n when a body of mass 1 kgm is hanging from the spring. If an identical body of mass 1 kgm is added, the scale should read 19.62 n, etc. (We have assumed here that 9.81 m/sec² is the free-fall acceleration at the location of our experiment.)

3–11 Motion of the center of mass. Although the motion of an isolated system of interacting particles may be quite complicated in its detail, the center of mass of the system moves in a simple way. From the experiments on conservation of momentum and the definition of the center of mass, we have learned that the center of mass of the system moves with constant velocity. We now wish to investigate the motion of the center of mass when one or more of the particles making up a system is acted upon by an external force.

As a first step in this direction, let us examine from the force point of view the motion of two bodies which interact only with each other. The force on body A arises only from body B. Let us call this force F_{ab}. The force on body B arises only from body A. Let us call this force F_{ba}. Then for bodies A and B we have

$$F_{ab} = \frac{dp_a}{dt} \tag{3-20}$$

and

$$F_{ba} = \frac{dp_b}{dt}. \tag{3-21}$$

But we know from our previous considerations of conservation of momentum, which led to Newton's third law, that F_{ab} and F_{ba} are equal in magnitude but oppositely directed. That is, since we have $F_{ab} = -F_{ba}$, when Eqs. (3–20) and (3–21) are added, we obtain

$$\frac{dp_a}{dt} + \frac{dp_b}{dt} = \frac{d(p_a + p_b)}{dt} = \frac{dp}{dt} = 0,$$

where $p = p_a + p_b$ is the total momentum and is equal to MV. Since $dp/dt = M(dV/dt)$ is zero, the center-of-mass velocity V must be constant. There is nothing new in all this, of course.

Suppose, on the other hand, that there is an external force on one of the bodies, say body B in Fig. 3–13. Then, making use of the principle of superposition of forces, we have for bodies A and B:

$$F_{ab} = \frac{dp_a}{dt}$$

and

$$F - F_{ba} = \frac{dp_b}{dt}.$$

When these two equations are added, we have

$$\frac{dp}{dt} = M\frac{dV}{dt} = F, \tag{3-22}$$

where, as before, $p = p_a + p_b = MV$. The acceleration (and therefore

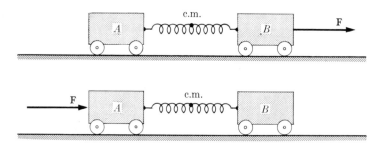

Fig. 3–13. The motion of the center of mass (c.m.) is determined by the external force and is independent of the point of application of force.

the subsequent motion) of the center of mass is determined completely by the external force F. Note carefully that if F had been applied to A we would have obtained the same result. Of course, if we wish to know the detailed motions of A and B, the forces F_{ab} and F_{ba}, which we shall call *internal forces* on the system $A + B$, must be taken into account. In the special case illustrated in Fig. 3–13, the two cars will oscillate to and fro as the whole system accelerates to the right under the influence of F. The motion of the individual cars will be complicated and will depend on the point of application of F, but *the center-of-mass motion is determined completely by the external force F and is independent of its point of application.*

What we have said about the motion of the center of mass of the two-body system can readily be extended to an arbitrary number of particles since, on the basis of the principle of superposition, the internal forces among the various bodies of the system cancel one another in pairs. The force on A from B is equal and opposite to the force on B from A, the force on A from C is equal and opposite to the force on C from A, etc. Thus the sum of the momentum transfers of all the internal forces is zero, and we find again that the only forces which can produce net momentum transfers to a system are external forces. Symbolically, we have

$$\sum_i F_i = M \frac{dV}{dt}. \qquad (3\text{--}23)$$

A rigid body is a special type of system of particles in which the particles (molecules, if we wish) maintain fixed distances from each other. Here also the forces between the particles cancel in pairs, and the center-of-mass motion is determined by the external forces. Again we should note carefully that so far as the center-of-mass motion is concerned, the point of application of the external force or forces is irrelevant. In Fig. 3–14(a) the line of action of the force goes through the center of mass of

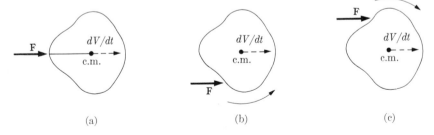

(a)   (b)   (c)

FIG. 3–14. The acceleration of the center of mass of a rigid body is independent of the point of application of a force. However, the motion of the body with respect to the center of mass *does* depend upon the point of application. Thus, in cases (b) and (c), when the force does not go through the center of mass, the force will also produce a rotation of the body in addition to the acceleration of the center of mass (see Chapter 12).

the rigid body, but in (b) and (c) it does not. In the two latter cases the force will produce a rotation of the body in addition to the acceleration of the center of mass. Although the rotation *does* depend upon the point of application the acceleration of the center of mass does not.

Which forces we call external and internal depends, of course, upon what we choose to define as our system. As an illustration, consider the two cars connected by a spring, as in Fig. 3–15. If we define our system I as the two cars (and the spring), the external force is just the force exerted by the rope on car B. The motion of the center of mass of the system (cars A and B) is determined by $F_{\mathrm{I}} = M_{\mathrm{I}}(dV_{\mathrm{I}}/dt)$, where $M_{\mathrm{I}} = m_a + m_b$ is the mass of the system, and V_{I} is the velocity of the center of mass of the system.

If, on the other hand, we choose to include in our system II whatever third body is responsible for the force F_{I}, the force F_{I} becomes an internal force, and the external force must include whatever external forces are on the third body. If the third body, C, is a motor-drive car as indicated in Fig. 3–15, the external force is the friction force (see Chapter 4) of the track on the driven wheels of the car. Then we have $F_{\mathrm{II}} = M_{\mathrm{II}}(dV_{\mathrm{II}}/dt)$, where $M_{\mathrm{II}} = m_a + m_b + m_c$ is the mass of system II, and V_{II} is the velocity of the center of mass of the system.

EXAMPLE. An elevator of mass m_2 is pulled up by means of a force F. A person of mass m_1 is inside the elevator. What is the contact force on the person from the floor (Fig. 3–16)?

If we consider the elevator and the person as a system, the external forces on the system are gravity, $(m_1 + m_2)g$, and the upward force, F. The total force in the upward direction is then $F - (m_1 + m_2)g$, and the corresponding upward acceleration is

$$a = \frac{F - (m_1 + m_2)g}{m_1 + m_2} = \frac{F}{m_1 + m_2} - g.$$

If we now isolate the person, we note that the forces on him are his weight, m_1g, directed downward and the contact force F_2 directed upward. The acceleration of the person is a, and the net force is $F_2 - m_1g$, directed upward:

$$m_1 a = m_1 \left(\frac{F}{m_1 + m_2} - g \right) = F_2 - m_1g,$$

$$F_2 = m_1g + \frac{m_1}{m_1 + m_2} F - m_1g = \frac{m_1}{m_1 + m_2} F.$$

EXAMPLE. As shown in Fig. 3–17, two cars A and B of masses $m_a = 2$ kgm and $m_b = 3$ kgm are connected by a spring of relaxed length $L = 0.5$ m and spring constant $K = 50$ n/m. The cars are originally at rest on a horizontal track. A constant force $F = 25$ n is applied on A in the direction toward B. (a) What is the initial acceleration of the center of mass of A and B? (b) What

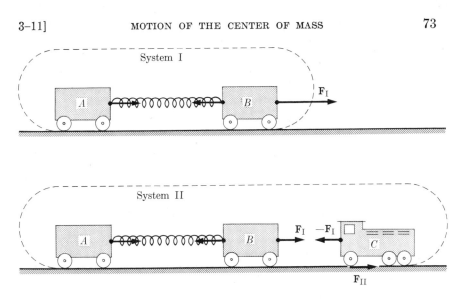

FIG. 3–15. The choice of the "system" determines which are external and which are internal forces.

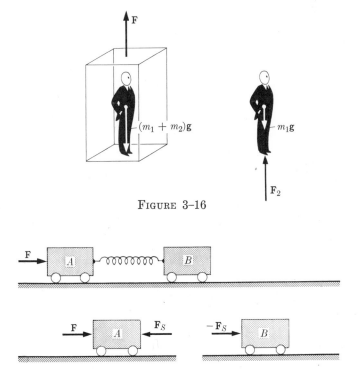

FIGURE 3–16

FIGURE 3–17

is the initial acceleration of A and of B? (c) What is the acceleration of A and B at the instant when the spring is compressed by an amount of 10 cm as A is acted upon by F?

(a) The initial acceleration of the center of mass of A and B is

$$\frac{dV}{dt} = \frac{F}{m_a + m_b} = \frac{25}{5} = 5 \text{ m/sec}^2.$$

(b) The initial acceleration of A is

$$\frac{dv_a}{dt} = \frac{F}{m_a} = \frac{25}{2} = 12.5 \text{ m/sec}^2,$$

since the spring force is initially zero. (c) At the instant when the spring is compressed 10 cm, body A is acted on by two forces, $F = 25$ n in one direction and the spring force $Kx = 50 \cdot 0.1 = 5$ n in the opposite direction, as indicated in Fig. 3–17. The acceleration of A is then

$$\frac{dv_a}{dt} = \frac{25 - 5}{2} = 10 \text{ m/sec}^2$$

and of B is

$$\frac{dv_b}{dt} = \tfrac{5}{3} \text{ m/sec}^2.$$

Equilibrium and statics. When the sum of all the external forces on a body (or system of particles) is zero, the acceleration of the center of mass is zero. Under these conditions the center of mass is said to be in *equilibrium* or, equivalently, the body is said to be in *translational equilibrium.* While bodies in equilibrium necessarily have zero center-of-mass acceleration, they do not necessarily have zero center-of-mass velocity. The study of the conditions and forces required for equilibrium, called *statics,* has wide practical applications, for example in the design of structures.

If a system or body is in translational equilibrium, it must be that

$$F = F_1 + F_2 + F_3 + \cdots = 0, \tag{3–24}$$

where F_1, F_2, F_3, etc., are the external forces. This is a necessary and sufficient condition for translational equilibrium. But this does not mean that all the parts of a system or body are in equilibrium. Only the center of mass has zero acceleration. There may be no net force on two cars connected by a spring, for example, and yet the cars may be oscillating to and fro.

Even when there is no net force on a *rigid* body, all parts of the rigid body are not necessarily in equilibrium. Imagine equal and opposite forces on the ends of a long plank and perpendicular to it. Certainly we are convinced that the center-of-mass acceleration of the plank will be

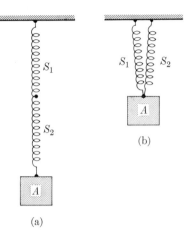

(a)

(b)

FIGURE 3–18

zero, yet clearly the plank has a tendency to rotate. (Rotational motion and conditions for rotational equilibrium will be considered in a later chapter.)

In investigating the conditions for translatory equilibrium or, for that matter, in finding the net force on a body so that its acceleration may be determined, it is most important to define precisely the system or body being considered. This ensures a clear distinction between internal and external forces, a separation that is essential since only the external forces are pertinent.

EXAMPLE. Two springs, S_1 and S_2, of negligible mass, with spring constants K_1 and K_2, respectively, are arranged to support a body A. In Fig. 3–18(a), the springs are coupled in "series" and in (b) they are in "parallel." What are the extensions of the individual springs in these two cases as a result of the force of gravity on A? Determine also the equivalent spring constant in the two cases.

In the first case the body is acted upon by two forces, the weight mg, and the spring force F_2. The spring S_2, in turn, is acted upon by F_2 at the lower end and by a contact force at the junction with S_1 at the upper end. Since the weight of the spring is negligible, the forces at the ends of the spring must cancel each other, that is, $F_1 = F_2$. Similarly, we find that spring S_1 is acted upon by opposite forces of magnitude F_2 at the two ends of the spring, as shown in Fig. 3–19. Finally, the support from which the spring S_1 is hanging is acted upon by a force F_2 downward. We have indicated all the forces acting upon the individual parts of the system, and can now impose the equilibrium conditions that the net force on A must be zero, i.e., $F_2 = Mg$. The extensions of the two springs can now be expressed in terms of mg and the spring constants:

$$x_1 = \frac{F_2}{K_1} = \frac{Mg}{K_1}, \qquad x_2 = \frac{F_1}{K_2} = \frac{Mg}{K_2}.$$

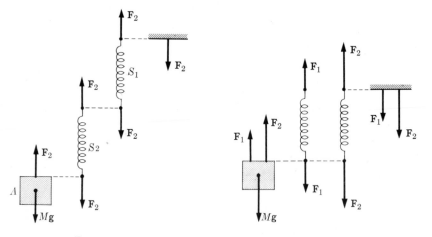

FIGURE 3-19   FIGURE 3-20

The total extension of the two springs is $x_1 + x_2 = Mg(1/K_1 + 1/K_2)$. In other words, the equivalent spring constant, $K_a = Mg/(x_1 + x_2)$, then becomes such that

$$\frac{1}{K_a} = \frac{1}{K_1} + \frac{1}{K_2}.$$

In case (b), the extensions of the two springs are the same:

$$x_1 = x_2 = x_b.$$

Body A is now acted upon by three forces, the weight and the two spring forces F_1 and F_2, as illustrated in Fig. 3-20, where the forces on the other parts of the system are also shown. We now have the relations

$$F_1 + F_2 = Mg,$$

and

$$F_1 = K_1 x_b, \qquad F_2 = K_2 x_b.$$

The condition for equilibrium of A then becomes

$$x_b(K_1 + K_2) = Mg,$$

$$x_b = \frac{Mg}{K_1 + K_2}.$$

Consequently the equivalent spring constant in this case becomes

$$K_b = K_1 + K_2.$$

In the special case when $K_1 = K_2 = K$, the equivalent spring constants in cases (a) and (b) become $K_a = K/2$ and $K_b = 2K$, respectively. In other words, the parallel coupling of the springs corresponds to a stiffness which is four times as large as that in the series coupling of the spring.

The flexible string. In our discussions we shall frequently find it convenient to exert forces on bodies by means of flexible strings. An idealized flexible string can exert only a pull, never a push, and the direction of the string force is always along the direction of the string. If a string runs over a frictionless pulley, the direction of a string force can be changed. The magnitude of the force exerted by a string is often called the *tension*. Hence if two boys at rest pull on opposite ends of a string with forces of 10 lb each, the string exerts 10-lb forces on each of the boys, and the tension in the string is 10 lb. A spring scale inserted at any point in the string would indicate this 10-lb tension. In most of the cases we shall discuss, the string mass will be much less than the mass of the bodies to which its ends are attached. Under these conditions we can neglect the mass of the string and assume that the forces it exerts on its two ends are equal (but opposite) even though the string may be accelerated.

EXAMPLE. *Acceleration experiments.* In experiments on motion with bodies sliding on a horizontal plane, a constant force is often required. It is then convenient to use the force of gravity of an external body transmitted in a horizontal direction by means of a flexible string running over a pulley, as shown in Fig. 3–21. However, it is important to note that when the system is accelerated the force transmitted to the body on the horizontal plane is *not* equal to the weight of the body at the other end of the string but is less, as we shall see below.

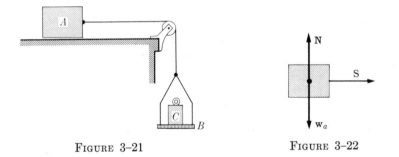

FIGURE 3–21   FIGURE 3–22

A body A on a horizontal frictionless table is connected to a string which runs over a pulley and carries a platform on its other end, as shown in Fig. 3–21. A body C is placed on the platform. The weights of A, B, and C are 10 lb, 2 lb, and 3 lb, respectively. What is the acceleration of A when the system is released from rest, and what is the tension S in the string? Determine the contact force between B and C.

We start by isolating the various bodies and indicating all the forces acting upon them. First we consider A. The forces on it are shown in Fig. 3–22. (The weight of A is balanced by the contact force N from the table.) Assume that the acceleration a of A is toward the right. The equation of motion is then

$$S = m_a a. \tag{3-25}$$

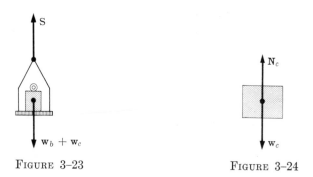

FIGURE 3–23   FIGURE 3–24

Next, we consider $B + C$ as a unit that moves downward, also with an acceleration a. The forces on $B + C$ are shown in Fig. 3–23. The equation of motion is

$$(w_b + w_c) - S = (m_b + m_c)a, \tag{3–26}$$

where we have here taken forces and accelerations positive when directed *downward*. The two unknown quantities a and S are obtained from these two equations. Thus, from Eqs. (3–25) and (3–26), we get

$$w_b + w_c = (m_a + m_b + m_c)a$$

$$a = \frac{w_b + w_c}{m_a + m_b + m_c} = \frac{m_b + m_c}{m_a + m_b + m_c}\, g,$$

since w is mg. Inserting numerical values, we obtain

$$a = \frac{2 + 3}{15}\, g = \frac{g}{3}.$$

From Eq. (3–26), the tension in the string is then

$$S = (w_b + w_c)\, \frac{m_a}{m_a + m_b + m_c} = \tfrac{2}{3}(w_b + w_c) = \tfrac{10}{3}\ \text{lb}.$$

In other words, the tension in the string is in this case only two-thirds of the weight of $B + C$.

Finally, to determine the contact force between B and C, we isolate body C, as shown in Fig. 3–24. We then find that

$$w_c - N_c = m_c a,$$

$$N_c = w_c - m_c a = m_c(g - a) = \frac{2m_c g}{3} = \tfrac{2}{3}w_c.$$

Note carefully that the tensions and contact forces are different in the equilibrium and nonequilibrium cases, as demonstrated in this example.

3–12 The force produced by a stream of particles. Rocket motion.
When a stream of particles either impinges upon or is emitted from an
object, a force is exerted on the object. This type of phenomenon is important to many situations in physics and engineering. Gas pressure,
certain types of drag force, and jet and rocket propulsion are examples.

Consider a stream of particles, each particle having a mass m and a
speed v, impinging on a rigid wall (Fig. 3–25). Let the number of particles
per unit volume in the stream be μ. Then the mass density in the stream
is $\rho = \mu m$. If the collisions that the particles make with the wall are
perfectly elastic, the particles will undergo a momentum change of $2mv$
at each collision, and so a momentum $2mv$ will be transferred to the wall
per collision.

If we wish to find the force on the wall, we must find the number of collisions per second, for the force (rate of momentum transfer) is the product
of the momentum transfer per collision and the number of collisions per
second. A particle which at one instant is a distance Δx from the wall will
reach the wall after a time $\Delta t = \Delta x / v$. In that time all particles in a
column of volume $A\,\Delta x = Av\,\Delta t$, where A is the area of the stream, will
have reached the wall (i.e., $\mu Av\,\Delta t$ particles), and the number of collisions
per second then will be $A\mu v$. The total momentum transfer per second
to the wall, or the force on the wall, is then

$$F = A\mu v(2mv) = 2A\mu mv^2 = 2A\rho v^2.$$

If, on the other hand, the collision is perfectly inelastic, the corresponding
force will be only half as much, because the momentum transfer is only
mv per collision.

Similarly, if a jet engine which is stationary on the ground discharges
a jet of speed v and density ρ, the momentum discharged per second from
the engine is $A\rho v^2$, and the corresponding force or "thrust" of the engine
has the same magnitude as that of the jet but is oppositely directed. If
the engine is free (not attached to the ground), it will acquire an initial

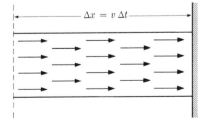

FIG. 3–25. In a stream of particles moving toward a wall at speed v, all the
particles within a distance of $v\,\Delta t$ from the wall will reach it in the next Δt sec.

acceleration dV/dt given by

$$M \frac{dV}{dt} = A\rho v^2,$$

where M is the total mass of the engine. As the engine gains speed, the speed of the jet stream relative to the ground decreases if its speed with respect to the engine remains constant. Furthermore, as the fuel is discharged, the total mass of the engine decreases, and the acceleration will vary with time.

EXAMPLE. Determine the thrust of a jet engine which discharges $Q = 200$ lb of air per second at a speed of $v = 2000$ ft/sec. Since $Q = (A\rho v)g$, we can express the force as

$$F = A\rho v^2 = \frac{Q}{g} v = \frac{200}{32} \cdot 2000 \simeq 12,500 \text{ lb.}$$

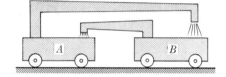

FIGURE 3–26

EXAMPLE. As shown in Fig. 3–26, two identical railroad cars travel along parallel tracks in the same direction but with different speeds V_a and V_b. Imagine that water is pumped from A to B at a rate of $R = \rho Av$ kgm/sec, where $A =$ area, $v =$ flow speed, $\rho =$ density. An identical amount of water is transferred from B to A. The rate of momentum transfer to B in the direction of motion is RV_a, and the rate of momentum transfer from B is RV_b. The net momentum transfer to B per second is $R(V_a - V_b)$; that is, the force on B is

$$F_b = \rho Av(V_a - V_b).$$

Similarly, the force on A is

$$F_a = \rho Av(V_b - V_a) = -F_b.$$

Note that the mass of each car remains constant. The force is produced by the exchange of fast-moving for slow-moving water.

A similar calculation will be performed in the kinetic theory of gases in the analysis of the *viscous force* between two layers of a gas which have different speeds. The exchange of fast-moving gas particles for slow-moving ones and vice versa produces a force between the layers.

The motion of a rocket. Basically, we can consider a rocket to consist of a container filled with fuel. As the fuel is burned, it leaves the container. The problem is to determine the equation of motion of the shell plus the unburned fuel.

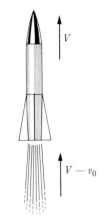

FIG. 3–27. Rocket motion.

Let us study just the simple case in which the rocket is in outer space, so that all external forces may be neglected. Let the original mass of the fuel be denoted by m_0, the mass of the fuel which *has been discharged* by m, and the mass of the rocket shell by M. The total mass of the rocket at this time is then $(m_0 - m) + M$, and if its speed is V, the total momentum is $(m_0 - m + M)V$. Now suppose that an additional fuel mass Δm is explosively separated from the rocket such that Δm is ejected with a velocity v_0 relative to the shell and in an opposite direction to V, as indicated in Fig. 3–27. After the explosion, the mass Δm has a momentum $\Delta m(V - v_0)$, and the momentum transfer to Δm in the separation is $(V - v_0)\Delta m - V\Delta m = -v_0\Delta m$. An equal amount of momentum is transferred to the rocket and its contents, which together now have a mass $(m_0 - m - \Delta m + M)$. We therefore have

$$(\Delta m)v_0 = (m_0 - m - \Delta m + M)\Delta V. \qquad (3\text{–}27)$$

If the separation takes place during a time interval Δt, the average acceleration is $\Delta V/\Delta t$. From Eq. (3–27), dividing by Δt, we thus obtain $(m_0 - m - \Delta m + M)(\Delta V/\Delta t) = (\Delta m/\Delta t)v_0$. If the mass discharge from the rocket is continuous, the average rates above can be replaced by the instantaneous rates dV/dt and dm/dt in the limit $\Delta t = 0$, and we obtain

$$\frac{dV}{dt} = \frac{v_0}{m_0 - m + M}\frac{dm}{dt}, \qquad (3\text{–}28)$$

where dm/dt = discharge rate. In this case, when there are no external forces on the system, we see that the acceleration of the rocket is proportional to the instantaneous mass discharge rate and the exit velocity relative to the rocket. Since m increases with time, it follows that the acceleration increases with time during the discharge period, even if the discharge rate and the exit velocity v_0 are constant.

PROBLEMS

3–1. A car A of mass 1000 kgm rolls on a horizontal track with a speed of 5 m/sec. It collides with car B of mass 2000 kgm moving in the opposite direction with a speed of 3 m/sec. After the collision, A is found to move with a speed of 5 m/sec opposite to its initial direction. What are the magnitude and direction of the velocity of B?

3–2. A body of mass M moves in outer space with a speed V. It is explosively separated into two equal parts such that the parts move along in the same direction as before. If the speed of one part is $V/3$, what is the speed of the other?

3–3. A rocket shell of mass 100 kgm is loaded with 10 kgm of hydrogen and 80 kgm of oxygen. The resulting water molecules are ejected from the rocket in such a way that their velocity *relative to the ground* is 2000 m/sec. If the velocity of the rocket was 300 m/sec before the burning started, what is it when the fuel is gone? Neglect the effect of earth's gravitation and other external effects on the motion.

3–4. Two boys of equal mass m stand facing each other on a frictionless ice pond. One has a large medicine ball with a mass $m/10$. The boys proceed to play a game of "catch," sliding the ball back and forth between them. Assume, for simplicity, that the speed of the ball relative to the ground is always the same as it travels between the boys. Describe in detail what happens and obtain the speed of the boys after the first throw and the first catch.

3–5. One of the isotopes of radium, Ra^{226}, has a mass of about $3.8 \cdot 10^{-22}$ gm. This atomic nucleus decays radioactively into an α-particle (nucleus of

helium, mass of about $6.7 \cdot 10^{-24}$ gm) and an isotope of radon (Rn^{222}, mass of about $3.7 \cdot 10^{-22}$ gm). In this "explosion" the α-particle is found to fly out with a speed of $1.5 \cdot 10^9$ cm/sec. What is the speed of the radon isotope?

3–6. A car B ($m_b = 2$ kgm) is at rest on a horizontal track 10 m from a rigid wall C. Car A ($m_a = 10$ kgm and $v_a = 10$ m/sec) collides with B and B later collides with C (see Fig. 3–28). Consider all collisions perfectly

FIGURE 3–28

elastic. (a) Where do A and B collide the second time? (b) What is the velocity of B just after the second collision with A?

3–7. Two balls of equal mass collide. The velocity of the first ball before the collision is V. What is the velocity of the second ball prior to collision in order that its velocity afterward is zero? The collision is perfectly elastic.

3–8. A puck A of mass $m_a = 0.3$ kgm travels with a velocity $v_a = 5$ m/sec on frictionless ice in a direction perpendicular to a wall, as indicated in Fig. 3–29. At a distance 20 m from the wall, the puck collides with a block B of mass $m_b = 0.2$ kgm, which is originally at rest. Five seconds after the collision, block B arrives at the wall at

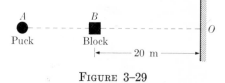

FIGURE 3–29

point O. (a) Where is A when B hits the wall? (b) What is the ratio between the final and initial relative velocities of the puck and the block?

3–9. Two similar cars A and B are connected rigidly together and have a combined mass of 4 kgm. Car C has a mass of 1 kgm. Initially, A and B have a velocity of 5 m/sec toward the right, and C, which is halfway between A and B, is at rest, as shown in Fig. 3–30.

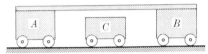

FIGURE 3–30

(a) Suppose the collision between A and C is *perfectly inelastic*. What is the final velocity of the system? (b) Suppose the collision between A and C is *perfectly elastic*, but that the collision between C and B is *perfectly inelastic*. What, then, is the final velocity of the system? Compare with part (a) and explain. (c) Suppose the collisions between A and C and between C and B are all perfectly elastic. What are the velocities of C after the first and second collisions?

3–10. A body A of mass $m_a = 1$ kgm is moving along a track with a velocity of $v_a = 2$ m/sec. When we start the clock, that is, at $t = 0$, this body passes a location which we shall consider as the origin, $x = 0$. At the same time body B of mass $m_b = 4$ kgm passes a location $x = 2$ m moving with constant velocity $v_b = 0.5$ m/sec in the same direction as A. (a) When and where will A and B collide? (b) When will A return to $x = 0$ if the collision is perfectly elastic? (c) Suppose m_a can be varied. What is the largest value of m_a/m_b, expressed in terms of v_b/v_a, for which body A will return after the collision?

3–11. A car A of mass m_a is at rest on a horizontal track. Another car B of mass m_b collides with A. What fraction of the initial momentum of B is delivered to A in the collision: (a) if the collision is perfectly elastic? (b) if the collision is perfectly inelastic? (c) Discuss the momentum transfer when m_a/m_b is very large and when it is very small. In a perfectly elastic collision, is there any upper limit to the velocity that car A acquires after the collision if the mass of car A is taken smaller and smaller?

3–12. An electron collides with a hydrogen atom in such a way that the motion is always along the same straight line. The mass of the hydrogen atom is $M = 1840m$, where m is the electron mass. If the hydrogen atom is originally at rest, what fraction of the initial momentum of the electron is transferred to the hydrogen atom if the collision is perfectly elastic?

3–13. Consider a perfectly elastic head-on collision between a neutron and a carbon nucleus. The mass of the neutron is m and the mass of the carbon nucleus is $M = 12m$. If the neutron is incident with a velocity v_0 on a carbon nucleus at rest, what is the magnitude of the velocity of the neutron after the collision?

3–14. Compute the center of mass of three particles with masses $m_1 = 4$ kgm, $m_2 = 3$ kgm, $m_3 = 5$ kgm and with coordinates $x_1 = -2$ m, $x_2 = 1$ m, $x_3 = 2$ m.

3–15. Determine the location of the center of mass of the earth-moon system. The mass of the earth is about 82 times the mass of the moon, and the distance between the moon and the earth is about 60 earth radii. Express the answer in terms of earth radii.

3–16. Analyze Problem 3–8 using the concept of center of mass. What is the velocity of the center of mass just before the block collides with the wall?

3–17. As illustrated in Fig. 3–31, a man of mass M stands at one end of a plank of length L which lies at rest on a frictionless surface. The man walks to the other end of the plank. How far has the man moved relative to the surface if the mass of the plank is $M/3$?

3–18. What force is required to accelerate a 2000-lb automobile from rest to a velocity of 50 mi/hr in 5 sec? Assume constant acceleration.

3–19. The velocity of a particle of mass 2 gm is plotted as a function of time in Fig. 3–32. From direct measurements on the graph, plot the force on the particle as a function of time. (a) What is the maximum force (approximately)? (b) What is the average force in the time interval 0 to 0.4 sec and in the time interval 0 to 0.8 sec?

3–20. A body B of mass $m_b =$ 2 kgm is originally at rest on a horizontal track. A body A of mass $m_a =$ 4 kgm and with initial velocity $v_a =$ 10 m/sec collides with B. If the duration of the collision is $\tau = 0.01$ sec, what is the average force on one of the bodies if the collision is perfectly elastic?

3–21. Three bodies, A of 1-kgm mass, B of unknown mass, and C of 3-kgm mass, are free to move (frictionfree) along a line so that A interacts with B, body B interacts with C, but A and C do not interact with each other. The velocities of A and C vary with time, as shown in Fig. 3–33. (a) At $t = 0$ the center-of-mass velocity of the three bodies is 1 m/sec and the velocity of B is 1.25 m/sec. What is the mass of B? (b) Make a labeled graph showing how the velocity of body B varies with time. (c) Make a

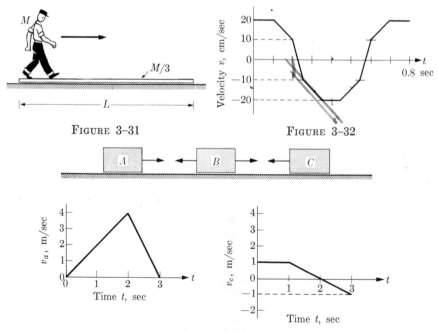

FIGURE 3–31

FIGURE 3–32

FIGURE 3–33

labeled graph showing how the *force on body A* varies with time. (d) Make a labeled graph showing how the *force on body B* varies with time.

3–22. A body A is shot straight upward with velocity $v_a = 100$ m/sec at $t = 0$. (a) What maximum height does it reach? (Neglect air drag.) (b) By what factor should you increase the velocity to make the body go twice as high? (c) At what time has the body reached half of its maximum height?

3–23. From a high cliff a man shoots a body A straight up and a body B straight down with the same initial speeds $v_0 = 10$ m/sec. When is the speed of B twice that of A? What then is the distance between the two bodies?

3–24. A bullet of mass $m = 10$ gm leaves a gun with a speed of 400 m/sec. The length of the barrel of the gun is $l = 60$ cm. Determine both the force and the time the bullet spends in the barrel, assuming the force is constant.

3–25. How far should a spring be stretched to produce an initial acceleration of 16 ft/sec^2 if the spring constant is 12 lb/ft and if the body attached to the spring has a weight of 8 lb?

3–26. When a spring with a relaxed length of 2 ft is supporting a 16-lb body at its lower end, its length is found to be 3 ft. (a) What is the spring constant? (b) If the body is lifted $\frac{1}{2}$ ft and then released, what is the initial acceleration of the body? (c) How far should the spring be stretched to produce upon release an upward acceleration g of the suspended body?

3–27. The friction force on a small falling sphere is known to be $F = 6\pi\eta rv$, where η is the coefficient of viscosity ($\eta = 18 \cdot 10^{-5}$ cgs units for air), r is the radius of the sphere, and v

is the speed (Stokes' formula). Estimate the terminal velocity of a drop of water of radius 0.05 cm if it falls vertically.

3–28. A train consists of ten cars, each of mass m, and a locomotive, of mass $10m$. The locomotive is acted upon by F, a forward force from the rail. Determine the forces on the couplings between the various cars of the train, starting with the force on the last car.

3–29. Two springs with relaxed lengths $l_1 = 20$ cm and $l_2 = 30$ cm and spring constants $K_1 = 40$ n/cm and $K_2 = 20$ n/cm, respectively, are attached to two rigid walls separated by a distance $l = 80$ cm. As shown in Fig. 3–34, the free ends of the two springs are then joined. (a) Determine the equilibrium position of the junction. (b) A body of mass $m = 2$ kgm is attached to the junction and displaced toward the left 5 cm and then released. Determine the initial acceleration.

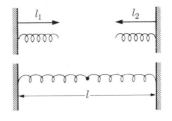

FIGURE 3–34

3–30. As shown in Fig. 3–35, a painter's platform hangs from a pulley. Consider the pulley as frictionless and weightless, the rope as weightless, and ignore the possibility that the platform may tip. The painter is on the platform, holding himself up. The platform weighs 80 lb, and the painter weighs 160 lb. (a) Find the tension in the ropes at points A, B, and C.

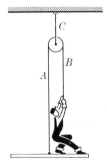

FIGURE 3–35

(b) Draw two separate force diagrams showing all the forces acting upon the painter and upon the platform. Label each force *clearly* as to magnitude and direction. (c) What is the contact force on the painter's feet? (d) The painter's "helper" leans out a convenient window and places a 100-lb drum of paint on the platform. What happens?

3–31. One end of a rope is attached to a rigid wall. On the other end a force F is applied, as shown in Fig. 3–36. What is the tension in the rope? If the rope is stretched between two men who each apply a force F, what then is the tension in the rope?

3–32. A 2-ft long string has one end held fixed in a wall and the other end pulled by a force of 100 lb, as shown in Fig. 3–37. The string is cut at its center point, and a spring of relaxed length 0.5 ft and spring constant $K = 200$ lb/ft is inserted, as shown. What, now, is the total combined length of the string-spring combination if a force of 100 lb is applied?

3–33. Two masses m_1 and m_2, where $m_1 > m_2$, are suspended a height h above the floor and are connected by a massless string over a massless pulley (Fig. 3–38). The masses are released. What is the tension in the string during the motion?

3–34. Consider the system of bodies

A, B, and C, and the system of strings and pulleys connecting them, shown in Fig. 3–39. Body A is prevented from falling by means of an additional string fastened to pulley D. In this case, the system is in equilibrium. What happens to body C when the string S is cut? The weight of the pulleys may be neglected. Determine both the tensions in the strings and the acceleration of C.

3–35. A stream of pebbles is poured into a box of weight 1 lb at a rate of $n = 100$ per second from a height of $h = 36$ ft above the box. Each pebble weighs 0.01 lb. The box is suspended by a rope. What is the (average) tension in the rope at a time $t = 10$ sec after the first pebbles start to fill the box? Consider the collision between the pebbles and the box perfectly inelastic.

3–36. A horizontal beam (cross-section area $= 1$ cm^2) of particles hits a rigid vertical wall. The number density of particles in the beam is $\mu = 1000$/cm^3 and the velocity of the beam is $v = 100$ m/sec. Each particle has a mass of $m = 0.001$ gm. The direction of motion is perpendicular to the wall. Assume that the collisions are inelastic. What is the rate of momentum transfer to the wall, that is, the (average) force on the wall? Indicate units.

On the basis of this simple analysis, how would the drag force on a satellite moving through space vary with the speed of the satellite as a result of collisions with air particles?

3–37. A jet engine develops a thrust of 10,000 lb. If the diameter of the nozzle is 20 in. and the mass per unit volume (density) of the exhaust gas is 0.001 gm/cm^3, what is the speed of the exhaust gas?

3–38. An open car of mass $M = 2$ kgm is moving on a track with a constant velocity $V = 5$ m/sec. It starts to rain, and the car begins to fill with water at a rate of $m = 5$ gm/sec. Draw a graph showing how the velocity of the car changes with time.

3–39. A continuous stream of particles, each of mass m and velocity v, is emitted from a source at a rate of n per second. The particles travel along a straight line, collide with a body of mass M, and are buried in this body. Determine the velocity of M (initial velocity $V = 0$) when it has received N particles.

3–40. A rocket starts from rest in free space. Consider the instant when only half of its initial fuel supply remains. What then should be the mass discharge rate of fuel so that the acceleration of the rocket is $5\,g$? The initial fuel mass $m_0 = 1000$ kgm is twice the shell mass, and the exhaust speed relative to the rocket is constant and equal to 1500 m/sec.

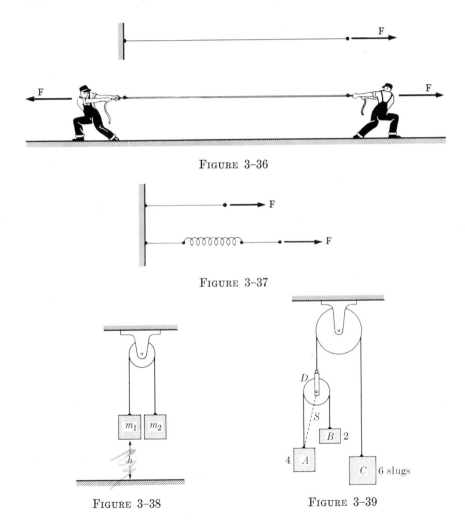

FIGURE 3–36

FIGURE 3–37

FIGURE 3–38

FIGURE 3–39

CHAPTER 4

MOMENTUM AND FORCE — II

Summary. Collision experiments in a plane establish the validity of conservation of momentum, and the considerations in Chapter 3 are extended to motion in two and three dimensions. The vector character of momentum and force is discussed, and the principle of superposition is obtained from an experiment on motion in a plane. The motion of the center of mass of systems of particles and rigid bodies then follows. Contact force (friction) is discussed, and examples of motion and equilibrium are given.

4-1 Conservation of momentum. It is only under very special conditions that a collision between two bodies is such that the motion of the bodies is along the same line both before and after the collision. In general, the bodies are free to move in any direction in a plane or in space, so that a collision between two bodies will involve motion in more than one direction. By performing experiments on collisions of bodies in a plane, we shall investigate whether the law of conservation of momentum can be extended to two dimensions.

Experimental arrangement. Rolling friction forces can be made very small, and this fact was used to advantage in our one-dimensional collision experiments with cars. Cars are not suitable for the collision experiments in a plane, however, and we shall instead use air-suspended pucks such as those illustrated in Fig. 4-1. The puck is a hollow cylindrical container that can be filled with compressed air, which can seep out through a small hole in the smooth, polished base. If the air flow is adjusted properly, the air cushion keeps the puck suspended, and the puck can then slide over a horizontal table practically without friction. A surprisingly small air flow is required.

Two air-suspended pucks are now made to collide in the plane. The velocities of the pucks before and after the collision are conveniently determined with the multiflash-photography technique described in Chapter 1. A photograph of this type is shown in Fig. 4-2.

Conservation of momentum: component form. Let us analyze the result of the collision illustrated in Fig. 4-2. The masses of the two bodies are $m_a = 2.0$ kgm and $m_b = 1.5$ kgm. The time interval between the flashes is 0.1 sec, and since the length scale can be found from the known diameter of the pucks, $d = 10$ cm, we can read the velocities directly from the photograph. We shall describe the motion of the bodies in terms of their x- and y-coordinates. Similarly, the velocities of the bodies will be described in terms of the components $v_{ax} = v_a \cos \theta_a$, $v_{ay} = v_a \sin \theta_a$, $v_{bx} = v_b \cos \theta_b$, and $v_{by} = v_b \sin \theta_b$. The values of the components of the

Air-suspended pucks

FIG. 4–1. In the experiments on motion in a plane, air-suspended pucks are used, sliding on a horizontal surface. Some typical experiments are illustrated below.

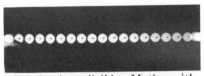

Friction is negligible. Motion with constant velocity

Puck at the end of a rubber band (central motion)

Collision

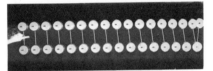

Translation of a rigid body

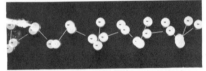

Combined translation and rotation of a rigid body

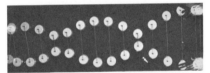

Motion of two interacting pucks

velocities before and after collision, obtained from the experiment shown in Fig. 4–2, are given in Table 4–1. Within the experimental accuracy, which is of the order of 3% or 4%, the components of the total momentum are conserved in the collision:

$$p_{ax} + p_{bx} = p'_{ax} + p'_{bx}, \qquad p_{ay} + p_{by} = p'_{ay} + p'_{by}. \qquad (4\text{–}1)$$

If we denote the total x- and y-components of the momentum by $p_x = p_{ax} + p_{bx}$ and $p_y = p_{ay} + p_{by}$, Eqs. (4–1) can be written as

$$p_x = p'_x, \qquad p_y = p'_y.$$

Variation of the experimental conditions, along the lines already discussed in the one-dimensional case, always leads to results which are consistent with the law of conservation of momentum.

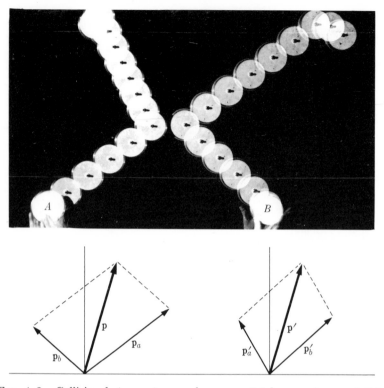

FIG. 4-2. Collision between two pucks, $m_a = 2.0$ kgm and $m_b = 1.5$ kgm, and a momentum vector diagram of the collision. Total momentum is conserved.

Conservation of momentum: vector form. Just as in the case of velocity, momentum can be described as a vector, $\mathbf{p} = m\mathbf{v}$. The components of this vector are $p_x = mv_x$ and $p_y = mv_y$. The two equations (4–1) expressing conservation of momentum in terms of components can then be condensed into one vector relation,

$$\mathbf{p}_a + \mathbf{p}_b = \mathbf{p}_a' + \mathbf{p}_b'. \tag{4-2}$$

Furthermore, if we introduce the total momentum vector $\mathbf{p} = \mathbf{p}_a + \mathbf{p}_b$, with the components $p_x = p_{ax} + p_{bx}$ and $p_y = p_{ay} + p_{by}$, we can express the law of conservation of momentum concisely by writing the relation

$$\mathbf{p} = \mathbf{p}'. \tag{4-3}$$

This important conservation law thus says that the total momentum vector before the collision is the same as the total momentum after the collision both in magnitude and direction, regardless of the momentum transfers between the individual bodies. In addition to the photograph

Table 4–1

Before collision		After collision	
m/sec	kgm·m/sec	m/sec	kgm·m/sec
$v_{ax} =$ 0.79 ·	$p_{ax} =$ 1.58	$v'_{ax} =$ −0.28	$p'_{ax} =$ −0.56
$v_{bx} =$ −0.64	$p_{bx} =$ −0.96	$v'_{bx} =$ 0.78	$p'_{bx} =$ 1.17
	$p_x =$ 0.62		$p'_x =$ 0.61
$v_{ay} =$ 0.60	$p_{ay} =$ 1.20	$v'_{ay} =$ 0.55	$p'_{ay} =$ 1.10
$v_{by} =$ 0.57	$p_{by} =$ 0.85	$v'_{by} =$ 0.62	$p'_{by} =$ 0.93
	$p_y =$ 2.0(5)		$p'_y =$ 2.0(3)

in Fig. 4–2 depicting a collision between two pucks, the momentum vector diagram for the same experiment is shown.

EXAMPLE. A particle of mass m_a = 10 gm travels along the positive x-axis with a velocity v_a = 20 cm/sec. It collides with a particle of mass m_b = 20 gm, which travels with a velocity v_b = 50 cm/sec in a direction making an angle of 53° with the positive x-axis, as shown in Fig. 4–3. After the collision the bodies stick together and travel as one. What is the velocity of this body after the collision?

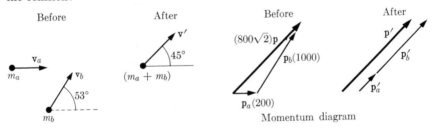

Momentum diagram

FIGURE 4–3

Let us denote the velocity after the collision by $\mathbf{v}'$. The components of $\mathbf{v}'$ are v'_x and v'_y. The law of conservation of momentum then gives the following relations for the determination of v'_x and v'_y:

$$m_a v_{ax} + m_b v_{bx} = (m_a + m_b)v'_x,$$

$$m_a v_{ay} + m_b v_{by} = (m_a + m_b)v'_y,$$

or

$$v'_x = \frac{m_a v_{ax} + m_b v_{bx}}{m_a + m_b} = \frac{200 + 600}{30} = \frac{80}{3} \text{ cm/sec},$$

$$v'_y = \frac{m_a v_{ay} + m_b v_{by}}{m_a + m_b} = \frac{0 + 800}{30} = \frac{80}{3} \text{ cm/sec},$$

in which we have inserted v_{ax} = 20, v_{ay} = 0, v_{bx} = 30, and v_{by} = 40 cm/sec.

Clearly the total momentum of the system before and after the collision is the same, with a magnitude of $800\sqrt{2}$ and making an angle of 45° with the positive x-axis, but the individual momenta of the bodies both change, as shown in the vector diagram in Fig. 4–3.

Many bodies. If we have a large number of bodies which can interact only among themselves, the *total momentum* of the system will be *conserved*, just as in the case of two bodies. This follows from the results of the previous collision experiments, when not more than two bodies in the system interact at a time. Later we shall return to this question and discuss the fact that conservation of momentum applies to an isolated system of bodies under *all* conditions, regardless of how and when bodies interact with each other. Momentum is simply passed around among the bodies, but the total remains the same throughout the entire interaction. This is illustrated by the examples of motion shown in Fig. 4–4.

In the first of these examples, two identical air-suspended pucks, connected by a rubber band, are bouncing against each other as they move forward. The other experiment shows the motion of three identical pucks

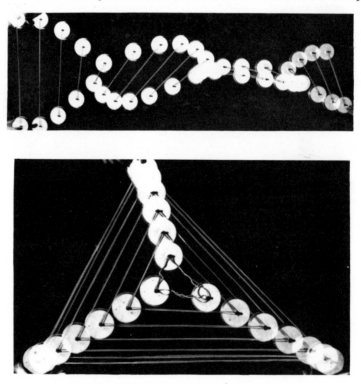

Fig. 4–4. Examples of motion of interacting bodies, demonstrating the law of conservation of momentum.

all connected by rubber bands. In both experiments the total momentum is constant.

Center of mass. The extension of the concept of center of mass to motion in two and three dimensions is straightforward. The center of mass of a number of particles m_a, m_b, m_c, m_d, ..., with coordinates (x_a, y_a, z_a), (x_b, y_b, z_b), etc., is defined by

$$X = \frac{m_a x_a + m_b x_b + m_c x_c + \cdots}{m_a + m_b + m_c + \cdots} ; \quad Y = \frac{m_a y_a + m_b y_b + m_c y_c + \cdots}{m_a + m_b + m_c + \cdots} ;$$

$$Z = \frac{m_a z_a + m_b z_b + m_c z_c + \cdots}{m_a + m_b + m_c + \cdots}. \tag{4-4}$$

If the locations of the bodies with respect to the common origin are described by the vectors $\mathbf{r}_a$, $\mathbf{r}_b$, $\mathbf{r}_c$, ..., the position vector of the center of mass is

$$\mathbf{R} = \frac{m_a \mathbf{r}_a + m_b \mathbf{r}_b + m_c \mathbf{r}_c + \cdots}{m_a + m_b + m_c + \cdots}, \tag{4-5}$$

and the velocity vector of the center of mass is then

$$\mathbf{V} = \frac{m_a \mathbf{v}_a + m_b \mathbf{v}_b + m_c \mathbf{v}_c + \cdots}{m_a + m_b + m_c + \cdots} = \frac{\mathbf{p}}{M},$$

that is,

$$M\mathbf{V} = \mathbf{p} = \mathbf{p}_a + \mathbf{p}_b + \mathbf{p}_c + \cdots, \tag{4-6}$$

where $\mathbf{p}$ is the total momentum of the system and M is the total mass. In other words, when the total momentum of a system of particles *is constant*, it follows that the center of mass of the system moves with *constant velocity*, no matter how complicated the motion of the individual particles.

It is interesting to apply the above concept to the motion of the center of mass of a *rigid body*. A rigid body may be considered as a particle system in which the distances between the particles remain constant. When a rigid body has a purely translational motion, that is, when all the particles in the body move along parallel paths, we can select the motion of any point in the body (not necessarily the center of mass) for the description of the translational motion of the whole body. However, the general motion of a rigid body involves rotation as well as translation. In Fig. 4–5 the motion of a rigid body is shown and although the individual points of the body have different and nonconstant velocities, we can see that the velocity $\mathbf{V}$ of the center of mass is constant. The total momentum of the body is

$$\mathbf{p} = M\mathbf{V},$$

where M is the total mass of the rigid body.

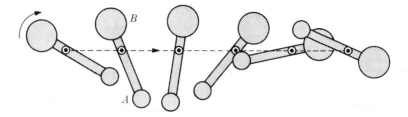

FIG. 4–5. Reproduced from flash photograph. The general motion of a rigid body involves translation as well as rotation. The broken line illustrates the path of the center of mass.

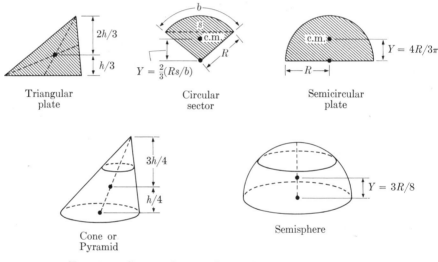

FIG. 4–6. Center of mass of some familiar-shaped bodies.

Center of mass of some bodies. In many bodies, such as a uniform straight bar, a sphere, or a circular cylinder, the center of mass can be obtained directly from symmetry. In other bodies the location of the center of mass is not always obvious but can be determined to any desired accuracy by dividing the body into small parts with known individual masses. The center of mass of the body is then obtainable directly from Eq. (4–4). In some cases the center of mass can be determined exactly, using the mathematical operation of integration. However, for the moment we shall be concerned only with bodies in which we can find the center of mass directly from symmetry or by appropriately subdividing the body into simple parts. The locations of the centers of mass of some familiar-shaped bodies are shown in Fig. 4–6.

EXAMPLE. *The center of mass of a uniform triangular plate.* Using plane geometry, we shall consider the problem of finding the center of mass of a uniform triangular plate with corners ABC, as shown in Fig. 4–7. If we divide the plate into bars parallel to the side AB, the center of mass (c.m.) on each bar is at its center, and consequently the center of mass of the plate must lie on the line connecting the centers of the bars; i.e., it must lie on the bisector CP_1. Similarly, the center of mass must lie on the bisector AP_2, and hence it must be the intersection O of CP_1 and AP_2. Now, draw a line through O parallel to CB which intersects AC at P_3. Draw a line that is parallel to AB through P_3P_4. We then obtain three identical triangles, shown crosshatched in Fig. 4–7, which divide CP_1 into three equal parts, of which OP_1 is one part. Therefore, the center of mass of the triangular plate lies on a bisector (of length d) a distance $2d/3$ from the corner of the triangle. (Why are the triangles congruent? Note that P_3P_4 is bisected by CP_1, and the line through P_3O is bisected by AP_2.)

EXAMPLE. Find the location of the center of mass of the uniform plate shown in Fig. 4–8. Let the mass of the plate be m_1 and the coordinate of the center of mass be X_1, as shown. We divide the plate into three identical triangular parts as shown, each of mass $m_1/3$. Since their centers of mass are located at the distances h, h, and $h/3$ from the left side of the plate, we obtain

$$m_1X_1 = \frac{m_1}{3}h + \frac{m_1}{3}h + \frac{m_1}{3}\frac{h}{3},$$

which gives

$$X_1 = \frac{7}{9}h.$$

Collisions between extended rigid bodies. When two rigid bodies of arbitrary shapes collide with each other, they usually spin or rotate, as well as translate. A collision may therefore be complicated in its details, but conservation of momentum still applies, since the two bodies taken together constitute an isolated collection of particles for which momentum is conserved. In other words, the combined velocity of the center of mass

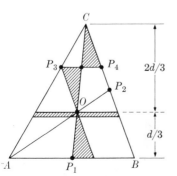

FIG. 4–7. Center of mass of a triangular plate.

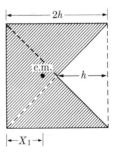

FIGURE 4–8

of the two bodies remains unchanged as a result of the collision, and the momentum lost by one rigid body is gained by the other. Although rotational motion of the bodies often results from the collision, translational motion of the system is governed by the law of conservation of momentum, and the *center of mass of the total system moves with constant speed along the same straight line.* Later, when we have studied rotation of bodies, we shall be in a position to formulate another conservation law which has to do with the "total rotation" of a system.

Perfectly elastic and inelastic collisions. In analogy with the one-dimensional case, a perfectly elastic collision is defined here as one in which the magnitudes of the relative velocities of the colliding bodies A and B are the same both before and after a collision, that is,

$$|\mathbf{v}_a - \mathbf{v}_b| = |\mathbf{v}_a' - \mathbf{v}_b'|.$$

Similarly, a perfectly inelastic collision is one in which the relative velocity after a collision is zero.

4–2 Force, a vector. The momentum transferred to a body moving in a plane or in space usually is not in the same direction as the momentum of the body. Denote the momenta of the body before and after a transfer as $\mathbf{p}_1$ and $\mathbf{p}_2$, respectively. The momentum transfer is represented by the vector

$$\Delta\mathbf{p} = \mathbf{p}_2 - \mathbf{p}_1,$$

as illustrated in Fig. 4–9.

The average rate of momentum transfer to the body is $\Delta\mathbf{p}/\Delta t$ if the transfer is accomplished in a time Δt. Therefore, the average force,

$$\overline{\mathbf{F}} = \frac{\Delta\mathbf{p}}{\Delta t}, \tag{4–7}$$

is a vector with the same direction as the momentum transfer $\Delta\mathbf{p}$. The vector $\Delta\mathbf{p}$ has the components Δp_x, Δp_y, and Δp_z, and similarly, the average force vector has the components

$$\overline{F}_x = \frac{\Delta p_x}{\Delta t}, \qquad \overline{F}_y = \frac{\Delta p_y}{\Delta t}, \qquad \overline{F}_z = \frac{\Delta p_z}{\Delta t}. \tag{4–8}$$

EXAMPLE. A body of mass $m = 10$ kgm slides over a smooth ice surface with constant velocity. The velocity components are $v_x = 3$ m/sec and $v_y = 2$ m/sec. A gust of wind transfers momentum to the body such that after the gust the velocity components are $v_x = -1$ m/sec and $v_y = 4$ m/sec. If the gust lasted for 2 sec, what were the magnitude and direction of the average force on the body during the gust?

Before the gust the momentum components were $p_{1x} = 30$ kgm·m/sec and

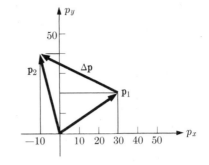

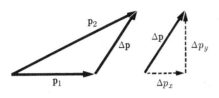

Fig. 4-9. The momentum transfer to a body usually is not in the direction of motion.

Fig. 4-10. Example of a momentum transfer.

$p_{1y} = 20$ kgm·m/sec, and after the gust they were $p_{2x} = -10$ kgm·m/sec and $p_{2y} = 40$ kgm·m/sec. The momentum transfer has the components

$$\Delta p_x = -10 - 30 = -40 \text{ kgm·m/sec}$$

and

$$\Delta p_y = 40 - 20 = 20 \text{ kgm·m/sec.}$$

The components of the average force are then

$$\overline{F}_x = \frac{\Delta p_x}{\Delta t} = -\frac{40}{2} = -20 \text{ n} \quad \text{and} \quad \overline{F}_y = \frac{20}{2} = 10 \text{ n,}$$

and the magnitude of the force vector is $|\overline{\mathbf{F}}| = \sqrt{20^2 + 10^2} = 10\sqrt{5}$ n with a direction given by $\tan \theta = +10/-20 = -1/2$, as shown in Fig. 4-10.

The *instantaneous values of the force components* are defined as the limiting values of $\Delta p_x/\Delta t$, etc., when $\Delta t = 0$. We have then

$$F_x = \frac{dp_x}{dt}, \quad F_y = \frac{dp_y}{dt}, \quad F_z = \frac{dp_z}{dt} \qquad (4\text{-}9)$$

which define the instantaneous force vector

$$\mathbf{F} = \frac{d\mathbf{p}}{dt}. \qquad (4\text{-}10)$$

If we restrict our discussion to motion in a plane, the magnitude of the force in terms of its components is

$$F = \sqrt{F_x^2 + F_y^2} = \sqrt{(dp_x/dt)^2 + (dp_y/dt)^2}, \qquad (4\text{-}11)$$

and the direction of the force vector is given by

$$\tan \theta = \frac{F_y}{F_x} = \frac{dp_y/dt}{dp_x/dt}, \qquad (4\text{-}12)$$

where θ is the angle between the force vector and the x-axis. If the mass is constant, the direction of the force vector is the same as that of the acceleration vector, which has the components dv_x/dt and dv_y/dt. It is clear that, in general, the direction of the acceleration vector or of the force vector *is not the same* as that of the velocity vector, since v_y/v_x, which defines the direction of the velocity vector, usually is different from $(dv_y/dt)/(dv_x/dt)$.

4–3 Analysis of an experiment.* Consider the motion of a body sliding over a plane, as shown in the multiflash photograph of Fig. 4–11. The body, an air-suspended puck, is attached to a rubber band which is held fixed at one end. The 10-cm diameter of the puck (mass $m = 1.5\,\mathrm{kgm}$) establishes the length scale of the picture.

We shall describe the motion of the puck in terms of the coordinates x and y. Our problem then is to obtain the velocity and force vectors as functions of time. At $t = 0$ (arbitrarily chosen) the x-coordinate is positive and the puck is moving in the positive x-direction, until at $t \simeq 0.5$ it starts in the negative x-direction. When $t \simeq 1.4$, the puck passes $x = 0$. The y-coordinate remains positive during the motion shown in the figure. The x- and y-coordinates are plotted in the first set of graphs in Fig. 4–12 as functions of time.

By measurement of the slope of the x vs. t curve, we obtain the velocity v_x, and from the slope of the v_x vs. t curve, the acceleration a_x is found.

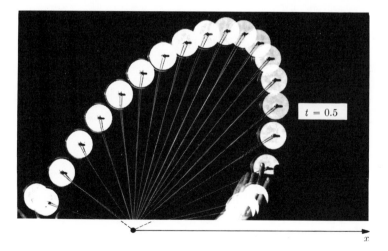

$t = 0.5$

FIG. 4–11. Air-suspended puck at the end of a rubber band. Time interval between flashes is $\Delta t = 0.1$ sec.

* This entire section may be omitted without loss of continuity.

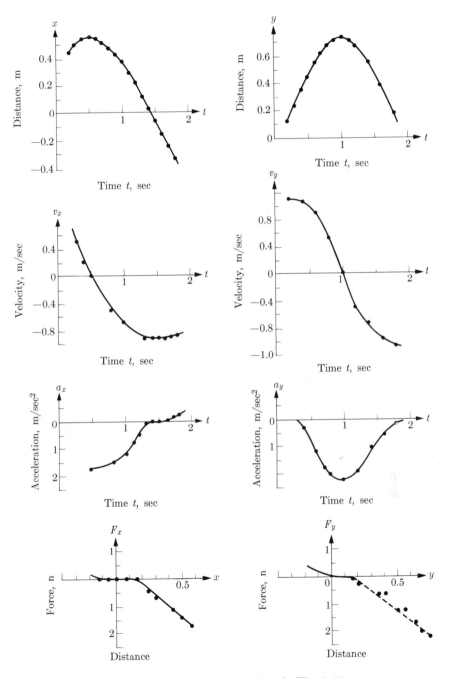

FIG. 4–12. Analysis of the motion in Fig. 4–11.

Similarly, we find v_y and a_y; the force components, $F_x = ma_x$ and $F_y = ma_y$, are then determined as functions of time. It is interesting to replot the force components in terms of the coordinates x and y. Although the accuracy is not high in this graphical procedure, we find that the force is essentially zero until the length of the rubber band exceeds its relaxed length. Beyond that length, the force appears to be at least approximately proportional to the amount by which the length of the rubber band is increased.

The magnitude of the velocity is obtained from $v = \sqrt{v_x^2 + v_y^2}$, and the angle between the velocity vector and the positive x-axis is $\theta = \tan^{-1}(v_y/v_x)$. For example, at $t = 0.8$ sec, we have $v_x \simeq -0.47$ m/sec and $v_y \simeq +0.50$ m/sec, and the magnitude of the velocity is $v = \sqrt{0.47^2 + 0.50^2} \simeq 0.68$ m/sec. The angle with the positive x-axis is $\theta \simeq 90° + 43°$.

Let us also determine the magnitude and direction of the force on the body at $t = 0.8$ sec. From the graphs of the acceleration components, in Fig. 4–12, we find $a_x \simeq -1.5$ m/sec^2 and $a_y \simeq -2$ m/sec^2, with the corresponding force components $F_x \simeq -2.25$ n and $F_y \simeq -3$ n. The magnitude of the force is then $F \simeq \sqrt{3^2 + 2.25^2} \simeq 3.7$ n and its direction is given by $\theta \simeq \tan^{-1}(-2/-1.5)$, that is, $\theta \simeq +180° + 53°$. As we expected, the force is directed along the line of the rubber band toward point O, as indicated in Fig. 4–13.

Instead of working with components x, y, v_x, v_y, etc., we can determine the velocity and force vectors in a more direct way. First, note that the direction of the velocity is always along the tangent to the trajectory of the body. The magnitude of the average velocity in time interval Δt is found by measuring the displacement Δs of the body in that time, as illustrated in Fig. 4–13. The average velocity is then

$$\bar{\mathbf{v}} = \frac{\Delta \mathbf{s}}{\Delta t}.$$

For example, between $t = 0.8$ and 0.9 sec, from direct measurement we obtain $\Delta s \simeq 0.065$ m and $\bar{v} = 0.65$ m/sec. Similarly, the average velocity between $t = 0.7$ and 0.8 sec is $\bar{v} = 0.70$ m/sec. Thus, to approximate a value of the instantaneous velocity magnitude at $t = 0.8$ sec, we may use the average of these two values, or $\bar{v} = 0.68$ m/sec. The tangent to the trajectory at $t = 0.8$ sec is found to make an angle of $90° + 47° = 137°$ with the positive x-axis, as before.

Similarly, the magnitude and direction of $\mathbf{F}$ are found from direct measurements of the velocity (or momentum) vectors. First, we draw the average momentum vectors in the intervals between $t = 0.7$ and

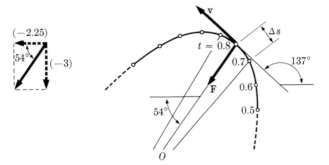

FIG. 4–13. The velocity vector is tangent to the trajectory and the magnitude is $v = ds/dt$.

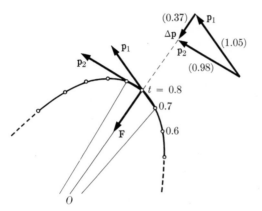

FIG. 4–14. The force can be determined not only from a_x and a_y, but directly from measurement of $\Delta \mathbf{p}$.

0.8 sec and between $t = 0.8$ and 0.9 sec. These vectors are shown in Fig. 4–14, drawn directly on the trajectory of the body, and also in a separate vector diagram in which the difference $\Delta \mathbf{p}$ between the vectors $\mathbf{p}_1$ and $\mathbf{p}_2$ is shown. The magnitudes of the individual vectors are obtained from the corresponding velocities as found earlier, that is, $p_1 = mv_1 = 1.5 \cdot 0.7 \simeq 1.05$ kgm·m/sec and $p_2 = 1.5 \cdot 0.65 \simeq 0.98$ kgm·m/sec. The length of the vector $\Delta \mathbf{p}$, as measured from the diagram, is 0.37 kgm·m/sec, and the direction of $\Delta \mathbf{p}$ is along the rubber band. Since $\Delta \mathbf{p}$ is the average momentum transfer to the body in an interval $\Delta t = 0.1$ sec centered around $t = 0.8$ sec, the average force in this interval is $|\Delta p/\Delta t| \simeq 3.7$ n. We see from our construction that the magnitude of the force is consistent with $\overline{F} = 3.7$ n, and its direction is along the rubber band toward O, as before.

4–4 The principle of superposition. The experiments with one-dimensional motion indicated that forces could be superimposed; we shall now investigate by experiments whether this principle can be extended to motion in two and three dimensions. As illustrated in Fig. 4–15, an air-suspended puck A is acted upon by a rubber band that is attached to a

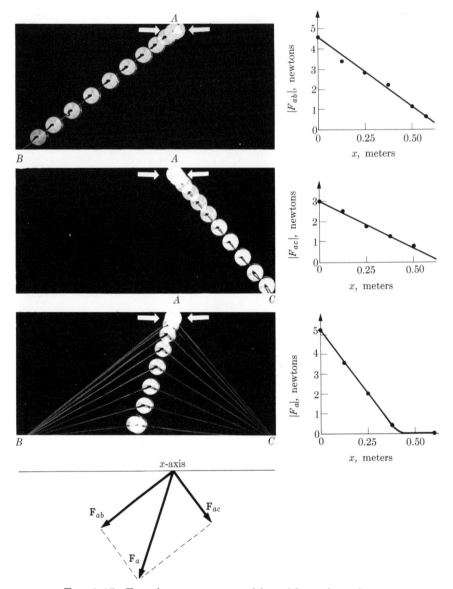

FIG. 4–15. Experiment on superposition of forces in a plane.

fixed point B. The motion of A can be considered as a result of the inter-action between A and B. We then analyze the motion, plotting location, velocity, and acceleration as functions of time and position, and obtain the magnitude of the force F_{ab} as a function of the distance of A from its initial position. We find that the magnitude of the force at the initial location is $F_{ab} \simeq 4.4$ n and that the force $\mathbf{F}_{ab}$ makes an angle of $143°$ with the positive x-axis.

Thereafter, we let A interact with C by means of a similar rubber band. An analysis of the resulting motion of A gives an initial force of magnitude $F_{ac} \simeq 3$ n, making an angle of $50°$ with the positive x-direction. Finally, we let A interact with both B and C at the same time, and find that the initial force makes an angle of $108°$ with the positive x-axis. Although the accuracy is only fair in an experiment and analysis of this kind, the result strongly indicates that the principle of superposition of forces still applies. That is, the effect of two interaction forces is the same as that of a single force which is the *vector sum of the two forces*. Thus, whether we deal with motion in one or two dimensions, the *superposition of forces* can be expressed as vector addition:

$$\mathbf{F}_a = \mathbf{F}_{ab} + \mathbf{F}_{ac}. \qquad (4\text{--}13)$$

The extension of this result to more than two forces follows by repeated application of Eq. (4–13), and the motion of a particle acted upon by several forces $\mathbf{F}_1, \mathbf{F}_2, \mathbf{F}_3, \ldots$, is determined by

$$m\,\frac{d\mathbf{v}}{dt} = \mathbf{F}_1 + \mathbf{F}_2 + \mathbf{F}_3 + \cdots = \sum \mathbf{F}_i = \mathbf{F}, \qquad (4\text{--}14)$$

where $\mathbf{F}$ is the vector sum of the forces, and $\sum$ symbolizes summation over $i = 1, 2, 3, \ldots$. (For further discussion, see Chapter 3.)

EXAMPLE. Two springs S_1 and S_2 of equal lengths $L = 0.5$ m, but with different spring constants $K_1 = 50$ n/m and $K_2 = 100$ n/m, are joined and fastened between two supports A and B which are a distance $2L$ apart, as shown in Fig. 4–16. A body C of mass $m = 2.5$ kgm is fastened to the springs at their junction and is pulled downward vertically until the length of each spring has doubled. The body is then released. What is the initial acceleration of the body?

We describe the acceleration in terms of its horizontal x- and vertical y-components. The body C is acted upon by three forces, the weight mg and the two spring forces, which have the magnitudes $F_1 = K_1(2L - L) = K_1L$ and $F_2 = K_2L$. We then project the forces in the x- and y-directions, respectively, and obtain

$$ma_x = K_2L \sin 30° - K_1L \sin 30° = \frac{K_2 - K_1}{2}\,L,$$

$$ma_y = (K_2 + K_1)L \cos 30° - mg.$$

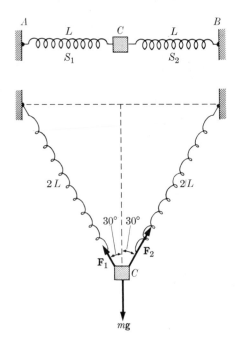

FIGURE 4–16

That is,

$$a_x = \frac{K_2 - K_1}{2} L = \frac{50 \cdot 0.5}{2 \cdot 2.5} = 5 \text{ m/sec}^2,$$

$$a_y = \frac{(K_1 + K_2)L \cdot \sqrt{3}}{2} - g \simeq 2.2 \text{ m/sec}^2.$$

4–5 Motion of the center of mass.

The relations

$$M \frac{d\mathbf{V}}{dt} = \sum \mathbf{F}_i = \mathbf{F} \tag{4–15}$$

or

$$M \frac{dV_x}{dt} = F_{1x} + F_{2x} + F_{3x} + \cdots = F_x,$$

$$M \frac{dV_y}{dt} = F_{1y} + F_{2y} + F_{3y} + \cdots = F_y,$$

determine the motion of the center of mass of a system of particles or of a
rigid body under the influence of a number of external forces that have
different directions and different points of application. This result follows
from arguments completely analogous to those dealing with one-dimensional motion presented in Chapter 3. The vector sum of all the internal

forces between the particles in the system is zero, and a net momentum transfer to the system, with a corresponding change in the center-of-mass velocity, can be produced only by external forces. It is important to note that although the details of the motion of a system of particles or of a rigid body depend upon the points of application of the external forces, the motion of the center of mass depends *only* upon the vector sum of the forces.

EXAMPLE. An unsymmetrical dumbbell consists of two balls, $w_1 = 1$ lb and $w_2 = 3$ lb, which are connected by a massless rod such that there is a separation of 2 ft between their centers. The dumbbell is at rest on a frictionless table; two horizontal forces of 3 lb and 4 lb are applied at $t = 0$, as shown in Fig. 4–17. The axis of the dumbbell is initially along the x-axis, with the small weight at the origin. The forces $\mathbf{F}_1$ and $\mathbf{F}_2$ remain constant in magnitude and direction regardless of the dumbbell's motion. What are the coordinates of the center of mass of the dumbbell after 3 sec?

The center of mass of the body is located a distance $[1/(1 + 3)] \cdot 2 = 0.5$ ft from the 3-lb body. Originally, then, the coordinates of the center of mass are $X_0 = 1.5$, $Y_0 = 0$.

The motion of the center of mass is governed by

$$M \frac{dV_x}{dt} = F_x, \qquad M \frac{dV_y}{dt} = F_y,$$

where F_x and F_y are the components of the external force, and V_x and V_y are the components of the velocity of the center of mass. Since $M = (1 + 3)/32 = 1/8$ slug, $F_x = 3$ lb, and $F_y = 4$ lb, we obtain the relations

$$\frac{dV_x}{dt} = 3 \cdot 8 = 24, \qquad \frac{dV_y}{dt} = 4 \cdot 8 = 32.$$

These in turn yield $dX/dt = V_x = 24t$ and $dY/dt = V_y = 32t$, since the velocity is zero at $t = 0$. Similarly, the coordinates of the center of mass can be obtained:

$$X - X_0 = 24 \frac{t^2}{2} = 12t^2, \qquad Y - Y_0 = 32 \frac{t^2}{2} = 16t^2.$$

With $t = 3$, $Y_0 = 0$, and $X_0 = 1.5$, the center-of-mass coordinates are then $X = 108 + 1.5 = 109.5$ ft and $Y = 144$ ft.

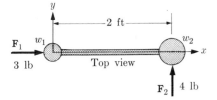

FIGURE 4–17

Another method of solving this problem uses the total force of 5 lb making an angle of 53° with the x-axis. After t sec, the center of mass will be a distance of $5 \cdot 8t^2/2 = 20t^2$ from its original position. If we multiply this expression by cos 53° and sin 53°, we obtain $X - X_0 = 12t^2$ and $Y - Y_0 = 16t^2$, respectively, as before. The center of mass thus moves along a straight line making an angle of 53° with the x-axis.

The trajectories of the 1-lb and 3-lb bodies are more complex. We leave it as an exercise to investigate at least the qualitative features of these motions.

4–6 The contact force. The origin of a contact force is the intermolecular forces between two bodies in contact. A detailed study of the contact force therefore requires a familiarity with atomic structure and will not be undertaken here. Rather, we shall simply discuss some of the experimental facts on a macroscopic rather than on a microscopic basis. When a body is placed on a horizontal surface, as shown in Fig. 4–18, it is in equilibrium under the influence of two forces acting upon it, the gravitational force (weight), and the contact force. Just as the total weight can be considered as the sum of the weights of the elementary parts of a body, but acting on the center of mass, also the contact force can be considered as the resultant of all the elementary contact forces which are distributed over the contacting surface.

In the present case, in which the body stands on a horizontal surface, the resultant contact force passes through the center of mass. However, in other situations this is not necessarily true. Since the gravitational force is vertical, the conditions for equilibrium require that the resultant contact force be vertical also, although the elementary contact forces need not be. The direction of the contact force at a certain point on the contact surface depends upon the nature of the irregularity of the surface at that point but, in this case, the resultant horizontal component of all the elementary contact forces is zero.

Friction. Although the components of the elementary contact forces in the direction of the contact plane are zero in the above example, this is not always the case, as we know from everyday experience. If it were, we would not be able to walk on a horizontal surface. To understand how a resultant tangential component of the contact force can come about, we shall picture the contact surface as two cog-tracks gripping into each other, as shown (very much enlarged) in Fig. 4–19. The elementary contact forces have horizontal components, but when the body is acted upon by only the gravitational force, the net contact force is vertical.

Now, if the body is pulled toward the left, as indicated in Fig. 4–19, the elementary contact forces denoted by C_2 are increased in magnitude, whereas those labeled C_1 decrease. The resultant contact force will then

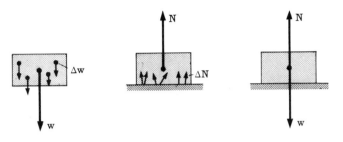

FIG. 4–18. The total contact force can be considered as the resultant of a number of elementary contact forces.

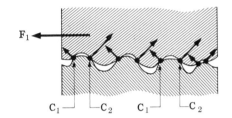

FIG. 4–19. Enlarged picture of two surfaces in contact.

have a horizontal component directed toward the right, and this is called the *friction force* on the body. As the external force $\mathbf{F_1}$ is increased continuously, the friction force F will also increase until the elementary $\mathbf{C_2}$ forces can no longer support the body and it starts to slip. This slip may be a result of the cogs slipping out of each other's grip, or of a breakage of a cog on one of the surfaces.

The maximum value of the friction force, that is, the value which exists just before slipping, is called the *fully developed static friction force*. From this simple picture of the friction force, it can be expected that the fully developed friction force will increase when the body is pressed against the horizontal plane.

For many surfaces the fully developed (maximum) static friction force is approximately proportional to N, the normal component of the contact force:

$$F = \mu N, \tag{4–16}$$

where the constant of proportionality, μ, is called the *static friction coefficient* between surfaces. It should be remembered that the friction force in Eq. (4–16) is the *maximum possible* value, so that when the external force $\mathbf{F_1}$ increases from zero, the friction force increases from zero up to this maximum value. When contacting surfaces move with respect to each other, the irregularities will not have an opportunity to grip deeply into one another and the force required to keep the body sliding, called the *sliding friction force*, should be smaller than the static friction force. Indeed, this is the case for most surfaces. Just as it was in the case of static friction force, the sliding friction force between many types of surfaces is found to be approximately proportional to the normal force. The corresponding constant of proportionality is called the *coefficient of sliding friction*.

As a demonstration of friction, the following experiment may prove instructive and amusing. A polished wooden block A that weighs 8 lb is resting on a long, smooth wooden board, as shown in Fig. 4–20. A string attached to A runs over a pulley and carries a weight at the other end. As the force on the string is increased by increasing the weight supported by it, the friction force on the block increases until the fully developed friction force F is reached. The block then starts to slip. If the fully developed friction force is found to be 2 lb, the corresponding friction coefficient is $\mu = 2/8 = 0.25$, since the normal component of the contact force is 8 lb.

Next, another wooden block B weighing 4 lb is placed on top of block A. The normal component of the contact force on A is then 12 lb. The maximum friction force is now found to be 3 lb, which gives $\mu = 3/12 = 0.25$, confirming the constancy of μ. Block B is then held fixed by means

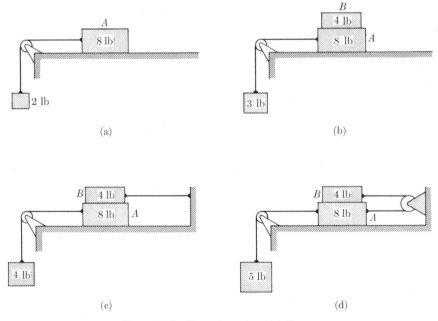

(a)   (b)

(c)   (d)

FIG. 4–20. Experiment on friction.

of a string, as shown in Fig. 4–20(c). There are now two contact surfaces
and two friction forces on A. The pull on the string required to make A
slip is now found to be 4 lb, which again is consistent with $\mu = 0.25$, if
the friction coefficients of both contacting surfaces are assumed equal.
Finally, the blocks are connected by a string over a pulley, as shown in
part (d) of the figure. The limiting weight now turns out to be 5 lb. We
leave it as a problem to show that the last two results are consistent
with $\mu = 0.25$ (Problem 4–28)..

EXAMPLE. A sled weighing 160 lb is standing on a horizontal plane that
has a friction coefficient $\mu = 0.25$. The sled is pulled by a rope which makes an
angle of $\theta = 30°$ with the horizontal, as shown in Fig. 4–21. With what force
must the rope be pulled to make the sled start sliding?

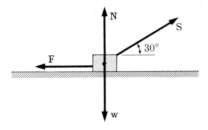

FIGURE 4–21

The sled is acted upon by three forces: gravitation, the contact force from the
plane, and the rope force. The rope force **S** is, of course, in the direction of the
rope. The contact force on the sled from the plane has both a normal (**N**) and a
tangential (**F**) component. Under the limiting conditions we are concerned with
here, the tangential component of the contact force, or the fully developed static
friction force, is

$$F = \mu N = 0.25N.$$

However, it should be noted that this relation *holds only when the body is on the
verge of slipping.*

Let us introduce a coordinate system with the x-axis in the plane and the
y-axis perpendicular to it. The sum of the x-components of the forces is then

$$S \cos 30° - \mu N = 0,$$

and the sum of the y-components is

$$S \sin 30° - w + N = 0.$$

We now have two equations with two unknowns, S and N. Eliminating N, we
obtain for S

$$S \sin 30° - w + \frac{1}{\mu} S \cos 30° = 0,$$

or

$$S = \frac{w}{\sin 30° + (1/\mu) \cos 30°} = \frac{160}{0.5 + 4 \cdot 0.866} \simeq 40.5 \text{ lb.}$$

The normal component of the contact force is then

$$N = \frac{1}{\mu} S \cos 30° = 4 \cdot 40.5 \cdot \sqrt{3}/2 \simeq 140.1 \text{ lb.}$$

PROBLEMS

4-1. Two bodies, A and B, move in a plane. Body A has a velocity with components $v_x = 3$ m/sec, $v_y = 4$ m/sec, and body B has components $v_x = 3$ m/sec, $v_y = 1$ m/sec. What is the angle between the trajectories of A and B, and what are the speeds of the two bodies?

4-2. A body of mass $m = 10$ kgm moves with a speed of 10 m/sec on an ice pond. A gust of wind causes the body to change its motion, so that after the gust the body is moving in a direction 30° off its original course with a speed of 12 m/sec. Determine the momentum delivered to the body by the gust.

4-3. The momentum vectors, $\mathbf{p}_a$ and $\mathbf{p}_b$, of two bodies add to zero. Which of the following statements regarding the motion of the bodies are correct? (a) The bodies necessarily move along the same straight line. (b) The trajectories of the bodies are parallel. (c) The bodies may move in parallel planes. (d) The bodies will eventually collide and contact each other.

4-4. In Fig. 4–22, P is a hockey puck of 0.16 kgm mass. It travels on frictionless ice toward a wall with a velocity of 5 m/sec. At a distance 28.8 m from the wall, P collides with a stationary wooden block B of 0.09 kgm mass. Five seconds after the collision, the block arrives at the wall at a point 9.6 m from the original line of travel

of the puck. (a) Where is the hockey puck 5 sec after the collision? (b) Draw a momentum vector diagram showing the momenta of the two bodies both before and after the collision.

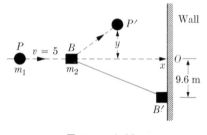

FIGURE 4–22

4-5. A body with a mass of 0.5 kgm is sliding with a constant velocity of 2 m/sec on a horizontal surface along the x-axis in a rectangular coordinate system. When the body passes $x = 3$ m (moving in the positive x-direction), it is hit by a bullet fired from the point $x = 0$, $y = 4$ m. After the collision, the body is found to move in a direction making an angle of 30° with the x-axis. The speed of the bullet was 500 m/sec before the collision. After the collision, it is embedded in the body. (a) Illustrate in a momentum vector diagram how the total momentum after the collision is related to the momentum vectors of the individual bodies before the collision. (b) By direct measurements on this vector diagram, estimate both the mass and the magnitude of the momentum of the bullet before the collision.

4-6. A stone A of mass $m_a = 1$ kgm is sliding on a smooth ice surface with a constant velocity $v_{ax} = 16$ m/sec. It collides with another stone B of mass $m_b = 4$ kgm, initially at rest. After the collision, A is traveling at right angles to its original direction with a velocity $v'_{ay} = 12$ m/sec. Find the magnitude and direction of the velocity of B after the collision.

4-7. Three bodies, A, B, and C, weighing 2 lb, 2 lb, and 4 lb, respectively, are connected by bars (neglect the weight of the bars), as shown in Fig. 4-23. The system is at rest on a *horizontal* table. ($AB = 4$ ft, $BC = 2$ ft.) (a) What are the coordinates of the center of mass? (b) A body with a momentum 10 lb·sec in the x-direction collides with A and comes to rest as a result of the collision. What is the velocity of the center of mass after the collision?

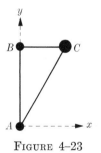

FIGURE 4-23

4-8. A body of mass $m = 40$ kgm moves parallel to the x-axis with a constant velocity $v = 0.1$ m/sec along the line $y = 2$ m. When the body arrives at $x = 0$, a shot is fired in the y-direction into the body. Some time after the shot, the body is found to pass the point $x = 3$ m, $y = 6$ m. (a) If the mass of the bullet is $m =$ 0.02 kgm, what was its velocity? (b) Determine the velocities of the center of mass of the system both before and after the collision.

4-9. Where is the center of mass of a uniform plate like that shown in Fig. 4-24?

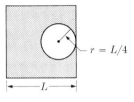

FIGURE 4-24

4-10. A ball weighing 0.32 lb and rolling on a horizontal surface with a speed of 2 ft/sec strikes a vertical wall at an angle of 30° to the wall. It rebounds with a speed of 5/3 ft/sec at an angle of 37° to the wall. Assume that the ball is in contact with the wall for a time 0.01 sec. Find the average contact force that the wall exerted on the ball during this time.

4-11. The momentum components of two bodies A and B colliding in a plane are plotted as functions of time in Fig. 4-25. (a) Complete the curves showing the momenta of B during and after the collision. (b) Show how the momentum vector $\mathbf{p}_a$ varies with time in a momentum diagram in which the vectors are drawn from a common point, and determine the magnitude and direction of the force on A as a function of time.

4-12. A body is moving in space along a trajectory described by a position vector $\mathbf{r}$. Which of the following statements concerning this motion are correct? Discuss your answers.

(a) The velocity is always along the direction of $\mathbf{r}$. (b) The velocity can be normal to $\mathbf{r}$. (c) The velocity is zero when the magnitude of $\mathbf{r}$ is constant.

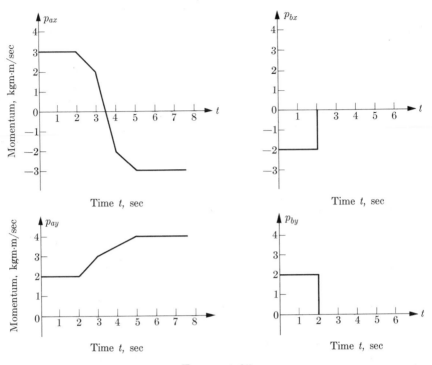

FIGURE 4–25

(d) The velocity is parallel to the tangent to the **r**-trajectory. (e) The force is normal to the momentum vector. (f) The force vector can be normal to the radius vector. (g) The force must be zero when dp/dt is zero (p = magnitude of **p**).

4–13. Draw a vector diagram illustrating how momentum varies with time in the motion of the puck shown in Fig. 4–11. Draw all the momentum vectors from one origin and connect their tips with a smooth curve. This curve is usually called the *hodograph* of the motion. Convince yourself that the tangent to the hodograph has the same direction as the force on the puck.

4–14. A body of mass 2 kgm is acted upon by three forces, $\mathbf{F}_1$ of magnitude 3 n in the x-direction, $\mathbf{F}_2$ of magnitude 4 n in the y-direction,

and $\mathbf{F}_3$ of magnitude 5 n directed into the fourth quadrant and making an angle of 45° with the x-axis. Determine the magnitude and direction of the additional force required, to produce an acceleration of 2 m/sec^2 in the negative x-direction. To produce equilibrium?

4–15. A body of mass m = 0.5 kgm is free to slide on a vertical frictionless bar, as shown in Fig. 4–26. One end of a spring of relaxed length 20 cm is attached to the body. The other end of the spring is fastened at a horizontal point B, a distance of 20 cm from the bar. The body is then released. It is found to come to equilibrium a vertical distance of 30 cm below B. (a) Plot a diagram isolating the body, showing all the forces acting upon it, and indicating the conditions for equilibrium.

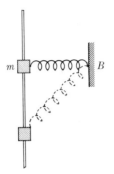

FIGURE 4–26

(b) Determine the spring constant of the spring and the magnitude and direction of contact force on the bar.

4–16. Two weights, each of mass m, are attached to opposite ends of a long rope and the rope is hung over pulleys a horizontal distance l apart. (a) What is the tension in the rope? (b) A third weight of mass M is hung on the rope midway between the pulleys, and the midpoint of the rope is observed to drop a distance $l/2\sqrt{3}$. How large, in terms of m, is M?

4–17. Two pith balls are attached to the ends of strings, as shown in Fig. 4–27. When the balls are electrically charged, they repel each other by a force $F = 9 \cdot 10^9 q_1 q_2 / r^2$ n, where r is measured in meters and q in coulombs. If the mass of each ball is 1 gm, $l = 100$ cm, and the angle of deflection is $\theta = 30°$, what then are the charges (assumed equal) on the pith balls?

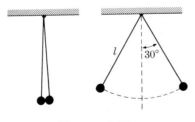

FIGURE 4–27

4–18. A body weighing 200 lb is supported by two ropes A and B, as shown in Fig. 4–28. Rope B runs over a pulley (neglect friction), and both ends of B are attached to the body. One end of A is attached to a fixed wall and the other to the body. If the angles of the ropes are as shown in the figure, determine the rope tensions.

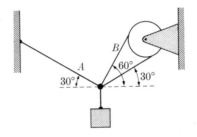

FIGURE 4–28

4–19. A small body A of mass m is attracted to the corners of a square (see Fig. 4–29) by forces which are proportional to the distances between A and the corners. The constants of proportionality are all the same and equal to K. Prove that the resulting force on A at an arbitrary point inside the square is $\mathbf{F} = -4K\mathbf{r}_a$, where $\mathbf{r}_a$ is the position vector of A.

FIGURE 4–29

4–20. Consider an arrangement similar to that in Fig. 4–26. If the spring constant this time is 20 n/cm, at what position should the body (mass = 0.5 kgm) be released in order that its initial acceleration should be g in the upward direction? If you cannot obtain an analytical solution, devise a numerical or a graphical method of solution.

4–21. Consider a frictionless hoop of radius r in a vertical plane. One end of each of two springs is attached to a body that can slide on the hoop. The other ends of the springs are fastened at the lowest and highest points of the hoop, as shown in Fig. 4–30. The springs are identical, each with a relaxed length of half the radius, and the spring constant is such that $Kr/2 = w$, where w is the weight of the body. (a) In a diagram, isolate the body and indicate all the forces on it. (b) Determine the acceleration of the body in terms of g when it is released from the position P indicated in the figure. What is the contact force on the hoop at that point?

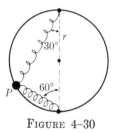

FIGURE 4–30

4–22. A ball is confined to sliding around a circle of radius r, in a vertical plane. The ball is repelled by forces at the endpoints A and B of the horizontal diameter of the circle. These forces are proportional to the distances from the ball to A and B, and the constants of proportionality are K_1 and K_2, respectively. That is, $F_1 = K_1 r_1$, $F_2 = K_2 r_2$. (a) Determine the angle ϕ at which equilibrium is established if the weight of the ball is w. (b) Determine the angle ϕ at which equilibrium is established if the weight of the ball is negligible. (c) Under some condition, can equilibrium be established for all angles ϕ if the weight of the ball is negligible?

4–23. Two weights, w_1 and w_2, are connected by a string of length l and placed on a smooth cylinder, as shown in Fig. 4–31. (a) Determine the relation between ϕ_1 and ϕ_2 at equilibrium. (b) What then are the tension in the string and the forces acting upon the cylinder?

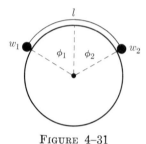

FIGURE 4–31

4–24. Three particles A, B, and C move in a plane. At a certain instant their positions are $x_a = 3$ m, $y_a = -2$ m; $x_b = 5$ m, $y_b = 1$ m; $x_c = -3$ m, $y_c = 3$ m; the corresponding momenta in kgm·m/sec are $p_{ax} = -1$, $p_{ay} = 2$; $p_{bx} = 3$, $p_{by} = 2$; $p_{cx} = 2$, $p_{cy} = -3$. The masses of the bodies are $m_a = 2$ kgm, $m_b = 3$ kgm, and $m_c = 1$ kgm. (a) Determine the location and the velocity of the center of mass when these conditions prevail. (b) From the information above, can you predict the future motion of the center of mass? If not, what information do you need? Discuss.

4–25. A mass $m_1 = 3$ kgm is attached to one end and a mass $m_2 = 1$ kgm to the other end of a bar 40 cm long. The bar is placed vertically on a frictionless plane at a point P, as shown in Fig. 4–32, and is then released. How far from P does mass m_1 strike the plane?

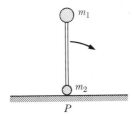

FIGURE 4–32

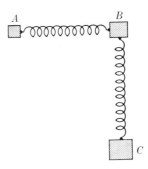

FIGURE 4–34

4–26. A closed box stands on a smooth horizontal plane. A pendulum consisting of a weight on a string of length l hangs inside from the cover of the box. The string passes through the center of mass of the box. The mass m of the pendulum equals that of the box. The pendulum is made to swing in a vertical plane between the angles $\phi = +90°$ and $\phi = -90°$. If one point of the box is at $x = 0$ (see Fig. 4–33) at the instant when $\phi = 0$, what is the location of that point when $\phi = +90°$?

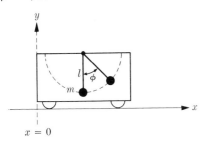

FIGURE 4–33

4–27. Consider three bodies A, B, and C on a frictionless horizontal plane. Their masses are $m_a = 4$ kgm, $m_b = 6$ kgm, and $m_c = 8$ kgm. The bodies are connected by springs, as shown in Fig. 4–34. The tensions in the springs AB and BC are 10 n and 15 n, respectively. The bodies are released from this position. Determine the initial accelerations (a) of A, B, and C; (b) of the center of mass of

the system $A + B$; and (c) of the center of mass of the system $A + B + C$.

4–28. Analyze the experiments shown in Fig. 4–20 of the text. In each experiment isolate each of the bodies involved, and indicate all the forces on each body. Determine the tensions in the strings involved.

4–29. A body is lying on an inclined plane, as shown in Fig. 4–35. The static friction coefficient between the body and the plane is μ. (a) Isolate the body and indicate all the forces on it. (b) If the inclination angle θ is increased continuously, at what angle does the body start to slide down the plane?

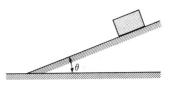

FIGURE 4–35

4–30. A block is resting on a platform, as shown in Fig. 4–36. The platform is moved with a constant acceleration equal to $g/4$, in the direction shown in the figure. What must be the friction coefficient of the contact surface to prevent the body from slipping?

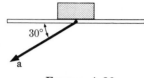

FIGURE 4–36

4–31. Two bodies A and B of masses $m_a = 2$ kgm and $m_b = 1$ kgm are connected by a string of negligible mass, as shown in Fig. 4–37. The friction coefficients at the contact surfaces of the two bodies are $\mu_b = 0.2$ and $\mu_a = 0.1$. (a) Isolate both A and B, and indicate all the forces on them. How many unknown forces and how many equations of motion are there? (b) What is the tension in the string as the bodies slide down the plane? The inclination angle of the plane is 30°.

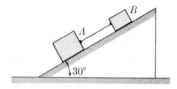

FIGURE 4–37

4–32. What is the range of acceleration, during which m_2 will not slip, that may be given to the cart shown in Fig. 4–38? The friction coefficients of the horizontal and vertical surfaces are μ_2 and μ_1, respectively.

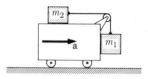

FIGURE 4–38

4–33. A container filled with water slides down an inclined plane, as shown in Fig. 4–39. Water is ejected from a hole in the container in the forward direction at a rate of ρ gm/sec with a constant speed v_0 relative to the box. The mass of the empty box is M, and the mass of the water is initially m_0. If the container starts sliding from rest at $t = 0$, determine its acceleration as a function of time, neglecting friction. The angle of inclination of the plane is θ.

FIGURE 4–39

CHAPTER 5

EXAMPLES OF FORCES AND MOTION — I

Summary. We shall start with a survey of the basic features of projectile motion in the local gravitational field. Having familiarized ourselves with this motion, we shall study qualitatively the nature of the trajectories of particles shot from an elevated position above the earth's surface at speeds ranging from very low to very high values. One of these trajectories must be a circle around the earth, and this particular trajectory is chosen for the study of circular motion. A brief discussion follows on the motions of charged particles in constant electric and magnetic fields. Electric force is analogous to local gravitational force, but magnetic force has the novel feature of being velocity-dependent. The chapter is concluded with a discussion of the mathematical method for determining motion when the force is time-dependent.

In previous chapters the basic concepts of momentum and force have been established and applied to several illustrative examples. However, there are certain forces and motions which are so important and common that they deserve special attention. We shall discuss in the present chapter several such examples, including the motion of a body in a constant force field (projectile motion) and circular motion. In addition, we shall investigate some aspects of the motion of electrically charged particles in both electric and magnetic fields. The essential properties of these motions can be properly described in terms of the general principles which we have so far treated.

5–1 Projectile motion. The analysis of motion along a vertical line, presented in the previous chapter, can easily be extended to the general case in which the initial velocity of a body also has a component in the x-direction. Experiment has shown that gravitational force is *independent of the velocity* of a body. The gravitational force near the surface of the earth always has the magnitude mg and is directed downward, *regardless of the speed or the direction* of the motion of a body. Consequently, in the horizontal direction, there will be no momentum transfer to a body as it moves under the influence of gravity. That is, the horizontal component of the velocity of the body remains constant, while the vertical velocity component changes just as in purely vertical motion.

An amusing demonstration of this property of projectile motion and the velocity-independence of gravitational force is the following. One of the cars used in the collision experiments of Chapter 3 is supplied with

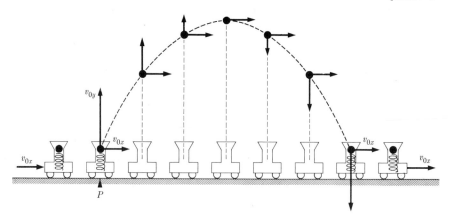

Fig. 5–1. An example of projectile motion, demonstrating that the horizontal component of the velocity remains constant.

a coil-spring "gun" loaded with a golf ball, as indicated schematically in Fig. 5–1. The car, which is free to move on a horizontal track, is set in motion and travels with a constant speed. When it passes the point P, the spring is released and the ball is ejected from the gun. As the ball is ejected, it has the same horizontal velocity as the car and, of course, receives a vertical velocity component also. We find that the horizontal component of the velocity indeed remains constant, since the horizontal positions of the ball and the car are seen to be the same throughout the motion until the ball finally lands in the car. The vertical velocity component, on the other hand, decreases at a constant rate until it becomes zero at the highest point of the path of the ball. Thereafter, it changes sign and its magnitude grows at the same rate, so that upon landing in the car, the ball resumes its initial speed.

We shall describe the motion of the ball with respect to a coordinate system that has a horizontal x-axis and a vertical y-axis. The origin of the coordinate system is chosen to be the position at which the ball is ejected, and time is measured from the instant of ejection. Thus at $t = 0$, the ball is ejected from $x = 0$, $y = 0$ with a speed v_0 and an elevation angle of θ. The horizontal and vertical velocity components are then $v_{0x} = v_0 \cos \theta$ and $v_{0y} = v_0 \sin \theta$. The equations of motion are

$$m \frac{dv_x}{dt} = F_x = 0, \qquad m \frac{dv_y}{dt} = -mg.$$

The velocity components at a later time t are then

$$v_x = v_{0x} = v_0 \cos \theta = \text{const}, \qquad v_y = v_{0y} - gt = v_0 \sin \theta - gt, \quad (5\text{–}1)$$

and the corresponding positions are given by

$$x = v_{0x}t = (v_0 \cos \theta)t, \qquad y = v_{0y}t - \frac{gt^2}{2} = (v_0 \sin \theta)t - \frac{gt^2}{2}. \quad (5\text{-}2)$$

Inserting $t = x/v_{0x} = x/v_0 \cos \theta$ into the expression for y, we obtain y as a function of x, which is the following parabolic trajectory:

$$y = \frac{v_{0y}}{v_{0x}} x - g \frac{x^2}{2v_{0x}^2} = \frac{v_{0y}}{v_{0x}} x \left(1 - \frac{g}{2v_{0x}v_{0y}} x\right). \quad (5\text{-}3)$$

We see that $y = 0$ for $x = 0$ and also for

$$x = l = \frac{2v_{0x}v_{0y}}{g} = \frac{v_0^2 \sin 2\theta}{g}. \quad (5\text{-}4)$$

The latter value of x represents the range l of the projectile. The maximum height h of the trajectory obtained for $x = l/2$ is

$$h = \frac{l}{4} \frac{v_{0y}}{v_{0x}} = \frac{l}{4} \tan \theta = \frac{v_{0y}^2}{2g}. \quad (5\text{-}5)$$

With the range and the height of the trajectory as indicated in Fig. 5-2, we now can write

$$\frac{y}{h} = 4 \frac{x}{l}\left(1 - \frac{x}{l}\right). \quad (5\text{-}6)$$

Clearly, l has a maximum value $l_m = v_0^2/g$, obtained for the angle $\theta = 45°$ when $\sin 2\theta = 1$. The maximum height, $h_m = v_0^2/2g = l_m/2$, is obtained when $\theta = 90°$. In other words, the maximum range is twice the maximum height of the projectile.

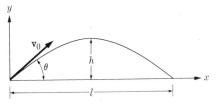

FIG. 5-2. Projectile motion.

Instead of starting with a given elevation angle as above, we shall now turn the problem around and start with a given position x_1, y_1 of a target and seek the elevation angle for which the trajectory will go through the target. The speed v_0 of the projectile is given. Then, using $1/\cos^2 \theta = 1 + \tan^2 \theta$, we obtain from the trajectory equation (5-3) the relation between the angle θ and the coordinates x_1, y_1:

$$y_1 = x_1 \tan \theta - \frac{g}{2v_0^2} x_1^2(1 + \tan^2 \theta).$$

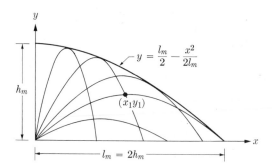

FIG. 5–3. The envelope of the various projectile trajectories obtained by varying the elevation angle.

Solving for tan θ gives

$$\tan \theta = \frac{l_m}{x_1} \pm \frac{1}{x_1} \sqrt{l_m^2 - x_1^2 - 2l_m y_1}, \qquad (5\text{–}7)$$

where $l_m = v_0^2/g$.

Note that there can be two different possible elevation angles that correspond to a given target, as illustrated in Fig. 5–3. When the target is located such that the square root of Eq. (5–7) vanishes, the two angles merge and there is only one possible orientation. The relation between y_1 and x_1 for which the square root is zero is

$$y_1 = \frac{l_m^2 - x_1^2}{2l_m} = \frac{l_m}{2} - \frac{x_1^2}{2l_m} = h_m - \frac{x_1^2}{2l_m}, \qquad (5\text{–}8)$$

which defines the curve indicated in Fig. 5–3. If the target point lies inside this curve, there are two possible angles θ; if the point lies *on* the curve, there is one possible angle; and if the point lies outside the curve, there is no possible angle at which the projectile will reach the target. Therefore, Eq. (5–8) defines a boundary line beyond which the projectile, with an initial velocity of v_0, cannot reach.

5–2 Circular motion. When the net force on a moving body is zero, the body moves along a straight line with a constant speed. The influence of a force on this motion, of course, depends upon the direction of the force. If the force is in the same direction as the velocity of the body, as in the case of a free fall, the effect of the force is merely to change the magnitude of the velocity. In order to produce a change of the direction of motion and a corresponding curvature of the trajectory, a force component perpendicular to the velocity is required. If the magnitude of the force is constant, the rate of change of direction and the corresponding curvature of the trajectory are maximum when the entire force is perpendicular to the velocity. This is illustrated by our discussion of projectile motion in the previous section, where we found a maximum curvature at the top of the trajectory.

This curvature of a trajectory depends not only upon the force perpendicular to the velocity, but also upon the speed of the projectile. To further illustrate this point, let us discuss qualitatively the trajectories of projectiles shot with different speeds in a horizontal direction from an elevated position P above the earth, as shown in Fig. 5–4. When the speed is zero, the projectile drops straight down, and when the speed is very great, that is, approaching infinity, the trajectory is very nearly a straight line. At intermediate speeds the curve of the trajectory, depending upon the speed, may be smaller or larger than the curvature of the earth's surface. Consequently, at a certain critical speed the trajectory will be such that the projectile always moves parallel with the earth's surface; i.e., the "fall" of the projectile in toward the earth is always "compensated" by curvature of the earth, so that the height of the projectile above the earth's surface remains constant. The trajectory illustrated by the dashed curve in Fig. 5–4 is then circular, and the force is always perpendicular to it, pointing in toward the center of the earth. We can readily determine the critical speed of the projectile corresponding to this circular orbit by investigating the relation that must exist between the (known) curvature of the circular path and the "deflection" of the projectile produced by its continuous fall in toward the earth.

Consider one segment of the circular path between two points, P_1 and P_2, separated a distance $R \, \Delta\theta = \Delta s$, where R is the radius of the circular

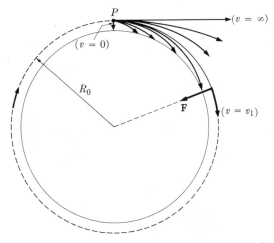

FIG. 5–4. The trajectories of projectiles shot with different velocities in a horizontal direction from an elevated point P.

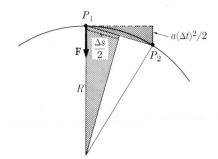

FIG. 5–5. The radius of curvature produced by a constant force that is perpendicular to the trajectory.

path, and Δs is the path length between P_1 and P_2, as shown in Fig. 5–5. If the speed of the projectile is v, the time of travel between P_1 and P_2 is $\Delta t = \Delta s/v$. As we have already pointed out, the force on the projectile and the corresponding acceleration a of the projectile are perpendicular to the velocity. Choosing the time interval Δt sufficiently small, we can consider the acceleration as constant in this interval. The distance which the projectile falls toward the earth in the time Δt is then $a(\Delta t)^2/2$, as indicated in the figure. Again taking Δt sufficiently small, the path distance Δs can be closely approximated by a straight line between P_1 and P_2. From Fig. 5–5 it follows directly that by comparing the similar triangles indicated in the figure, we obtain

$$\frac{\Delta s/2}{R} = \frac{a(\Delta t)^2/2}{\Delta s}$$

or

$$a = \frac{(\Delta s/\Delta t)^2}{R} = \frac{v^2}{R}. \tag{5–9}$$

In other words, if the speed of the projectile is $v = \sqrt{aR}$, as it is shot out from P under the influence of the acceleration a perpendicular to the path, the "fall" of the projectile in the direction of the acceleration will be such that the trajectory becomes a circle of radius R. Note that as the direction of motion changes so does the direction of the force, so that the force and the corresponding acceleration always are perpendicular to the velocity in circular motion. The speed of the projectile then remains constant. For other speeds of projectiles the trajectories are not circular, and in the direction of motion there will be a force component which speeds or slows the projectile. Compare this motion with that in the previous section, where small projectile speeds were considered. The case in which the velocity is larger than $v = \sqrt{aR}$ will be treated in Chapter 10. The critical speed at which the projectile is sent into orbit around the earth can be estimated if we use $R = 6.4 \cdot 10^6$ m and $g = 9.8$ m/sec^2. The corresponding value of the critical speed is then $v_1 \simeq 8000$ m/sec or about 5 mi/sec.

So far as circular motion is concerned, the origin or nature of the force is irrelevant. Instead of the gravitational force, we may have a constant force provided by a string, a rigid bar, a track, etc., or we may have an electromagnetic force acting to keep the moving body in a circular path. As in the trajectory around the earth, the force on a body moving in a circular orbit is always perpendicular to the trajectory and directed in toward the center of the circle. The magnitude of the force is related to the speed v of the body and the radius R of the circle by the equation

$$F = ma = \frac{mv^2}{R}, \tag{5–10}$$

which follows from Eq. (5–9).

It is important to note that when a body moves in a circle it is often forced to do so by a "constraint" such as a circular wire or a track of some kind. In such cases there is frequently more than one force acting on the body, for example, gravity and one or more contact forces. As the body moves in the circle, the acceleration toward the center of the circle always has the magnitude v^2/R, even if the speed varies from one point to another. The sum of all the force components in the direction toward the center of the circle then must equal mv^2/R. Of course, these forces can also have components in the tangential direction that make the velocity of the body vary as it moves around the circle.

EXAMPLE 1. A pendulum consists of a 3-ft string, fixed at one end and carrying a 4-lb body at the other (Fig. 5–6). As the pendulum swings back and forth in a vertical plane, the velocity is found to be 10 ft/sec when the angular deflection is 45°. At this instant, what is the tension in the string?

There are two forces acting upon the body at the end of the string, its weight mg and the tension $\mathbf{S}$ in the string. The acceleration toward the center of the circular path of the body is v^2/R. The resulting force component in this direction is $S - mg \cos \theta$, as indicated in the figure. Consequently, we have

$$S - mg \cos \theta = \frac{mv^2}{R}$$

or

$$S = \frac{mv^2}{R} + mg \cos \theta.$$

Using the numerical values $v = 10$ ft/sec and $m = 4/32$ slug, $mg = 4$ lb, $R = 3$ ft, and $\theta = 45°$, we obtain

$$S = \frac{4}{32} \cdot \frac{10^2}{3} + 4 \frac{\sqrt{2}}{2} \simeq 7.01 \text{ lb.}$$

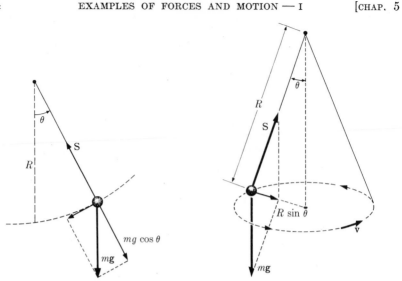

FIGURE 5-6   FIGURE 5-7

EXAMPLE 2. We shall let the pendulum of the previous example move coni-
cally, so that the body at the end of the string moves in a horizontal rather
than a vertical circle, and the string generates the surface of a cone, as shown in
Fig. 5-7. (Such motion is employed in centrifugal regulators.) What speed is
required to make the angle between the string and the vertical 45°, and what is
the corresponding tension in the string?

If the length of the string is R, the radius of the horizontal circle is $R \sin \theta$,
where θ is the angle between the string and the vertical. There are two forces on
the body, its weight mg and the tension $\mathbf{S}$ in the string. The acceleration in the
vertical direction is zero, and we have $S \cos \theta - mg = 0$, or $S = mg/\cos \theta$.
The acceleration in the horizontal direction is toward the center of the circle
and we have

$$S \sin \theta = \frac{mv^2}{R \sin \theta}$$

or

$$v^2 = Rg \tan \theta \sin \theta.$$

With the numerical values $R = 3$ ft, $g \simeq 32$, and $\theta = 45°$, we obtain

$$v \simeq \sqrt{3 \cdot 32 \cdot 1 \cdot 0.7} \simeq 8.2 \text{ ft/sec.}$$

The corresponding tension in the string is

$$S = \frac{mg}{\cos \theta} \simeq 5.7 \text{ lb.}$$

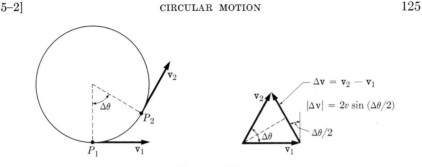

FIGURE 5–8

EXAMPLE 3. We shall illustrate another derivation of the expression for the relation between the force and the speed of a particle in circular motion. We shall start directly from the definition of the average vector acceleration, $\bar{\mathbf{a}} = (\mathbf{v}_2 - \mathbf{v}_1)/(t_2 - t_1) = \Delta\mathbf{v}/\Delta t$, and investigate the limiting value of this acceleration when $\Delta t = 0$. Consider a body moving with constant speed in a circle of radius R. Determine the average acceleration of the body in the interval between two points, P_1 and P_2, separated by an angle $\Delta\theta$, as illustrated in Fig. 5–8.

The change in velocity between these points, $\Delta\mathbf{v} = \mathbf{v}_2 - \mathbf{v}_1$, has a magnitude $|\Delta\mathbf{v}| = 2v \sin (\Delta\theta/2)$ and a direction which makes an angle of $\Delta\theta/2$ with the vertical. The body goes from P_1 to P_2 in the time $\Delta t = R\,\Delta\theta/v$,* so that the average acceleration $\bar{\mathbf{a}} = \Delta\mathbf{v}/\Delta t$ has the magnitude

$$\bar{a} = \frac{v^2}{R} \frac{\sin (\Delta\theta/2)}{\Delta\theta/2}.$$

To find the instantaneous acceleration at P_1, we determine the limiting value of this acceleration when Δt (and $\Delta\theta$) is zero. Since the limiting value of

$$\frac{\sin (\Delta\theta/2)}{\Delta\theta/2}$$

is unity, we see that the magnitude of the instantaneous acceleration at P_1 is $a = v^2/R$, as before. Since the average acceleration makes an angle $\Delta\theta/2$ with the vertical, it follows that in the limit when Δt and $\Delta\theta$ approach zero, the direction of the instantaneous acceleration at P_1 is vertical; that is, the acceleration is directed toward the center of the circle. Clearly, the same result applies to an arbitrary point on the circle.

Polar coordinates. In the discussion of projectile motion, the location of the body was specified by the rectangular coordinates x and y. These coordinates define the position vector $\mathbf{r}$ of the body. In addition to de-

---

* Here the angle $\Delta\theta$ is measured in radians. Recall that a full circle is 360° or 2π radians, and that the length of circular arc subtended by an angle α is $r\alpha$, where r is the radius of the circle and α is measured in radians.

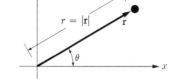

FIG. 5–9. Polar coordinates r and θ.

fining $\mathbf{r}$ by x and y, we can also specify it by its length r, and its direction as given, for example, by the angle θ between $\mathbf{r}$ and the fixed x-axis. The two quantities r and θ are called the *polar coordinates* of the body. With reference to Fig. 5–9, the following relations between the rectangular and polar coordinates may be obtained:

$$x = r \cos \theta, \qquad y = r \sin \theta, \tag{5–11}$$

or

$$r = \sqrt{x^2 + y^2}, \qquad \tan \theta = \frac{y}{x}.$$

As the body moves, both the radial and angular coordinates, r and θ, will usually change. The rates of change of r and θ are called the *radial* and the *angular* velocities, respectively. Thus the radial velocity is

$$v_r = \frac{dr}{dt}, \tag{5–12}$$

and the *angular velocity* is

$$\omega = \frac{d\theta}{dt}. \tag{5–13}$$

In the special case of circular motion, the radius r remains constant (R), and the radial velocity is zero. The angular velocity is related in a simple way to the speed of the particle. A displacement ds along the circle corresponds to an angular displacement $d\theta = ds/R$, and the angular velocity is then $d\theta/dt = (1/R)(ds/dt)$, or

$$\omega = \frac{v}{R}, \qquad v = \omega R. \tag{5–14}$$

In circular motion, then, the magnitude of the acceleration toward the center can be expressed as

$$a = \frac{v^2}{R} = \omega^2 R. \tag{5–15}$$

If the angle θ is measured from the positive x-axis, and if we set $t = 0$ when $\theta = 0$, we have $\theta = \omega t$ if the angular velocity ω is constant.

The rectangular coordinates, $x = r \cos \theta$ and $y = r \sin \theta$, of a particle moving in a circular path with *constant* speed are then

$$x = R \cos \omega t, \qquad y = R \sin \omega t. \tag{5–16}$$

The corresponding components of the velocity and the acceleration are

$$\frac{dx}{dt} = v_x = -R\omega \sin \omega t, \qquad \frac{dy}{dt} = v_y = R\omega \cos \omega t \tag{5–17}$$

and

$$\frac{dv_x}{dt} = a_x = -R\omega^2 \cos \omega t = -\omega^2 x,$$

$$\frac{dv_y}{dt} = a_y = -R\omega^2 \sin \omega t = -\omega^2 y. \tag{5–18}$$

The motions of the coordinates are oscillatory and are called *harmonic motions*. These two special and related types of motion, harmonic and circular, have wide general significances in physics. We can see, from Eq. (5–18), that in harmonic motion acceleration is proportional but oppositely directed to displacement. This interesting property of motion is the same as that of a body under the influence of a spring force, $F = -Kx$, as given by Eq. (3–19) in Chapter 3. We shall later find that a mass at the end of a spring does indeed perform harmonic motion.

5–3 Motion of electrically charged particles. *Electrostatic force.* Electrostatic forces are perhaps not so familiar or as frequently encountered as are gravitational, contact, and spring forces, but certainly we are all aware of their existence. A plastic comb when rubbed on a piece of woolen cloth becomes "charged" and tends to attract a piece of paper. This attractive force is called an electrostatic force. Electrostatic forces are responsible for the peculiar and annoying behavior of dust on a phonograph record. More important, interatomic forces are largely of electrostatic origin.

The basic force law of electrostatics was first given by Coulomb in 1785; however, long before that it was known that such a force existed. The basic law, known as Coulomb's law, is

$$F = Cq_1 q_2 / r^2 \qquad (C = 9 \cdot 10^9 \text{ n·m}^2/\text{coul}^2), \tag{5–19}$$

where F is the electrostatic force between two point charges q_1 and q_2 which are separated by a distance r. The constant C depends, of course, on the choice of units. When the length is in meters, the charge in coulombs, and the force in newtons, C has the value given in Eq. (5–19). Coulomb's law was first found from static, or equilibrium, experiments. We shall not discuss possible equilibrium experiments that would lead to this law, or possible definitions of the charge q. For now, we shall merely point out that the law of electrostatics is very similar in form to the gravitational law of Newton, with gravitational mass replaced by electric charge. While we know of only one type of gravitational mass, the electric charge on a body may be either positive or negative. When two bodies have either *both negative* or *both positive* charges, the force between them is *repulsive;* when one of two bodies has a negative charge and the other a positive charge, the force between them is *attractive.* (Gravitational force, so far as is known, is always *attractive.*) It should be noted that a direct application of Eq. (5–19) to bodies of finite size is possible only when their separation is large compared with their own dimensions.

In experiments performed in the laboratory, we find that the electrostatic force between objects is generally much larger than the corresponding gravitational force. The motion of electrons in vacuum tubes and in some cathode-ray oscilloscopes is determined entirely by electrostatic forces. Electron motion is, of course, determined by these forces acting on the electron as it travels through space.

Both the gravitational and the electrostatic forces can act through empty space and need no material contact between interacting bodies. It is therefore very useful to consider space as possessing a *field* (gravitational or electrostatic), which is defined as the force per unit mass (gravitational field) or per unit charge (electric field) on a body placed in the field. A field, of course, results from the presence of bodies, but in many problems of motion the field may be specified as a function of the location in space and of time. (In practice, a field may change as a result of the introduction of a body, since the body will affect the sources of the field by interactions with the sources.)

The space about the earth possesses a gravitational field, and when a body is introduced into this region, it will be acted upon by gravitational force. If the mass of this body is m_1, the force on it is $F = m_1(Gm_2/r^2)$. The quantity inside the parentheses is the gravitational *field strength,* gravitational *force* being proportional to the mass of the body and the field strength. Close to the surface of the earth, the field strength is constant and equal to g, and is directed downward.

Similarly, the force on an electric charge q_1 placed in the region about another charge q_2 can be considered as a result of an electric field $E = Cq_2/r^2$, produced by q_2. The force can be written as

$$F = q_1E. \tag{5–20}$$

If the field strength is measured in *newtons per coulomb* (sometimes called *volts per meter*) and the charge is measured in *coulombs*, the force is expressed in *newtons*. In general, the electric field, E, is a result of a distribution of charges and will vary in space in accordance with the charge distribution. The expression for the electric field is then not simply Cq_2/r^2, as above. However, the electric field at a specified point is always defined, both in magnitude and in direction, by the force on a particle with a unit of positive charge, placed at this point. Since force is proportional to charge, in an arbitrary electric field the force on a particle is then given by $F = qE$. The force is independent of the velocity of the particle. In the particular case of a large, uniformly charged plane, the electric field outside the plane will be constant, just as the gravitational field close to the surface of the earth is constant. Similarly, the region between two oppositely charged plates, separated a distance that is small compared with the dimensions of the plates, for all practical purposes is constant. The force on a positively charged particle between such plates is then constant and in a direction perpendicular to the plates, from the positive plate toward the negative.

EXAMPLE. A stream of electrons passes between a pair of plates on an oscilloscope, as shown in Fig. 5–10. The length of the plates is l cm, and the separation is d cm. The screen in the oscilloscope is L cm distant from the plates, as shown. If the strength of the electric field between the plates is E, what is the vertical deflection on the screen? The velocity of the electrons entering between the plates is v_0 m/sec.

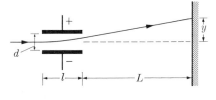

FIGURE 5–10

The electrostatic force $F = qE$ is constant, and the trajectory of the electron is the same as that of a projectile in the local gravitational field. The x-component of the velocity therefore remains constant, and the y-component is $v_y = (F/m)t = (q_m)(E/v_0)x$. As the particle leaves the plate, the y-component of the velocity is $(qE/mv_0)l$. This component remains constant, and after a distance L and a corresponding time L/v_0 of travel to the screen, the displacement at the screen in the y-direction is $(qE/mv_0^2)lL$. There is, in addition, the (small) displacement between the plates, $(F/m)t^2/2 = (qE/mv_0^2 2)l^2$, and we find that the total displacement $y = (qE/mv_0^2)lL(1 + l/2L)$.

Magnetic force. The force on a charge moving in an electrostatic field, as we have seen, is independent of the velocity of the particle. The situation is entirely different when the charged particle moves in the region between the poles of a magnet. In this case experiments show that the force is proportional both to the charge q of the particle and to its velocity

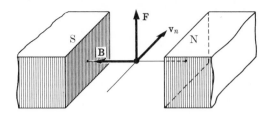

FIG. 5–11. The force on a charged particle moving in a magnetic field.

component v_n in the plane of the pole pieces, that is, $F = \text{const} \cdot qv_n$. The direction of the force is also in the same plane as the pole pieces, but it is perpendicular to the velocity, as shown in Fig. 5–11. The region between the pole pieces is said to possess a *magnetic field*. The magnitude B of the field is defined as the constant of proportionality in the force equation above, so that we have

$$F = qv_nB. \tag{5-21}$$

The direction of the magnetic field is chosen to be perpendicular both to **v** and to **F**, as shown in the figure. This direction, which is the same as that of a magnetic needle placed in the field, defines the direction of the magnetic-field lines, which are used for visualization of the field. When the force is measured in newtons, the velocity in m/sec, and the electric charge in coulombs, the magnetic-field strength as defined by Eq. (5–21) is obtained in the unit n·sec/m·coul, which is called webers/m^2. Since the force is perpendicular to the velocity of the particle, the magnitude of the velocity will not change, but the direction will. Therefore when the velocity is perpendicular to a uniform magnetic field the trajectory of the particle will be circular.

EXAMPLE. A particle with an electric charge q and of mass m moves in a direction perpendicular to the field lines between the poles of a magnet. The magnetic field B is constant. The force on the particle then has the constant magnitude qvB and is perpendicular to the velocity, i.e., the conditions correspond to those for circular motion. The trajectory is indeed circular, and the radius of the circle is given by

$$\frac{mv^2}{R} = F = qvB,$$

that is,

$$R = \frac{m}{q}\frac{v}{B} = \frac{p}{qB}.$$

The time for one round-trip is then $t = 2\pi R/v = 2\pi(m/qB)$, and the corresponding angular frequency is

$$\omega = \frac{2\pi}{t} = \frac{q}{m}B.$$

It is interesting to find that the period t is *independent* of the speed of the particle, a result which is the basis for magnetic-type particle accelerators, such as the cyclotron. The corresponding characteristic frequency is called the *cyclotron frequency*.

5–4 Time-dependent force. Frequently the force on a particle is given as a function of time, as in the case of an electrically charged particle in an electric field that varies with time. The instantaneous rate of change of momentum and the acceleration of the particle are therefore given as functions of time, but if we wish to determine the velocity or trajectory of the particle, we have to solve the equation of motion,

$$m \frac{dv}{dt} = m \frac{d^2x}{dt^2} = F(t). \tag{5–22}$$

There are similar equations for the y- and z-components. The problem is to find v and x from this equation. If v and x are given functions of time, the force is found geometrically from the slope of the p vs. t curve (Chapter 3), or analytically by differentiation. The analytical aspects of this problem are purely mathematical, and we refer the reader to standard texts on calculus* for details. We shall present merely a brief review of the basic procedure involved in such an analysis.

To express that a quantity, for example x, is time-dependent, we write $x = x(t)$, where t is the argument of the function x. The functional dependence of t may be $x(t) = Ct^2$, $x = A \sin \omega t$, etc. Suppose now that from a given $x(t)$ we wish to find the corresponding velocity $v(t)$ and acceleration $a(t)$. As an illustration, consider a simple function like $x = Ct^2$. The value of the constant C depends upon the units of x and t, and we shall assume that they are chosen in such a way that the constant is equal to unity. We have then

$$x = t^2.$$

To determine the instantaneous velocity, which, by definition, is the limiting value of $\Delta x/\Delta t$ when $\Delta t = 0$, we first determine the value of Δx, that is, the increase in the x-coordinate of the body when time increases from t to $t + \Delta t$. Clearly, this increase is

$$\Delta x = x(t + \Delta t) - x(t) = (t + \Delta t)^2 - t^2$$
$$= t^2 + (\Delta t)^2 + 2t\,\Delta t - t^2 = 2t\,\Delta t + (\Delta t)^2. \tag{5–23}$$

---

* For example, George B. Thomas, Jr., *Calculus and Analytic Geometry*, Addison-Wesley Publishing Company, Inc., Reading, Massachusetts, 3rd ed., 1960.

Consequently, we obtain

$$\frac{\Delta x}{\Delta t} = 2t + \Delta t,$$

which becomes the instantaneous velocity when we set $\Delta t = 0$:

$$v = \frac{dx}{dt} = 2t.$$

Thus, when the body is located at $x = t^2$, its velocity is $v = 2t$. Similarly, we can find the acceleration by calculating the limiting value of $\Delta v/\Delta t$:

$$a = \frac{dv}{dt} = \lim_{\Delta t=0} \frac{\Delta v}{\Delta t} = \lim_{\Delta t=0} \frac{2(t + \Delta t) - 2t}{\Delta t} = 2.$$

If we start with a more general time dependence, such as $x = t^n$, the velocity is found to be

$$v = \frac{dx}{dt} = nt^{n-1}, \tag{5-24}$$

and for $n = 2$, this reduces to $2t$, as before. The corresponding acceleration is

$$a = \frac{dv}{dt} = \frac{d^2x}{dt^2} = n(n-1)t^{n-2}.$$

Similarly, when the location is $x = kt^n$, where k is a constant, the velocity becomes $v = knt^{n-1}$.

When a function is a sum of terms, its derivative is merely the sum of the derivatives of the individual terms. For example, if $x = t^2 + t^3$, the derivative is $dx/dt = 2t + 3t^2$. If the function $x = x(t)$ is the product of two functions of time, $x = f(t)g(t)$, its derivative is $dx/dt = f(t)(dg/dt) + g(t)(df/dt)$. We can easily convince ourselves that this relation is consistent with the formulas above by considering, say, $x = t^5$. According to Eq. (5-24), the derivative of this function is $dx/dt = 5t^4$. If we consider t^5 as the product of t^2 and t^3, the "product formula" gives $dx/dt = 2t \cdot t^3 + t^2 \cdot 3t^2 = 5t^4$.

The derivatives of more complicated functions can always be found from the general definition and procedure given by Eq. (5-23). Furthermore, extensive tables of dx/dt for a large number of functions $x(t)$ are available.*

EXAMPLE. The location of a body is given by $x = 4t - 3t^3$, where x is measured in meters and t in seconds. When is the velocity of the body equal to zero, and what then is the acceleration? (t is positive.)

Using the general expression in Eq. (5-24), we obtain the time derivative of x,

$$v = \frac{dx}{dt} = 4 - 9t^2 \text{ m/sec.}$$

If we set $v = 0 = 4 - 9t^2$, we find $t = (\pm)\frac{2}{3}$ sec. Similarly, the acceleration is obtained by differentiating the expression for the velocity:

$$a = \frac{dv}{dt} = -18t.$$

When $t = \frac{2}{3}$ sec, the acceleration is -12 m/sec^2.

Let us now consider the reverse situation in which $F(t)$ is given and $v(t)$ and $x(t)$ are sought. We start with the familiar case of a constant acceleration a_0, and we have

$$m\frac{dv}{dt} = F_0 \qquad \text{or} \qquad \frac{dv}{dt} = \frac{F_0}{m} = a_0.$$

Since the rate of momentum transfer is constant, it follows that in time t the net change of momentum equals $F_0 t$. Thus if at $t = 0$ the momentum of the body is p_0, the momentum at time t is

$$p(t) = p_0 + F_0 t \qquad \text{or} \qquad v = v_0 + \frac{F_0}{m} t = v_0 + at.$$

Next we shall consider a force which is proportional to time, that is,

$$\frac{dp}{dt} = F = kt,$$

where k is a constant. When the force is $F = kt$, the momentum p must be a function of time such that its derivative dp/dt equals kt. In our example,

$$p(t) = k\frac{t^2}{2} + \text{const}, \tag{5–25}$$

since differentiation of dp/dt gives the force $F(t) = dp/dt = kt$. The constant has been added to account for the value of the momentum which exists at $t = 0$ or at any other time. For if the force is $F = kt$, any of the parallel curves, $p(t) = kt^2/2 + \text{const}$, illustrated in Fig. 5–12,

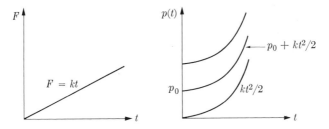

Fig. 5–12. The momentum corresponding to the force $F_x = kt$ is $p(t) = kt^2/2 + C$.

is a possible momentum function. In order to select the curve that applies to a particular problem, we must specify the motion by describing, for example, the conditions under which the motion started, i.e., the value of the momentum at $t = 0$. If this value is $p(0)$, the constant in Eq. (5–25) is simply $p(0)$, and we have

$$p(t) - p(0) = k \frac{t^2}{2}.$$

If, instead, we know the value $p(t_1)$ of the momentum at time t_1, rather than at $t = 0$, we find that const $= p(t_1) - kt_1^2/2$. We incorporate this with Eq. (5–25) to obtain

$$p(t) - p(t_1) = k \frac{t^2}{2} - k \frac{t_1^2}{2}. \tag{5–26}$$

In principle, the procedure of calculating the momentum from a given force, illustrated by the special examples above, clearly can be applied to an arbitrary force function. In other words, with the force $F(t)$ given as a function of time, the momentum equals that function of time which has a derivative equal to the force function. As in the examples given, there always will be an undetermined constant involved, which, however, can be determined from knowledge of the momentum at an instant of time, and which leads to a relation analogous to Eq. (5–25) for the increase in momentum.

The function that has a derivative equal to $F(t)$ is denoted $\int F(t)\, dt$, the *integral* (function) of $F(t)$. Thus, in general, we have

$$p(t) = \int F(t)\, dt + \text{const.} \tag{5–27}$$

The integral function of $F(t) = kt$ was found to be $\int F(t)\, dt = kt^2/2$. Once the momentum function has been obtained, the position of the particle is obtained analogously from $m(dx/dt) = p(t)$.

EXAMPLE. A body starts at $t = 0$ from $x = 5$ m, with velocity $v = 3$ m/sec in the positive x-direction. In the time interval from $t = 0$ to 3 sec, it is acted upon by a force $F = 4t^3$ n in the positive x-direction. What are the velocity and the location of the body at $t = 1$ sec? The mass of the body is 0.5 kgm.

The acceleration is $dv/dt = a(t) = 4t^3/0.5 = 8t^3$, so that $v(t) = 8t^4/4 + C$. At $t = 0$, $v(0) = 3$ m/sec, so that $C_1 = 3$ and $v(t) = 2t^4 + 3$. The location is obtained from $dx/dt = v(t) = 2t^4 + 3$, that is, $x = 2t^5/5 + 3t + C_2$. At $t = 0$, we have $x = 5$, so that $C_2 = 5$. Consequently, $x = 0.4t^5 + 3t + 5$. Therefore at $t = 1$, we obtain $v = 5$ m/sec and $x = 0.4 + 3 + 5 = 8.4$ m.

The trajectory. Once the velocity components and the position coordinates have been obtained from Eq. (5–22) as functions of time, the trajectory of the particle is given in parametric form; i.e., the relation between y and x (in plane motion) is expressed indirectly in terms of the parameter t (time). By elimination of t, we obtain the equation for the trajectory, as illustrated previously in connection with projectile motion.

EXAMPLE. The motion in a plane of a particle of mass m is determined by the relations

$$x = 3t^2, \qquad y = 2t^3,$$

where x is given in meters and t is in seconds. (a) What are the magnitude and direction of the force on the particle at time $t = \frac{1}{2}$ sec? (b) What is the angle between the force and the velocity vectors? (c) What is the equation of the trajectory of the particle (y as a function of x)?

(a) The velocity components are

$$v_x = \frac{dx}{dt} = 6t, \qquad v_y = \frac{dy}{dt} = 6t^2,$$

and the acceleration components are

$$a_x = \frac{dv_x}{dt} = 6, \qquad a_y = \frac{dv_y}{dt} = 12t.$$

At time $t = \frac{1}{2}$ sec, the acceleration components are $a_x = 6$ and $a_y = 6$. The magnitude of the acceleration is then $a = 6\sqrt{2}$ in a direction making an angle of 45° with the x-axis. The force has the magnitude $|F| = ma$ and has the same direction as the acceleration.

(b) The velocity vector at $t = \frac{1}{2}$ has the components $v_x = 3$ and $v_y = \frac{6}{4}$. The direction of v makes an angle with the x-axis of $\theta_v = \tan^{-1}(v_y/v_x) = \tan^{-1}[6/(3 \cdot 4)] = \tan^{-1}(\frac{1}{2}) = 26.6°$. The angle between the force and the velocity vectors is then $45 - 26.6 = 18.4°$.

(c) Elimination of t leads to $t = \sqrt{x/3}$, and hence

$$y = 2\left(\frac{x}{3}\right)^{3/2}.$$

PROBLEMS

5–1. A body A is dropped from a cliff which is a height h over a horizontal plane. Simultaneously and from the same point, another body B is shot horizontally from the cliff with a speed v. Which of the bodies reaches the ground first (neglect air friction)?

5–2. A projectile is shot from the ground with a speed of 400 m/sec at an elevation angle of 45°. How long does it take to return to the ground (neglect air friction)?

5–3. A projectile is shot from the ground such that its range is l, and the highest point of its trajectory is at a height h. What are the initial speed and the elevation angle of the projectile in terms of h, l, and g (neglect air friction)?

5–4. A particle of mass 100 gm is shot at an elevation angle of 30° with a velocity of 200 m/sec. (a) Where does the projectile hit the ground? (b) If the distance in (a) is denoted by l, determine the magnitude and direction of the momentum vector when the x-coordinate of the particle is $x = 0$, $l/4$, $l/2$, $3l/4$, and l. (c) Choosing the same origin for all the vectors determined in (b), draw a momentum vector diagram of the motion. Convince yourself that the tips of the momentum vectors lie on a vertical line and that the rate of change of the momentum vector equals mg. (d) What is the total change of momentum of the particle during its motion? (e) Note that the direction of the force and the velocity vectors are different at all times. When is the velocity vector perpendicular to the force vector? [Neglect air friction throughout.]

5–5. A gun at position $x = 0, y = 0$ has a maximum range of l_m. Determine the two elevation angles which cor-respond to a target located at

$$x_1 = l_m/2, \qquad y_1 = l_m/4.$$

5–6. A projectile is shot from a point on the ground in such a way that its predicted range and flight time are l and T, respectively. At the highest point of its trajectory, the projectile explodes and divides into two equal parts. After the explosion, the two parts travel in the same plane as the initial trajectory. At a time $3T/4$ after the explosion, one of the parts hits the ground a distance $3l/4$ from the initial point. Where is the other part at that time? Where and when will the other part hit the ground?

5–7. If an artificial satellite is to orbit at a height of 300 km above the earth's surface, what must be the velocity of the satellite? The radius of the earth is 6370 km. Use $g = 9.8$ m/sec². How often does the satellite orbit around the earth, and how long is it visible from a point on the earth?

5–8. A body of mass 2 kgm is attached to the end of a spring of relaxed length 0.5 m with a spring constant of 400 n/m. The body is whirled around in a horizontal circle on a frictionless table while one end of the spring is held fixed on the table. (a) If the radius of the circle is found to be 1 m, what then is the speed of the body? (b) If the speed is increased by a factor of two, what will be the new radius of the circle?

5–9. In a laboratory testing vehicle, a person fastened in a seat at the end of a horizontal arm 15 ft long is whirled around as the arm rotates about a vertical axis through its other end. How many revolutions per second must the arm make to produce a radial acceleration of the person of $10\,g$? ($g = 32$ ft/sec².)

5-10. A string of length l carries on one end a body of weight w. The other end of the string is held fixed as the body moves in a vertical circle. (a) What is the smallest speed the body can have at the bottom of the circle and remain in the circular path? (b) What is the difference in the tension in the string at the bottom and at the top?

5-11. A motorcyclist drives in a horizontal circle on the wall of a vertical cylinder of radius r. What is the smallest speed which will keep him in motion if the friction coefficient between the wheels and the wall is μ? In particular, set $r = 5$ m and $\mu = 0.25$.

5-12. A body attached to the end of a string moves in a vertical circle. As the string makes an angle of 45° with the vertical (upward) direction, the tension of the string becomes zero. What is the speed of the body at that point? Describe the subsequent motion of the body. Where is the body when the string becomes stretched again? (Solve graphically if you wish.)

5-13. A car goes around a horizontal curve which has a radius of curvature r. (a) If the road is horizontal and the friction coefficient is μ, what is the maximum speed the car can attain before it starts to skid? (b) At what angle should the road slope inward in order for the contact force on a car moving with speed v to be normal to the road? (c) What influence does the mass of the car have on this result?

5-14. The radius of curvature at the bottom and at the top of a roller coaster is r. The contact force between a car and the rail is not to exceed six times the weight of the car. What, then, is the maximum speed of a car at the bottom? What is the highest speed that the car can have at the top in order that the contact force on the car is zero at that point?

5-15. In the Bohr model of the hydrogen atom, an electron was assumed to move in a circular path about a small positively charged nucleus. The electrostatic force between the electron and the nucleus is given by

$$F = \frac{2.3 \cdot 10^{-19}}{r^2} \text{ dyne,}$$

where r (in cm) is the separation of the electron and nucleus. What must be the order of magnitude of the velocity of the electron if its orbital radius is $r \simeq 10^{-8}$ cm? The mass of the electron is $m = 9.1 \cdot 10^{-28}$ gm.

5-16. A small particle moves in a gravitational orbit close to the surface of a sphere of density ρ. What is the round-trip time of the particle?

5-17. A particle with an electric charge q and mass m passes through a constant electric field E between two plane parallel plates of length x_0. The particle enters the field with a velocity v perpendicular to the electric field. What is the exit velocity of the particle?

5-18. A particle of mass m and electric charge q is projected into a constant magnetic field in such a manner that its velocity v makes an angle ϕ with the magnetic-field lines. Describe the motion.

5-19. In the previous problem, suppose there is added an electric field of intensity E, parallel with the magnetic-field lines. What then is the nature of the motion?

5-20. A particle moves with constant angular velocity ω in a circular path of radius r. The angular position θ of the particle is measured with respect to the x-axis and $t = 0$ is chosen when $\theta = 0$, so that we have $\theta = \omega t$. (a) At the position of the particle, draw the velocity vector at time t and determine the projections of this vector on the x- and y-axes. (b) Draw the acceleration vector and determine its projections on the x- and y-axes. Compare your answers with the results given in Sec. 5–3.

5–21. A particle of mass m moves along a straight line, starting from rest at $t = 0$ under the influence of a force $F_1 = F_0(t/t_0)$, where F_0 and t_0 are constants. At $t = t_0$ the force suddenly becomes zero and a new force $F_2 = -F_0[(t - t_0)^2/t_0^2]$ starts to act. When and where does the particle start to return to the origin?

5–22. A body is moving in a path described with respect to an xy-coordinate system as follows:

$$x = at^2, \quad a = 3 \text{ cm/sec}^2,$$
$$y = bt^3, \quad b = 2 \text{ cm/sec}^3,$$

where t is the time. (a) At what time t_2 is the velocity vector of the body parallel with the line $x = y$? (b) At what time t_1 is the acceleration vector parallel with the line $x = y$? (c) What is the average velocity (magnitude and direction) in the time interval $t_2 - t_1$?

5–23. From the known distance from the sun to the earth, the known mass of the earth, and the known time for the earth's trip around the sun, find the force that must be acting on the earth.

A good-quality nylon rope of $\frac{1}{2}$-in. diameter will support a weight of 20,000 lb. How many ropes of this type would be necessary to hold the earth in its orbit, in the absence of gravitational force?

CHAPTER 6

IMPULSE AND WORK

Summary. If the position of a body, as a function of time, is known, the detailed behavior of the force on the body can be determined. Conversely, if the force on the body, as a function of time or position, is known, the details of the motion of the body can be predicted. If, on the other hand, only the net changes of momentum or speed of a body are known, only certain integrated effects of the force, known as the impulse and the work respectively, can be determined. Conversely, from known values of the impulse and the work the net changes of momentum and kinetic energy, respectively, can be found. The impulse, which is equal to the momentum change, is a vector. The work, which is related to the kinetic energy change, is a scalar quantity.

As has been mentioned before, the study of motion is concerned, broadly speaking, with two types of problem. In one type, the motion as obtained from experiments is known in advance, and the force acting on the body is to be found. This type of problem is most basic to physics and we have treated several examples in the preceding chapters. Classic examples are Newton's development of the gravitational force law and Rutherford's investigations which led to the nuclear atom (see Chapter 10). In the other type of problem, the forces are known (or thought to be known) and the motion of a body is to be determined. Here we are attempting to predict phenomena in advance—what will be the motion of a satellite or comet, how many bounces will a rubber ball make before it "stops," what is the motion of a charged particle in a known field, etc.? Of course, when we say the forces are known, what we really mean is that the motion of other bodies in a similar environment has already been investigated by us or by others, and from these investigations we know, or think we know, the forces and how they depend on time, speed, mass, electric charge, and other parameters which characterize the body, its motion, and its environment.

However, sometimes one is not concerned with a description of motion in all its detail. For example, in the collision experiments discussed in previous chapters we usually were not able to determine the positions of the colliding bodies as functions of time, during the short interval of collision; only the net changes of momenta were found. Similarly, when a bullet is shot from a gun it is relatively simple to determine the muzzle speed of the bullet, but it is not as simple to determine the position of the bullet, as a function of time, as it passes through the barrel. In problems of this kind, only net changes of motion are observed, and the detailed

139

behavior of the force as a function of time or position cannot be determined. Only certain average or integrated values of the force during the interval of time or distance under consideration can be determined. In the case of a collision between two bodies, we shall find that, from the momentum changes of the bodies, the time integral of the force acting upon one of the bodies during the collision can be found. If the duration of the collision is known the (time) average of the force can also be found. The time integral of the force, which is the same as the (time) average force multiplied by the duration of the collision, is called the *impulse of the force*. Similarly, in the cited example concerning the bullet, we shall find that the quantity $mv^2/2$, the kinetic energy of the bullet, is related to the space integral of the force over the length of the barrel. From the known length of the barrel, the (space) average of the force can be obtained. The space integral of the force, which is the same as the (space) average force multiplied by the displacement of the bullet, is called the *work of the force*. Work of a force, then, is essentially the product of force and length, and impulse is the product of force and time.

If the impulse and work of a force are known, the net changes of the momentum and the kinetic energy, respectively, can be predicted. Even if the force is known in detail as a function of time or position, we may not always be interested in predicting the details of the motion of the body, but merely the changes in momentum or kinetic energy. These changes can then be determined directly from the impulse and the work of the force, without the need of a calculation of the position of the body as a function of time. We shall find that the use of the work of a force for the calculation of changes of the speed of a body is particularly valuable in cases of so-called constrained motion, in which a body is forced or constrained to follow a certain path. Typical examples of constrained motion are the motion of a car on a roller coaster and the motion of a pendulum. The quantitative aspects of the concepts of impulse and work will be established with the help of simple experiments with a car on a horizontal track or with an air-suspended puck on a horizontal plane, under the influence of a constant force.

6–1 Impulse of a force. In developing the concepts of impulse and work we shall start with the simple experiment illustrated schematically in Fig. 6–1. A car is pulled along a horizontal track with a constant force F which acts in the direction of the track. The magnitude of the force can

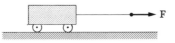

FIGURE 6–1

be read from a spring scale inserted between the pulling mechanism and the car. (The motion is one-dimensional, and for the moment we need not be concerned with the vector character of the force.) We pull the car, which starts from rest, with the constant force for a time Δt, and measure the velocity acquired by the car at the end of this interval. If we repeat the experiment with cars of different masses we note that the final velocities of the cars are different, but the momenta delivered to the cars by the force are all the same and equal to $F \Delta t$. That is, the change of momentum produced by the constant force F during the time $\Delta t = t_2 - t_1$ is

$$\Delta p = F \Delta t,$$

regardless of the mass of the body. This result, of course, follows directly from the definition of the force as the rate of change of momentum. The quantity $F \Delta t$ is called the *impulse, J*, of the (*constant*) force during the time Δt:

$$J = F \Delta t = F(t_2 - t_1). \tag{6–1}$$

We should keep clearly in mind that the effect of a given impulse is to produce a momentum change, and this momentum change is independent of the mass of a body. Hence a net force of one dyne acting for one second produces a momentum change of one gm·cm/sec whether the force is applied to a grain of sand or to an ocean liner. Of course, although changes in momentum do not depend upon mass, changes in velocity do.

If force is plotted as a function of time (Fig. 6–2), the impulse of the force is geometrically proportional to the area under the force curve. The constant of proportionality depends upon the scales of F and t, and hereafter we shall assume that this has been taken into account when we speak of impulse as an area. Impulse is measured in n·sec, lb·sec, dyne·sec, etc.

Let us now vary the force in steps, as illustrated in Fig. 6–3, between the times t_1 and t_2. In the first interval Δt the force is F_1, in the second it

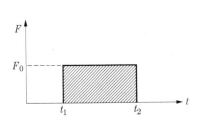

FIG. 6–2. Impulse of a constant force.

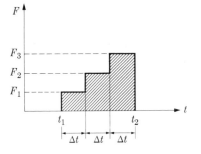

FIG. 6–3. Impulse of a force varying in steps.

has changed to F_2, etc. The total momentum change in a time interval $t_2 - t_1$ is now the sum of the net momentum transfers in the various intervals and we have

$$J = F_1 \, \Delta t + F_2 \, \Delta t + F_3 \, \Delta t + \cdots.$$

Again, the total impulse of the force in the interval $t_2 - t_1$ is proportional to the area under the force curve between these limits.

Next, we let the force vary continuously with time, as illustrated in Fig. 6–4. We can approximate $F(t)$ by a succession of constant forces as shown, and the total impulse is then represented by the area under the step-curve. As the time intervals are made smaller and smaller, the step-curve approaches the force curve, and the total impulse of the force can again be represented by the area under the force curve between t_1 and t_2.

As we have already remarked, we sometimes encounter the situation where, having observed the motion of an object, we wish to know something about the force on it. Suppose, for example, we have observed the velocity of an object of mass m at t_1 and t_2. We then know that the impulse of the *net* force acting upon the body must have been $J = \Delta p = mv_2 - mv_1$. Although a knowledge of J is not sufficient for a detailed description of the force during the interval Δt, it does enable us to determine the time average of the force,

$$\overline{F} = \frac{J}{\Delta t} = \frac{p_2 - p_1}{t_2 - t_1}. \tag{6–2}$$

The average force is such that $\overline{F}(t_2 - t_1)$ is represented by the total area under the force curve $F(t)$, as indicated schematically in Fig. 6–4. The maximum value of the force in the time interval is always at least as large as $\overline{F}$, and is equal to $\overline{F}$ when the force is constant.

The above one-dimensional considerations regarding the impulse of a force can be applied directly to the *components* of an arbitrary force. Thus, if the force **F** is constant during a time interval Δt, the vector $\mathbf{J} = \mathbf{F} \, \Delta t$ is the impulse of the force in the interval Δt and the corresponding

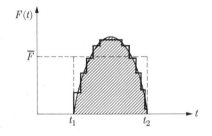

FIG. 6–4. Impulse of a continuously varying force.

change of momentum is given by

$$\Delta \mathbf{p} = \mathbf{J} = \mathbf{F}\,\Delta t. \qquad (6\text{–}3)$$

If the force is not constant in the interval Δt, the relation (6–3) still applies if $\mathbf{F}$ is replaced by the average force $\overline{\mathbf{F}}$.

The interpretation of the impulse as an area still applies to the components of the force. That is, the x-component of the impulse can be represented by the area under the curve of F_x versus t.

EXAMPLE 1. A baseball weighing 6 oz arrives at the batter's box with a velocity of 85 ft/sec along a horizontal line. The ball leaves the bat at an elevation angle of 30°, with a speed of 170 ft/sec. What is the impulse of the force on the baseball by the bat? What is the average force on the bat if the contact time between the ball and the bat is 0.01 sec?

The weight of the baseball is $mg = 6/16$ lb, and the magnitudes of the momenta before and after the collision are

$$p_1 = mv_1 = \frac{6}{16}\frac{85}{32} \simeq 1 \text{ lb·sec}, \qquad p_2 = mv_2 = \frac{6}{16}\frac{170}{32} \simeq 2 \text{ lb·sec}.$$

The magnitude of the momentum transfer is then

$$\Delta p = \sqrt{(1 + 2\cos 30°)^2 + (2\sin 30°)^2} \simeq 2.9 \text{ lb·sec}.$$

The magnitude of the average force is then

$$\overline{F} = \frac{\Delta p}{\Delta t} = \frac{2.9}{0.01} \simeq 290 \text{ lb}.$$

The direction of the average force is the same as that of $\Delta \mathbf{p}$, illustrated in Fig. 6–5.

EXAMPLE 2. A body of mass $m = 2$ kgm moves along the x-axis in a horizontal plane and enters a region where it is acted upon by a force in the x-direction which depends upon time, in the manner shown in Fig. 6–6.

The net "area," in n·sec, under the force curve in the interval 0.1 to 0.5 sec is seen to be $(0.4 - 0.1)(30/2) - (0.5 - 0.4)(10/2) = 4.5 - 0.5 = 4$ n·sec,

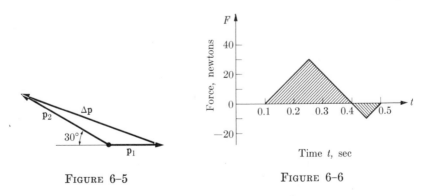

FIGURE 6–5   FIGURE 6–6

which equals the impulse of the force in the interval 0.1 to 0.5 sec. As a result the velocity of the body will change by an amount $\Delta v = \frac{4}{2} = 2$ m/sec.

Impulse as an integral of the force. Suppose now that the force on a body varies continuously and that it is given in mathematical form as a function of time. We wish to express the impulse of the force in the interval $t_2 - t_1$. For the x-component of the momentum we then have

$$\frac{dp_x}{dt} = F_x(t).$$

According to the discussion in Sec. 5–4, the function which has a derivative equal to $F_x(t)$ is denoted mathematically by $\int F_x(t)\, dt$, the *integral* (function) of $F_x(t)$. Thus, in general, we have

$$p_x(t) = \int F_x(t)\, dt + \text{const.} \qquad (6\text{--}4)$$

To obtain the impulse of a force in the time interval $t_2 - t_1$, we simply evaluate $p_x(t_2) - p_x(t_1)$, that is, the difference between the values of the function $\int F_x(t)\, dt$ at t_2 and t_1. Again, as we know from mathematics, this difference is denoted by $\int_{t_1}^{t_2} F_x(t)\, dt$, the *definite* integral of $F_x(t)$. Thus we have

$$J_x = p_x(t_2) - p_x(t_1) = \int_{t_1}^{t_2} F_x(t)\, dt. \qquad (6\text{--}5)$$

We should bear in mind that $\int_{t_1}^{t_2} F_x(t)\, dt$ can be interpreted as the area under the force curve between the limits t_1 and t_2, as described previously.

This discussion can be extended directly to two and three dimensions. Thus if the components of the force on a body are F_x, F_y, and F_z, the impulse components are given by

$$J_x = \int_{t_1}^{t_2} F_x\, dt, \qquad J_y = \int_{t_1}^{t_2} F_y\, dt, \qquad J_z = \int_{t_1}^{t_2} F_z\, dt. \qquad (6\text{--}6)$$

These relations may be replaced by the vector equation

$$\mathbf{p}_2 - \mathbf{p}_1 = \mathbf{J} = \int_{t_1}^{t_2} \mathbf{F}\, dt. \qquad (6\text{--}7)$$

Equation (6–7) usually is called the *impulse-momentum relation*, although we should remember that it is a direct consequence of the definition of force.

Impulse on a system of particles or on a rigid body. In our previous work we have seen that the motion of the center of mass of a system of particles is determined completely by *external forces*. That is, we showed that

$$\mathbf{F} = M\frac{d\mathbf{V}}{dt},$$

where M is the total mass, $\mathbf{V}$ is the center-of-mass velocity, and $\mathbf{F}$ is the net external force. From this, it follows immediately that if the external forces are known as functions of time, the quantity $\Delta\mathbf{P} = M\,\Delta\mathbf{V}$ may be found, where $\Delta\mathbf{V}$ is the change of the velocity of the center of mass.

$$\mathbf{J} = \Delta\mathbf{P} = \int_{t_1}^{t_2} \mathbf{F}\, dt. \tag{6–8}$$

If a given impulse $\mathbf{J}$ acts on a rigid body, for example, the center-of-mass motion will not depend upon the point of application of $\mathbf{J}$. If $\mathbf{J}$ is applied *at* the center of mass, the body will just translate; if $\mathbf{J}$ is applied some distance away from the center of mass, the body will rotate as well as translate, as we shall see in Chapter 12. So long as the impulse $\mathbf{J}$ is the same in the two cases, the center-of-mass motion will be the same.

6–2 Work of a force. Let us return now to the experiment with the one-dimensional motion of a car pulled along a horizontal track by a constant force, as was shown in Fig. 6–1. When the force was applied over a given constant *time* interval Δt, the momentum change of the car was always the same, regardless of the mass of the car. Now we pull the cars with a constant force F over a given *distance*, say from $x = 0$ to $x = x_1$. A heavier car will take a longer time than a light one to cover the distance x_1, and consequently a larger impulse and more momentum are delivered to the heavier car. Since the force is constant, the car will be uniformly accelerated, and we have

$$x_1 = \frac{1}{2}\frac{F}{m}t^2 \qquad \text{and} \qquad v_1 = \frac{F}{m}t.$$

When t is eliminated from these two expressions, we obtain

$$v_1 = \sqrt{2Fx_1/m}$$

or

$$p_1 = mv_1 = \sqrt{2mFx_1}\,. \tag{6–9}$$

Now the momentum delivered to the car by the force is not independent of the car's mass, as it was when the force was applied for a given time. Rather, the momentum is proportional to the square root of the mass m. However, we see from Eq. (6–9) that there is another quantity which *is* the same for all bodies, regardless of their masses, namely,

$$\frac{p_1^2}{2m} = \frac{mv_1^2}{2} = Fx_1.$$

That is, when bodies, starting from rest, are acted upon by a constant force over a specified *distance* they acquire the same value of the quantity

$p^2/2m = mv^2/2$. This quantity, called the *kinetic energy* and denoted by E, clearly will play an important role in the theory of motion, since it is related to the force in this very simple way.

We could also, of course, pull the car over a longer distance x_2. Then we have

$$E_2 = \frac{mv_2^2}{2} = Fx_2,$$

and the kinetic energy change $\Delta E = E_2 - E_1$ between x_1 and x_2 is

$$\Delta E = F(x_2 - x_1) = F\,\Delta x.$$

The kinetic energy change in the interval $x_2 - x_1$ depends only upon the product of the (constant) force and the displacement, $F(x_2 - x_1) = F\,\Delta x$, and not upon the mass of the body. This quantity is called the *work* of the force. Just as a given impulse produces the same momentum change regardless of mass, a given amount of work produces the same kinetic energy change.

The relation $\Delta E = F\,\Delta x$ (or $F = \Delta E/\Delta x$) is clearly valid even if the force is not constant, provided that F is taken as an average force. Then in the limit $\Delta x = 0$ we have

$$F = \frac{dE}{dx}. \qquad (6\text{--}10)$$

Force is the time rate of change of momentum and, as well, is the spatial (distance) rate of change of kinetic energy.

In the derivation of the above relation, we started from the simple case of a constant force in the direction of motion and used the well-known relations for uniform acceleration to obtain v as *a function of x*. However, we can obtain the result (6–10) in a mathematically more elegant way from $F = dp/dt$ as follows: Start from $\Delta p/\Delta t$. If v is the average velocity in the interval Δt, we have $\Delta x = v\,\Delta t$. Replacing Δt by $\Delta x/v$, we get $\Delta p/\Delta t = v(\Delta p/\Delta x)$. In the limit $\Delta x = 0$, this may be expressed as

$$F = v\frac{dp}{dx} = mv\frac{dv}{dx} = \frac{d(mv^2/2)}{dx} = \frac{dE}{dx}. \qquad (6\text{--}11)$$

When force is given as a function of x, we can obtain the kinetic energy from Eq. (6–10) as

$$E = \int F_x(x)\,dx + C,$$

where C is the constant of integration. The difference between the kinetic energies at x_1 and x_2 can be obtained by eliminating this constant, and we have

$$E_2 - E_1 = \int_{x_1}^{x_2} F_x(x)\, dx = W, \qquad (6\text{–}12)$$

where $W = \int_{x_1}^{x_2} F_x(x)\, dx$ is the *work* done by the force in the interval $x_2 - x_1$. It should be recalled from the discussion of impulse that the work can be interpreted as the area under the curve F_x versus x between the limits x_1 and x_2, as indicated in Fig. 6–7. Equation (6–12) is usually referred to as the work-energy relation, although, just as in the case of the impulse-momentum relation, it follows as a consequence of the definition of force.

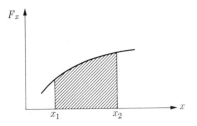

FIG. 6–7. The work done by a force is represented by the area under the F_x versus x curve.

EXAMPLE 1. A body of mass m is released from a height h above ground. What is its velocity when it hits the ground?

The force mg and the displacement h are both in the same direction, therefore the work done is mgh. This work serves to increase the kinetic energy, and we have

$$\frac{mv^2}{2} = mgh, \qquad v = \sqrt{2gh}.$$

EXAMPLE 2. Consider a spring with a spring constant K. When the spring is relaxed, its end is located at $x = 0$ (see Fig. 6–8). The spring is now compressed by an external force, the magnitude of which must increase in proportion to the compression of the spring; that is, the external force must be Kx, where K is the spring constant and is equal to 100 n/m. What is the work done

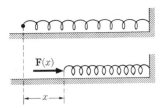

FIGURE 6–8

by the external force on the spring to compress it a distance $x_1 = 4$ m? Graphically, the F versus x curve is as shown in Fig. 6–9. The work done in a compression, or push, from $x = 0$ to x_1 is represented by the area under the curve and is

$$W = \frac{Kx_1^2}{2} = \frac{100 \cdot 16}{2} = 800 \text{ n·m.}$$

Analytically,

$$W = \int_0^{x_1} F \, dx = \int_0^{x_1} Kx \, dx = \frac{Kx_1^2}{2},$$

and $W = 800$ n·m, as before.

EXAMPLE 3. The force on a body varies with position, as illustrated in Fig. 6–10. What is the work done by the force?

In this case we do not have an analytical expression for the force. However, we can at least approximate a value for the work by estimating the area under the curve. We can, for example, approximate the force curve by a triangle which has an area of $(0.5 - 0.1)(100/2) = 50 \cdot 0.4 = 20$ n·m.

Units of energy and work. In the British system of units, the unit of work is one foot·pound, and there is no special name given to this unit. In the cgs system the unit of work is one dyne·cm, which is called one *erg.* Correspondingly, in the mks system, the work unit is one newton·meter, which is called one *joule.* One joule is equal to 10^7 ergs. Other conversion factors will be found in Appendix A.

Work by several forces. "No-work" forces. We started our discussion of kinetic energy with the motion of a body along a straight line under the influence of one single force component F_x in the direction of motion. The work done by this single force, $\int_{x_1}^{x_2} F_x \, dx$, was shown to equal the change in the kinetic energy in this interval, $\Delta E = mv_2^2/2 - mv_1^2/2$.

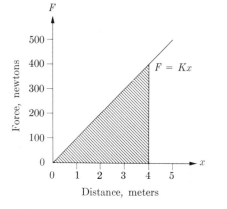

FIG. 6–9. F versus x curve for the compression of a spring.

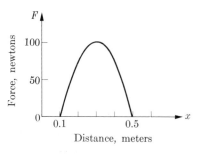

FIGURE 6–10

Now, if the body is acted upon by several forces $\mathbf{F}_1$, $\mathbf{F}_2$, $\mathbf{F}_3$, ... as it moves in the x-direction, the principle of superposition tells us that the motion of the body is not changed if these forces are replaced by the resultant force $\mathbf{F} = \mathbf{F}_1 + \mathbf{F}_2 + \mathbf{F}_3 + \cdots$ having x-components $F_x = F_{1x} + F_{2x} + F_{3x} + \cdots$. Hence, the kinetic energy E will be equal in both cases, and the change in E is given by $\Delta E = F_x \Delta x = W$. However, since $F_x \Delta x = F_{1x} \Delta x + F_{2x} \Delta x + F_{3x} \Delta x + \cdots$, the total work can be obtained as the sum of the individual work contributions, $W_1 = F_{1x} \Delta x$, etc. In other words, we can determine the change of kinetic energy of the body as the sum of the individual work contributions by the various forces acting on the body.

Conversely, when a force is represented by its components, the sum of the work done by the components is the same as the work done by the resultant, a fact which we shall use in a later discussion.

In practice, when we wish to calculate the kinetic energy of a body as it moves under the influence of several forces, we frequently find that one or more of the forces is perpendicular to the displacement of the body. For example, the force of gravity and the normal component of the contact force on the car in Fig. 6–1 do not influence the motion in the plane, and hence do not contribute to the kinetic energy and work done. Similarly, a car on a frictionless roller coaster (Fig. 6–11) moves under the influence of two forces, gravity and the normal force that the tracks exert on the car. Of course, the car has no velocity normal to the track and all the kinetic energy of the car is a result of its motion along the track. Only gravitational force has a component along the track, thus this is the only force doing any work. The normal force on the car therefore is called a "no-work" force.

"No-work" forces, then, are those which are perpendicular to the direction of a body's motion and so do not contribute to kinetic energy changes. A motion which is restricted to a prescribed path, like a track or a wire, or to a prescribed plane, is called a *constrained* motion. In such a motion no-work forces are present but knowledge of them is not necessary for the calculation of changes of kinetic energy.

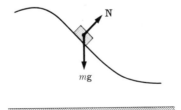

Fig. 6–11. The normal force is a "no-work" force.

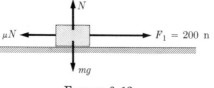

FIGURE 6–12

EXAMPLE. A body of mass $m = 50$ kgm is pulled horizontally along a surface by a string. The applied horizontal force on the body is $F_1 = 200$ n (Fig. 6–12). The friction coefficient at the contact surface is $\mu = 0.2$. If the body starts from rest, what is its velocity when it has been pulled a distance $d = 5$ m?

The forces contributing to the work are F_1 and the friction force $F_x = -\mu N$. The work done by the string force is $W_1 = +F_1 d$, and by the friction force is $W_2 = -\mu N d$. Therefore the total work is $W = W_1 + W_2 = (F_1 - \mu N) d$. The normal component of the contact force is $N = mg \simeq 50 \cdot 9.81 \simeq 490$ n. The total work is then $W = (200 - 0.2 \cdot 490) \cdot 5 = 102 \cdot 5 = 510$ n·m (joules). The increase in kinetic energy is then $mv^2/2 = W$, so that the velocity at the end of the 5-m slide is

$$v = \sqrt{2W/m} = \sqrt{2 \cdot 510/50} \simeq 4.5 \text{ m/sec.}$$

Motion along a curved path. The results obtained concerning work and kinetic energy can easily be extended to the case when the motion of a body is along an arbitrary curved path rather than along a straight line (see Fig. 6–13). The path can be approximated by a succession of straight-line segments. If such a segment is Δs, as in the figure, and the average force over the line segment is **F**, the work done by **F** as the body moves is

$$\Delta W = F_s \, \Delta s = F \, \Delta s \cos \theta_s, \tag{6-13}$$

where θ_s is the angle between **F** and Δs. The magnitudes of the force and the line element are F and Δs, respectively. The component of **F** in the direction of Δs is $F_s = F \cos \theta_s$.

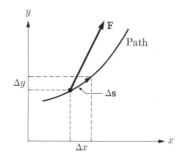

FIG. 6–13. Motion along a curved path in a plane.

It should be noted, from Eq. (6–13), that the elementary work can be interpreted in two ways, either as *the product of the magnitude* Δs *and the component* $F \cos \theta_s = F_s$ in the direction of Δs, or as *the product of the magnitude of the force* $\mathbf{F}$ *and the component* $\Delta s \cos \theta_s$ in the direction of the force. Using the latter interpretation, we can express the elementary work directly in terms of the force components F_x and F_y. Thus, we replace $\mathbf{F}$ by its force components and determine then the work of $\mathbf{F}$ as the sum of the work of each of its components. The work of F_x, as we have just indicated, is the product of F_x and the projection Δx of Δs in the x-direction. Similarly, the work of F_y is the product of F_y and the projection Δy of Δs in the y-direction. The total work, in terms of the force components, is then

$$\Delta W = F_x \, \Delta x + F_y \, \Delta y.$$

We conclude that work can be expressed in three different ways:

$$\Delta W = F_s \, \Delta s = F \, \Delta s \cos \theta_s = F_x \, \Delta x + F_y \, \Delta y. \tag{6–14}$$

Similarly, if we consider motion in space, there is another contribution $F_z \, \Delta z$ to the work:

$$\Delta W = F_x \, \Delta x + F_y \, \Delta y + F_z \, \Delta z.$$

The total work done by force $\mathbf{F}$ as the body moves from one point (x_1, y_1, z_1) to another point (x_2, y_2, z_2) can then be expressed as

$$W = \int_{x_1}^{x_2} F_x \, dx + \int_{y_1}^{y_2} F_y \, dy + \int_{z_1}^{z_2} F_z \, dz$$
$$= \int_{(1)}^{(2)} (F_x \, dx + F_y \, dy + F_z \, dz), \tag{6–15}$$

which, for short, can be written as

$$W = \int_{(1)}^{(2)} F_s \, ds.$$

This work is equal to the increase in the kinetic energy, $\frac{1}{2}mv^2$, where v is the magnitude of the velocity. The kinetic energy can be expressed in terms of the velocity components as

$$\tfrac{1}{2}mv^2 = \tfrac{1}{2}mv_x^2 + \tfrac{1}{2}mv_y^2 + \tfrac{1}{2}mv_z^2.$$

Since v_x depends only upon the F_x-component, we have

$$\int_{x_1}^{x_2} F_x \, dx = \tfrac{1}{2}mv_{x_2}^2 - \tfrac{1}{2}mv_{x_1}^2.$$

Similar expressions can be obtained for the y- and z-components.

The results given by Eq. (6–15) can also be obtained in a formal way directly from $dp/dt = \mathbf{F}$ as follows. We have

$$\frac{dp_x}{dt} = v_x \frac{dp_x}{dx} = \frac{d(mv_x^2/2)}{dx} = F_x.$$

Consequently,

$$d(mv_x^2/2) = F_x \, dx.$$

Similarly,

$$d(mv_y^2/2) = F_y \, dy \quad \text{and} \quad d(mv_z^2/2) = F_z \, dz.$$

Summing these relations, we obtain

$$dE = d(mv^2/2) = F_x \, dx + F_y \, dy + F_z \, dz,$$

from which Eq. (6–15) follows.

EXAMPLE 1. A body is sliding down an inclined plane and the sliding friction coefficient at the contact surface is μ (Fig. 6–14). What is the velocity of the body as it moves from rest a distance d down the plane?

There are three forces acting upon the body. The work by the normal component of the contact force $\mathbf{N}$ is zero, since it is always perpendicular to the displacement of the body. The work by the friction force is $Fd = \mu N d$ and the work by the gravitational force is $mgd \sin \theta$. Then, with $N = mg \cos \theta$, we get

$$v = \sqrt{2g \, d(\sin \theta - \mu \cos \theta)}.$$

EXAMPLE 2. A pendulum consisting of a body at the end of a string of length R is released from an angle θ, as shown in Fig. 6–15. What is the velocity of the body as the pendulum passes through its lowest point?

The body is acted upon by two forces, the tension $\mathbf{S}$ in the string and the weight $m\mathbf{g}$ of the body. The work by $\mathbf{S}$ is zero, since $\mathbf{S}$ is perpendicular to the velocity of the body at all times. The work by the gravitational force (weight) is the product of the force mg and the displacement in the direction of the force. This displacement is $R - R \cos \theta = R(1 - \cos \theta)$ and the net work is

$$\tfrac{1}{2}mv^2 = mgR(1 - \cos \theta).$$

For the velocity we thus obtain

$$v = \sqrt{2gR(1 - \cos \theta)}.$$

Work as a scalar product of vectors. Work and kinetic energy are both scalar quantities; each can be specified by a single number. For example, kinetic energy depends only upon the magnitude of the velocity of a body, not upon its direction. However, it is interesting to note that although work is a scalar quantity, two *vectors* are involved in the calculation of work, the force vector $\mathbf{F}$ and the displacement vector $\Delta\mathbf{s}$ or $\Delta\mathbf{r}$ as indicated in

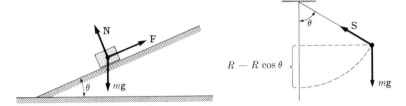

FIGURE 6–14   FIGURE 6–15

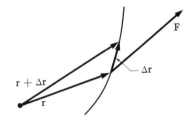

FIGURE 6–16

Fig. 6–16. In terms of the components of these vectors, as we have seen, the work is

$$\Delta W = F_x \, \Delta x + F_y \, \Delta y + F_z \, \Delta z.$$

This product of the components is called the *scalar product* $\mathbf{F} \cdot \Delta \mathbf{r}$ of the two vectors $\mathbf{F}$ and $\Delta \mathbf{r}$, as mentioned in Chapter 1. We have then

$$\mathbf{F} \cdot \Delta \mathbf{r} = F_x \, \Delta x + F_y \, \Delta y + F_z \, \Delta z = F \, \Delta r \cos \theta, \qquad (6\text{–}16)$$

where F and Δr are the magnitudes of $\mathbf{F}$ and $\Delta \mathbf{r}$, and θ is the angle between these vectors.

If we rewrite the relation (6–15) in terms of the scalar product, we get

$$W = \int_{(1)}^{(2)} \mathbf{F} \cdot d\mathbf{r}. \qquad (6\text{–}17)$$

In a general discussion, this method of expressing work is often convenient, but in numerical calculations we must use one of the methods given in Eq. (6–16).

Power. The work done by a force depends only on the force and the displacement, or in other words, work determines the kinetic energy change and is independent of how fast this change takes place. In many instances it is useful to have a quantity that can be used to describe how fast work is done, or how fast the kinetic energy changes. This quantity is called *power*, and it is defined by

$$P = \frac{dW}{dt}. \tag{6–18}$$

An amount of work ΔW done by a force $\mathbf{F}$ when it acts through a displacement $\Delta \mathbf{r}$ can be written as $\mathbf{F} \cdot d\mathbf{r}$. But $d\mathbf{r}/dt$ is just the velocity, $\mathbf{v}$, and so we have

$$P = \mathbf{F} \cdot \mathbf{v} = Fv \cos \theta, \tag{6–19}$$

where θ is the angle between $\mathbf{F}$ and $\mathbf{v}$.

Power is measured in units of energy (or work done) per unit time. Hence power has the units joules/second or watts in the mks system, ergs/second in the cgs system, and foot·pounds/second in the British system. One watt is 10^7 ergs/second, and one horsepower is 746 watts or 550 foot·pounds/second.

EXAMPLE. A car of mass m accelerates uniformly from rest to a speed v_0 in t_0 sec. As a function of time, what is the power delivered to the car?

The acceleration is v_0/t_0, and so the horizontal force that the road must exert on the wheels is mv_0/t_0, while the car's velocity is v_0t/t_0. The power is

$$P = Fv = \frac{mv_0}{t_0} \cdot \frac{v_0 t}{t_0} = \frac{mv_0^2}{t_0^2} t.$$

Hence if a 3200-lb car $(m = 100$ slugs) accelerates to 60 mi/hr (88 ft/sec) in 10 sec, the power at the end of the 10-sec interval must be

$$P = \frac{100 \cdot 88^2 \cdot 10}{10^2} = 77{,}500 \text{ ft·lb/sec} = \frac{77{,}500}{550} = 141 \text{ hp.}$$

The power delivered by the engine must be considerably larger than this, of course, because the forces of wind, friction, etc., do negative work on the accelerating car. Note that very little power is required in the early part of the acceleration period. Why is this?

Work done by an external force on a collection of particles. Imagine a collection of particles having a total mass M. The collection may comprise a rigid body, for example, although the discussion which follows is applicable even when the particles do not maintain fixed distances between one another. We have seen that the center-of-mass motion of a collection of particles is determined completely by the external forces. That is, we have $\mathbf{F} = M \, d\mathbf{V}/dt$, where $\mathbf{F}$ is the net external force and $\mathbf{V}$ is the center-of-mass velocity. Multiplication of both sides of this equation by $\mathbf{V}$ yields the scalar product

$$\mathbf{F} \cdot \mathbf{V} = M \frac{d\mathbf{V}}{dt} \cdot \mathbf{V} = \frac{dE_t}{dt}, \tag{6–20}$$

where $E_t = MV^2/2$ is the translational kinetic energy. The term $\mathbf{F} \cdot \mathbf{V}$ is the scalar product of the external force and the center-of-mass velocity. Expression (6–20) is equivalent to

$$\mathbf{F} \cdot \Delta\mathbf{S} = \Delta E_t, \qquad\qquad (6\text{–}21)$$

where $\Delta\mathbf{S}$ is the displacement of the center of mass. While this expression is similar to the familiar work-energy relation, it differs in two important respects. First, $\Delta\mathbf{S}$ is the center-of-mass displacement, not the distance through which the force acts. Second, E_t is the translational kinetic energy only, and does not include the kinetic energy which a rigid body, for example, may have by virtue of its rotational motion. A more complete form of the work-energy relation, which will be discussed in Chapter 12, equates the quantity $\mathbf{F} \cdot \Delta\mathbf{s}$ to ΔE, where $\Delta\mathbf{s}$ is the force displacement and E is the total kinetic energy.

As a simple example of the use of Eq. (6–21), consider a rigid body in the earth's gravitational field. The net external force is $M\mathbf{g}$ directed downward. If the center of mass falls a distance h, the term $\mathbf{F} \cdot \Delta\mathbf{S}$ is Mgh, and this must be equal to the change in the translational kinetic energy, $MV^2/2$. The fact that the rigid body simultaneously may be going through a complicated rotational motion makes no difference. The center of mass of the rigid body behaves just like a mass point of mass M.

PROBLEMS

6–1. A body of mass $m = 2$ kgm drops from a tower 100 m high. (a) What impulse does the body receive during the first second? during the second second? What is the total impulse received during t sec of free fall? (b) What is the momentum of the 2-kgm mass at $t = 1$ and 2 sec? What is the momentum at t sec? (c) If the mass hits the ground and stops in 0.2 sec, what impulse did it receive? What was the average force on the mass during the stopping period?

6–2. Imagine a square billiard table. Assume that the collisions that a ball makes with the cushions are perfectly elastic. (a) How should the ball be shot so that it follows a square path? (b) What impulse does the ball receive at each collision? Assume an 8-oz ball shot at 10 ft/sec. Specify the magnitudes and directions of the impulses.

6–3. A body of 1.5-kgm mass moves along the y-axis in a horizontal plane with a constant momentum $p_y = 10$ kgm·m/sec. It then enters a region where it is acted upon by a force with time-dependent components, as shown in Fig. 6–17. (a) What are the magnitude and direction of the total impulse of this force? (b) What is the (vector) velocity of the body at $t = 5$ sec?

6–4. Three balls A, B, and C, weighing 2 lb, 2 lb, and 4 lb, respectively, are connected by bars of negligible weights, as shown in Fig. 6–18, and are at rest on a horizontal table (neglect the friction). Ball A is given an impulse of 10 lb·sec in the x-direction and B is given an impulse of 15 lb·sec in the positive y-direction. What is the resulting velocity of the center of mass?

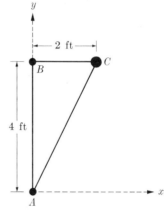

FIGURE 6–18

6–5. The force on a 2-kgm body is $F = F_m \sin (2\pi t/T)$, where $F_m = 20$ n and the period $T = 0.5$ sec. (a) What is the momentum of the body as a

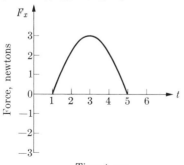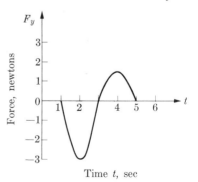

FIGURE 6–17

function of time if the velocity of the body is zero at $t = 0$? (b) What is the impulse of the force in the interval from $t = 0$ to $t = T/2$? (c) What is the impulse in the interval from $t = 0$ to $t = T$?

6-6. A force has components $F_x = F_0(t/t_0)$ and $F_y = F_0(t/t_0)^2$ in the interval from $t = 0$ to $3t_0$. At $t = 0$ the body on which this force acts is at rest. (a) What is the momentum of the body as a function of time? (b) Is the momentum vector ever parallel with the force vector? (c) What is the total impulse of the force? Specify both magnitude and direction.

6-7. A 1.6-oz golf ball is hit and is in flight for a horizontal distance of 200 yd. The club and ball are in contact for 0.01 sec. What minimum impulse and average force did the club exert on the ball?

6-8. A mass of 0.5 kgm confined to one-dimensional motion has a kinetic energy which depends upon x, as shown in Fig. 6-19. (a) Plot the force on the mass as a function of x. (b) What velocity does the mass have at $x = 0$, 1, 2, 5 m? (c) Find how x varies with time. (d) What impulse did the body receive as it traveled from $x = 0$ to $x = 5$ m?

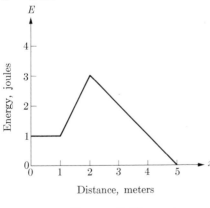

Distance, meters

FIGURE 6-19

6-9. An impulse of 50 dyne·sec is given first to a grain of sand (10^{-5} gm), then to a cubic centimeter of ice (1 gm), then to a small automobile (10^6 gm). Assume that all three bodies are initially at rest. In each case, specify the momentum change, final velocity, and the acquired kinetic energy.

6-10. An impulse of 2 n·sec is given to a 0.1-kgm ball. What momentum and kinetic energy changes does the ball undergo if (a) the ball is initially at rest, (b) the ball has initially a velocity of 1, 5, 10, 100 m/sec in the direction of the impulse, and (c) the ball has initially a velocity of 1, 5, 10, 100 m/sec directed at right angles to the impulse?

6-11. Ten joules of work are done on a body of mass $m = 1$ kgm. (a) If the force doing the work acts in the same direction as the body's initial motion, is the momentum change greater for small or large initial velocities? (b) If the initial velocity is 1.5 m/sec, what is the change of speed? Does your answer depend upon the direction of the force? (c) Would your answer to (b) be the same for changes in momentum and velocity?

6-12. A body slides along the x-axis and is propelled by two forces, F_1 and F_2. The force F_1 varies with x, as shown in Fig. 6-20, and F_2 is constant and equal to 100 lb. (a) Determine the work done by F_1 when the body moves from $x = 0$ to 30 ft. (b) What is the corresponding work done by F_2? (c) What is the velocity of the body at $x = 30$, if it starts from rest at $x = 0$ and if the weight is 800 lb?

6-13. A bullet of mass $m = 50$ gm is shot from a gun at a speed of $v_0 = 400$ m/sec. The length of the gun barrel is $d = 1$ m. The force on the bullet

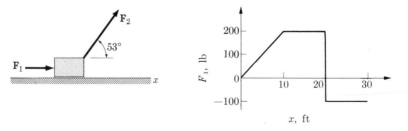

FIGURE 6–20

is assumed to be constant in the barrel. What then is the force? What is the power delivered to the bullet, as a function of its position in the gun barrel?

6–14. A block of mass m is pulled with a string inclined at θ to the horizontal along a level plane. The coefficient of sliding friction between the block and plane is μ. (a) When the block has been pulled a distance x, what is its velocity? (b) Where is the block t sec after the pulling starts? (c) What force is required to keep the block moving at constant velocity? How much work is being done per second by the force in this case?

6–15. A bead of 1-gm mass is free to slide on a vertical frictionless hoop of wire of 100-cm radius. (a) If the bead is released from the top of the hoop, what is its kinetic energy when it reaches the bottom? (b) Why is the normal force between the hoop and the bead a "no-work" force? (c) Are the x- and y-components of the normal force no-work forces? How does the bead acquire an x-component of velocity?

6–16. As shown schematically in Fig. 6–21, a bead of mass m slides down a frictionless chord of a vertical circle. How does the travel time, B to A, depend upon θ?

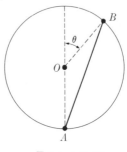

FIGURE 6–21

6–17. A rocket is moving in a horizontal direction under the action of a force $F_x = F_0(1 + x/x_0)$ in the region from $x = 0$ to $x = 5x_0$, and the force of gravity $F_y = -mg$. Under the influence of these forces the rocket moves from $x = 0$, $y = 5x_0$, to $x = 4x_0$, $y = 2x_0$, in t_0 sec. (a) What is the change in kinetic energy of the rocket in this interval? (b) What is the average power delivered to the rocket in this interval?

6–18. A force has the components $F_x = 10(1 + x/2)$ and $F_y = 20(1 + y)^2$ n, where x and y are measured in meters. (a) What is the work done by this force when the body, acted on by the force, moves from $x_1 = 0$, $y_1 = 1$ m, to $x_2 = 4$ m, $y_2 = 2$ m? (b) If the body has a mass $m = 0.5$ kgm, what is the velocity of the body at (x_2, y_2) if it starts from rest at

(x_1, y_1)? (c) Would the body actually move from (x_1, y_1) to (x_2, y_2) under the initial conditions stated if it were under the influence of no other forces?

6–19. An electron is accelerated to an energy of 4 Mev = $4 \cdot 10^6$ ev in a high-energy machine. What is the final velocity of the electron? (The electron mass = $9.1 \cdot 10^{-28}$ gm, 1 ev = $1.6 \cdot 10^{-12}$ erg, 1 Mev = $1.6 \cdot 10^{-6}$ erg.) Compare this velocity with the speed of light. Do you think your calculation is valid?

6–20. Estimate your own power output in (a) running up a flight of stairs, (b) riding a bicycle up a 10° slope, (c) accelerating from rest to 10 m/sec in 1 sec, (d) rising from a sitting to a standing position.

6–21. A mass m_1 and a mass m_2 are initially at rest on the ground. Mass m_1 is carried to a height h_1, and then m_2 is carried to a height h_2. Compute the work W_1 and W_2 required to carry these masses to their respective heights. Show that the result is the same as the work required to carry a mass $m_1 + m_2$ to the height of its center of mass.

6–22. A body of mass 2 kgm passes point 1 $(x_1 = 0, y_1 = 0)$ with a speed of 2 m/sec and passes point 2 $(x_2 = 2, y_2 = ?)$ with a speed of $3\sqrt{3}$ m/sec. The body is acted upon by two forces, one of which has the components $F_{1x} = 6x + 1$, $F_{1y} = 0$ and the other the components $F_{2x} = 0$, $F_{2y} = -2y + 6$. (Here forces are in newtons; x and y are in meters.) (a) What was the total work done on the body as it traveled from point 1 to point 2? (b) What was the work done on the body by the force F_1? (c) What was the work done on the body by the force F_2, and what is the value of y_2?

6–23. Two particles, A and B, of equal mass m, are connected by a

spring of spring constant K. The system is initially at rest on a frictionless horizontal surface, and the spring is relaxed. An instantaneous impulse, J, is applied to A, as shown in Fig. 6–22. What is the velocity of A immediately after the impulse, and what is its kinetic energy? What is the velocity of the center of mass?

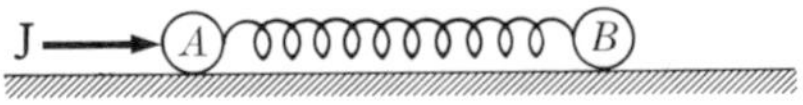

FIGURE 6–22

6–24. Body A of mass m is at rest on a horizontal table. Another body B of mass $2m$, moving along a straight line on the table, collides with A. The velocities of body B immediately before and immediately after the collision are v and $v/2$, respectively. The motion after the collision is along the same straight line as before.

(a) What is the velocity of A immediately after the collision? (b) What fraction of the original kinetic energy is lost in the collision? (c) What is the total impulse delivered to A by B and to B by A? (d) What is the work done by B on A in the collision and what is the work done by A on B? (e) Because of friction on the table (this is the unavoidable effect of the presence of other bodies), both bodies will eventually come to rest. What is the ratio between the impulse given by the table to body A to bring it to rest, and the corresponding quantity for body B?

6–25. As shown in Fig. 6–23, a wooden block of mass m_2 is resting on a horizontal surface. The coefficient of friction is μ. One end of a spring with spring constant K is attached to the block, and the other end to a solid wall. The spring is unstretched. A bullet of mass m_1 hits the block and becomes embedded in it. Find the initial velocity of the bullet in terms of the maximum deflection x of the spring and m_1, m_2, K, μ, and g.

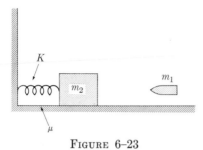

FIGURE 6–23

6–26. A small block of mass $m = 2$ gm is initially at rest on top of a smooth hemisphere of radius $R = 20$ cm (Fig. 6–24). At a certain instant the block is given a very small horizontal push so that it starts to slide down the hemisphere. Neglecting friction, find (a) the contact force as a function of position, and (b) the angle (measured from the vertical) at which the block leaves the surface of the hemisphere.

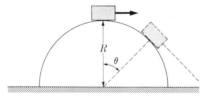

FIGURE 6–24

6–27. A 10-gm body on a frictionless surface is observed to move along the x-axis with a kinetic energy that increases by 20 ergs/cm. (a) What is the rate of change of momentum? (b) Two constant forces, $\mathbf{F}_a$ and $\mathbf{F}_b$, are acting upon the body. Force $\mathbf{F}_a$ is 10 dynes in the positive y-direction. What is the magnitude of $\mathbf{F}_b$? (c) At a certain point on the x-axis the body is observed to have a velocity of 10 cm/sec. How far does the body move

during the next three seconds? (d) How much work was done on the body during this 3-sec period?

6–28. Consider a collision between two small cars A and B on a horizontal track. Car B is originally at rest. Car A has a kinetic energy that varies with location, as shown in Fig. 6–25. The masses of A and B are $m_a = 2$ kgm and $m_b = 2/3$ kgm. (a) Draw a graph of the force on A (in newtons) as a function of the position of A. (b) Draw a graph of the kinetic energy of B as a function of the position of B. (c) What is the time rate of change of the kinetic energy of A at position $x = 3$?

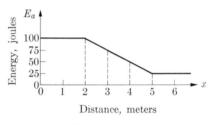

FIGURE 6–25

6–29. A charged particle A moves at high speed v_0 along a straight line and passes a distance d from another charged particle B, which is originally at rest. The two particles repel each other with a force K/r^2, where r is the distance separating A and B, and K is a constant (Fig. 6–26).

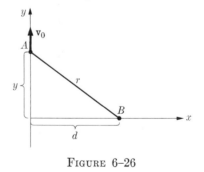

FIGURE 6–26

Since A moves very fast, its effect on B may be considered as an instantaneous impulse normal to the line of motion of A; in other words, body B does not start to move until A has passed. Determine, under these assumptions, the energy transferred to B.

6-30. A cannon on an inclined plane ($\theta = 30°$) rests against a stop, as shown in Fig. 6-27. After a projectile is fired in the *horizontal* direction, the cannon starts to slide up the plane (neglect friction).

The weight of the cannon alone is $Mg = 1600$ lb and the weight of the projectile is $mg = 80$ lb. The velocity of the projectile when it leaves the cannon is $v = 1000$ ft/sec.

(a) What is the velocity of the cannon immediately after firing? (b) How far up the plane does the cannon move? (c) If it takes a time of 0.01 sec for the projectile to leave the cannon, what is the average normal force on the plane during that time?

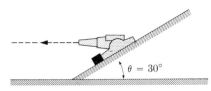

FIGURE 6-27

6-31. A body of mass $m = 1$ kgm is pushed along a frictionless horizontal plane with a force which delivers a constant power $P = 10$ watts. (a) If the velocity of the body at time $t = 0$ is $v_0 = 1$ m/sec, what is the force at that time? (b) At what time will the velocity be $2v_0$?

6-32. A 10-gm body moves with constant velocity in the negative x-direction on a plane (neglect friction). When it passes $x = 0$ a force of 100

dynes starts to act on the body in the positive x-direction. The body returns to $x = 0$ ten seconds after the force started to act. (a) Find the initial velocity. (b) When and where does the particle reverse its direction? (c) What is the total work done by the force during the first 10 sec? (d) What is the instantaneous power delivered by the force when the body passes $x = 0$ in the positive x-direction?

6-33. A wooden block of mass $M = 98$ gm rests on a frictionless horizontal table. A bullet of mass $m = 2$ gm, traveling horizontally with a velocity $v_1 = 300$ m/sec, embeds itself in the block. (a) What is the velocity of the block after the collision? (b) What is the ratio between the mechanical energy lost in the collision and the incident kinetic energy of the bullet?

6-34. Consider two bodies m_1 and m_2 which start from rest and interact only with each other by means of a spring. The force between them is proportional to the separation between them. If the original separation is d, what is the ratio of the kinetic energies of the bodies when they collide?

6-35. A ball released from rest a distance h above the ground bounces up and down. With each bounce a fraction e of its kinetic energy just before the bounce is lost. How long does it take for the ball to come to rest?

6-36. A body of mass m starts from rest, slides along a 37° declined plane for a distance of 10 ft, collides with a wall, and rebounds along the plane (Fig. 6-28). *In terms of the work-energy relation*, compute the distance x of closest approach to the starting position after the return, assuming that no kinetic energy is lost during

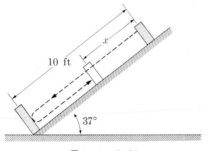

10 ft

x

37°

FIGURE 6–28

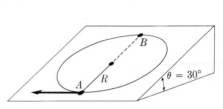

B

R

A

$\theta = 30°$

FIGURE 6–29

the collision and that the coefficient of sliding friction is $\mu = \frac{1}{4}$.

6–37. What is the location x, as a function of time, of a mass which starts from rest at $x = 0$ and is acted upon by a constant force F? By a force that develops a constant power P?

6–38. A small body of mass m is sliding on a circular hoop of radius R in a vertical plane. If the body is started with a velocity v_0 at the bottom of the hoop, determine the contact force on the hoop as a function of the position of the body. What must be the value of v_0 in order that the contact force be zero at the top of the hoop?

6–39. A body is attached to one end of a string, of length $R = 1$ m, which has its other end fixed on an inclined plane, as shown in Fig. 6–29. The inclination angle of the plane is $\theta = 30°$. The mass of the body is $m = 2$ kgm. How much kinetic energy does the body lose in traversing the semicircular path from A to B? The coefficient of sliding friction between the mass and the plane is $\mu = 0.25$.

CHAPTER 7

ENERGY

Summary. When the forces on a body are of a certain type (conservative), we can introduce the concept of potential energy, V, and formulate the law of conservation of the total mechanical energy, $H = E + V$, where E is the kinetic energy of the body. Since H is a constant of motion and V depends only on position, the kinetic energy and the speed of the body also depend on position only. The motion can be described conveniently and vividly by means of energy diagrams, from which the general features of the motion can be observed. After an analysis of these questions of motion of a body under the influence of a conservative force, the extension of the energy concept is discussed, and a qualitative survey of the various forms of energy is given. In its general form energy, like momentum, is a conserved quantity in nature.

The concept of kinetic energy would be a rather sterile one if it had no significance beyond that which we have encountered so far. We have seen that when the net force on a body is known as a function of position, the work of the force can be calculated, thereby enabling the prediction of the kinetic energy and the speed of the body as functions of position. This, to be sure, is a very important and useful property of kinetic energy because in many situations the force is known as a function of position. But the importance of the energy concept extends far beyond this work-energy relation. We shall see eventually that it leads to a conservation law of great generality and importance. The full impact of this concept will emerge slowly, for energy manifests itself in a variety of forms, and therefore requires more than one kind of measurement to detect its presence. Heat, we shall see, is a form of energy and often when kinetic energy "disappears" it has not disappeared at all but merely has been converted into the random kinetic energy of atoms. There is energy in light, radio, and sound waves, there is energy associated with mass, and there is nuclear as well as chemical energy. It should be borne in mind, therefore, that all the motivation for our stress on the energy concept has not yet appeared explicitly, and we shall ultimately see that this concept has a status fully equal to that of momentum.

7-1 Potential energy. In our momentum considerations we have observed that the total momentum before a collision is always equal to the total momentum after the collision. We have also seen that the total momentum is unchanged even *during* a collision.

Now imagine a perfectly elastic one-dimensional collision in which two identical cars move toward each other with equal speeds. After the collision the bodies move away from each other with the same speed as they had initially and, consequently, the total kinetic energy after the collision is the same as the total kinetic energy before the collision. (Later in this chapter, we shall see that the total kinetic energy after is the same as that before a collision in all perfectly elastic collisions, regardless of the initial conditions.) But can we make a statement which is analogous to that made in connection with momentum conservation, and say that the kinetic energy is conserved even *during* the collision? Certainly not, for at one instant during the collision both cars are instantaneously at rest, and so have no kinetic energy whatever! Clearly, the kinetic energy is constant before the collision, decreases as soon as the cars begin to interact, eventually becomes zero, increases again, and then regains and maintains its initial value after the collision.

If the cars interact with each other via a spring, there will be work done on the spring while it is being compressed. From the work-energy relation, it follows that the magnitude of this work is equal to the decrease in the kinetic energy of the cars. Since the cars regain their kinetic energy during the expansion cycle of the collision, the spring must do the same amount of work on the cars during its expansion as it absorbed during its compression. In other words, the work done on the spring during compression can be considered as stored in the spring, and this stored work, as we have seen in the previous chapter, can be expressed as $Kx^2/2$, where x is the compression of the spring and K is the spring constant. Note that the work stored in the spring at a certain moment does not depend on whether the spring is in the process of expansion or compression; it depends only on the length of the spring at that moment, and consequently only on the position of each car. We shall call this stored work the *potential energy V*. Then, although the kinetic energy E does not remain constant during the collision, the *sum of the kinetic and potential energies* does. In other words, if the concept of energy is extended to include the potential energy, we can formulate a law of conservation of energy:

$$E + V = \text{const} = H. \tag{7-1}$$

The sum of the kinetic and potential energies, called the *total mechanical energy H*, remains constant during the interaction. As we shall discuss in more detail shortly, the concept of potential energy is useful only when the force between the interacting bodies depends solely upon the distance between the bodies and not upon their relative speeds, for example. Then there is a unique relationship between the potential energy and the force between the bodies, and the potential energy can be determined in advance from the known force.

In order to further discuss potential energy and to investigate the relationship between the potential energy and the force, we shall consider only one of the interacting bodies. For simplicity, let one end of the spring be held in a fixed position (which corresponds to the case in which one of the interacting bodies has a very large mass), as shown in Fig. 7–1. Suppose the body moves toward the spring with a constant kinetic energy of, say, 50 ergs. The free end of the relaxed spring is located at $x = 0$. As the body collides with the spring, it slows down. If we could measure the kinetic energy at various points, we might find, for example, that during the first centimeter of compression the kinetic-energy loss is 2 ergs; during the next centimeter, 6 ergs; etc.; and that the kinetic energy varies with position, as is indicated in Fig. 7–1. At $x = -5$ cm, the kinetic energy is zero and the body starts to turn. We now find that in each interval the body gains a kinetic energy precisely equal to the amount lost in this interval during the compression. That is, when the body passes, say $x = -2$ cm, it has exactly the same kinetic energy, 42 ergs, as it had when it passed this point during the compression. It is this property of the spring force which guarantees that the kinetic energy lost in the compression will be regained in the expansion, and it is this property of the spring force which permits us to define and use the potential energy. If a spring did not have this property, that is, if a body lost an amount of kinetic energy ΔE when it compressed a spring from x_1 to x_2 but regained less than ΔE when the spring expanded from x_2 to x_1, the concept of potential energy would be useless, for what then would be meant by a stored kinetic energy at x_1 or at x_2? A body which

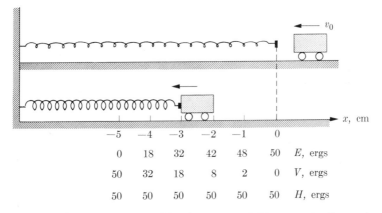

-5	-4	-3	-2	-1	0	
0	18	32	42	48	50	E, ergs
50	32	18	8	2	0	V, ergs
50	50	50	50	50	50	H, ergs

FIG. 7–1. The car has an initial kinetic energy of 50 ergs. As the spring is compressed by the car, some and eventually all of the kinetic energy is converted into potential energy. The kinetic energy of the car is regained when the spring expands, and during the entire motion the total mechanical energy $H = E + V$ remains constant.

started at x_1, moved to x_2, and then returned to x_1 would have less energy than a body which remained stationary at x_1.

In more general terms, for a potential energy to be associated with a force F, this force F must be such that if a body gains an amount of energy ΔE when moving through Δx in one direction, it loses exactly that same amount of energy when moving through this *same* displacement Δx in the opposite direction. This means that the force F must *not* depend upon the speed or direction of motion of the body, but must depend at most on the position x of the body. From this we see that a potential energy cannot be associated with a sliding friction force, for sliding friction forces are always directed oppositely to the direction of motion and, consequently, depend not only on the position of the body but on the direction of motion as well. The kinetic energy is lost by the body whether Δx is moved through from the right or from the left. A potential energy can be associated with constant forces (both magnitude and direction must be constant) or forces which depend only on x, for then the force on the body is completely independent of which way or how fast the body moves and the kinetic-energy changes through Δx and $-\Delta x$ will surely be equal and opposite. Forces with which a potential energy can be associated are called *conservative* forces (total mechanical energy conserved). Forces with which a potential energy cannot be associated are called *nonconservative* forces.

If the change of the kinetic energy is ΔE when the body goes from x to $x + \Delta x$, the corresponding change in the potential energy will be

$$\Delta V = -\Delta E, \qquad (7\text{–}2)$$

and the total mechanical energy $H = E + V$ must remain constant. Clearly, the potential energy of the body is related to the force on the body, and this relation is obtained directly if we recall that the force on a body can be expressed as $F = \lim (\Delta E/\Delta x)$. Then, with $\Delta E = -\Delta V$, it follows that

$$F = -\frac{dV}{dx} \qquad (7\text{–}3)$$

or

$$V = -\int F(x)\, dx + \text{const.} \qquad (7\text{–}4)$$

In other words, when the force depends on only the position of the body, the potential energy can be calculated once and for all from Eq. (7–4). The constant of integration is of no particular significance, since in all calculations involving the potential energy we are interested ultimately in the difference between the potential energies at two points. Therefore, in each particular case, the constant is chosen to make the expression for the potential energy as simple as possible. This will be apparent in the following.

It follows now from the above discussion that, for a given total mechanical energy, the kinetic energy, as well as the potential energy, depends on only the position of the body. We can therefore prepare a diagram or "map" of the potential and the kinetic energies of the body from a knowledge of the force and the total mechanical energy. The total mechanical energy can be determined as the sum of the kinetic and the potential energies of the body at any arbitrary point. If, at a certain point, the potential energy is zero, the total mechanical energy is simply the kinetic energy at that point. Conversely, if the kinetic energy is zero at some point, the total mechanical energy is the same as the potential energy at that point. Although in the foregoing discussion a spring-type force has been implied, these considerations apply to any conservative force, such as the gravitational force and the electrostatic force.

If we must, in addition to conservative forces, consider friction forces, we can see that the total mechanical energy will not remain constant but will decrease continuously as a result of the negative work of the friction forces on the moving body. In problems of this kind that involve non-conservative forces, it is usually most convenient to apply the work-energy principle in the calculation of the kinetic energy of the body.

The potential-energy concept, of course, does not introduce anything that is basically new to us. All that can be done with this concept can be done with the work-energy principle. However, we find that it does offer a new viewpoint and, most important, it serves to introduce the general principle of the conservation of energy, which we shall discuss later in this chapter and again in connection with thermodynamics.

7–2 Examples. Energy diagrams. In order to better establish the idea of potential energy, we shall apply it to motion in the local gravitational field and then study in more detail the motion of a body under the influence of the spring-type force. We shall present graphically the relationship between the potential, kinetic, and total mechanical energies by means of so-called energy diagrams. Even if the motion cannot be expressed explicitly in mathematical form, we can always obtain immediately a qualitative idea of the motion directly from an energy diagram.

Consider the motion in the local gravitational field. An object of mass m is thrown upward with an initial velocity $v_y = v_0$ from a height $y = y_0$ above the earth. What will be the kinetic energy and the speed v of the body when it reaches height y? First, we shall solve the problem by use of the work-energy principle. The positive direction of the position coordinate y is upward, and therefore the force on the body is $F_y = -mg$; the work done on the body as it moves from y_0 to y is $F_y(y - y_0) =$

$-mg(y - y_0)$. This work is equal to the change of the kinetic energy $(mv^2/2) - (mv_0^2/2)$; that is,

$$-mg(y - y_0) = \tfrac{1}{2}mv^2 - \tfrac{1}{2}mv_0^2.$$

The speed v can be obtained directly from this equation in terms of y, y_0, and v_0. We can rewrite the expression in the following form:

$$\tfrac{1}{2}mv^2 + mgy = \tfrac{1}{2}mv_0^2 + mgy_0. \qquad (7\text{-}5)$$

The quantity on the left relates to the body at position y, and that on the right is the same quantity evaluated at $y = y_0$. This quantity, then, is a constant of motion that represents the total mechanical energy of the body, and the quantity mgy is evidently the potential energy which, when it is added to the kinetic energy, makes the sum constant.

In order to better understand the formal discussion of potential energy in the previous section, we now solve the problem using the concept of potential energy from the start. The force is given and, in this particular case, is a constant, $F_y = -mg$. From the given force we determine the potential energy by means of the relation (7–4):

$$V = -\int F_y \, dy + \text{const} = mgy + \text{const.} \qquad (7\text{-}6)$$

As we indicated earlier, the choice of the constant of integration depends on the point at which we wish to set the potential energy equal to zero. In this particular case it is convenient to choose the zero point at ground level, that is, at $y = 0$. This means that the constant in (7–6) becomes zero. Having found the expression for the potential energy, we can use the law of conservation of the total mechanical energy to obtain

$$\tfrac{1}{2}mv^2 + mgy = H.$$

The constant H can be evaluated as the sum of the kinetic and potential energies at any point. At the starting point $y = y_0$, we know both the kinetic and potential energies, that is, $H = (mv_0^2/2) + mgy_0$. Thus we obtain

$$\tfrac{1}{2}mv^2 + mgy = \tfrac{1}{2}mv_0^2 + mgy_0, \qquad (7\text{-}7)$$

which is the same result as Eq. (7–5). Note that this same relation would have been obtained regardless of the choice of the constant of integration in Eq. (7–6), since this constant would have appeared on both sides of Eq. (7–7). If we wish to evaluate the speed of the body as it strikes the ground, we simply insert $y = 0$ into the above relation and obtain $v^2 = v_0^2 + 2gy_0$.

It is illuminating to present the relation between the potential, kinetic, and total energies in a diagram, in which the potential energy (known in

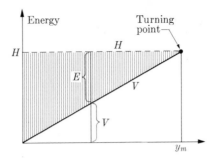

FIG. 7-2. Energy diagram for a body in the local gravitational field.

advance from the known force) is plotted as a function of the position coordinate of the body. In the present example, we have $V = mgy$, which is a straight line in the diagram of Fig. 7-2. The total mechanical energy H can be represented by a horizontal line in the diagram, and the kinetic energy $E = H - V$ is then represented simply by the vertical distance between the H-line and the potential-energy curve, as shown.

When the body reaches its highest point, y_m, the kinetic energy is zero, and the potential energy mgy_m at that point equals the total mechanical energy of the body. As the body falls, the potential energy is continuously converted into kinetic energy, so that the sum $E + V = H$ remains constant. At $y = 0$ all the energy is kinetic. Since the potential energy V can never exceed the total mechanical energy H, motion is possible only in the regions of y in which the H-curve is above the V-curve in the energy diagram. The point at which the two curves intersect represents a turning point in the motion, and at this point the kinetic energy is zero.

Let us now reconsider the motion of a body under the influence of a spring-type force, and determine the speed of the body as a function of its position when the initial conditions are known. Again, for the purpose of illuminating the potential-energy concept, we shall first solve the problem by using the familiar work-energy relation, and then by using potential energy and the law of conservation of total mechanical energy. The equations we obtain in the two cases obviously can be brought into the same form; nevertheless, it is useful to carry through their derivation in detail.

Suppose the body is attached to the end of a compressed spring and then released, as indicated in Fig. 7-3. The body is acted on by the force $F_x = -Kx$, and if the body starts its motion at $x = -x_0$, the work done by the force when the body reaches x is $W = \int_{-x_0}^{x} F_x \, dx = \int_{-x_0}^{x} (-Kx) \, dx = (Kx_0^2/2) - (Kx^2/2)$. The kinetic energy at x is then given by

$$\tfrac{1}{2}mv^2 = \int_{-x_0}^{x} F_x \, dx = \tfrac{1}{2}Kx_0^2 - \tfrac{1}{2}Kx^2. \tag{7-8}$$

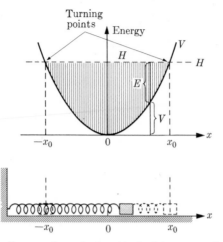

FIG. 7-3. Energy diagram for a body attached to one end of a spring. The other end of the spring is held fixed.

Now, to solve the same problem by use of the concepts of potential energy and conservation of total mechanical energy, we proceed as follows. We determine the potential energy that corresponds to the given force from the relation (7–4), $V = -\int F_x\, dx + C$, which, in the present case, is $V = Kx^2/2 + C$. If we choose $V = 0$ when $x = 0$, we get $C = 0$ and $V = Kx^2/2$. From the conservation of energy, $V + E = H = $ const, we then obtain

$$\tfrac{1}{2}Kx^2 + \tfrac{1}{2}mv^2 = \text{const} = H.$$

The constant energy H can be evaluated from the known conditions at one point. In particular, we have $v = 0$ at $x = -x_0$. Here the total energy is entirely potential, and we have $H = Kx_0^2/2$. Thus, we get

$$\tfrac{1}{2}Kx^2 + \tfrac{1}{2}mv^2 = \tfrac{1}{2}Kx_0^2,$$

which is the same as Eq. (7–8).

The energy diagram for the body at the end of the spring is illustrated in Fig. 7–3. The potential energy $V = Kx^2/2$ is represented by a parabola. The initial potential energy is $Kx_0^2/2$, which is also the total mechanical energy, since $E = 0$ initially. The potential energy can never exceed H and, consequently, the magnitude of the displacement of the body from the equilibrium position cannot exceed x_0; the motion is limited to the region $-x_0 < x < x_0$. The turning points of the motion are defined by the intersection of the total energy line, $H = $ const, and the potential-energy curve. The kinetic energy is a maximum at $x = 0$, at which point all the energy is kinetic.

The speed and travel time in one-dimensional motion. Here we shall summarize in general terms the observations made in the previous section that regard one-dimensional motion of a body under the influence of a conservative force.

If the potential energy of the force is $V = V(x)$ and the kinetic energy of the body is E, we have $E + V = H = $ const, and the speed of the body is given by

$$v = \sqrt{\frac{2(H - V)}{m}}.$$ (7–9)

Since H is a constant and V is a function of x only, it follows that the speed also is a function of the position only. We have $v = dx/dt$, and the time of travel of the body between the positions x_0 and x can be expressed as

$$t = \int_{x_0}^{x} \frac{dx}{v} = \int_{x_0}^{x} \sqrt{\frac{m}{2[H - V(x)]}}\, dx,$$ (7–10)

which is valid if the velocity does not change sign in the region from x_0 to x.

As an illustration of the use of these general results, let us consider vertical motion in the local gravitational field. Suppose a body is projected upward from the ground with an initial velocity such that the body reaches a maximum height y_m. The total mechanical energy is then $H = mgy_m$. The travel time from the ground to the maximum height, according to the general formula (7–10), is then

$$t = \int_{0}^{y_m} \sqrt{\frac{m}{2mg(y_m - y)}}\, dy = \sqrt{\frac{2y_m}{g}},$$ (7–11)

a result that is well known from Chapter 3.

Similarly, in the example of motion of the body at the end of a spring, we obtain for the time of travel between $x = -x_0$ and $x = x_0$:

$$t = \int_{-x_0}^{x_0} \sqrt{\frac{m}{2(Kx_0^2/2 - Kx^2/2)}}\, dx = \pi \sqrt{\frac{m}{K}}.$$ (7–12)

This result will be obtained in a different manner, and discussed further, in Chapter 8.

7–3 Potential energy—motion in a plane and in space.

The extension of the potential-energy concept to include motion in a plane and in space follows directly from our considerations of motion along a line. We have seen in the case of motion along a line that a body may have a latent or potentially available kinetic energy which is specified by the position of the body along the line. For the potential-energy idea to be useful in the analysis of the motion of a body in space, we must be able to specify a latent or potentially available kinetic energy according to a body's position in space. Let us see how this idea applies in two familiar examples.

Consider first the local gravitational force, but now let the body be free to move in the x- and z-directions as well as in the y-direction. From the work-energy principle, we have

$$\Delta E = F_x \,\Delta x + F_y \,\Delta y + F_z \,\Delta z.$$

But there is no force in the x- or z-directions, and the kinetic energy changes only as a result of motion in the y-direction. Therefore, the potential energy is just the same as before, mgy, but now, instead of the potential energy having fixed values along a vertical line, we may regard it as having fixed values on parallel horizontal planes. Whenever a body passes from the plane defined by y_1 to that defined by y_2, its potential energy changes from mgy_1 to mgy_2, and so the kinetic-energy change is $\Delta E = -\Delta V = -mg(y_2 - y_1)$.

EXAMPLE. Consider a simple pendulum that consists of a point mass m suspended on the end of a light pivoted rod of length l. There are two forces on the mass, its weight mg and the tension T in the rod. The tension T is a no-work force, for as m moves back and forth its velocity is always perpendicular to T. The potential energy is therefore determined by y, the distance at which the mass is above its lowest point. If we take the potential energy to be zero at this lowest point, we have

$$V = mgy = mgl(1 - \cos \theta).$$

From Fig. 7–4, we see that for angles not far from $\theta = 0$ the potential-energy curve is very similar in shape to the potential-energy curve for a mass connected to a spring. If a pendulum bob has a small total mechanical energy H_1, the total energy is larger than V only in a limited region of θ, as shown, and the pendulum will swing back and forth between θ_m and $-\theta_m$. If, on the other hand, the total mechanical energy is larger than $H_2 = 2mgl$, the bob will swing completely around the pivot, and H is larger than V everywhere. At the top of a swing, where $\theta = \pi$, the potential energy is a maximum, and so the kinetic energy will have its smallest value.

Consider next the spring-type force, but now imagine the fixed end of the spring to be arranged such that the spring and the body to which it is attached are free to move on a horizontal frictionless plane about a pivot. (Fig. 7–5). The kinetic-energy change imparted to a body by the spring, and the corresponding change of the potential energy, is simply a matter of the amount of compression or expansion of the spring, and this is determined by the radial distance r from the pivot to the end of the spring at which the body is attached. This follows from the fact that the spring force is directed along the spring, and only displacements in this direction will produce work and a change of the potential energy. In the one-dimensional case we found that the potential energy had values fixed by

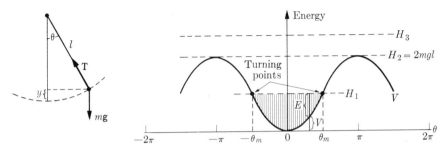

FIG. 7–4. Energy diagram for a simple pendulum. If the total mechanical energy is less than $H_2 = 2mgl$, we have H larger than V only in a limited region of θ and the pendulum swings between the turning points θ_m and $-\theta_m$. If, on the other hand, $H > 2mgl$, we have H larger than V everywhere and the motion is possible for all angles, i.e., the bob will swing in a complete circle.

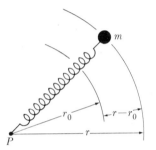

FIG. 7–5. The spring is free to pivot about the point P. The potential energy is $V = \frac{1}{2}K(r - r_0)^2$ and the equipotential-energy surfaces are spheres centered on P.

the position of the body along a line. Now, however, the potential energy is determined by the distance of the body from the pivot, and all positions on a circle of given radius have the same potential energy. If the body on the spring were to move in space about the pivot and if the gravitational force were absent, all points on a sphere of given radius would have equal potential energies.

The surfaces on which a body can move with no potential-energy change are called *equipotential-energy surfaces*. In the example above, the equipotential-energy surfaces are spheres that are centered on the spring pivot. In the gravitational case mentioned earlier, the equipotential-energy surfaces were the parallel horizontal planes. (Actually these parallel horizontal planes are small portions of earth-centered spheres entirely similar to the pivot-centered spheres associated with the spring force.)

The spring force that we have discussed is a special example of a very important class of forces, that is, those which depend at most on distance and are directed along a line that connects two interacting bodies. The potential-energy concept, as discussed below, is valid with *all* forces of this class. Then, if one of the interacting bodies is fixed in space (corresponding to the pivot in the case of the spring, or the sun in the case of planetary motion), and if this fixed point is chosen as the origin of a coordinate system, the force on the moving body is always in the radial direction (toward the center or away from it). A force of this kind is called *central*. If, in addition, the magnitude of the force depends only on the radius r, work is done by the force only when the body is displaced in the radial direction. If the force is $F(r)$, taken as positive when directed away from the center, the expression for the potential energy is analogous to Eq. (7–4). We have

$$V(r) = -\int F(r)\,dr + \text{const.} \qquad (7\text{–}13)$$

Electrostatic and gravitational forces are central forces which depend only on r, and therefore their potential energies can be obtained from (7–13).

Although central forces of this kind are the most important ones, it is interesting to ask whether a potential energy can be introduced for other types of forces involved in motion in a plane or in space. We might be tempted to say that introduction of potential energy is possible if the force depends only on the position of the body. However, a little thought reveals that this requirement, although sufficient in one dimension and for central forces, is not sufficient in general. We must require, in addition, that the work done by the force when the body moves around an arbitrary closed path is zero. If this work were not zero a body could gain any amount of kinetic energy by just going around the same closed path over and over again. Then we could certainly not specify a latent or potentially available energy from a knowledge of just the body's position, since the same point in space would correspond to many different values, depending on the previous history of the motion.

It is important that we realize that energy considerations give us information about both the kinetic energy and the speed of a body, but do not tell us anything about the direction of the motion. In one-dimensional considerations, for example, a knowledge of the kinetic energy does not tell us whether the body is moving toward the right or the left, and when a body can move in space it may have velocity components in all of the x-, y-, and z-directions. From energy considerations alone, we can find only the value of $v^2 = v_x^2 + v_y^2 + v_z^2$.

Energy relation in an inverse-square force field. As an example of the use of the concepts of potential energy and total mechanical energy, we shall discuss briefly the motion of a body when acted upon by a force with a magnitude of the form K/r^2. Both gravitational and electrostatic forces are of this type. Gravitational forces, so far as is known, are always attractive, and we have $F = -K/r^2$, if K is a positive constant. The planets, the moon, satellites, meteors, and comets move under the influence of gravitational forces. Electrostatic forces may be either attractive or repulsive, and we have $F = \pm K/r^2$, and this depends upon whether the electric charges of the two bodies are alike $(+)$ or unlike $(-)$. Atomic electrons move under the influence of electrostatic forces. In both cases, electrostatic and gravitational, the force is directed along a line which connects the two interacting bodies. The force is zero only at $r = \infty$ and it is convenient to choose the potential energy to be zero also at $r = \infty$. Then the constant in Eq. (7–13) is zero, and for a repulsive force we have

$$V(r) = -\int \frac{K}{r^2}\, dr = \frac{K}{r}.\qquad(7\text{–}14)$$

Here, when r increases, the potential energy decreases, and so the kinetic energy increases.

Suppose that a body of mass m is subject to a repulsive (K/r^2)-force, and that at a distance r_0 from the force center, the kinetic energy is E_0. The total energy $E + V$ must be constant and at $r = r_0$ its value is then known to be $H = E_0 + K/r_0$. The kinetic energy at an arbitrary value of r is therefore obtained from

$$E + \frac{K}{r} = E_0 + \frac{K}{r_0}.\qquad(7\text{–}15)$$

(The direction of motion cannot be determined from energy considerations alone.) Note that the kinetic energy becomes zero at the radius r_1 given by $K/r_1 = E_0 + K/r_0$, and the body can come no nearer than r_1 to the force center. As the body moves toward infinity, its kinetic energy approaches the value of the total energy, $E_0 + K/r_0$. As indicated earlier, motion is restricted to the region of space where H is larger than V, that is, where the H-curve is above the V-curve in the energy diagram of Fig. 7–6. The curves intersect at $r = r_1$ and the motion is restricted to the region $r > r_1$.

If, on the other hand, the force is attractive, so that $V = -K/r$, and the kinetic energy is E_0 at $r = r_0$, the kinetic energy at an arbitrary value of r is given by

$$E - \frac{K}{r} = E_0 - \frac{K}{r_0}.\qquad(7\text{–}16)$$

Now, the body gains kinetic energy as it approaches the force center, and

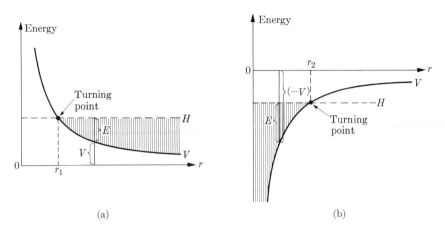

FIG. 7–6. Energy diagram for (K/r)-type forces: (a) a repulsive force $+K/r^2$, and (b) an attractive force $-K/r^2$. If, in the attractive case, the total energy is greater than zero, all values of r are accessible. If the total energy is less than zero, the body is trapped. The planets, for example, are trapped by the gravitational force of the sun.

loses kinetic energy as it moves away. The kinetic energy becomes zero at $r = r_2$ where $K/r_2 = K/r_0 - E_0$, and the body can move no farther away. Only in the region $r < r_2$ is H larger than V, as can be seen in Fig. 7–6. The body is trapped in this region.

The total mechanical energy in the attractive-force case is

$$H = E - \frac{K}{r}. \tag{7–17}$$

If H is greater than zero, the kinetic energy will be greater than zero even when r becomes infinite. If H is less than zero, the kinetic energy is zero at some finite value of r_1 and, as was mentioned before, the body is trapped. If H is exactly zero, the kinetic energy approaches zero as the body approaches infinity. The total mechanical energy of all the planets in the solar system is negative. They are trapped in the sun's gravitational force field. Similarly, all comets are apparently trapped and so have a negative total mechanical energy. Some meteors, on the other hand, do have positive energies and could, if they did not strike the earth and either stop or burn up, escape again into the spaces between stars from which they came.

7–4 Superposition of potential energies. In Chapter 4, we observed that when many forces act on a body they may be represented by their *vector* sum. This is a basic, important property which justifies the introduction of the force concept. In the calculation of the kinetic energy of

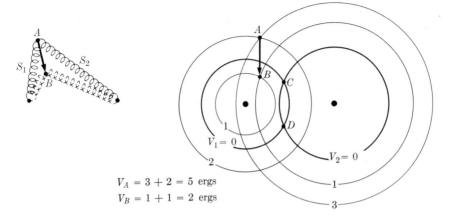

$$V_A = 3 + 2 = 5 \text{ ergs}$$
$$V_B = 1 + 1 = 2 \text{ ergs}$$

FIG. 7-7. A body moves from A to B under the influence of two springs. Its potential-energy change is the sum of the potential-energy changes which arise from each of the two springs. In the trip from A to B, therefore, a body would gain 3 ergs of kinetic energy.

a body under the influence of several forces, the potential-energy concept is particularly useful, for the potential energies which arise from many forces acting on a body can be added *algebraically*, as discussed below. Of course, if we wish detailed information about the time dependence of the motion, for example, we must consider the detailed forces and their vector sum. However, the potential energy allows us to find the kinetic energy as a function of position, and this is both valuable and easily obtained.

Consider first the familiar spring-type force. Imagine a body connected to two springs, each of which is pivoted at one end (Fig. 7-7). If we arrange things so that we start from a position at which both springs have their relaxed lengths, and then pull the body away so that both springs are stretched, the work done on the body by the springs is the sum of the work contributions from each spring force, as we have seen in Chapter 6. That is, the potential energy of the body is now equal to the algebraic sum of the potential energies which arise from each of the springs.

More generally, when a body is under the influence of several forces, each of which is conservative (i.e., of the type with which a potential energy can be associated), it will undergo a kinetic-energy change $\Delta E = \mathbf{F} \cdot \Delta \mathbf{r}$ when displaced through $\Delta \mathbf{r}$. Here $\mathbf{F}$ is the *vector sum* of all the conservative forces, $\mathbf{F}_1 + \mathbf{F}_2 + \mathbf{F}_3 + \cdots$. The kinetic-energy change is therefore

$$\Delta E = \mathbf{F}_1 \cdot \Delta \mathbf{r} + \mathbf{F}_2 \cdot \Delta \mathbf{r} + \mathbf{F}_3 \cdot \Delta \mathbf{r} + \cdots, \qquad (7\text{-}18)$$

or the *algebraic* sum of the work done (scalar quantities) by the individual forces. Each of the work terms, when integrated, is just minus the potential-energy change associated with that force alone, and so the kinetic-energy change is simply $\Delta E = -\Delta V$, where V is the net (algebraic sum) potential energy:

$$V = V_1 + V_2 + V_3 + \cdots \qquad (7\text{-}19)$$

EXAMPLE 1. A vertical spring of length $2L$ and spring constant K is suspended at one end. A body of mass m is attached to the other end of the spring. The spring is compressed to half its length and then released. Determine the kinetic energy of the body, and its maximum value, in the ensuing motion.

The body is acted on by two conservative forces, the spring force and gravity. If the position of the body is measured from the *relaxed* position of the spring by the coordinate y (positive upward), and if the potential energy is set equal to zero at $y = 0$, the potential energies that correspond to the two forces are $Ky^2/2$ and mgy, respectively. The total potential energy is then

$$V = \tfrac{1}{2}Ky^2 + mgy.$$

The law of conservation of energy, $E + V = H = \text{const}$, then gives the following expression for the calculation of the kinetic energy E:

$$E + \tfrac{1}{2}Ky^2 + mgy = \text{const} = H. \qquad (7\text{-}20)$$

The constant value of H is determined from the fact that $E = 0$ when $y = L$ (the initial conditions). Therefore we get $H = KL^2/2 + mgL$, and from (7-20) we find that the kinetic energy is then

$$E = \frac{K}{2}(L^2 - y^2) + mg(L - y).$$

The kinetic energy will have a maximum and the potential energy a minimum value where $dE/dy = 0$ or $dV/dy = 0$, that is, at the point y_0 given by $Ky_0 = -mg$ or

$$y_0 = -\frac{mg}{K}.$$

This is the static equilibrium point of the body. The maximum kinetic energy then is

$$E_{\max} = \frac{K}{2}(L^2 - y_0^2) + mg(L - y_0)$$

$$= \frac{K}{2}(L^2 - y_0^2) - Ky_0(L - y_0) = \frac{K}{2}(L - y_0)^2,$$

and the corresponding minimum value of the potential energy is

$$V_{\min} = -\tfrac{1}{2}Ky_0^2.$$

It is interesting to look at the energy diagram representing this motion. The potential-energy curve shown in Fig. 7-8 is the sum of the function $Ky^2/2$,

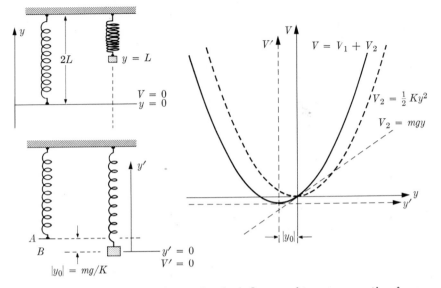

FIG. 7-8. Example of motion under the influence of two conservative forces. Note that the treatment of this problem is simplified if the position and the potential energy are measured from the equilibrium position B, rather than from the relaxed-spring position A.

which is represented by a parabola, and the function mgy, which is represented by a straight line. The total potential energy is again a parabola with the minimum value $V_{\min} = -Ky_0^2/2$ at the point $y = y_0$. The potential energy can then be expressed as

$$V - V_{\min} = \frac{K}{2}\,(y - y_0)^2.$$

In other words, if we measure the position of the body from the equilibrium position, rather than from the relaxed-spring position, and if we choose the potential energy to be zero at that point, the expression for the potential energy simplifies to

$$V' = \frac{K}{2}\,y'^2,$$

where $V' = V - V_{\min}$ and $y' = y - y_0$.

The problem then reduces to the determination of the motion of a body under the influence of a spring force only. This latter choice of the coordinates and the zero point for the potential energy is recommended in studies of motion of a body under the influence of a spring force and a constant force (such as gravity), since then we need not include the potential energy that corresponds to the constant force. Its effect enters only in the determination of the equilibrium position.

EXAMPLE 2. A body of 0.5 kgm mass is connected to three equal springs each of 1-m relaxed length. The spring constant for each of the springs is $K = 2$ n/m, and in their relaxed state the springs are fixed to three corners of an equilateral triangle, as shown in Fig. 7–9. The mass m is displaced to point A, then released. What will be the kinetic energy of m if it returns to point B?

When m is at A, springs a and c are 0.87 m long and therefore are compressed 0.13 m. Spring b, on the other hand, is expanded 0.5 m. The total potential energy at A is the sum of the potential energies associated with each of the springs, and so is

$$V_A = \tfrac{1}{2}Kx_a^2 + \tfrac{1}{2}Kx_b^2 + \tfrac{1}{2}Kx_c^2 \simeq 0.017 + 0.017 + 0.25 \simeq 0.28 \text{ joule.}$$

When the mass is at B, its potential energy is zero, and so its kinetic-energy gain must be $E = 0.28$ joule, and its speed is $v \simeq 1$ m/sec.

When a body moves under the influence of only friction or other non-conservative forces, the potential-energy concept is useless, for a potential energy cannot be associated with forces of this type. When a box slides across the floor and stops, its initial kinetic energy has been converted into heat energy, and we note that the box does not have a latent kinetic or potential energy which can be reconverted into kinetic energy.

Many situations in nature involve a mixture of conservative and non-conservative forces. A car rolling down a hill is subject to wind drag and friction (nonconservative) and gravity (conservative). If the energy concept is useful in these situations, and it often is, the work-energy principle can always be used. One simply equates the net work done by *all* forces, conservative and nonconservative, to the kinetic-energy change, and entirely ignores the potential energy. Alternatively, the work done by conservative forces may be included in the potential energy as usual. Then the work done by the nonconservative forces must be evaluated separately. We shall call W_{nc} the work done by the nonconservative forces and from the work-energy relation and the definition of potential energy, we immediately have

$$W_{nc} = \Delta E + \Delta V. \tag{7–21}$$

Since the total mechanical energy is $H = E + V$, we may say that the work done by the nonconservative forces serves to change the total mechanical energy. Clearly, a friction force, for which W_{nc} is always a negative quantity, serves to decrease the total mechanical energy.

EXAMPLE. A body of mass m has an initial velocity v_0 directed up a plane that is at an inclination angle θ to the horizontal. The coefficient of sliding friction between the mass and the plane is μ. What distance d will the body slide up the plane before coming to rest? (See Fig. 7–10.)

There are two forces on the body, its weight and the force of the plane. The force of the plane has two components, N which is normal to the plane and f

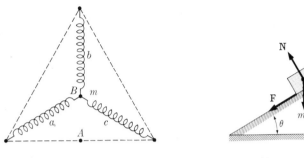

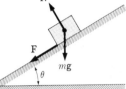

FIGURE 7-9   FIGURE 7-10

which is directed down the plane. N is a no-work force (perpendicular to the motion) with a magnitude of $mg \cos \theta$, and so the friction force is $f = \mu mg \cos \theta$.

If we apply the work-energy principle, we have $-f\,d$ for the work done by the friction force and $-mg\,d \sin \theta$ for the work done by the gravitational force because the component of the weight in the direction of the displacement is $-mg \sin \theta$. The net work is therefore $-\mu mg\,d \cos \theta - mg\,d \sin \theta$, and this must be equal to $\Delta E = -mv_0^2/2$. We have therefore

$$d = \frac{v_0^2}{2g(\mu \cos \theta + \sin \theta)}.$$

The friction force is nonconservative, and the work done by it alone is $W_{\text{nc}} = -\mu mg\,d \cos \theta$. Of course, the gravitational force is conservative, and if the potential energy is taken as zero at the start of the motion, it is $mg\,d \sin \theta$ at d. The potential-energy change is $\Delta V = mg\,d \sin \theta$, and the kinetic-energy change is $\Delta E = -mv_0^2/2$. We have

$$W_{\text{nc}} = \Delta E + \Delta V = -\frac{mv_0^2}{2} + mg \sin \theta,$$

$$-\mu mg\,d \cos \theta = -\frac{mv_0^2}{2} + mg\,d \sin \theta,$$

as before.

Equipotential-energy surfaces. We have already mentioned the equipotential-energy surfaces (for example, equally spaced parallel horizontal planes and concentric spheres) that are associated with the local gravitational force and distance-dependent forces. On these surfaces a body may move with no potential-energy change, and hence also with no kinetic-energy change, if there are no nonconservative forces. For example, a satellite that moves in a circular path around the earth has a constant kinetic energy on the surface of an equipotential-energy sphere.

Similar but more complicated equipotential-energy surfaces exist when more than one conservative force acts on a body. Figure 7-11, for example, shows cross sections of the equipotential-energy surfaces for a body under the influence of two forces, either electrostatic or gravitational, one originating from B and one from C. Whenever a body crosses over from one equipotential-energy surface to another, its kinetic energy will change by a sufficient amount to keep the total mechanical energy constant.

The family of equipotential-energy surfaces is, of course, intimately related to the net force on a body. Suppose that some equipotential-energy surfaces are as shown in Fig. 7–12. When a body moves from the V_1-surface to the V_2-surface, it gains kinetic energy if V_1 is larger than V_2 and loses kinetic energy if V_1 is less than V_2. There must be a force on the body for otherwise the kinetic energy would not change, and the force is in the direction of decreasing potential (increasing kinetic) energy. The kinetic energy of a body will change (with distance) most rapidly when the body is displaced in the direction of the force on it. Therefore the force, at a given place on the V_1-surface, must be in the direction of

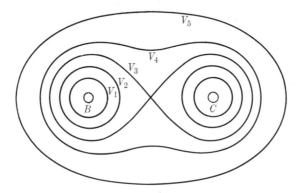

Fig. 7–11. Equipotential-energy surfaces (in cross section) for two electrostatic or two gravitational forces, one from B and one from C. (Imagine the surfaces generated when the figure is rotated about a line through BC.)

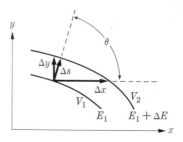

Fig. 7–12. A body which moves from line V_1 to line V_2 has a kinetic-energy change $\Delta E = -\Delta V$. The magnitude of the total force is $\overline{F} = -\Delta V/\Delta s$ and its direction is perpendicular to the equipotential surfaces. The component of the force in the x-direction is $\overline{F}_x = \overline{F} \cos \theta = -\Delta V/\Delta x$.

the shortest distance to the V_2-surface, and this direction is perpendicular to the V_1-surface if the two surfaces are sufficiently close together, i.e., if V_1 and V_2 differ by a sufficiently small amount.

The magnitude of the force is given by the rate of change of the kinetic energy with distance. If the shortest distance between the V_1 and V_2 surfaces is Δs (Fig. 7–12), and the kinetic energy at V_2 is larger than that at V_1 by an amount ΔE, the average force in the interval Δs is $\overline{F} = \Delta E/\Delta s = -\Delta V/\Delta s$, where ΔV is the corresponding change of the potential energy. To reach the V_2-surface in any other direction requires a displacement larger than Δs and the corresponding force component in that direction is smaller than $\overline{F}$. In particular, if the angle between Δs and the x-axis is θ, the force component in the x-direction is $\overline{F}_x = \overline{F} \cos \theta = (-\Delta V/\Delta s) \cos \theta = -\Delta V/\Delta x$, where $\Delta x = \Delta s/\cos \theta$. Note that the displacement Δx is *not* the projection of Δs on the x-axis, but rather, is the distance required to produce a change ΔV of the potential along the x-axis. In the displacement Δs both x and y vary, but in the displacement along the x-axis, y remains constant. The corresponding derivative of V with respect to x then represents the rate of change of V when y is held constant. This derivative is called the *partial derivative of V with respect to x* and it is denoted by $\partial V/\partial x$. The components of the force in the x- and y-directions then can be expressed in terms of the potential V, as follows:

$$F_x = -\frac{\partial V}{\partial x}, \qquad F_y = -\frac{\partial V}{\partial y}. \tag{7–22}$$

7–5 Kinetic energy in collisions. *Kinetic-energy changes.* We have seen that regardless of the nature of a collision, the total momentum of the colliding bodies always remains constant. We have classified collisions phenomenologically as perfectly inelastic (relative velocity decreased to zero), inelastic (relative velocity decreased), perfectly elastic (relative velocity unchanged in magnitude), and explosive (relative velocity increased). What relations to changes in the total kinetic energy of the colliding bodies do these collision types bear? Kinetic energy is a much more significant quantity than is relative velocity.

Let us examine the total kinetic energy of two colliding bodies and compare the values before and after a collision (see Fig. 7–13). The important points of our discussion will emerge more vividly and with a minimum of algebraic complication if our consideration is restricted to collisions in which two bodies of equal and opposite momenta approach and collide with each other. Of course, their momenta after the collision will remain equal and opposite also. The center of mass will be at rest, but we shall later extend our results to the more general case in which the center of mass moves.

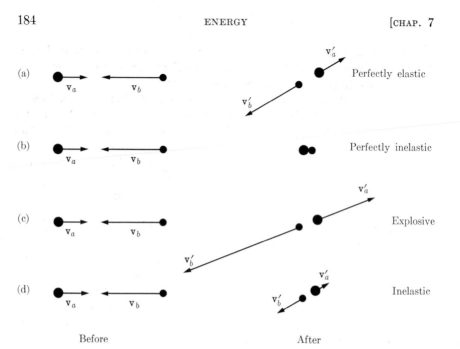

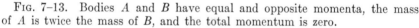

Before   After

FIG. 7–13. Bodies A and B have equal and opposite momenta, the mass of A is twice the mass of B, and the total momentum is zero.

Consider a perfectly inelastic collision between two identical bodies, A and B, which approach each other with equal speeds, $v_a = v_b$. They have a total kinetic energy $m_a v_a^2/2 + m_b v_b^2/2$. After the collision, both bodies will have zero velocity because the total momentum before the collision was zero, and the relative velocity after the collision is zero. Here, all the kinetic energy of the colliding bodies has disappeared.

Consider next a perfectly elastic collision. The magnitude of the velocities of A and B must remain unchanged in this type of collision. This is true because if the velocity of A did change by a certain fraction, the velocity of B would have to change by that same fraction in order to guarantee that the total momentum remain zero. But if both velocities change by the same factor, the magnitude of the relative velocity will change also, and this is not the case in a perfectly elastic collision. Neither A nor B have changed magnitudes of velocity, and therefore the kinetic energy is unchanged by the perfectly elastic collision. (See also Chapter 11.)

Similarly, when we study an inelastic collision we find that the relative velocity decreases and the total kinetic energy decreases. In an explosive-type collision the relative velocity increases and the total kinetic energy increases.

Of course, each of these types of collision has special features of its own, but the perfectly elastic collisions are, in one important sense, in a class apart from the others. When bodies take part in a perfectly elastic collision, their physical states are unchanged, while bodies involved in inelastic or explosive-type collisions always undergo some definite physical change. If two cars collide inelastically, the metal at the collision surface may be dented or the putty which cushioned the collision may be flattened. If two cars separate explosively, the spring which was compressed assumes its relaxed length, or the firecracker which was of one chemical composition becomes an entirely different chemical compound.

These physical changes (or lack of physical changes in the case of perfectly elastic collisions) are of importance because, as mentioned before, energy *is conserved* in nature. Kinetic energy is just one type of energy, and when we note in an experiment that kinetic energy has seemingly been "created" or "destroyed," we find that, in reality, energy has merely been transformed from one type to another. The physical changes we have mentioned are simply manifestations of this energy transformation. Of course, these qualitative observations do not show that energy is conserved, and we shall have to study, one by one, the physical changes that take place when kinetic energy is apparently created or destroyed.

Energy transfer in perfectly elastic one-dimensional collisions. When a body in motion collides with a body at rest, kinetic energy is transferred. In this section, we shall investigate briefly some of the properties of such an energy transfer, e.g., how it varies with the masses of the colliding bodies. The problem is closely related to important problems in engineering and applied physics. We shall consider here one-dimensional motion.

Let body A of mass m_a be moving with velocity v_a toward body B of mass m_b, which is at rest. From our previous experiments, we know that if A and B are of equal mass, after the collision A comes to rest and its velocity is taken up by B. All the kinetic energy of A is transferred to B. Further, if the mass of A is very small compared with that of B, for instance, as in a collision between a tennis ball and a freight car, very little energy will be transferred from A to B. On the other hand, if the mass of A is much greater than that of B (a moving freight car collides with a stationary tennis ball), very little energy will be transferred from A to B. Our analytic results must confirm these observations.

We wish now to find the fraction of the kinetic energy of A transferred to B, that is, $E_b'/E_a = m_b v_b'^2 / m_a v_a^2$. We start with two basic relationships. The first,

$$m_a v_a = m_b v_b' + m_a v_a', \qquad (7\text{–}23)$$

expresses conservation of momentum, and the second,

$$v_a = -(v_a' - v_b') \qquad \text{or} \qquad v_a' = v_b' - v_a, \qquad (7\text{–}24)$$

expresses the fact that the collision is perfectly elastic. When v_a' from (7–24) is substituted into (7–23) we obtain $2m_a v_a = v_b'(m_a + m_b)$, and from this it follows that

$$\frac{E_b'}{E_a} = \frac{4(m_b/m_a)}{(1 + m_b/m_a)^2}. \tag{7–25}$$

When m_b is much larger than m_a (a moving tennis ball hits a stationary freight train), the kinetic energy transfer is very small, as we have pointed out. Likewise, the fractional kinetic energy transfer is small when m_a is very much larger than m_b (a moving freight train hits a stationary tennis ball). But when m_a and m_b are of equal mass, E_b'/E_a is equal to unity and all the kinetic energy of A is transferred to B. Figure 7–14 is a graph of E_b'/E_a versus m_b/m_a.

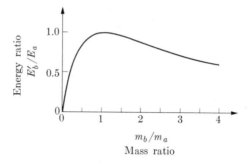

FIG. 7–14. Body A collides perfectly elastically with body B which was originally at rest. When A and B are of equal mass, all the kinetic energy of A is transferred to B.

An interesting question arises which is related to the problem we have just discussed: If A and B are of unequal mass, can the fraction of the energy transferred to B be increased by inserting a third body, C, between A and B, so that first A collides with C, then C collides with B? A simple extension of our method indicates that the answer is "yes," and that the optimum mass of the third body is $m_c = \sqrt{m_a m_b}$, the geometric mean of m_a and m_b. The kinetic energy of B can be further increased if bodies of mass $\sqrt{m_a m_c}$ and $\sqrt{m_b m_c}$ are inserted between A and C and between B and C, respectively. This process can be continued indefinitely and, in the limit, when we have inserted an indefinitely large number of masses, *all* of the kinetic energy of A can be transferred to B. (Despite one's first impression, there is no violation of momentum conservation here. Why?)

When the center of mass of two colliding bodies is not at rest, the algebraic details of determining kinetic energy become complicated. Certain special cases which are given as problems at the end of the chapter can be worked out easily, however.

The determination of kinetic-energy transfer between the bodies is best discussed from the viewpoint of an observer who moves with the velocity of the center of mass of the colliding bodies. Then to him *all* collisions are of the type in which the center of mass is at rest. In a later chapter, a method will be given for relating the total kinetic energy E^* of two colliding bodies as measured by an observer moving with the center-of-mass velocity, and the total kinetic energy E as measured by an observer at rest. This method yields $E = MV^2/2 + E^*$, where M is the total mass of the two bodies, and V is the center-of-mass velocity. Note that when two bodies have been in a perfectly inelastic collision, they each have the velocity of their center of mass. Then E^*, the kinetic energy measured by the moving observer, is zero, since according to our moving observer both bodies are at rest. (See Chapter 11.)

7–6 Nonmechanical forms of energy. In the preceding chapters, we have been concerned with the gross motion of bodies and it is therefore natural that we have concentrated our attention on the mechanical forms of energy, kinetic and potential. As we have emphasized before, kinetic and potential energies would be hardly more than mathematical conveniences in problem-solving were it not for the fact that whenever the total mechanical energy changes, a definite compensating energy change occurs somewhere in the surroundings.

A bullet is fired from a gun thereby suddenly acquiring kinetic energy. Here, chemical energy has been converted into kinetic energy. Similarly, when a person throws a ball, the chemical energy from the food he eats is ultimately the source of the ball's kinetic energy.

A block slides along a table and comes to rest. The kinetic energy of the gross motion of the block has disappeared, only to reappear as heat or the random kinetic energy of the molecules of the block, table, and air.

A steam locomotive starts from rest. Chemical energy, the burning coal, is converted into heat. The heat serves to boil water and create steam under pressure. There is energy associated with the high-pressure steam, and the steam does mechanical work on the piston. This work, in turn, is converted into the kinetic energy of the moving train.

An elevator starts from the ground floor and carries us upward. The elevator is run by an electric motor. The electric energy may have been acquired from the mechanical energy of water, a coal- or oil-burning steam engine, or even from a nuclear reactor. In the latter case, nuclear energy is the ultimate source of our increasing potential energy.

A rock falls from a cliff into a lake. Some of the energy of the rock serves to heat the water and the rock, but some is carried off in the wave motion of the water. A floating stick some distance away may acquire mechanical energy as the waves pass. There is energy in waves.

Energy in each of these forms—mechanical, chemical, nuclear, heat, sound waves, liquid waves, waves in solids, electromagnetic waves—is a subject for intensive study in itself. All these forms of energy are subject to one general law, the *conservation of energy*, or more formally, the *first law of thermodynamics* (see Chapter 17). Perpetual-motion machines, that is, machines that put out more energy of one kind, say mechanical, than they take in of another kind, say chemical or heat, would be contrary to the first law of thermodynamics. This does not, of course, prove that perpetual-motion machines are impossible, for energy conservation is an experimental law of nature. However, this conservation law has been subject to so many tests, in so many different fields, over so many years, that people nowadays are inclined to say that perpetual-motion machines are impossible in view of the first law of thermodynamics. This is equivalent to saying that perpetual-motion machines are impossible because no one has ever made one. (This is probably a safe attitude, but is nonetheless not a logical necessity.)

Heat and some of the wave forms of energy will be discussed in subsequent chapters. Here we shall discuss briefly the chemical, nuclear, and mass forms of energy.

Chemical energy. An exploding shell, a burning lump of coal, a boy running up a hill are all examples of the conversion of chemical energy into some other type of energy. A qualitative understanding of the basic features of chemical energy may be obtained if we consider the energy diagram of a molecule (see Fig. 7–15). In the figure, energy is shown as a function of the distance between, say, the carbon atom and the oxygen molecule which, when combined, form a molecule of carbon dioxide. When the carbon atom and oxygen molecule are very far apart there is no force between them, and their mutual potential energy is zero. Carbon and oxygen do not combine readily except at high temperatures where they have a relatively large kinetic energy. The reason for this is that in region I, the potential energy is positive; to the right of I the force between the atoms is repulsive. But if the kinetic energy is large enough, larger than the activation energy V_a, they can slide over the hump at I, and

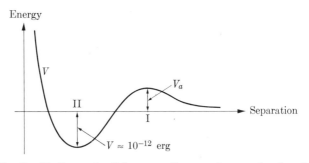

FIG. 7–15. Qualitative potential-energy diagram for a molecule which, when formed, releases energy.

enter the region II of small separation where the potential energy is negative. If the total energy were to remain constant, the kinetic energy would be very large in this region and there would be nothing to prevent the newly formed molecule from dissociating again. However, in the trip from region I to region II, energy can be lost to the surroundings. Light can be emitted, usually in the infrared region, and thus can lower the total mechanical energy. Or, more commonly, the oxygen molecule will dissociate, one atom staying with the carbon to form carbon monoxide and the other leaving with kinetic energy. In either case, the total energy of the new molecule will be less than zero because energy has been carried off to the surroundings. The emitted light waves or the ejected oxygen atom collide quickly with nearby matter, thereby increasing the temperature of the matter.

In plant life, the reverse process takes place. Plants take in carbon dioxide from the air, and by photosynthesis, this carbon dioxide is dissociated into carbon compounds and oxygen. This process requires energy, and this energy is provided in the form of sunlight.

The reaction $C + O_2 \rightarrow CO_2$ is exothermic, since energy (heat) is liberated. The reaction $2C + H_2 \rightarrow H_2C_2$, which forms acetylene, is endothermic. This means that acetylene, if it were to decompose into carbon and hydrogen, would release energy. The energy diagram of acetylene is indicated schematically in Fig. 7–16.

The energy released in chemical reactions is typically 10^{-12} erg per molecule.

Nuclear energy. Conceptually, nuclear energy is due to phenomena entirely similar to the phenomena which lead to chemical energy. When the nuclei of two light atoms, say two protons (hydrogen nuclei) or two α-particles (helium nuclei), are brought nearer and nearer to each other,

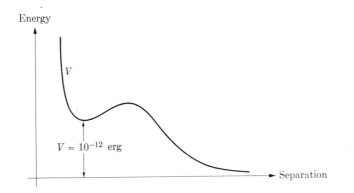

Fig. 7–16. Qualitative potential-energy diagram for a molecule which, upon dissociation, releases energy.

the potential-energy curve is qualitatively as shown in Fig. 7–17. Activation energies corresponding to temperatures of the order of a thousand degrees may be necessary to cause a chemical reaction, but the corresponding temperatures for nuclear fusion are of the order of millions of degrees. On the other hand, in a nuclear reaction about a million times more energy is released when the two nuclei arrive in region II. Fusion is the source of energy in our sun, in the stars, and in the H-bomb. The reaction is violently exothermic.

Nuclear fission, however, has its analogy in the acetylene-chemical case. Nuclei of certain atoms, say those of barium and krypton, have a mutual potential-energy curve as shown in Fig. 7–18. When the two nuclei are in the region II, they form a nucleus of uranium. An existent nucleus of uranium, if it can be made to divide into krypton and barium nuclei, releases the amount of energy labeled $V \approx 10^{-4}$ erg. Liquid acetylene will divide into its constituents, carbon and hydrogen, if given a sudden jolt or some other rather weak disturbance; uranium, because of the large hump which exists in its potential-energy curve, is quite stable but can be induced to divide when it absorbs a neutron. Neutrons are emitted by the dividing nucleus, and this is what makes possible self-sustaining or chain-reacting piles or bombs.

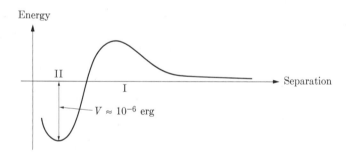

FIG. 7–17. Qualitative potential-energy curve for nuclear fusion.

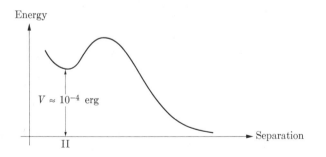

FIG. 7–18. Qualitative potential-energy curve for nuclear fission.

Mass–energy. We have mentioned previously that, according to Einstein's special theory of relativity, mass and energy are intimately related. That is, a mass that moves at a velocity v has an associated energy given by

$$U = \frac{m_0 c^2}{\sqrt{1 - (v^2/c^2)}}, \qquad (7\text{–}26)$$

where m_0 is the mass as measured when it is at rest or moving at velocities much less than c, the velocity of light. Newtonian mechanics, of course, provides a correct description of bodies that move at velocities much less than c, and if the above energy expression is correct, it must agree with the results of newtonian mechanics in this limiting case. When v is zero, we have $U = m_0 c^2$; however, when v is small, but finite, we have

$$U = m_0 c^2 \left(1 + \tfrac{1}{2} \frac{v^2}{c^2} + \cdots \right), \qquad (7\text{–}27)$$

where the radical has been expanded in a binomial series. (Note that for $v^2/c^2 = 0.02$ we have $1/\sqrt{1 - (v^2/c^2)} = 1/\sqrt{0.98} \simeq 1.01$, in agreement with the expansion we have used.) When (7–27) is multiplied out, we obtain

$$U = m_0 c^2 + \tfrac{1}{2} m_0 v^2 + \cdots = m_0 c^2 + E + \cdots,$$

where E is the kinetic energy. In other words, the special theory of relativity associates with a mass m_0 both a so-called rest energy $m_0 c^2$ and a kinetic energy. The rest energy associated with a 1-gm mass is evidently $m_0 c^2 = 1 \cdot (3 \cdot 10^{10})^2 = 9 \cdot 10^{20}$ ergs or $9 \cdot 10^{13}$ joules, a fantastic amount of energy when we recall that a 1-gm mass must travel 45 m/sec to have a kinetic energy of 1 joule.

Only in distinctly nuclear phenomena have mass changes associated with the release or absorption of energy ever been measured. For example, when a nucleus of deuterium, a heavy isotope of hydrogen, is formed from a free neutron and a free proton, the mass of the deuterium nucleus is nearly 0.1% smaller than the mass of the neutron and proton from which it is made. The extra mass is carried off in the form of electromagnetic energy, a γ-ray.

There are situations in which particles are totally annihilated. A positron, a particle like an electron but with a positive rather than a negative electric charge, can annihilate an electron. Both particles disappear, and two γ-rays—two oppositely moving electromagnetic waves—are left. These electromagnetic waves have energy, and associated with this energy is a mass that is equal to the combined electron-positron mass. Similarly, the recently discovered antiprotons and antineutrons can annihilate ordinary protons and neutrons. Conversely, high-energy particles (protons, neutrons, etc.) and high-energy γ-rays can, by means of a loss of their own kinetic energy, produce other particles that have mass.

Reversibility. Although we have stated that energy is conserved when it is transformed from one form to another, we do not wish to imply that such transformations can always be accomplished easily or completely. We find it quite simple to pull the trigger of a gun and so convert chemical to mechanical and heat energy. However, the reverse process, the collection of the gases, heat, and the moving bullet, and reformation of the original chemical state of the shell, would be practically impossible. Similarly, it is all too easy to convert mechanical energy into heat. We need only provide some friction forces. But the reverse process is much more difficult. We shall treat these questions more fully in Chapter 19 when we discuss the second law of thermodynamics.

PROBLEMS

7-1. A body of 0.5-kgm mass slides along a frictionless horizontal surface and collides with the end of a spring, the other end of which is held fixed. The body then reverses its motion. (a) If the initial velocity of the body was 2 m/sec and if the spring had a maximum compression of 10 cm, what was the spring constant K? (b) Draw an energy diagram and include the potential, kinetic, and total mechanical energies. (c) What impulse did the body receive as a result of the collision with the spring?

7-2. A body of mass m is held at a height y_0 above the surface of the earth and is then dropped. Draw an energy diagram assuming the potential energy to be zero at $y = 0$. Include in the diagram a representation for the possibility of m dropping into a hole in the ground.

7-3. Bodies below the surface of a liquid are subject to a buoyant force equal to the weight of the displaced liquid. Determine, as a function of the vertical position y, the potential energy of a cube of density ρ and include regions above and below a water surface. Consider the densities $\rho = 10$, 1, and 0.5 gm/cm³ for the cube. The density of water is 1 gm/cm³.

7-4. The force characteristics of a spring depend upon how the coils of the spring are wound. Imagine a spring for which $F_x = -Kx$ for displacements to the right of the relaxed position, and for which $F_x = -Cx^3$ for displacements to the left of the relaxed position. Find the potential energy as a function of the displacement x.

7-5. A particle of mass 4 gm enters a region in which its potential energy is as shown in Fig. 7-19. It enters from the right, and for very large values of x, where its potential energy is zero, it has a kinetic energy of 16 ergs. (a) What is the kinetic energy at points A, B, and C? (b) While it is at point A, the particle suddenly loses half its *total energy*. (The potential-energy graph is unaffected.) Describe qualitatively the subsequent motion, giving the range of values of x over which the particle can move.

7-6. On a frictionless horizontal table, a body moves back and forth colliding alternately with springs at either end of the table. The spring on the left has a force constant $K = 10$

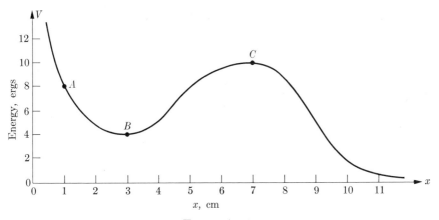

FIGURE 7–19

lb/ft and the spring on the right has a force constant $K = 20$ lb/ft. When the motion starts the body has a kinetic energy of 2 ft·lb and is in contact with the left spring, which is compressed 6 in. (a) What will be the maximum compressions of the two springs? (b) Draw an energy diagram.

7–7. Refer to Fig. 7–4 and the discussion of the energy of a simple pendulum. How does the tension in the string vary with the angle θ? Is there any angle θ for which the tension is zero?

7–8. Refer to Fig. 7–7. If the distance between the fixed ends of the two springs is 2.4 cm, what are the force constants, K_1 and K_2, of the two springs? Consider the motion of a body which moves along a line which passes through C and D. Sketch the potential-energy curve as a function of distance along this line, and show also the kinetic and total mechanical energies of a body which has 2 ergs of kinetic energy when it is at C.

7–9. When two parallel wires carry electric currents in the same direction, the wires are attracted to each other with a force which is inversely propor-

tional to the distance r between the wires: $F_1 = C/r$, where C is a constant. In Fig. 7–20 are shown two horizontal parallel wires A and B with currents in the same direction. Wire B is held fixed a distance $2L$ from a wall, and wire A is attached to two identical springs, each with a relaxed length L and spring constant $K/2$. The other ends of the springs are fastened to the wall. If the constant $C = 5KL^2/36$, determine (a) the force on the wire A as a function of the displacement x

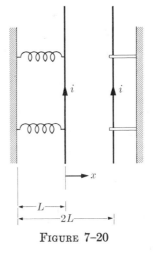

FIGURE 7–20

from the relaxed position of the spring and (b) the potential energy of the wire A as a function of x, setting $V = 0$ at the relaxed position of the springs. Draw an energy diagram. (c) Where is the equilibrium position of the wire? (d) Determine the total mechanical energy H below which the motion of wire A is oscillatory. Discuss qualitatively the motion for larger values of H. Indicate, in the diagram, the turning points of the motion, and the regions in which motion is possible for different values of H.

7-10. The earth's gravitational force on a 1-kgm mass is given by GM_e/r_e^2, where r_e is the distance to the earth's center. Similarly, the moon's gravitational force on a 1-kgm mass is given by GM_m/r_m^2, where r_m is the distance to the moon's center. (a) Where, on the earth-moon line, is the net gravitational force zero? (b) If the potential is, as usual, taken as zero at infinity, is the net potential energy zero anywhere else on the earth-moon line?

7-11. Refer to the previous problem. Suppose a 1-kgm mass is released between the earth and the moon from the point at which the net gravitational force is zero. The mass is given a very small initial velocity toward the earth. (a) What is the kinetic energy of the mass when it arrives at the earth's surface? (b) Suppose the mass is released from a point the same distance from the earth, but from the side of the earth away from the moon. What then will be the kinetic energy at the earth's surface?

7-12. What minimum velocity must a body have at the earth's surface in order to be able to reach the moon? By what fraction must this velocity be increased if the body is to be able to escape the earth's gravitational force field?

7-13. The moon travels around the earth in 27.3 days and is about 3.84 · 10^8 m from the earth's center. What is the moon's velocity? If the direction of the moon's velocity could be changed so that it would travel away from, rather than around, the earth, could it escape? If not, how far away could it go?

7-14. The force between two charged particles is $F = kq_1q_2/r^2$, where q_1 and q_2 are the charges on the two particles measured in coulombs, k is $9 \cdot 10^9$ n·m^2/coul^2, and r is the distance between the particles measured in meters. The elementary unit of charge is the charge on an electron, $1.6 \cdot 10^{-19}$ coul. What is the potential energy of an electron in a hydrogen atom, where the proton-electron distance is about $5 \cdot 10^{-11}$ m or 0.5 angstrom? (1A = 10^{-8} cm.) The proton has the same charge value as the electron, but the electron's charge is negative and the force is attractive.

7-15. A 2000-lb car starts from rest and rolls down a 30° decline. At the bottom of the decline, which is 400 ft long, the car's speed is 60 mi/hr. (a) What energy must have been expended by dissipative or nonconservative forces? (b) What weight (in lb) would have a potential energy at the top of the decline equal to the energy dissipated by the car?

7-16. A 16-lb block starting from rest is pushed up a 3-ft-long, 45° incline by the force of a man's hand. The coefficient of sliding friction between the block and the incline is 0.2. At the top of the incline, the block has a speed of 10 ft/sec. (a) How much work was done by the man's hand? (b) With what constant force did the man push? (c) What time elapsed before the block reached the top?

7-17. A 32-lb empty barrel falls from a height of 50 ft and reaches the ground in 2 sec. Assume that the air-drag force was constant. (a) What was the magnitude of the drag force? (b) How much mechanical energy was lost? (c) What was the velocity of the barrel just before it hit the ground?

7-18. A body of mass m, at rest on a vertical spring of spring constant K, compresses the spring a distance y_0 from its relaxed position. From what height must m be dropped for the spring to compress a distance $3y_0$ from its relaxed position?

7-19. A particle moves in the x-direction under the influence of a force such that the potential energy is $V(x) = 6x^2 - 3x^3$ joules (x in m). (a) What is the force on the particle? (b) What is the maximum value of the total mechanical energy at which oscillatory motion is possible? (c) Obtain an expression for the travel time between $x = 0$ and $x = x_1$.

7-20. A ballistic pendulum provides a simple method for the determination of bullet velocities. A block of wood thick enough to stop the bullet is suspended on a long light string. Before the bullet enters the wood, the block is at rest and it starts to swing only after the bullet has become embedded in it. Show how a bullet velocity can be obtained from observations of the maximum angle of swing of a ballistic pendulum. A typical bullet may have a mass of 10 gm and a speed of 300 m/sec.

7-21. A small car of mass m is free to move without friction on the outside of a vertical track of radius R. The car moves under the influence of the track (a no-work force), gravity, and a spring which has one end attached to a pivot a distance $R/2$ above the center of the track. The spring, of force constant K, has its relaxed length when the car is at the top of the circle. This is an example that is difficult to work out in detail, but many features of the motion can be obtained easily

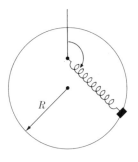

FIGURE 7-21

from energy considerations. (a) Find the potential energy of the car as a function of the angular position of the car with respect to the center of the circle, and draw a potential-energy diagram showing V versus θ. (b) What minimum kinetic energy must the car have at the top position in order to go all the way around the track? (c) If the car has the kinetic energy of part (b), what force does the track exert on the car at the top and at the bottom points of the track?

7-22. Prove relation (7-11).

7-23. Prove relation (7-12).

7-24. A body of mass m collides perfectly elastically with another body which is originally at rest. What should be the mass of the second body if it is to acquire half of the kinetic energy of the incident body? Assume a one-dimensional collision.

7-25. Body A of mass m_a has a velocity v_a and body B of mass m_b has a velocity v_b. All motion is confined to a straight line. Show that if $v'_b - v'_a = -(v_b - v_a)$, the total kinetic energy is unchanged as a result of the collision.

7-26. In the kinetic theory of gases, gas pressure results from the collision of gas molecules with the wall of a container. We shall be concerned with the collisions of gas molecules with a moving wall (a piston). Consider a perfectly elastic collision between a very light particle of mass m and velocity v, and a very heavy body of mass M and velocity V. Assume v and V to have the same directions initially. In the limit of $m/M = 0$, what is the velocity of the particle after the collision? What is the loss in kinetic energy of the small particle in the same limit? Show that this loss in kinetic energy is approximately proportional to the velocity of the large body when $v/V \gg 1$.

7–27. A particle A of mass m_a collides perfectly elastically with a particle B of mass m_b that is initially at rest. (a) Under what conditions can A transfer all its kinetic energy to B? (b) Under what conditions will A continue after the collision to travel in the same direction it had before? (c) Under what conditions will A travel after the collision in an opposite direction to that it had before? (d) Can B ever travel in the direction opposite to that A had initially?

7–28. In a one-dimensional perfectly inelastic collision, body A of mass m_a collides with body B of mass m_b which is initially at rest. What should be the ratio m_a/m_b for B to acquire the largest possible amount of kinetic energy? What should be the ratio m_a/m_b for A to lose the smallest possible amount of kinetic energy?

7–29. Two bodies, each of 1-gm mass, are involved in a perfectly inelastic collision, and after the collision the total kinetic energy is found to be 100 ergs. The bodies move along the same straight line. (a) What was the velocity V of the center of mass before the collision? (b) What was the total momentum before the collision? after the collision? (c) When the same two bodies with the same initial motion as

above collide *perfectly elastically*, the total kinetic energy after the collision is found to be 200 ergs. What were the velocities of the bodies before they collided?

7–30. A 1-gm mass and a 100-gm mass approach each other along the same line, each with a momentum of 1000 gm·cm/sec. (a) What is their relative velocity? (b) What is their total kinetic energy? (c) After the two masses collide, the 1-gm mass leaves the collision center with a velocity of 200 cm/sec and with a deflection of 30° from its original path. What is the velocity of the 100-gm mass? (d) After the collision, what is the total kinetic energy? Which mass lost the larger fraction of its initial kinetic energy?

7–31. A 10-gm body moves at 20 cm/sec and collides head-on with a 20-gm body that moves at 15 cm/sec. The velocity vector of the 10-gm body is deflected 60° as a result of the collision but this body maintains its initial speed. What was the total kinetic-energy change which resulted from the collision?

7–32. A puck of mass m collides elastically with a second puck also of mass m which is initially at rest. In the collision, kinetic energy is conserved. Prove that the angle between the trajectories of the two pucks after the collision is 90°.

7–33. In a one-dimensional perfectly elastic collision, body A of mass m_a collides with body B of mass m_b which is initially at rest. In Sec. 7–5, it was pointed out that unless $m_a = m_b$, only a fraction of the kinetic energy of A is transferred to B. Show that a larger kinetic energy can be transferred to B if another body C is inserted between A and B. Show also that the optimum mass for C is $m_c = \sqrt{m_a m_b}$.

CHAPTER 8

EXAMPLES OF FORCES AND MOTION — II

Summary. In this chapter, we start with a discussion of the conditions that lead to oscillatory motion, and a simple example of oscillation, the "particle in a box" or "square-well" oscillator, is analyzed. The linear (harmonic) oscillator is then considered in some detail. Quantitative discussion of other than linear oscillators is difficult, but qualitative features of the motion follow directly from the potential-energy diagram. As examples, the simple pendulum and molecular vibrations are discussed. The effect of damping on a "free" linear oscillator is treated, and the forced motion of the linear oscillator is analyzed. Finally, a brief survey of the mechanical frequency spectrum is given.

In Chapter 5, a few special examples of forces and motion were treated in some detail. Now, having enlarged upon the basic principles of motion in terms of the concepts of work-energy, potential energy, and the total mechanical energy and its conservation, we shall pause to study some specific problems in which these new concepts prove particularly convenient and valuable. The problems we have selected to analyze deal with oscillations, in particular with the so-called *linear* or *harmonic oscillator*, which plays an important role in all aspects of physics. Whether we deal with the vibrations of molecules or of bridges, familiarity with the properties of the linear oscillator is essential.

8–1 Oscillations. We shall consider a body in equilibrium and study what happens when the body is displaced from its equilibrium position and then released, or when it is given an initial velocity away from its equilibrium position. Several situations, in which a ball is at rest on different types of surfaces, are illustrated schematically in Fig. 8–1. In this figure, the surfaces also represent the potential-energy curves of the particle. In (a), the surface is simply a horizontal plane. When the ball is displaced from its initial position and released, it will again be in equilibrium, and if it is given an initial velocity, it will remain in motion with a constant speed. The position on the horizontal plane has no influence on the equilibrium. In Fig. 8–1(b), the ball is at rest on the top of a curved surface, and it is obvious that when the ball is displaced in any direction and then released, it will continue to move farther away from the equilibrium position. The body is then said to be in unstable equilibrium. A somewhat similar situation is illustrated in Fig. 8–1(c) as another example of unstable equilibrium.

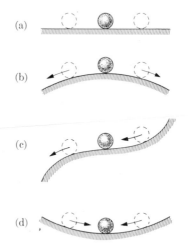

Fig. 8-1. Illustrations of equilibrium. In (d), oscillatory motion will result when the body is displaced from its (stable) equilibrium position.

Of more interest here is the case illustrated in Fig. 8-1(d), in which the ball is at rest on the bottom of a curved surface. The force on the ball tends to return it to its equilibrium position, regardless of the direction of the initial displacement of the velocity. Under these conditions, the equilibrium is said to be stable. When displaced from its equilibrium position and released, the ball will be accelerated toward the equilibrium position. By the time the ball arrives at this position, it has acquired momentum and so "overshoots." The force on the ball in the direction of motion reverses and the ball slows down, eventually changing its direction of motion. It returns to the equilibrium position, overshoots again, and proceeds to oscillate back and forth about the equilibrium position. Friction forces, of course, will ultimately bring the ball to rest. In other words, whenever a body is displaced from a stable equilibrium position and then released, it will perform an oscillatory motion. In nature, there are countless examples of this type of motion. Molecules, pendulums, violin strings, structures, etc., all have oscillatory motion similar to that of a mass attached to a spring, and in all these cases the bodies move under *conservative* forces (neglecting friction) that are always oppositely directed to the displacements. The potential energy, in all cases, has a minimum at the equilibrium position.

The spring-type force, $F = -Kx$, which we discussed in Chapter 3, has a minimum potential energy at $x = 0$. The magnitude of the force increases linearly with x, the displacement from the equilibrium position. An oscillator with a force of this type is called a *linear* or a *harmonic* oscillator, and the corresponding oscillation is called *harmonic motion*.

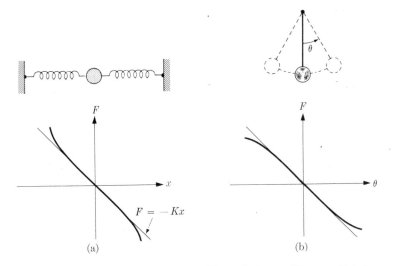

FIG. 8–2. The restoring force in an oscillator is linear ($F = -Kx$) for sufficiently small amplitudes of oscillation.

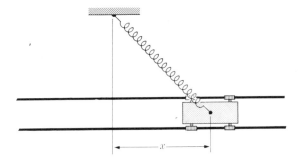

FIG. 8–3. Example of an oscillator which is nonlinear, even for small amplitudes of oscillation.

If the force depends on x in any other way, the oscillator is called *nonlinear*. We find that although many oscillators are nonlinear, most are linear or approximately so, at sufficiently small amplitudes of oscillations. For example, the force produced by an ordinary coil-spring is given by $F = -Kx$, for sufficiently small values of x, as mentioned in Chapter 3. As x is increased, the spring becomes "stiffer," and the force increases faster with x than in the linear region. In the case of a pendulum, on the other hand, the reverse situation holds true, as can be seen from Fig. 8–2, where the behavior of the forces in the mass-spring oscillator and in the pendulum are compared.

There are nonlinear oscillators even for small amplitudes, and a simple example is shown in Fig. 8–3. It is left as an exercise to show that the magnitude of the restoring force on the car along the track is not proportional to the displacement x from the equilibrium position, but to x^3 for small values of x (Problem 8–1).

8–2 The "particle in a box" or "square-well" oscillator.

As a very simple introductory example of an oscillation, we shall consider the motion of a body, for example, a car that moves back and forth along a level track between two fixed points, as shown in Fig. 8–4. These turning points, P_1 and P_2, can be rigid parallel walls between which the car oscillates after perfectly elastic collisions with the walls. The force is zero between the walls, but increases instantaneously to a very large (infinite) value at the walls. The corresponding potential-energy curve then forms a rectangular "well" with vertical sides, as shown in Fig. 8–4.

The two walls are located at $x = x_0$ and $x = -x_0$. If we measure the time from the instant when the car collides with the right-hand wall, we have $x = x_0$ and $v = 0$ when $t = 0$. As the car moves out from the wall, its velocity is $v = -v_0$, and the position coordinate decreases until the car collides with the other wall. The corresponding graphs, x vs. t and v vs. t, are shown in Fig. 8–5. This choice of the origin of the time coordinate, of course, is arbitrary. For example, if we prefer to start the clock when the car passes the midpoint between the walls, we have $x = 0$ when $t = 0$. Then if the car moves to the right, we have $v = v_0$ when $t = 0$. The corresponding graphs for x vs. t and v vs. t are then obtained from Fig. 8–5 by measuring t from the origin O_1.

The maximum excursion x_0 of the car from $x = 0$ is called the amplitude of oscillation. The car completes the round-trip $P_1 \rightarrow P_2 \rightarrow P_1$ in

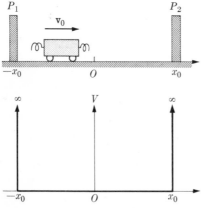

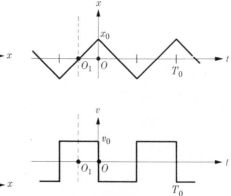

FIG. 8–4. An oscillator with a "square-well" potential-energy curve.

FIG. 8–5. The time dependence of the displacement and the velocity of the car in the "square-well" oscillation in Fig. 8–4.

the time $T_0 = 4x_0/v_0$, the *period* of oscillation. The number of complete oscillations per second is called the frequency of oscillation, $f_0 = 1/T_0$.

8-3 The linear oscillator. Let us consider again the car on the horizontal track, shown in Fig. 8-4. The car is now attached to one end of a spring, the other end of which is held fixed. Then, as the car is displaced a distance x from the relaxed position of the spring, the spring force on the car is given by

$$F = -Kx. \tag{8-1}$$

The corresponding potential energy is

$$V = \frac{Kx^2}{2},$$

as is shown in Fig. 8-6. When the car is released from a position $x = x_0$, it is set in oscillatory motion. If the clock is started at the moment the car is released, we have $x = x_0$ at $t = 0$. The speed of the car, of course, will not be constant as in the case of the "square-well" oscillator, but will increase gradually to a maximum value v_0 when it passes the equilibrium position $x = 0$. The fact that total mechanical energy is conserved, $mv^2/2 + Kx^2/2 = H$, requires that the corresponding maximum kinetic energy $mv_0^2/2$ of the car equal the maximum potential energy, $Kx_0^2/2$. The maximum speed of the car, i.e., the speed at $x = 0$, is then

$$v_0 = \sqrt{\frac{K}{m}}\, x_0. \tag{8-2}$$

After it has passed the equilibrium position $x = 0$, the car moves an

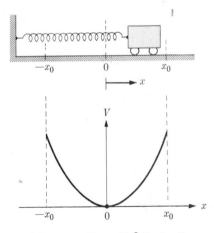

FIG. 8-6. Potential energy $V = Kx^2/2$ of a linear oscillator.

equal distance in the opposite direction, where it turns and moves to $x = x_0$ again, and so on. Since the speed of the car does not change abruptly, the graphs, which represent the position x and the velocity v as functions of time, are no longer successions of straight-line segments with sharp turns as in the "square-well" oscillator, but are now smooth curves, as indicated in Fig. 8–7. (For comparison, the broken lines in this figure indicate the motion of the corresponding "square-well" oscillator.) If we choose $t = 0$ when $x = x_0$, as mentioned earlier, we see that the curves in Fig. 8–7 for x vs. t and v vs. t are similar to a cosine function and a (negative) sine function, respectively. If time is measured from the instant when the car passes its equilibrium position with a velocity $v = +v_0$, the origin of the time coordinate in Fig. 8–7 is O_1, rather than O. The x vs. t curve is then similar to a sine curve, rather than a cosine curve.

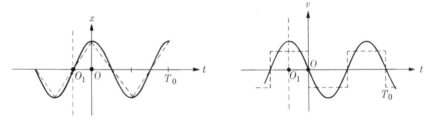

FIG. 8–7. The displacement and velocity as functions of time for the oscillator of Fig. 8–6. Time is measured from the instant when $x = x_0$. For comparison, the corresponding curves (broken lines) of the "square-well" oscillator of Fig. 8–4 are shown.

After these introductory observations, we shall now proceed to prove that the displacement and velocity of the car in this linear oscillator, indeed, do correspond to cosine and sine functions. First, we can prove this statement experimentally by comparing the displacement of the car with the x-coordinate of a body moving in a circle with a constant angular velocity. The body can be attached to a bar that is rotated by means of an electric motor. The x-coordinate is known in advance to be $x_0 \cos \omega t$, where ω is the angular velocity of the circular motion and x_0 is the radius of the circle (see Chapter 5). The comparison of this motion with the motion of the car can easily be made by shadow projection on a screen, so that the x-coordinate of the circular motion is shown beside the corresponding projection of the car. By adjusting the periods of the circular motion and the linear oscillator so that they are the same, we find that the motion of the car is identical with the circular motion of the shadow of the body. Of course, the amplitudes of the two motions are assumed to have been adjusted to the same value.

In the mathematical analysis of motion, we start from the expression (8-1) for the force on the car, and thus obtain for the acceleration

$$\frac{d^2x}{dt^2} = -\frac{K}{m}\,x, \tag{8-3}$$

where m is the mass of the car. The acceleration is proportional to the displacement but is oppositely directed. The mathematical problem is to obtain a solution, that is, a function $x(t)$, which both satisfies this equation and corresponds to the particular choice of the starting point for the time t in relation to the displacement x. It is not difficult to find a function that meets the requirement that the second derivative (acceleration) be proportional to the negative value of the function itself. The experiment described above strongly indicates that the oscillating car performs the same motion as the x-coordinate, $x = x_0 \cos \omega t$, of a body moving in a circle with radius x, if the angular velocity (that is, the speed of the motor in the experiment) is adjusted to the proper value. We now convince ourselves that $x = x_0 \cos \omega t$ does satisfy the equation of motion of the car, provided $\omega^2 = K/m$.

Thus, starting from the harmonic motion $x = x_0 \cos \omega t$, we obtain for the velocity $v = dx/dt = -\omega x_0 \sin \omega t$, and for the acceleration $dv/dt = d^2x/dt^2 = -\omega^2 x_0 \cos \omega t = -\omega^2 x$. As expected, the function $x = x_0 \cos \omega t$ satisfies the requirements of Eq. (8-3), in the sense that the value of the acceleration is proportional to the negative value of the displacement. In Eq. (8-3), the constant of proportionality is K/m, and in the harmonic motion it is ω^2. Therefore, the harmonic motion $x = x_0 \cos \omega t$ satisfies the equation of motion for the oscillator that has a spring constant K and a mass m, if the angular velocity is

$$\omega_0 = \sqrt{\frac{K}{m}}. \tag{8-4}$$

The argument $\omega_0 t$ that appears in $x = x_0 \cos \omega_0 t$ is the angular displacement in the circular motion, as indicated both in Chapter 5 and in Fig. 8-8. A complete oscillation corresponds to an angular displacement of 2π. The time T_0 required for this angular displacement is then

$$T_0 = \frac{2\pi}{\omega_0} = 2\pi \sqrt{\frac{m}{K}}. \tag{8-5}$$

This is the so-called *period* of the oscillator. The corresponding *frequency* of oscillation, that is, the number of periods in a second, is

$$f_0 = \frac{1}{T_0} = \frac{1}{2\pi} \sqrt{\frac{K}{m}}, \tag{8-6}$$

often called the *characteristic frequency* of the oscillator.

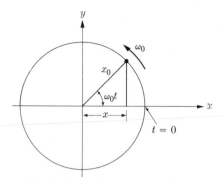

FIG. 8–8. The x-coordinate of a point moving with constant angular velocity ω_0 in a circle of radius x_0 has the harmonic motion $x = x_0 \cos \omega_0 t$. One complete oscillation corresponds to the angular displacement $\omega_0 T = 2\pi$.

It is important to note that the period of the linear oscillator is *independent of the amplitude* of oscillation x_0. It depends on *only* m and K, the characteristic constants of the oscillator. The explanation for this result is that the maximum speed v_0 is proportional to the amplitude x_0; that is, $v_0 = \omega_0 x_0$. The average speed $\bar{v}$ of the car in one period is proportional to v_0; in fact, $\bar{v} = (2/\pi)v_0$ (see Problem 8–13). The distance traveled by the car in one period is $4x_0$, and the period can then be expressed as $T = 4x_0/\bar{v}$. Since the average speed $\bar{v}$ is proportional to x_0, it follows that T must be independent of x_0.

If the spring is nonlinear, the amplitude independence of the period no longer applies. For example, the nonlinearity of the spring shown in Fig. 8–2(a) leads to a period which decreases with increasing amplitude, whereas the opposite holds true when the nonlinearity is similar to that of the pendulum of Fig. 8–2(b).

Energy considerations. The total mechanical energy of the oscillator, $H = E + V$, can be expressed as the maximum potential energy $V_m = Kx_0^2/2$, or as the maximum kinetic energy $E_m = mv_0^2/2 = m\omega_0^2 x_0^2/2$. It should be observed that the time averages $\bar{E}$ and $\bar{V}$ of the kinetic and potential energies are $\bar{E} = E_m/2$ and $\bar{V} = V_m/2$. Clearly, we have $\bar{E} = \bar{V} = H/2$.

EXAMPLE. Consider the mass-spring oscillator of Fig. 8–6. The weight of the car is 8 lb. If the car is hung vertically at the end of a spring, the equilibrium length of the spring is $d = \frac{1}{4}$ ft longer than its relaxed length. What will be the period of oscillation of the car when it is moving on the track, as shown in Fig. 8–6?

The spring constant K can be determined from the observed value of d; that is, $Kd = mg$ or $K = mg/d$. The period of oscillation is then $T_0 = 2\pi\sqrt{m/K} = 2\pi\sqrt{md/mg} = 2\pi\sqrt{d/g} = 2\pi\sqrt{\frac{1}{4} \cdot 32} \simeq 0.55$ sec.

With a maximum displacement of $x_0 = 0.5$ ft in this oscillation, what is the total energy of the oscillation? What are the maximum speed and the average speed of the car? The total energy can be expressed either as the maximum potential energy or as the maximum kinetic energy, $H = Kx_0^2/2 = mv_0^2/2$. With $K = mg/d = 32$ lb·ft, we obtain $H = 32 \cdot 0.5^2/2 = 4$ ft·lb. The maximum speed is $v_0 = \sqrt{K/m}\, x_0$, which, with $m = 8/32$ slug, becomes $v_0 = \sqrt{32 \cdot 32/8}\ 0.5 \simeq 5.6$ ft/sec. The corresponding average speed is $\bar{v} = (2/\pi)v_0 = 4x_0/T_0 \simeq 3.6$ ft/sec.

Phase. So far, in the discussion of the linear oscillator, we have used the instant when $x = x_0$ as the starting point for the time. Suppose now that $t = 0$ is chosen at another instant, for example, at the time when $x = x_0 \cos \phi$. The displacement at a later time t is then given by

$$x = x_0 \cos (\omega_0 t + \phi) = x_0 \cos \left(\frac{2\pi t}{T_0} + \phi \right), \qquad (8\text{–}7)$$

as indicated in Fig. 8–9. The angle ϕ is called the *phase*, or the *phase angle*, of the oscillator. For example, if $\phi = \pi/2$ we have

$$x = x_0 \cos \left(\omega_0 t + \frac{\pi}{2} \right) = -x_0 \sin \omega_0 t,$$

or if $\phi = -\pi/2$ we have

$$x = x_0 \cos \left(\omega_0 t - \frac{\pi}{2} \right) = x_0 \sin \omega_0 t.$$

EXAMPLE 1. The harmonic motion of a body with a period $T_0 = 2$ sec is described by $x = x_0 \cos \omega_0 t = x_0 \cos (2\pi t/T_0)$. As the body reaches $x = -x_0$, it is caught and held there for a time $\tau = 0.5$ sec, and then it is released. If the time is measured from the same starting point as before, what then is the expression for the ensuing harmonic motion?

The body reaches $x = -x_0$ at time $t_1 = T_0/2$, and at that time we have $\omega_0 t_1 = \omega_0 T_0/2 = \pi$. As the body is released at time $T_0/2 + \tau$, the argument of the cosine function must still be π. Therefore, if we assume that the phase

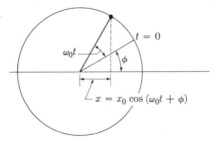

FIG. 8–9. When t is measured from the instant when $x = x_0 \cos \phi$, the displacement at a later time t is $x = x_0 \cos (\omega t + \phi)$. The angle ϕ is the phase or the phase angle of the oscillator.

angle in the new motion is ϕ, we obtain $\omega_0(T_0/2 + \tau) + \phi = \pi$ or $\phi = -\pi/2$. Therefore, the ensuing motion is given by

$$x = x_0 \cos \left(\omega_0 t - \frac{\pi}{2} \right) = x_0 \sin \omega_0 t.$$

EXAMPLE 2. The motion of a body at the end of a spring has a displacement $x = x_0 \cos \omega_0 t$. When the body is at $x = -x_0$, that is, when $t = T/2$, the body receives an impulse J in the positive x-direction. Determine the amplitude and the phase of the oscillation after the impulse. The time is measured from the same starting point as before.

At the point $x = -x_0$ the velocity of the oscillator before the impulse is zero, and after the impulse it is $v' = J/m$, where m is the mass of the body. The total mechanical energy of the oscillator after the impulse is then $H' = Kx_0^2/2 + mv'^2/2 = Kx_0^2/2 + J^2/2m$. The new amplitude of oscillation, x_0', is then given by $H' = Kx_0'^2/2$; that is, $x_0' = \sqrt{x_0^2 + (J^2/Km)}$. The phase ϕ of the new oscillation must be such that the displacement at $t = T/2$ is still $-x_0$, or such that the velocity at $T/2$ is J/m. Thus, we have $-x_0 = x_0' \cos (\omega_0 T/2 + \phi) = -x_0' \cos \phi$, or $\cos \phi = x_0/x_0'$.

8–4 Small oscillations of a simple pendulum. As another example of a linear oscillator, we shall study small oscillations of a pendulum. The pendulum, shown in Fig. 8–10, is assumed to have its entire mass m concentrated in one point at a distance l from the fixed point of suspension. This concentration of mass, of course, is an idealization, and a pendulum of this type is often called a mathematical, or simple, pendulum to distinguish it from a physical pendulum which has a distributed mass. The mathematical pendulum can be approximated by a small heavy ball fastened to the end of a light string.

The pendulum is set in oscillation in a vertical plane, and the deflection of the pendulum is measured by the angle θ from the equilibrium position, as shown in the figure. As usual, θ is chosen positive in the counterclockwise direction. Instead of θ we can use the distance of displacement s

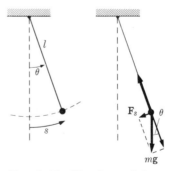

FIG. 8–10. Simple pendulum.

along the circular path of the bob of the pendulum. We have

$$s = l\theta. \tag{8-8}$$

If the mass of the bob is m, the equation of motion is

$$m\frac{d^2s}{dt^2} = F_s, \tag{8-9}$$

where F_s is the component of all forces acting on the bob of the pendulum in the direction of s. There are two forces on the bob, the tension in the string and the weight $w = mg$. Only the latter has a component in the s-direction, $F_s = -w\sin\theta$, as indicated in Fig. 8–10. For sufficiently small angles, say $\theta < \pi/6$, the approximation $\sin\theta \simeq \theta = s/l$ is good, and the force component in the s-direction can be written as $F_s = -(w/l)s$. The equation of motion, (8–9), then reduces to

$$\frac{d^2s}{dt^2} = -\frac{w/l}{m}s. \tag{8-10}$$

This equation is completely analogous to the equation $d^2x/dt^2 = -(K/m)x$, which was obtained for the mass-spring oscillator, and by comparison we see that, in the pendulum, the quantity w/l corresponds to the spring constant K. In the mass-spring oscillator, the spring constant is independent of the mass, and the characteristic frequency $f_0 = (1/2\pi)\sqrt{K/m}$ then decreases with the square root of the mass. In the pendulum, on the other hand, the restoring force is caused by gravity, and the corresponding spring constant is proportional to the mass of the bob, $w/l = mg/l$. As a result, the characteristic frequency and the period of the pendulum are *independent of the mass:*

$$\omega_0 = 2\pi f_0 = \sqrt{\frac{g}{l}}, \qquad T_0 = \frac{1}{f_0} = 2\pi\sqrt{\frac{l}{g}}. \tag{8-11}$$

Since g varies with position, so also does the period of a pendulum; when the pendulum is on the moon, the period will be longer than if the pendulum were on the earth. The period of a mass-spring oscillator, on the other hand, is independent of position. That the period of a pendulum is independent of the mass follows from the fact that the weight w and hence the gravitational mass are proportional to inertial mass (see Chapter 2).

EXAMPLE. What should be the length of a simple pendulum that has a period of 1 sec? What is the total mechanical energy of the pendulum, if the maximum angle of excursion is $\theta_m = \pi/8$? With $g = 981$ cm/sec^2 and $T_0 = 1$ we obtain $l = 981/(2\pi)^2 \simeq 25$ cm. The total mechanical energy of the pendulum equals the maximum potential energy, which can be expressed as $V_m = K's^2/2$, where K' is the equivalent spring constant $K' = w/l = mg/l$. With $s = l\theta$ the maximum potential energy then becomes $V_m = mgl(\theta^2/2)$. With $m = 1$ gm, we get $V_m \simeq 1900$ ergs. For an arbitrary angle of excursion, the maximum potential energy is determined from $mgl(1 - \cos\theta)$, as was shown in Chapter 7. For small angles of θ, we have $\cos\theta \simeq 1 - (\theta^2/2)$, and the general expression reduces to the result obtained above.

8–5 The two-body oscillator. Reduced mass.

In the study of, for example, the vibrations of a diatomic molecule, we deal with the oscillations of two interacting bodies, as illustrated in Fig. 8–11. Here, two bodies of masses m_1 and m_2 are connected with a spring of force constant K. If the spring is compressed, and then released, the bodies will oscillate to and fro with the same frequencies. Sometimes the center of mass is at rest but, in general, there is a translational motion superimposed on the oscillations. In any event, the oscillatory motion is the motion of the bodies with respect to the center of mass. We wish to determine the characteristic frequency of the oscillation and the ratio between the oscillation amplitudes and energies of the two bodies.

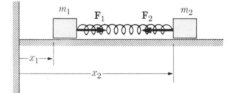

FIG. 8–11. Two-body oscillator.

If the position coordinates of the two bodies are x_1 and x_2 with respect to a fixed coordinate system as shown in Fig. 8–11, the length of the spring is $x_2 - x_1$, and if the relaxed length is d, the extension of the spring is $x = x_2 - x_1 - d$. The force on m_2 is then $F_2 = -Kx$ and the force on m_1 is $F_1 = Kx$. Thus the equations of motion for the two bodies become

$$m_2 \frac{d^2x_2}{dt^2} = -Kx \qquad (8\text{–}12)$$

and

$$m_1 \frac{d^2x_1}{dt^2} = Kx. \qquad (8\text{–}13)$$

If we multiply Eq. (8–12) by m_1, and Eq. (8–13) by m_2, and then subtract the equations, we obtain

$$\frac{m_1 m_2}{m_1 + m_2} \frac{d^2x}{dt^2} = -Kx, \qquad (8\text{–}14)$$

where $x = x_2 - x_1 - d$. In other words, the extension x of the spring satisfies an equation which is the same as that for a single-mass oscillator where one end of the spring is held fixed and the other carries the mass μ:

$$\mu = \frac{m_1 m_2}{m_1 + m_2}. \tag{8–15}$$

The quantity μ is called the *reduced mass* of the oscillator.

The characteristic angular frequency of the oscillation, which is the same for both m_1 and m_2, is then

$$\omega_0 = \sqrt{\frac{K}{\mu}}. \tag{8–16}$$

The energy of the oscillation can be expressed either as the maximum potential energy $V_m = Kx_m^2/2$, where x_m is the maximum extension of the spring, or as the sum of the maximum kinetic energies of the two bodies at the moment when the spring is relaxed. These kinetic energies can be expressed as $E_1 = p_1^2/2m_1$ and $E_2 = p_2^2/2m_2$, where p_1 and p_2 are the momenta of the bodies *as measured with respect to the center of mass*. Thus we have $p_1 = p_2 = p$, and the total mechanical energy of oscillation is

$$H = \frac{1}{2}Kx_m^2 = \frac{1}{2}p_m^2\left(\frac{1}{m_1} + \frac{1}{m_2}\right) = \frac{1}{2}\cdot\frac{p_m^2}{\mu}.$$

Clearly, the ratio between the energies of oscillation of the two bodies is

$$\frac{E_1}{E_2} = \frac{m_2}{m_1}.$$

If the magnitudes of the displacement amplitudes of the two bodies are X_1 and X_2, we have $X_1/X_2 = m_2/m_1$ and $x_m = X_1 + X_2$. From these relations, we can determine X_1 and X_2, in terms of x_m.

If the center of mass is not at rest, but has a velocity V, the total energy of the system (mass $M = m_1 + m_2$) is the sum of the center-of-mass energy $MV^2/2$ and the oscillatory energy, as will be discussed in more detail in Chapter 11. Thus, by subtracting the center-of-mass energy $MV^2/2$ from the total energy (which often is known), we obtain the mechanical energy of oscillation, from which the properties of the oscillatory motion can be found as shown above.

EXAMPLE. Two bodies of masses m_1 and m_2 are free to move along a horizontal straight track. They are connected by a spring with spring constant K. The system is initially at rest. An instantaneous impulse J is given to m_1 along the direction of the track. Determine the motion of the system after the impulse. In particular, determine the energy of oscillation of the bodies.

After the impulse, the center of mass of the system moves with a velocity $V = J/M$, where $M = m_1 + m_2$, and the corresponding energy of translation is $E_t = MV^2/2 = J^2/2M$. If we consider the motion of m_1 alone, we note that the momentum acquired by m_1 immediately after the impulse is $p_1 = J$, and the corresponding kinetic energy of m_1 is $p_1^2/2m_1 = J^2/2m_1$. Since the spring is relaxed at that moment, this quantity is the total energy of the system. If we then subtract the energy of the center of mass from this quantity, we obtain the energy of oscillation:

$$H_0 = \frac{J^2}{2}\left(\frac{1}{m_1} - \frac{1}{M}\right) = \left(\frac{J^2}{2m_1}\right)\frac{m_2}{m_1 + m_2}.$$

In other words, the fraction $m_2/(m_1 + m_2)$ of the total energy delivered to the system goes into the oscillatory motion. The maximum compression of the spring can then be determined from $Kx_m^2/2 = H_0$.

8–6 Molecular vibrations. In the linear oscillator, the relation between the force and the displacement is particularly simple and, as we have seen, the details of motion then can be described quantitatively by simple mathematical formulas. As indicated earlier, the linear-oscillator approximation ordinarily applies only when the amplitude of oscillation is sufficiently small. At larger amplitudes a quantitative description is, in general, considerably more complicated.

However, even if the detailed quantitative description is complicated, the basic qualitative features of the motion can readily be understood from the potential-energy curve of the oscillator. As an illustration, let us consider a potential-energy curve of the type shown in Fig. 8–12. A potential-energy curve like this is typical for many examples of motion. For example, it is known to apply to an atom that interacts with another atom. The coordinate x then represents the separation of the atoms. When the atoms or molecules are far apart, the force between them is, of course, nearly zero. As the atoms come closer to each other, the initial force may be repulsive, and the potential energy increases. For small distances, less than x_b in Fig. 8–12, the potential energy decreases and the force becomes attractive. However, the force does not indefinitely remain attractive (negative) as the separation decreases. (If this were so, all matter would "collapse.") Rather, the force becomes repulsive again, and the potential-energy curve has a minimum that corresponds to a stable equilibrium separation of the atoms.

For convenience in the present discussion, we shall measure the potential energy V from the minimum point, where we shall set $V = 0$. Although we have a stable equilibrium point at x_0, the atoms or molecules are never at rest relative to each other but always have some energy, as we shall discuss further in Chapter 16. The character of the relative motion between the atoms depends strongly upon the magnitude of this energy. For example, it can be seen from Fig. 8–12 that for an energy H_1, motion is possible only in the valley of the potential-energy curve between

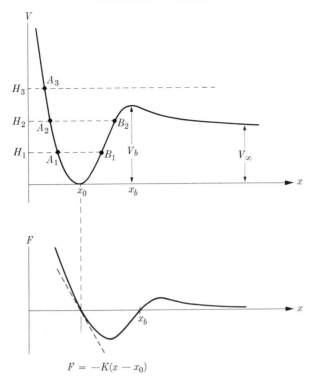

$$F = -K(x - x_0)$$

FIG. 8–12. Energy diagram for the interaction between two atoms.

the points A_1 and B_1. The atoms then have oscillatory motion, in which the energy is continuously transformed from a kinetic to a potential form, just as in the case of a linear oscillator. The atoms are then "bound" together at an average separation that is approximately equal to x_0. If H_1 is sufficiently small, the force F vs. x is nearly a straight line, $F = -K(x - x_0)$, as shown in the figure, and the corresponding potential energy is then $K(x - x_0)^2/2$. (What would happen if the potential energy were proportional to x^4 for small values of x? See Problem 8–11.) Incidentally, on the atomic or molecular scale, the linear relation between F and x, for small x, is responsible for the similar relation between forces and deformations of matter in bulk, for example, as in the case of a coil-spring.

As energy is increased, say to the value H_2 in Fig. 8–12, the oscillation has a sufficiently large amplitude so that it exceeds the linear range of the force. As indicated in the figure, the restoring force then increases more slowly with the displacement, for $x > x_0$, than for $x < x_0$. Consequently, the atom "reaches out" farther on the outside than on the inside, and the average separation of the atoms becomes somewhat larger than the equilibrium separation. Qualitatively, this asymmetry of the restoring force and the potential-energy curve is responsible for the thermal expansion of a solid, as will be discussed further in Chapter 17.

If the energy of oscillation is further increased, say to the value H_3 in Fig. 8–12, such that it exceeds the value V_b at the barrier at x_b, the motion will no longer be oscillatory; the atoms will no longer be bound together. One of the atoms escapes over the barrier and is soon outside the force range of its neighbor. Eventually if it collides head-on with a new atom, it will pass the potential barrier, enter into the potential valley, and move up to the point of closest separation (A_3 in the figure). Since we have assumed a perfectly elastic collision, the atom will turn and move away with the same speed it had before the collision. If, on the other hand, the collision is not perfectly elastic, the mechanical energy of the atom will decrease, and if the energy goes from H_3 to H_2, the atoms will combine and form a molecule as a result of the collision.

This separation of atoms, which occurs when the energy of oscillation exceeds a certain critical value, is the essence of the "molecular" explanation of such phenomena as the dissociation and recombination of a diatomic or polyatomic gas at high temperature, the melting of a solid, or the boiling of a liquid, as we shall discuss in a later chapter.

8–7 The effect of damping on free oscillations. So far we have neglected the influence of friction in the discussion of oscillations. The friction force is always in the opposite direction to the displacement and, obviously, produces a gradual reduction of the amplitude of oscillation. In order to study quantitatively this decaying motion, we must set up the equation of motion that includes friction force, and then seek the appropriate solution to this equation.

Friction forces in mechanical systems are usually complicated and difficult to describe quantitatively in an accurate way. The friction force between two smooth surfaces is approximately constant for small velocities, but is subject to wide variations when humidity, detailed surface conditions, etc., are taken into account. The drag force on a small sphere moving slowly through a fluid is proportional to the velocity (Stokes' law), and the drag force on an object moving through a very rare gas is proportional to the square of the velocity. The drag force, under other conditions, depends critically upon the shape of the body, and the velocity dependence is so complex that a numerical analysis must be performed to determine the influence of the drag force on the motion. Only for special types of simple friction forces can the motion be described in terms of simple mathematics. An example of this kind is a force which is proportional to the velocity, as in Stokes' law, and we shall consider this case here.

Since friction force is always oppositely directed to the velocity, we can express the friction force as $F_f = -R(dx/dt)$, where R is a constant. If we consider the motion of a body that is acted on both by a spring force and by a friction force of this type, the equation of motion for this body is given by

$$m \frac{d^2x}{dt^2} = -Kx - R \frac{dx}{dt}. \qquad (8\text{–}17)$$

Suppose we are interested in the motion which results when we release the body from rest, at the position $x = x_0$, at time $t = 0$. The solution to Eq. (8–17) which corresponds to this initial condition is

$$x = x_0 e^{-t/\tau} \left(\cos \omega t + \frac{1}{\omega \tau} \sin \omega t \right), \qquad (8\text{–}18)$$

in which

$$\tau = \frac{2m}{R}$$

and

$$\omega = \omega_0 \sqrt{1 - (1/\omega_0 \tau)^2} = \omega_0 \sqrt{1 - (T_0/2\pi\tau)^2},$$

and the period is

$$T = \frac{2\pi}{\omega} = \frac{T_0}{\sqrt{1 - (1/\omega_0 \tau)^2}}.$$

It is recommended that the reader convince himself that Eq. (8–18) satisfies Eq. (8–17), and that $x = x_0$ and $v = 0$ when $t = 0$ (Problem 8–28). Note that the frequency of oscillation is decreased and the period of oscillation is prolonged somewhat by the presence of friction. However, this effect usually is very small. In most oscillators, the time τ is considerably larger than one period, and so the correction term $(T_0/2\pi\tau)^2$ in the square root is much less than $(1/2\pi)^2 \simeq 0.025$, which means that the frequency and the period are changed by less than 1%. Therefore, in most practical applications, the period T_0 can be used.

The quantity $\tau = 2m/R$ is a characteristic time which is a measure of how long the oscillations will last. In this sense, it can be regarded as a measure of the *lifetime* of the oscillator. After the oscillator has been in motion during time τ, the amplitude has been reduced by a factor of $e^{-1} \simeq 1/2.718$, or, in other words, approximately equal to $\frac{1}{3}$ of its initial value. The lifetime τ is a certain fraction of the period $T_0 = 2\pi/\omega_0$ of the undamped oscillator, and this fraction is $\tau/T_0 = \omega_0 \tau/2\pi = Q/\pi$, where we have introduced the symbol $Q = \omega_0 m/R$. The angular displacement corresponding to the lifetime is then $\omega_0 \tau = 2Q$.

In addition to the variation of the amplitude of the oscillator with time, which was expected, we have noted that the period of oscillation has

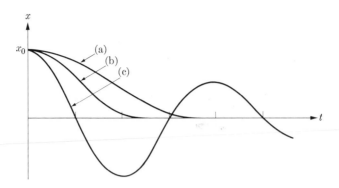

FIG. 8–13. Typical curves of x versus t for an oscillator with (a) $Q < \frac{1}{2}$, (b) $Q = \frac{1}{2}$, and (c) $Q > \frac{1}{2}$.

also been influenced by the friction force. This latter result is reasonable if we consider the extreme case in which the friction force is so large that the oscillator practically "sticks" to the surface. In such a case, the period, if any, must obviously be much larger than the period T_0 of the undamped oscillator. The mathematical analysis in Eq. (8–18) reveals that the period indeed becomes infinitely long when $\omega_0\tau = 1$, i.e., when $Q = \frac{1}{2}$ or $R = 2\omega_0 m$. Under these conditions, the oscillator is said to be *critically damped*. The body will then approach the equilibrium position $x = 0$ without any oscillation or "overshoot." If Q is larger than $\frac{1}{2}$, the motion will be oscillatory, and if it is less than $\frac{1}{2}$, it is nonoscillatory (overdamped). The time dependence of overdamped, critically damped, and underdamped (oscillatory) motion is shown in Fig. 8–13.

The quantity $Q = \omega_0 m/R = \pi\tau/T_0 = \omega_0\tau/2$, sometimes called the *quality*, can be interpreted physically in several ways. If the damping is small, it can be shown (Problem 8–31) that $2\pi/Q$ is the fractional change of the total mechanical energy lost in one period of the motion. We may also express Q in terms of the magnitude of the friction impulse in relation to the maximum momentum. The impulse by the friction force, as the body moves from $x = 0$ to $x = x_0$, is $\int F_f \, dt = R\int v \, dt = Rx_0$, and the momentum of the body as it passes the equilibrium position is mv_0. The ratio between the maximum momentum and the friction impulse is then $mv_0/Rx_0 \simeq m\omega_0/R = Q$, if we use the approximate relation $v_0 \simeq \omega_0 x_0$. Finally, if Q is expressed as $Q = \omega_0\tau/2 \simeq \pi(\tau/T_0)$, we see that for sufficiently large values, Q can be interpreted as π times the number of complete oscillations in the lifetime τ, since then, as we have seen, the period of the oscillator is very nearly T_0.

8–8 Forced motion of a linear oscillator. The oscillations that we have studied so far are characteristic of free oscillators. A free oscillator is one which, with the possible exception of external friction effects, does

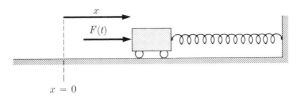

FIG. 8–14. Forced motion of a linear oscillator.

not interact with other bodies. It performs its own motion as determined by the inertia and the restoring force in the system. Although these oscillations are very important in themselves, we shall find many problems in physics which involve oscillators that are acted on by external forces.

For the purpose of illustration, we again shall use the linear oscillator that consists of a car, at the end of a spring, moving on a horizontal track, as shown in Fig. 8–14. The car is assumed to be acted on by an external force $F(t)$ which varies harmonically with time. In addition, the car is acted on both by the spring force and a friction force from the track. The characteristic frequency of oscillation of the oscillator, if we neglect the effect of friction, is denoted by f_0 and we have $2\pi f_0 = \sqrt{K/m}$. We shall consider $F(t)$ to be harmonic, with a frequency f which is usually different from the characteristic frequency f_0. As a result, the car will be forced into oscillatory motion with the *same* frequency f as the driving force. Initially, in addition, there will be a "transient" characteristic oscillation of the oscillator, but this eventually disappears because of the friction force, and the system settles down in a steady-state oscillation of frequency $f = \omega/2\pi$.

We shall describe the displacement of the car in the steady-state motion by $x = x_0 \cos \omega t$, where the amplitude x_0 is yet to be determined in terms of the driving force and the properties of the oscillator. What driving force is required to produce the displacement $x = x_0 \cos \omega t$? To answer this question, we shall consider the various forces acting on the car. If, as before, we use a friction force F_f which is proportional to the velocity, i.e., $F_f = -R(dx/dt)$, the equation of motion is

$$m \frac{d^2x}{dt^2} = F(t) - Kx - R \frac{dx}{dt},$$

and the driving force required to produce the displacement x is then

$$F(t) = Kx + m \frac{d^2x}{dt^2} + R \frac{dx}{dt}. \qquad (8\text{–}19)$$

Now, if we insert the expression $x = x_0 \cos \omega t$ into this equation, we find the following expression for the force required to produce the motion:

$$F(t) = Kx_0 \cos \omega t - m\omega^2 x_0 \cos \omega t - R\omega x_0 \sin \omega t$$

$$= Kx_0 \left(1 - \frac{\omega^2}{\omega_0^2}\right) \cos \omega t - R\omega x_0 \sin \omega t. \qquad (8\text{–}20)$$

In the first part of Eq. (8–20) the three terms represent the forces required to overcome the spring stiffness, the inertia of the car, and the friction, respectively. In the second part of the equation we have taken together the two $\cos \omega t$ terms and introduced the expression for the characteristic frequency of the undamped oscillator, $K/m = \omega_0^2 = (2\pi f_0)^2$.

In contrast to the characteristic frequency f_0 of the given oscillator, the driving frequency f does not depend on the properties of the oscillator, but is determined by the driving mechanism alone. One of the essential problems in the study of forced motion is to determine the response of the oscillator to different driving frequencies. We shall find that one can distinguish between three basically different types of oscillator responses that correspond to the three frequency regions $\omega < \omega_0$, $\omega \simeq \omega_0$, and $\omega > \omega_0$.

Let us start with the first region, where the driving frequency is less than the characteristic frequency of the oscillator. In this region we have $\omega/\omega_0 < 1$, and as ω approaches zero, the relation between the driving force and the oscillator displacement is simply $F \simeq Kx_0 \cos \omega t = Kx$. This driving force is only that required to compress the spring; the effect of the inertia in the oscillator is negligible. In this region $\omega \ll \omega_0$, the oscillator is said to be *stiffness-controlled*. Note that as ω approaches zero, the displacement and the force are in phase with each other; they can both be described by a $\cos \omega t$ function. Furthermore, when ω is sufficiently small, the ratio between the magnitude of the driving force and the displacement is independent of frequency.

In the high-frequency region $\omega \gg \omega_0$, on the other hand, inertia plays the dominant role. We have $\omega/\omega_0 \gg 1$, and as the frequency approaches infinity, the important force contribution in Eq. (8–20) comes from the inertia term $F \simeq -(\omega/\omega_0)^2 Kx_0 \cos \omega t = -\omega^2 m x_0 \cos \omega t$. The driving force is no longer in phase with the displacement but has a phase angle of π, since $-\cos \omega t = \cos (\omega t + \pi)$. It should be observed that the relation between the force amplitude $F_0 = \omega^2 m x_0$ and the displacement amplitude is now frequency-dependent. In order to maintain a constant displacement, as the frequency increases, the force amplitude must also increase as ω^2. Conversely, if the force amplitude is kept constant, the displacement decreases as $1/\omega^2$. In this high-frequency region $\omega \gg \omega_0$, the oscillator is said to be *mass-controlled*.

Finally, in the frequency region $\omega \simeq \omega_0$, where the driving frequency is about equal to the characteristic frequency, we have $\omega/\omega_0 \simeq 1$, and the factor $1 - \omega^2/\omega_0^2$ is close to zero. In fact, in the absence of friction and if $\omega = \omega_0$, no force is required to maintain the oscillation $x = x_0 \cos \omega_0 t$. This result is expected, of course, since this motion is identical with that of the free oscillator; the force contributions by inertia and stiffness then cancel each other. Conversely, if the driving force were different from zero when $\omega = \omega_0$, the amplitude of oscillation would be infinite, were it not for the limiting influence of friction and nonlinear effects. We say that the driving frequency is *in resonance* with the characteristic frequency, or more simply, that the oscillator is driven at resonance. The amplitude-controlling factor is now friction, and the relation between the driving force and the displacement is $F = -R\omega_0 x_0 \sin \omega_0 t$. It is interesting to express this result in terms of the Q-value of the oscillator. We recall that $Q = \omega_0 m/R = K/R\omega_0$, and by use of this relation, we find that $F = -(Kx_0/Q) \sin \omega_0 t$. In other words, the force amplitude required to produce a displacement amplitude x_0 at resonance is Q times smaller than the *static value* Kx_0. Conversely, if the force amplitude is kept constant, the displacement amplitude at resonance is Q times larger than the static value x_0.

In order to obtain a relation between the force and the displacement that is valid in the entire frequency region, we return to the original equation (8–20). If we start with the idealized case of zero friction, this relation is simply $F = Kx_0(1 - \omega^2/\omega_0^2) \cos \omega t = F_0 \cos \omega t$. The corresponding relation between the force amplitude F_0 and the displacement amplitude is then

$$F_0 = Kx_0 \left(1 - \frac{\omega^2}{\omega_0^2}\right) \quad \text{or} \quad x_0 = \frac{F_0/K}{1 - (\omega/\omega_0)^2}. \qquad (8\text{–}21)$$

In our approach to the analysis of forced motion, we started with the problem of finding the driving force required to produce a certain oscillatory displacement. Once the answer to this problem is obtained, clearly, we can turn it around and consider the displacement a result of a given driving force. Thus, if the driving force amplitude F_0 is known, we obtain the corresponding x_0 from Eq. (8–21). This relation is shown in Fig. 8–15. The amplitudes of the oscillatory motions are always taken to be positive, and the change of sign that occurs in the denominator of Eq. (8–21) as ω passes through ω_0 is expressed as a change of the phase angle from 0 to π, as shown in Fig. 8–15.

We shall now extend the analysis to include the effect of friction. It follows from Eq. (8–20) that the force is now of the form $F(t) = A \cos \omega t - B \sin \omega t$, where $A = Kx_0(1 - \omega^2/\omega_0^2)$ and $B = R\omega x_0$. Since the force is harmonic, it can be expressed in the form $F = F_0 \cos (\omega t + \phi)$, where the force amplitude F_0 and the phase ϕ are functions of ω and the oscillator parameters m, K, and R. In order to find F_0 and ϕ in terms of the known quantities A and B, we use the well-known identity $\cos(\alpha + \beta) = \cos \alpha \cos \beta - \sin \alpha \sin \beta$, and thus obtain

$$F_0 \cos(\omega t + \phi) = (F_0 \cos \phi) \cos \omega t - (F_0 \sin \phi) \sin \omega t.$$

Consequently, we have

$$A = F_0 \cos \phi \quad \text{and} \quad B = F_0 \sin \phi,$$

and therefore

$$F = \sqrt{A^2 + B^2} = K x_0 \sqrt{(1 - \omega^2/\omega_0^2)^2 + (R\omega/K)^2}$$

and $\tan \phi = B/A$. The expression for the displacement amplitude is then

$$x_0 = \frac{F_0/K}{\sqrt{(1 - \omega^2/\omega_0^2)^2 + (R\omega/K)^2}} = \frac{F_0/K}{\sqrt{(1 - \omega^2/\omega_0^2)^2 + (\omega/\omega_0 Q)^2}},$$

$$(8\text{–}22)$$

and the phase angle is given by

$$\tan \phi = \frac{B}{A} = \frac{R\omega}{K(1 - \omega^2/\omega_0^2)}.$$

These relations are shown in Fig. 8–15 for some different values of Q. The displacement amplitude is expressed in terms of the static value $x_{\text{st}} = F_0/K$.

Demonstration of forced oscillatory motion. In order to experimentally demonstrate forced harmonic motion in accordance with the treatment given above, we should have at our disposal a force with harmonic time dependence and with a variable frequency. This force is to be applied to the mass in a mass-spring oscillator. The amplitude of the force preferably should be independent of the frequency. However, it is much simpler to produce a controlled harmonic *displacement* rather than a harmonic force, and an experiment like that of Fig. 8–16 can be done simply. Here, the end of a spring is displaced in harmonic motion, $x = x_0 \sin \omega t$, and the corresponding displacement of the mass at the other end of the spring is observed. This type of experiment, type A, does not completely correspond to the initial type of forced motion, type B, where a given harmonic force was applied to the mass of the oscillator on one end of a spring, the other end of which is held fixed. However, so far as the motion of the mass in the oscillator is concerned, the two cases are completely equivalent. We leave it as a problem to show that the motion produced in A by a

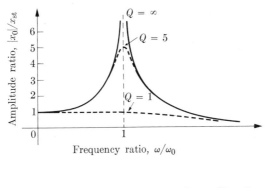

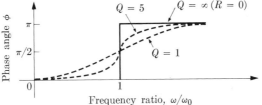

FIG. 8–15. The magnitude of the displacement amplitude and the phase difference ϕ between the driving force and the displacement in a harmonic oscillator. The displacement amplitude is expressed in terms of the value $x_{st} = F_0/K$ that corresponds to $\omega = 0$.

given harmonic displacement $x = x_0 \sin \omega t$ is the same as the motion produced in B by a force $F = Kx_0 \sin \omega t$, where K is the spring constant (Problem 8–39).

The type of forced motion which we have designated as B can be demonstrated by the simple arrangement shown in Fig. 8–17. The figure shows a car which is held on a track between two stretched springs. The car is set in oscillation by periodically tilting the track a small angle $\theta = \theta_0 \sin \omega t$ about the horizontal equilibrium position. If the angle is sufficiently small, the external force component in the direction of the track is $F = mg \sin \theta \simeq mg\theta = mg\theta_0 \sin \omega t$, which is a harmonic driving force with the amplitude $F_0 = mg\theta_0$. (It should be pointed out that

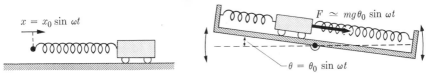

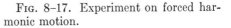

FIG. 8–16. Experimental demonstration of forced harmonic motion.

FIG. 8–17. Experiment on forced harmonic motion.

in this experiment, there is a small extraneous effect which is caused by the motion of the coordinate system. See Chapter 11.)

There are, of course, several other ways of producing a harmonic force with a constant amplitude, in particular, we could use an electromagnetic device similar to an ordinary loudspeaker. Here the force on an electric current in a magnetic field is utilized, the force being proportional to the current. When the electric current is varied harmonically with time, the desired driving force is produced.

Energy considerations. We have seen that the force required to produce the oscillatory displacement $x = x_0 \cos \omega t$ is $F = F_0 \cos (\omega t + \phi)$, where the phase angle ϕ goes from 0 to π when ω goes from 0 to ∞. The instantaneous power delivered by the force to the oscillator is Fv, where v is the velocity, $v = -\omega x_0 \sin \omega t = -v_0 \sin \omega t$. This power varies with time; it is positive when F and v have the same direction and negative when they oppose each other. If there is no friction in the oscillator, the positive and negative work delivered in a period cancel each other and the average power is then zero. However, in the presence of friction it is clear that energy is dissipated. We leave it as an exercise to show that the time average of the power delivered is then

$$\text{Average power} = \tfrac{1}{2}F_0 v_0 \sin \phi = \tfrac{1}{2}Rv_0^2. \qquad (8\text{--}23)$$

(See Problem 8–40.)

8–9 The mechanical frequency spectrum. Among the various kinds of mechanical oscillators, frequencies of oscillation range from 0 up to about 10^{13} cycles/sec. Just as the human eye is sensitive to only part of the electromagnetic spectrum, the human ear can detect only part of the mechanical frequency spectrum, from about 20 to 15,000 cycles/sec. Frequencies below 20 cycles/sec are encountered in various kinds of mechanical structures, buildings, bridges, etc. Frequencies above 15,000 cycles/sec are often encountered in fluid mechanics and can be generated under controlled conditions by means of piezoelectric crystals, or other so-called electromechanical transducers. Such vibrations, usually referred to as *ultrasonic vibrations* or *ultrasound*, have numerous industrial applications and recently, frequencies as high as 3000 megacycles/sec ($3 \cdot 10^9$ cycles/sec) were generated by means of such electromechanical transducers. The upper limit of the frequency of vibrations in solids corresponds to that of the thermal vibrations, with a frequency of the order of 10^{13} cycles/sec (see Chapter 17).

PROBLEMS

8–1. By reference to Fig. 8–3, show that the restoring force that tends to accelerate the car towards the equilibrium position is proportional to x^3 for small values of x. Determine the potential energy for an arbitrary value of x, and draw an energy diagram.

8–2. The energy of oscillation in a "square-well" oscillator is H. If the period is T, what is the amplitude of oscillation?

8–3. Convince yourself that $x = x_0 \cos \omega_0 t$, $x = x_0 \sin \omega_0 t$, $x = x_0 \cos (\omega_0 t + \phi)$ all satisfy the differential equation (8–3) if $\omega_0 = \sqrt{K/m}$.

8–4. A cantilever beam deflects 1.00 inch when a one-ton weight is hung on its free end. What is the frequency of oscillation, neglecting the mass of the cantilever?

8–5. The frequency of oscillation of a molecule in thermal motion is about 10^{13} cycles/sec. The mass is of the order of 10^{-22} gm. What is the equivalent spring constant?

8–6. A body, when placed on a vertical spring, compresses the spring statically by 10 cm. What is the characteristic frequency of oscillation of the body on this spring?

8–7. From a reasonable guess as to the mass of a car and its period of vertical oscillation, estimate the effective spring constant of the springs on its four wheels.

8–8. A body of mass $m = 0.5$ kgm performs harmonic motion at the end of a spring. The characteristic angular frequency is $\omega_0 = 10 \sec^{-1}$. What is the spring constant? If the body is displaced 20 cm from its equilibrium position and then released, what are the maximum values (amplitudes) of the displacement, speed, and acceleration in the ensuing motion? What are the total, the maximum potential, and the maximum kinetic energies?

8–9. A body of mass m, on a horizontal frictionless plane, is attached to the junction of two horizontal springs, with spring constants K_1 and K_2. The relaxed lengths of the two springs are the same and equal to L. The free ends of the springs are pulled apart and fastened to two fixed walls a distance $3L$ apart, as shown in Fig. 8–18. (a) Determine the equilibrium position of the body. (b) What is the frequency of oscillation of the car about the equilibrium position?

8–10. Suppose a body of mass m is attached to two springs, as shown in Fig. 8–19. What then is the frequency of oscillation when the springs are (a) in series and (b) in parallel?

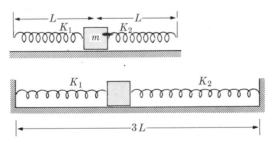

FIGURE 8–18

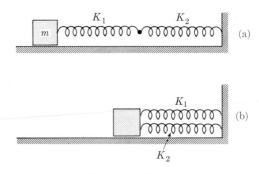

FIGURE 8–19

8–11. Suppose that the potential energy for small values of x is $V = Ax^4$. Will the corresponding oscillatory motion be harmonic? How do you think the period would vary with the amplitude in these oscillations?

8–12. In the diagram of Fig. 8–20, the spring is of negligible mass and has a length of 1 ft when not stretched.

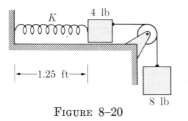

FIGURE 8–20

A 4-lb body, attached to the spring, can move on a frictionless horizontal surface. One end of a string that runs over a frictionless pulley is attached to the 4-lb weight. The other end of the string supports an 8-lb weight. The system is originally at rest in the position shown, and the length of the spring is 1.25 ft. The string is then cut and the 4-lb body starts to oscillate in a simple harmonic motion. (a) What is the amplitude of oscillation? (b) What is the period of oscillation? (c) What is the total mechanical energy of the oscillator?

8–13. Show that the average speed $\bar{v}$ in a harmonic motion is $(2/\pi)$ times the maximum speed. Convince yourself that the period of oscillation can be written as $T_0 = 4x_0/\bar{v}$, where x_0 is the maximum displacement. Prove that T_0 is independent of x_0. Also prove that the time average of the kinetic energy is half the total energy.

8–14. Prove from energy considerations that, in a harmonic oscillator, the velocity can be written as $v = \omega_0\sqrt{x_0^2 - x^2}$ and that the time t can be expressed as $t = \int dx/(\omega_0\sqrt{x_0^2 - x^2})$. Integrate this equation and show that $x = x_0 \cos(\omega_0 t + \phi)$ results.

8–15. A mass of 10 gm oscillates as $x = 10 \cos(\omega_0 t + \pi/4)$, where x is in centimeters and $f_0 = \omega_0/2\pi = 20$ cycles/sec. Find the position and the velocity of the oscillating mass at $t = 0$. What is the value of the spring-type force constant K?

8–16. A wooden block of mass M is attached to one end of a spring (spring constant K) and is at rest on a horizontal table (neglect friction). The other end of the spring is held fixed, as shown in Fig. 8–21. A bullet of mass m is shot at a speed v into the block in the direction of the spring. The collision takes place in a very short time, so that the spring can be

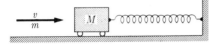

FIGURE 8-21

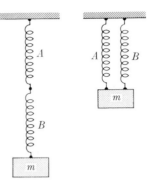

FIGURE 8-22

considered to be in the relaxed position during the collision. (a) What is
the total mechanical energy in the
subsequent oscillation? (b) What is
the maximum compression of the
spring? (c) Using the numerical values
$M = 1$ kgm, $m = 5$ gm, $v = 300$ m/
sec, and $K = 400$ n/m, determine the
numerical answers to (a) and (b). Indicate units.

8-17. On a horizontal table, a body
attached to the end of a spring performs harmonic motion (neglect friction). (Mass $m = 0.5$ kgm; spring
constant $K = 50$ n/m.) The amplitude of oscillation is $x_0 = 0.2$ m. An
impulse is delivered to the oscillator
in order to increase the amplitude to
twice the given value. What should
be the respective magnitudes of such
an impulse if it is applied at the point
of maximum displacement? at the
point of maximum velocity? Discuss.

8-18. A thin wooden bar of length l
has a weight w on its lower end, so
that in water it maintains a vertical
position with half its length submerged.
The bar is displaced vertically and
released from its equilibrium position.
Discuss the ensuing motion. What is
the period of oscillation? Introduce
symbols for all the quantities that
must be included in the discussion.
Is the oscillator linear for all amplitudes of oscillation?

8-19. Consider a body of mass m
supported by two identical springs A
and B, each with a spring constant K.
Now, consider the two arrangements
shown in Fig. 8-22. (a) If the static
deflections, i.e., the changes of the
equilibrium position of the body

caused by the weight of the body, in
the two cases are x_1 and x_2, determine x_1/x_2. (b) What is the ratio
between the resonance frequency of
each oscillator? (c) What is the ratio
between the total mechanical energies
of the oscillators, if they oscillate with
the same displacement amplitude?

8-20. A mass m at the end of a
spring oscillates with a displacement
given by $x = x_0 \sin \omega_0 t$. When the
mass reaches $x = x_0$ it receives an
instantaneous impulse J in the positive
x-direction. Determine the new expression for the displacement, considering the changes both in amplitude and
phase. Time is still measured from the
same starting point as before.

8-21. A simple pendulum 8 ft long
swings with an amplitude of 1 ft, measured along the circular path of the bob
of the pendulum. (a) Compute the
velocity of the pendulum at its lowest
point. (b) Compute its acceleration
at the ends of its path. (c) What is
the period of oscillation?

8-22. When a body is hung at the
end of a vertical spring, it stretches the
spring statically to twice its initial
length. This system can be set into
oscillation either as a simple pendulum
or as a mass-spring oscillator. Which
of the corresponding frequencies is the

larger? What is the ratio between the two frequencies?

8–23. A pendulum and a mass-spring oscillator have identical periods on the earth. What is the ratio of their periods on a planet where bodies weigh eight times more than they do on earth?

8–24. Masses of 10 gm and 40 gm are suspended from a common point on 1.5-m lengths of very light thread. They are released simultaneously from 5° and 10°, as shown in Fig. 8–23. Where and when do they collide? Explain and discuss your answer briefly.

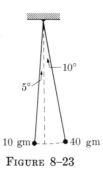

10 gm   40 gm

FIGURE 8–23

8–25. It has been shown in the text that the period of a simple pendulum is independent of the amplitude of oscillation, if the angles of excursion are small enough. For large amplitudes this independence does not apply. (a) Does the period of the pendulum increase or decrease with increasing amplitude? Discuss this question and illustrate the qualitatively large-amplitude motion by means of an energy diagram. (b) Refer to Eq. (7–10) and obtain an expression (an integral) for the period of the large-amplitude pendulum. (c) Obtain a similar expression for the period of the nonlinear oscillator, shown in Fig. 8–3 in the text.

8–26. Two bodies of masses $m_1 = 1$ kgm and $m_2 = 3$ kgm are free to slide along a straight line on a horizontal surface. They are connected by a spring of spring constant $K = 300$ n/m and relaxed length L. The spring is compressed $x_0 = 20$ cm from its relaxed length, and then the bodies are released in such a way that the center of mass stays at rest. (a) What is the frequency of the ensuing oscillations? (b) What is the maximum kinetic energy of m_1 and of m_2?

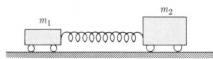

FIGURE 8–24

8–27. To the ends of a spring (spring constant K) of negligible mass are attached equal masses m, at rest on a frictionless table (Fig. 8–25). The system is set in motion by compressing the spring a distance d, with one of the bodies resting against a wall, and then releasing the system from rest. (a) How far does body 1 move before body 2 starts moving? (b) After body 2 has lost contact with the wall, what is the velocity of the center of mass of the system and what is the amplitude of oscillation?

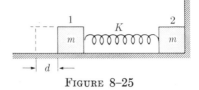

FIGURE 8–25

8–28. Prove that the expression (8–18) for damped oscillations satisfies the equation of motion (8–17).

8–29. A 1-kgm mass is hung on a spring of spring constant 100 n/m. (a) What is the frequency of oscillation? (b) It is observed after 30 cycles that the amplitudes of the oscillations drop to $1/e$ of their initial amplitude. What is Q? What is the lifetime of the oscillator? (c) What is R, the coefficient that relates the damping force to the velocity? (d) If the oscillations are started by displacing the mass 10 cm from equilibrium, how large are the actual damping forces?

8-30. Consider a mass at the end of a spring performing damped free oscillations. Consider small damping. What then is the net impulse delivered in half a period (from $-x_0$ to $+x_0$) (a) by the spring force? (b) by the friction force $F_f = -R(dx/dt)$? (c) Discuss qualitatively the modification, if any, of the answers to (a) and (b) if the restriction of small damping is relaxed.

8-31. Consider an oscillator with small damping. Show that the fractional change of the total energy in one period is $2\pi/Q$.

8-32. Consider a harmonic oscillator with damping. Prove the relation $dH/dt = -(2R/m)E$, where H is the total energy and E is the kinetic energy. (*Hint*. Start from $m(dv/dt) = -Kx - Rv$ and multiply both sides by $v = dx/dt$.)

8-33. (a) Consider a spring (spring constant K) fixed at one end and driven at the other end in such a way that $x = x_0 \cos \omega t$ (see Fig. 8-26). What must be the driving force F_1? (b) A body of mass m is driven by a force F_2 such that it moves with the same motion as in (a), $x = x_0 \cos \omega t$.

What is F_2? (c) The mass m of (b) is now attached to the spring of (a), and the mass and spring are driven by a force F_3 such that $x = x_0 \cos \omega t$. What is F_3? (d) If the driving frequency in (c) is $\omega_0 = \sqrt{K/m}$, what then is the force F_3 required to sustain the oscillation? (e) At frequencies very much larger than ω_0, the system in (c) behaves approximately like either (a) or (b). Which one? Explain.

8-34. A block of wood rests on a horizontal platform. The platform moves vertically with a displacement $y = y_0 \cos \omega t$, where y_0 is 3 cm and ω can be varied. (a) Find the force of the platform on the block as a function of the frequency $f = \omega/2\pi$. (b) At what frequency will the block leave the table?

8-35. A platform weighing 100 lb is supported by springs that rest on a foundation. The characteristic frequency of oscillation is 10 cycles/sec. The platform is driven by a vertical harmonic force with an amplitude of 5 lb. What are the amplitude of the displacement of the platform and the amplitude of the force from the springs on the foundation when the driving frequency is 1 cycle/sec? 9 cycles/sec? 10.5 cycles/sec? 20 cycles/sec? Neglect damping.

8-36. Find the instantaneous power delivered by the driving force to a mass m if m has no other forces acting on it and moves such that $x = x_0 \cos \omega t$. Next, suppose m is connected to a spring of spring constant K.

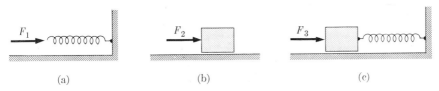

(a) (b) (c)

FIGURE 8-26

What then is the instantaneous power? Is there any net energy delivered over a complete cycle?

8–37. A ballistic pendulum consists of a wooden block of mass 10 kgm that is suspended on a string 3 m long. (a) What is the period T of the oscillatory motion? (b) The pendulum, when at rest in the equilibrium position, is struck by a bullet of mass 5 gm moving with a speed of 200 m/sec. What is the amplitude of the resulting oscillatory motion? (c) If bullets are fired once every T sec, show how the amplitude of the motion increases with time. Sketch the motion. (d) What will be the motion if the bullets are fired once every $T/2$ sec? once every $3T/2$ sec? (e) If the pendulum is swinging, when should a bullet be fired in order to transfer the maximum possible additional oscillatory energy to the pendulum?

8–38. Consider the forced motion of a linear oscillator. The friction force is proportional to the velocity, and the constant of proportionality is R. If the amplitude of the driving force is F_0, show that the velocity amplitude v_0 is given by $v_0 = F_0/\sqrt{R^2 + X^2}$, where $X = \omega m - K/\omega$.

8–39. In the text, the discussion of forced motion cited a situation in which the mass-spring oscillator was driven by a force applied to the mass when one end of the spring was held fixed. Consider now the resulting motion when, instead of being held fixed, the (massless) end of the spring is forced to move with a displacement $x_0 \sin \omega t$. (a) What then is the displacement of the mass m at the other end of the spring? Prove that this displacement is the same as that which would result if the force $Kx_0 \sin \omega t$ were applied to the mass when the other end of the spring is held fixed. (b) If the characteristic frequency of the oscillator is f_0, what is the amplitude of oscillation when $f = f_0/2$? (c) At what other frequency is the amplitude the same as in (b)? (d) What force is required at the free end of the spring to maintain the displacement $x = x_0 \sin \omega t$ at this point?

8–40. Prove the relation (8–23) in the text. [*Hint.* The power is the time average of $Fv = -F_0 \cos (\omega t + \phi)v_0 \sin \omega t = -F_0 v_0 (\cos \omega t \cos \phi -\sin \omega t \sin \phi) \sin \omega t$. Find the time averages of the terms $\sin \omega t \cos \omega t \cos \phi$ and $\sin^2 \omega t \sin \phi$.]

CHAPTER 9

ANGULAR MOMENTUM

Summary. When the force on a particle is central, that is, directed always toward or away from a fixed point in space, the angular momentum of the particle remains constant. We introduce angular momentum by a study of the properties of plane motion of a particle acted on by a series of instantaneous central impulses. The law of conservation of angular momentum is formulated and is extended to a system of two or more centrally interacting particles, including rigid bodies. The vector nature of angular momentum is then discussed and the total angular momentum of a system of particles is divided into two parts, the orbital angular momentum that results from the translational motion of the system and the spin angular momentum that results from the motion with respect to the center of mass. Finally, we study the change in the angular momentum which is produced by external impulses and forces, and the concept of torque as the rate of change of angular momentum is introduced.

Conservation laws play a basic role in physics. Thus far we have discussed the laws of conservation of momentum, mass, and energy. These conservation laws are important not only because they make very general statements about nature, but also because they offer short-cut solutions to specific problems, at the same time permitting partial solutions to or partial understanding of very complicated problems and phenomena. In this chapter we shall develop another conservation law, the conservation of angular momentum.

If two or more particles interact only among themselves, their total momentum remains constant. We have assumed that this conservation law applies to all types of interaction and it requires that the mutual interaction forces between any two particles be equal in magnitude but oppositely directed. Although the relative orientations of the two interaction forces (called a *force pair*) are established in this manner by the law of conservation of momentum, no restriction is imposed on the absolute orientation of the force pair. The forces must be parallel but may be directed along the line that connects the particles or in any arbitrary direction in space. However, experiments have shown that most interaction forces are *central*, that is, directed along the line which connects the interacting bodies. As a consequence of this property of the interaction forces, we shall find that, in addition to momentum, another quantity, called

227

angular momentum, is conserved. Momentum relates to the translational motion, whereas angular momentum relates to the rotational motion of a system. The gravitational and electrostatic forces are perhaps the most familiar and important examples of central forces.

9–1 Central force on a single particle. Conservation of angular momentum. In an introductory discussion of angular momentum, it is convenient to consider the motion of one particle acted on by a central force which is always directed toward one fixed point in space. This situation represents a central interaction between two particles when one of the particles is considered to be at rest. The motion of the earth as described with respect to a coordinate system attached to the sun is an example. Likewise, the motion of the moon as seen from a coordinate system attached to the earth and the motion of a body attached to the end of a spring that is fastened to the earth are examples of motion that results from central forces.

In a discussion of projectile motion in the *local* gravitational field of the earth, it is perfectly natural and most convenient to use a cartesian coordinate system (x, y), since then the only force on the projectile, its weight, can be expressed in terms of one force component $(F_y = -mg)$ only. By the same token, it usually is most convenient to use a polar coordinate system (see Chapter 7) when the force on a body is central, i.e., directed along the position vector $\mathbf{r}$. Then, instead of a discussion in terms of the x- and y-components of the momentum of a body we consider the momentum components in the r- and θ-directions (see Fig. 9–1).

Now, in the case of projectile motion, where cartesian coordinates are used, the x-component of the momentum is constant because the force has only a y-component. In the case of a central force, there is a force component only in the r-direction and this suggests, by analogy, that

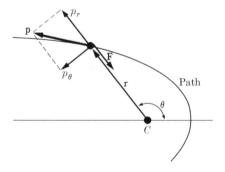

Fɪɢ. 9–1. Polar coordinates and the radial and tangential components of momentum.

there might be a property of the motion which remains constant when expressed in terms of polar coordinates.

We might be led to guess that since $F_\theta = 0$, p_θ is constant. However, it is easy to show that this guess is erroneous. If p_θ is to be constant when there is a central force, it must also be constant in the special case when the force is zero. If the force is zero, the mass point must, of course, move along a straight line with constant momentum. There is no lack of generality in the discussion if, as in Fig. 9–2, we let this straight line of motion be parallel to the y-axis. Then we have $p_x = 0$, $p_y = p$. From the figure, the *polar* components of the momentum are

$$p_\theta = p \cos \theta = p \frac{d}{r}, \qquad p_r = p \sin \theta, \qquad (9\text{–}1)$$

where d is the perpendicular distance from the line of motion to the reference point O. We see that p_θ is *not* constant. In fact, as the mass point travels out toward infinity $(r \to \infty)$, p_θ approaches zero and p_r approaches p. Note, however, that p_θ varies in a very simple way and that the product

$$p_\theta r = pd \qquad (9\text{–}2)$$

remains constant and equal to the product of the momentum p and the perpendicular distance d from the line of motion to the reference point. The distance d we shall often refer to as the *lever arm* of **p**. It is clear immediately that the same result is obtained if the line of motion of the mass point is not parallel with the y-axis as in the discussion above, but has an arbitrary direction in the plane at a perpendicular distance d from the reference point O. Again, the product $p_\theta r$ remains constant and equal to pd.

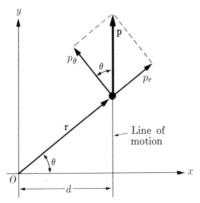

FIG. 9–2. The mass point moves under the influence of no force. The momentum has components p_r and p_θ.

We are now ready to consider the effect of a central force, or, specifically, a central instantaneous impulse. Certainly, we cannot expect p_θ to remain constant, because, as we have seen, it is not constant even when there are no forces. But let us examine $p_\theta r$, and determine the effect of a central impulse on it.

In Fig. 9–3 is shown the trajectory of a mass point that has been subjected to an *instantaneous central impulse* **J** at point A. The initial momentum of the mass point is $\mathbf{p}_1$ and its final momentum is $\mathbf{p}_2$. We have shown (Fig. 9–2) that $p_{1\theta}r$ is constant and equal to $p_1 d_1$ along path 1, and $p_{2\theta}r$ is constant and equal to $p_2 d_2$ along path 2, for there are no forces on the mass point along these paths. We now must answer the following question: is it possible that $p_1 d_1$ and $p_2 d_2$ are equal? Because **J** is an *instantaneous* impulse, the position vector $\mathbf{r}_a$ (and the angle θ_a) of the mass point is the same just before and just after the impulse is delivered. Because **J** is a *central* impulse, the θ-component of momentum just before the impulse, $(p_{1\theta})_a$, must be the same as that just after the impulse, $(p_{2\theta})_a$. Therefore, $(p_{1\theta})_a r_a = (p_{2\theta})_a r_a$. But we found before that, for all points along path 1, we have $p_{1\theta}r = p_1 d_1$ and, consequently, $(p_{1\theta})_a r_a = p_1 d_1$. Similarly, along path 2, we have $p_{2\theta}r = p_2 d_2$, so that $(p_{2\theta})_a r_a = p_2 d_2$. It follows that $p_1 d_1 = p_2 d_2$; that is, the central impulse at A did *not* change the value of the quantity $p_\theta r$.

Clearly, we can repeat the same argument for an arbitrary number of central impulses $\mathbf{J}_1$, $\mathbf{J}_2$, $\mathbf{J}_3$, etc., all directed toward O but applied at different points A, B, C, etc., such that the path consists of a succession of line segments, as shown in Fig. 9–4. The time spacing of these impulses can be made arbitrarily small, so that, in principle, we can simulate a continuously acting central force as closely as we please. Thus, we conclude that a continuously acting central force on a particle does not change the quantity $p_\theta r = pd$. This quantity is called the *angular mamentum l*, and

$$l = p_\theta r = pd. \qquad (9\text{–}3)$$

It is sometimes convenient to express the angular momentum in terms of the angular velocity $\omega = d\theta/dt$ with respect to O, the force center. The velocity component in the θ-direction is $v_\theta = r(d\theta/dt) = r\omega$, and so from (9–3), we can express angular momentum as

$$l = (mr^2)\omega. \qquad (9\text{–}4)$$

Note carefully that the angular momentum refers to a particular point in space. If this point is the force center, i.e., the point toward which the central impulses or central force on the particle are directed, the angular momentum of the particle is conserved.

The dimension and unit of angular momentum are, of course, different

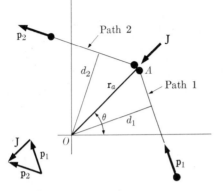

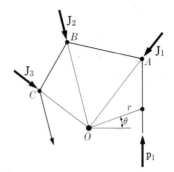

FIG. 9–3. **J** is an *instantaneous central* impulse, and $\mathbf{p}_2 = \mathbf{p}_1 + \mathbf{J}$. The angular momentum p_1d_1 is equal to p_2d_2, and so is unchanged by the impulse.

FIG. 9–4. Motion resulting from a series of central impulses.

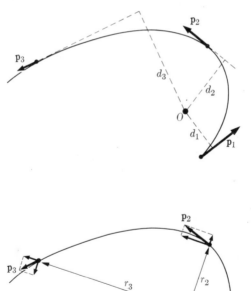

FIG. 9–5. A continuously acting central force acts on the mass point. The angular momentum $p_\theta r = pd$ is constant for all points on the path.

from those of momentum. Angular momentum, being the product of momentum and length, has the dimension $[M][L]^2[T]^{-1}$ and the unit in the mks system is then kgm·m^2/sec.

The angular velocities corresponding to the two possible senses of rotation in the plane of motion are distinguished by positive and negative signs. Similarly, angular momentum will be counted positive and negative in the same manner as ω.

EXAMPLE 1. An air-suspended puck, the mass of which is 1.5 kgm, slides over a horizontal surface. A light string is attached to the puck. As the puck arrives at A, it is given an impulse toward O by means of a sudden pull on the string which runs through a ring at O, as shown in Fig. 9-6. Another impulse is delivered at point B. An analysis of this motion shows that the speed before the impulse at A is $v = 1.38$ m/sec and the lever arm is $d_1 = 0.6$ m, so that the angular momentum is $l_1 = mv_1d_1 = 1.24$ kgm·m^2/sec. Similarly, the speed and the lever arm between A and B are $v_2 = 1.5$ m/sec and $d_2 = 0.55$ m, respectively, with a corresponding angular momentum $l_2 = 1.23$ kgm·m^2/sec. In the same way we find that the angular momentum beyond B is $mv_3d_3 = 1.22$ kgm·m^2/sec. Thus, within the errors in the measurements, we find that the angular momentum is the same throughout the motion. This result, of course, is expected from the above analysis so long as no forces other than the pull toward O influence the motion of the puck. It is clear from the experimental results above that the effect of the friction force on the puck is not large enough to affect, to any great extent, the angular momentum of the puck.

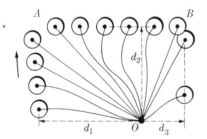

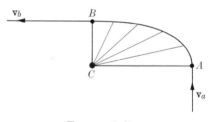

FIG. 9-6. An experiment that illustrates conservation of angular momentum.

FIGURE 9-7

EXAMPLE 2. A man of mass $m = 80$ kgm slides along a frictionless horizontal surface with a velocity $v_a = 3$ m/sec. A long rope stretched a distance $d = 2$ m has one end attached to a ring that is free to slide without friction about a post at point C. The man grabs the other end of the rope at point A, and while the path of the man turns (he interacts with the post via the rope), he pulls himself to within a distance $d/2 = 1$ m of the post. When the direction of his velocity is normal to his initial velocity, he lets go of the rope. What then is the speed of the man?

We do not have to analyze the detailed spiral-like motion of the man. He interacts only with the post (a central force) and so his angular momentum about C must remain constant. The angular momentum is known at point A (and before A for that matter, since both v_a and d_a are given), and is $l_a = p_a d_a = 3 \cdot 80 \cdot 2 = 480 \text{ kgm·m}^2/\text{sec}$. At point B, we have $d_b = 0.5d_a$, and from $p_b d_b = l_b = l_a$, we find that $p_b = 2p_a$. Thus, $v_b = 2v_a = 6 \text{ m/sec}$.

Note that the kinetic energy of the man has increased by a factor of four, since his velocity increased by a factor of two. (Whence did he acquire this energy?)

EXAMPLE 3. An earth satellite of mass m moves in an elliptic orbit. Its maximum and minimum distances from the surface of the earth are 1587 mi and 219 mi, respectively. The maximum speed is 18,470 mi/hr. What are the speeds at $r = r_{\min}$ and $r = r_{\max}$? The radius of the earth is 3964 mi.

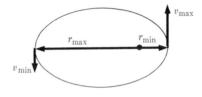

FIGURE 9-8

Since the satellite moves under the influence of a central force (gravity), its angular momentum remains constant. Therefore, when r is small, the velocity must be large. Since in the elliptical orbit the velocity $\mathbf{v}$ is perpendicular to the position vector at $r = r_{\min}$ and $r = r_{\max}$, the constant angular momentum of the motion is

$$l = mv_{\max}r_{\min} = mv_{\min}r_{\max}.$$

With an earth radius of 3964 miles, we have $r_{\max} = 3964 + 1587 = 5551$ mi and $r_{\min} = 3964 + 219 = 4183$ mi. For $v_{\min}$, we have

$$v_{\min} = \frac{r_{\min}}{r_{\max}} v_{\max} = \frac{4183}{5551} \cdot 18{,}470 = 13{,}900 \text{ mi/hr.}$$

The sector velocity. One of Kepler's three empirical laws of motion (see Chapters 1 and 10) states that in planetary motion the radius vector from the sun to the planets sweeps over equal areas in equal times. The area swept over per unit of time is often called the *sector velocity*. It is easy to show that the Keplerian law of a constant sector velocity is equivalent to the law of conservation of angular momentum, when related to the motion of a planet about the sun. This means that the force on the planet is central, that is, directed toward the sun at all times during the motion.

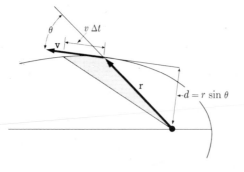

FIG. 9-9. The sector velocity, $rv_\theta/2 = r^2\omega/2$, is proportional to the angular momentum. When a mass point moves under the influence of a central force, the radius vector sweeps out equal areas in equal times.

In order to see the connection between the sector velocity and the angular momentum, consider Fig. 9-9. Let us calculate the area swept over by the radius vector from the central reference point to the body in a small time Δt. In this time, the planet has moved a distance $v\,\Delta t$ and the radius vector has moved forward through an angle $\Delta\theta$. The corresponding triangular area swept over by the radius is then $(v\,\Delta t)(r\sin\theta)/2$, and the average sector velocity during this time Δt is then $(vr\sin\theta)/2$. This can also be expressed as $v_\theta r/2$, where $v_\theta = v\sin\theta$, or, with $v_\theta = r\omega$, we have

$$\text{Sector velocity} = \frac{rv_\theta}{2} = \tfrac{1}{2}r^2\omega.$$

Thus, we see that the sector velocity is proportional to the angular momentum $l = mr^2\omega$ of the particle; in fact,

$$\text{Sector velocity} = \frac{l}{2m}. \qquad (9\text{-}5)$$

9–2 Conservation of angular momentum of two or more interacting particles in a plane. In the previous section, we assumed the existence of a central force acting on a particle, and we did not concern ourselves with what caused this force. The assumed motion was, say, planetary or satellite motion, or the motion of a body at the end of a spring which is attached to the earth. In such cases, it is reasonable to assume that one of the interacting bodies is at rest (the sun in planetary motion, and the earth in the satellite and the spring motion), since it can be considered to have infinite mass in comparison with the mass of the moving particle. On the other hand, when the masses of the two interacting particles are of the same order of magnitude, we must consider the motion of both particles.

If the interaction between the particles is central, the forces on the particles pass through the center of mass of the system, and if the total momentum of the particles is zero, the center of mass is at rest. Each particle then moves under the influence of a central force that is directed toward a fixed point in space (the center of mass). It follows from our previous discussion that the angular momentum of each particle, and thus the total angular momentum since it is the sum of the individual angular momenta, is conserved.

To be specific, let us consider two particles of masses m_a and m_b, respectively, that are connected by a coil-spring, as indicated in Fig. 9–10. Suppose the spring is pulled apart, and as the system is released to move in a plane, it is caused to spin. Now, in addition to the oscillations to and fro, the particles are in orbital motion about the stationary center of mass. If at a certain moment, the distances from the center of mass to the two particles are r_a and r_b, respectively, the total angular momentum of the system can be expressed as $L = p_{\theta a} r_a + p_{\theta b} r_b$. Since the center of mass is at rest, we have $p_{\theta a} = p_{\theta b} = p_\theta$, and the total angular momentum reduces to

$$L = p_\theta(r_a + r_b) = p_\theta d.$$

The quantity $d = r_a + r_b$ is, of course, the separation between the two particles.

Since the straight line that connects the two particles must always go through the center of mass, the angular velocities of the two particles are the same and $\omega_a = \omega_b = \omega$. Therefore, using Eq. (9–4), we find that the total angular momentum of the system can be expressed as

$$L = (m_a r_a^2 + m_b r_b^2)\omega = I_0\omega. \tag{9–6}$$

The quantity

$$I_0 = m_a r_a^2 + m_b r_b^2$$

is the *moment of inertia* of the system with respect to the center of mass. In general, this quantity varies during the motion, since r_a and r_b vary. Only in the special case when, as in a rigid body, the distance between

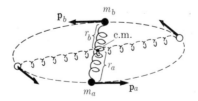

Fig. 9–10. Combined oscillation and rotation of two particles that are connected by a spring.

the two particles is constant, do the moment of inertia and the angular velocity remain constant. However, when I_0 varies, the angular velocity will also vary to keep the angular momentum constant. When the spring is stretched, so that d is large, the angular velocity is small, and vice versa.

An illustrative and amusing demonstration of this behavior is illustrated in Fig. 9-11. The system, a man holding two weights, is on a turntable that spins about a vertical axis. The masses m_a and m_b of the foregoing discussion are represented by the weights, and the spring is represented by the man, who can change the moment of inertia of the system by moving the weights closer to and farther from his body. The man then can regulate the angular velocity with the aid of the weights; as he holds his arms outstretched, the angular velocity is small, and when he pulls the weights close to his body, his angular velocity increases.

The result obtained in the study of the conservation of angular momentum of a particle (mass point) would be of limited value unless we can show that this conservation law can be extended to apply to a real body. Such a body can be considered as a collection of particles, and it is natural then to consider next the influence of a central force on such a collection of particles. A particle in the system is acted on by two types of forces. First, we have the internal forces that result from interactions with other particles in the system. Second, the particle is acted on by external central forces. In this case, we are concerned with only one external force or impulse which is directed toward a fixed point in space. Although this problem will be considered in more detail later, we can point out that, indeed, the conservation of angular momentum applies also to a collection of particles, provided that the mutual interactions between the particles are central. To illustrate this statement, consider two particles P_1 and P_2 in a system in a plane (Fig. 9-12). Suppose that P_1 acts on P_2 with an instantaneous impulse $\mathbf{J}_{21}$. As a result, P_2 will acquire an additional momentum component $\mathbf{J}_{21}$ in the direction toward P_1, and an angular momentum $\mathbf{J}_{21}D$ with respect to the reference point O, where D is the lever arm of the impulse. However, the general property of interaction forces, derived from the conservation of momentum, requires that there will be an equal and opposite impulse $\mathbf{J}_{12} = -\mathbf{J}_{21}$ on P_1 as a result of the interaction with P_2. Then, P_1 will receive a change of momentum $\mathbf{J}_{12}$ toward P_2 and an angular momentum with a magnitude $J_{12}D$. Since $\mathbf{J}_{12} = -\mathbf{J}_{21}$, it follows that the angular momentum transferred from P_1 to P_2 is equal in magnitude but opposite in sign to the angular momentum transfer from P_2 to P_1. Therefore the interaction between P_1 and P_2 does not change the total angular momentum of the system.

A completely analogous argument is applicable to any pair of particles in the system, and we find that the *total* angular momentum remains

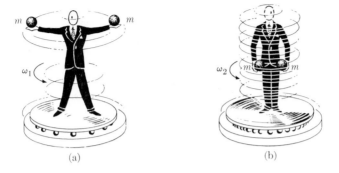

FIG. 9–11. Demonstration of the law of conservation of angular momentum.

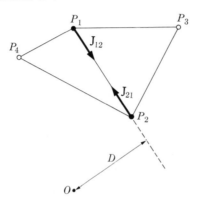

FIG. 9–12. Central interaction forces among the particles in a system do not change the total angular momentum of the system.

constant when the internal forces are central. The angular momentum of each particle may change, of course. Since we have seen that the internal forces or impulses do not contribute to the total angular momentum, it remains to consider the influence of only the external impulse. The result obtained for a single particle can then be applied to the *total* angular momentum of a particle system with central internal interactions.

So far as the total angular momentum is concerned, although the particles can move arbitrarily far from or close to each other, the total angular momentum always remains the same. One can even imagine a situation in which the particles "fuse" to form a new composite particle, still with no change of the angular momentum. The new particle then must possess a "spin" angular momentum which is the same as the original total angular momentum. Conversely, if a particle explodes into several parts, its original angular momentum will be the sum of the angular momenta of the fragments. The total angular momentum, like momentum, is conserved in an arbitrary interaction that involves central forces.

The earth and the sun both possess spin angular momenta. Also, on the atomic and subatomic scales, we find that particles often possess spin angular momenta of the order of $(h/2\pi) \simeq 10^{-34}$ kgm·m²/sec, where h is Planck's constant.

There are numerous other illustrative examples, such as diving, figure-skating, ski-jumping, and other athletic events, in which the angular momentum conservation plays an important role and in which the angular velocity is regulated by variations of the moment of inertia of the body. Returning to the example of the man on a turntable, we observe not only that the man can vary his angular velocity with variations of the moment of inertia, but also that he can start from rest, and by properly moving the weights turn himself from one angular position to another, in just about the same manner as a falling cat manages to turn himself so that he always lands on his feet (Problem 9–13). This manipulation of the cat is a matter of conservation of angular momentum, and evidently involves, to a large extent, the motion of the tail. But the technique involved in distributing the total angular momentum among the tail, rear legs, etc. varies somewhat from one cat to another. (Even cats that have no tails manage to land on their feet.)

EXAMPLE. Three bodies, A, B, and C, with the directions and velocities as shown in Fig. 9–13, approach a region R in space. Upon entering the region, A, B, and C interact with one another only, and it is finally observed that bodies B and C leave R, while A remains at rest. If B has the velocity and path shown, what must be the velocity and path of C?

In problems where we are concerned with more than two particles, or in situations where little or no information is given about the interaction involved, the motion cannot easily be detailed. We know only that the laws of conservation of momentum and angular momentum must be satisfied. Therefore, in the present case, we start by writing the conditions for conservation of momentum and angular momentum, as follows:

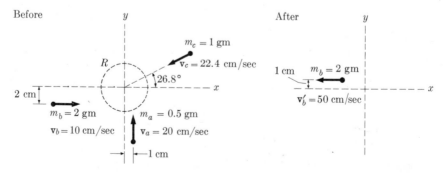

FIGURE 9–13

Conservation of momentum:

x-direction: $2 \cdot 10 - 1 \cdot 22.4 \cdot \cos \theta = -2 \cdot 50 + 1 \cdot v_{cx}$,

y-direction: $1 \cdot v_{cy} = 0.5 \cdot 20 - 1 \cdot 22.4 \cdot \sin \theta$.

With $\theta = 26.8$, we then obtain

$$v'_{cx} \simeq 100, \qquad v'_{cy} \simeq 0.$$

Conservation of angular momentum: Assume that the lever arm of v_c is y with respect to O. The angular momentum with respect to O is then

$$0.5 \cdot 20 \cdot 1 + 2 \cdot 10 \cdot 2 = 2 \cdot 50 \cdot 1 - v'_{cx}y,$$

in which the left- and right-hand sides of the equation represent the conditions before and after the interaction, respectively. This equation gives

$$y = \frac{50}{100} = \frac{1}{2}.$$

We note that the kinetic energy after the collisions is larger than before. During interaction, energy must have been released from some potential or internal energy of the particles.

The moment of inertia of a rigid body. A rigid body can be considered as a collection of particles which are separated by fixed distances. If the body rotates about an axis, all particles describe circular paths with the same angular velocity, as illustrated schematically in Fig. 9–14. Thus, if particles of masses m_1, m_2, m_3, etc. are located at distances r_1, r_2, r_3, etc. from the axis, it follows from Eq. (9–4) that the total angular momentum of the body is

$$(\textstyle\sum mr^2)\omega = I_0\omega. \tag{9–7}$$

The quantity $I_0 = \sum mr^2 = m_1r_1^2 + m_2r_2^2 + \cdots$ is the moment of inertia of the particle system with respect to the axis of rotation, and it

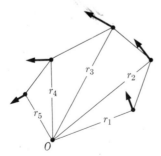

FIG. 9–14. All the mass points in a rigid body have the same angular velocity. Their speeds are ωr_1, ωr_2, etc.

is seen to be dependent upon the geometry and mass distribution of the system.

When the body consists of a continuous mass distribution, rather than a finite number of discrete mass points, the summation of a finite number of terms of the form mr^2 is only an approximate expression for the moment of inertia of the body. The correct result can be given in terms of the integral

$$I = \int r^2 \, dm,   (9\text{–}8)$$

where the integration is extended over the entire body. For bodies of simple geometry, such as straight bars and circular cylinders, the integral (9–8) can be evaluated exactly, as demonstrated by the following examples. If the distance r is measured from an axis which goes through the center of mass of the body, we denote the moment of inertia by I_0. It should be pointed out that even for bodies with a continuous mass distribution, the moment of inertia can be evaluated approximately from a finite number of terms mr^2 that represent the contributions from a finite number of mass elements into which the body is divided.

EXAMPLE 1. Consider a straight, uniform bar of length L and total mass M, and determine the moment of inertia with respect to the center-of-mass axis that is perpendicular to the bar, as indicated in Fig. 9–15.

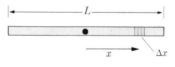

FIGURE 9–15

Let us first use the approximate method in which the bar is divided into a finite number of mass elements, and then we use $I_0 \simeq \sum mr^2$ for the calculation of the moment of inertia. Let us choose four equal parts, each of mass $M/4$. Each half of the bar then contains two elements with the center-of-mass distances $r_1 = L/8$ and $r_2 = 3L/8$. The moment of inertia then becomes approximately equal to

$$I_0 \simeq 2 \cdot \frac{M}{4}\left[\left(\frac{L}{8}\right)^2 + \left(\frac{3L}{8}\right)^2\right] = \frac{10}{128}\,ML^2 = \frac{ML^2}{12.8}\,.$$

The larger the number of elements we use, the closer is the result to its exact value. In the limit of an infinite number of elements, the calculation, of course, involves evaluation of the integral (9–8). In the present example, we choose the mass element Δm to be a length Δx of the bar, as shown in Fig. 9–15. The element is located a distance x from the center of the bar, and has the elementary mass $\Delta m = (\Delta x/L)M$. Its contribution to the moment of inertia is $(\Delta m)x^2$. The total moment of inertia with respect to the center of mass is then

$$I_0 = \int_{-L/2}^{+L/2} x^2\, dm = 2 \int_0^{L/2} x^2\, dm = 2 \int_0^{L/2} \frac{M}{L} x^2\, dx$$

$$= 2\, \frac{M}{L}\, \frac{L^3}{24} = \frac{ML^2}{12}\,.$$

It is interesting to find that even with the relatively small number of four elements, the approximate method of evaluation is quite good.

EXAMPLE 2. In order to calculate the moment of inertia of a circular disc with respect to an axis that is through the center of mass and perpendicular to the disc, we choose as the mass element the ring between r and $r + \Delta r$, as shown in Fig. 9–16. If the total mass of the disc is M and its radius is R, the mass of the element is $\Delta m = (2\pi r\, \Delta r/\pi R^2)M$. The total moment of inertia is

$$I_0 = \int_0^R r^2\, dm = \frac{2M}{R^2} \int_0^R r^3\, dr = \frac{MR^2}{2}\,.$$

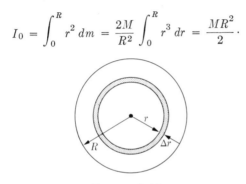

FIGURE 9–16

The radius of gyration. The moment of inertia is of the dimension $[M][L]^2$. In other words, it is always possible to express the moment of inertia as the product of the total mass M of the body and the square of a certain length k, the radius of gyration of the body, such that

$$I = Mk^2.$$

Here again we use the symbols I_0 and k_0 when we refer to an axis through the center of mass of the body.

The radius of gyration can be interpreted in the following way. A body that rotates with an angular velocity ω about a fixed axis has an angular momentum $I\omega$. If now we take a point element with the same total mass M as the body, and let this point describe a circle of radius k with an angular velocity ω, the angular momentum of the point mass is the same as that of the body. In this sense, the problem of rotation of a rigid body in a plane can be replaced by the simpler problem of the motion of a single point mass. For example, a circular disc of radius R that rotates about the center-of-mass axis, perpendicular to the disc, is equivalent to a point mass that rotates with the same angular velocity in a circle of radius $k_0 = R/\sqrt{2}$.

9–3 Angular momentum as a vector. *Motion in a plane.* The two possible directions of rotation of the position vector and the corresponding angular velocities of a particle in a plane are distinguished by plus and minus signs, and the angular momentum is given the same sign as the angular velocity, as mentioned in connection with Eq. (9–4). In principle, the choice of the positive direction of rotation is arbitrary, and when we are concerned with the motion in one plane, the choice is unimportant, so long as it is consistent. However, when we consider more general types of motion, the direction of the angular momentum will play an important role, and in order to gain experience with this question we shall discuss here the manner in which the choice of positive direction of rotation in a plane is made.

When we view the plane of motion from one side, the radius vector from the reference point to the particle turns in either the clockwise or counterclockwise direction. We can choose, for example, the counterclockwise direction as positive. However, this description is not unique. For if the plane is horizontal, the sign of the angular momentum, according to this description, depends on whether we view the motion from above or from below the plane. In other words, to establish uniquely the sign of the angular momentum, we must specify, in some way, the side from which motion is to be viewed. This specification is made by introducing a coordinate axis that is perpendicular to the plane. In a cartesian coordinate system, the z-axis has a definite direction in relation to the xy-plane. In a *right-handed coordinate system* this direction is related to the directions of the x- and y-axes as follows. Turn the $+x$-axis toward the $+y$-axis. This turn defines a direction of rotation which we denote as $x \rightarrow y$. If a right-handed screw is turned in the same manner, the direction of advance of the screw defines the direction of the z-axis. We shall introduce the symbol $x \rightarrow y \rightarrow z$ for this relationship between the directions of the axes. The direction of rotation $x \rightarrow y$ defines the positive direction of the angular velocity and angular momentum of the motion in the xy-plane. Thus, viewed from the positive z-axis this positive sense of rotation is in the counterclockwise direction (see Fig. 9–17).

Since angular momentum is so closely related to a direction perpendicular to the plane of motion, it is natural, even at this point, to describe a positive angular momentum in the xy-plane by a vector that is directed

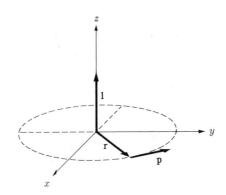

FIG. 9–17. Right-handed coordinate system, and the vector description of angular momentum.

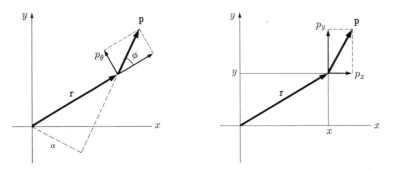

FIG. 9–18. The magnitude of the angular momentum of a particle in a plane can be expressed as $pd = p_\theta r = pr \sin \phi$. Furthermore, in terms of rectangular coordinates, we have $l = xp_y - yp_x$.

along the positive z-axis, as indicated in Fig. 9–17. We have seen that the magnitude of the angular momentum is $pd = p_\theta r$. This may be interpreted as the product of the momentum and the component of the position vector perpendicular to the momentum vector, or as the product of the magnitude of the position vector and the component of the momentum perpendicular to the position vector. In any case, the magnitude of the angular momentum is $|\mathbf{p}|\,|\mathbf{r}| \sin \phi$, where ϕ is the angle between the directions of $\mathbf{r}$ and $\mathbf{p}$, as shown in Fig. 9–18.

The angular momentum can also be expressed in terms of the components of the vectors $\mathbf{r}$ and $\mathbf{p}$ (Fig. 9–18). If we decompose $\mathbf{p}$ into the components p_x and p_y, we find that the angular-momentum contribution from p_y is $+xp_y$ (positive sense of rotation), and the contribution from p_x is $-yp_x$ (negative sense of rotation). The total angular momentum then is

$$l = xp_y - yp_x. \tag{9–9}$$

This addition of the angular-momentum contributions from p_x and p_y is completely consistent with the other expressions pd, $p_\theta r$ and $rp \sin \phi$ for the total angular momentum (see Problem 9–22). In addition to the magnitude of the angular momentum, Eq. (9–9) also gives the sign of the angular momentum.

We have then a procedure for determining both the magnitude and the direction of the angular momentum from the vectors $\mathbf{r}$ and $\mathbf{p}$, and, clearly, the angular momentum is uniquely specified by these vectors. An accepted symbolism to express the relationships among the three vectors $\mathbf{l}$, $\mathbf{r}$, and $\mathbf{p}$, both in regard to magnitude and direction, is

$$\mathbf{l} = \mathbf{r} \times \mathbf{p}.$$

The product $\mathbf{r} \times \mathbf{p}$ is called the *vector product* of the vectors $\mathbf{r}$ and $\mathbf{p}$. This product is a vector with the magnitude $l = rp \sin \phi$ and has a direction given by the advance of a right-handed screw, as described previously.

A study of Fig. 9–19 should help in understanding the direction of $\mathbf{l} = \mathbf{r} \times \mathbf{p}$. Note that when $\mathbf{r}$ and $\mathbf{p}$ are mutually perpendicular ($\phi = 90°$), $\mathbf{l}$ has its largest magnitude, and when $\mathbf{r}$ and $\mathbf{p}$ are directed along the same line, $\mathbf{l}$ has zero magnitude.

It should be noted carefully that in this type of multiplication of vectors, reversal of the order of the factors reverses the sign, and hence the direction, of the vector product. The reason for this rests on the fact that we defined the direction of $\mathbf{r} \times \mathbf{p}$ in terms of a rotation in which $\mathbf{r}$ (the first factor) is rotated toward $\mathbf{p}$ (the second factor). In the product $\mathbf{p} \times \mathbf{r}$, $\mathbf{p}$ is turned toward $\mathbf{r}$, and so the direction is opposite to that of $\mathbf{r} \times \mathbf{p}$. Consequently, for a vector product of two arbitrary vectors $\mathbf{A}$ and $\mathbf{B}$, we have

$$\mathbf{A} \times \mathbf{B} = -\mathbf{B} \times \mathbf{A}.$$

The magnitude of the vector product $\mathbf{r} \times \mathbf{p}$ can be interpreted geometrically in terms of the area of a parallelogram formed by the vectors $\mathbf{r}$ and $\mathbf{p}$, as shown in Fig. 9–20. The height of the parallelogram is $d = r \sin \phi$ and the area is $p(r \sin \phi)$.

Motion in three dimensions. Our previous discussions of angular momentum have been restricted to cases in which all motion was confined to a plane. In the case of one particle which moves under the influence of a central force, e.g., the earth's motion about the sun, the motion is always in one single plane. However, when many particles or rigid bodies are involved, the motion usually is not confined to a single plane.

Consider, for example, a flywheel on a turntable, mounted so that its axle is horizontal. If just the flywheel rotates, the motion is in a plane, but if, in addition, the turntable rotates, we have three-dimensional motion.

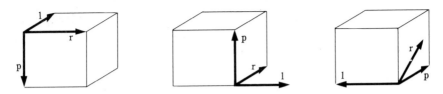

FIG. 9–19. The vector $\mathbf{l} = \mathbf{r} \times \mathbf{p}$ is perpendicular to both $\mathbf{r}$ and $\mathbf{p}$, and is in the direction of the advance of a right-handed screw when $\mathbf{r}$ is (imagined to be) rotated toward $\mathbf{p}$.

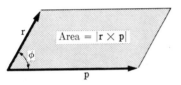

FIG. 9–20. The magnitude of the vector product is equal to the area of the parallelogram formed by $\mathbf{r}$ and $\mathbf{p}$.

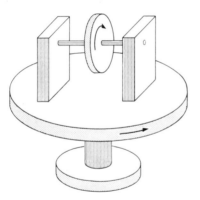

FIGURE 9–21

There are numerous examples of this kind, particularly in the mechanics of spinning bodies, where we must re-examine the concept of angular momentum. We shall study several specific examples of this kind in some detail in Chapter 13. At present, it will be sufficient to indicate, in principle, how the concept of angular momentum as developed for motion in a plane is extended to include motion in three dimensions.

We recall that in the case of motion in a plane, the angular momentum was introduced as the quantity that remained constant when the forces involved were central. It will become clear that this idea of angular momentum can be carried over, in a natural way, to an arbitrary motion by decomposing this motion into plane motions on the three coordinate planes in an xyz-coordinate system. For each of these plane motions, we can apply the previous analysis and thereby determine the conditions under which the angular momentum in each plane is conserved. This will lead to the introduction of three angular-momentum components and an angular-momentum vector.

To develop these ideas, we must first recall that angular momentum can be interpreted in terms of the sector velocity of the particle concerned. In other words, we can picture the magnitude of the angular momentum in terms of the area swept over by the radius vector in one second. The angular momentum is simply $2m$ times this area, where m is the mass of the particle.

Consider now one of the particles in a group which moves in space, as shown in Fig. 9–22. The position of the particle is described with respect to a right-handed, cartesian, rectangular xyz-coordinate system. During a sufficiently short time interval, the trajectory of the particle can be considered to be a straight-line element, and the motion can be considered to take place in the plane that contains this line element and the origin of the coordinate system. Then, from our previous considerations on plane motion, the angular momentum of the particle can be represented by the sector velocity, as shown. In a similar manner, we can construct planes and sectors that represent the angular momenta of the other particles in the group, but since, as a rule, these planes do not coincide, we have no way of knowing the significance, based on our previous considerations of angular momentum, of the sum of these individual momenta. In order to make such an addition of angular momenta meaningful, the motions of the particles must be referred to one plane. Although this is not possible when we use the total momenta of the particles, it

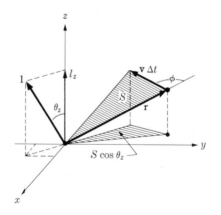

FIGURE 9–22

can be accomplished if we use the projections of the motions of the particles on the three coordinate planes. Then in each of these planes, we have motions and trajectories that refer to the particles in the group, and we can introduce sector velocities and angular momenta of these plane motions. These sector velocities and angular momenta then can be added as before.

Let us look more closely at the projection of the motion of one of the points on the xy-plane, as shown in Fig. 9–22. The sector velocity of the projection in the xy-plane is simply the total sector velocity of the particle multiplied by the cosine of the angle between the trajectory plane and the xy-plane. This angle is the same as the angle between the normals of the planes, that is, the angle θ_z between the z-axis and the normal to the sector plane, as shown. Thus, if the magnitude of the sector velocity is S, the sector velocity in the xy-plane is $S_{xy} = S \cos \theta_z$. Instead of using the notation S_{xy}, it is more convenient and equally descriptive to use S_z, so that $S_z = S \cos \theta_z$. In other words, S_z is the sector velocity associated with the motion about the z-axis in the plane perpendicular to the z-axis. In a completely analogous manner, we can obtain $S_x = S \cos \theta_x$ and $S_y = S \cos \theta_y$ for the sector velocities in the yz- and zx-planes, respectively. Here the angles θ_x and θ_y are the angles between the normal to the sector plane and the x- and y-axes, respectively.

Just as there is an angular momentum $l = 2mS$ associated with the sector velocity S, we shall similarly introduce the angular-momentum components $l_x = 2mS_x = l \cos \theta_x$, $l_y = 2mS_y = l \cos \theta_y$, and $l_z = 2mS_z = l \cos \theta_z$, where we have used $S_x = S \cos \theta_x$, etc., and $l = 2mS$. Using this interpretation of the angular-momentum components, we can define an angular-momentum vector with the components l_x, l_y, and l_z. The component l_z is then directed along the z-axis, and represents the angular momentum associated with the motion in the xy-plane. Similarly, the components l_x and l_y are related to the angular momenta in the yz- and zx-planes, respectively. Together they form an angular-momentum vector which is perpendicular to the initial sector plane, as shown in Fig. 9–22. (The angle between the resultant vector and the z-axis is given by $\cos \theta_z = l_z/l$, and so on, i.e., the direction of $\mathbf{l}$ is the same as the direction of the normal to the sector plane, since $l_z/l = S_z/S$.)

It should be emphasized that angular momentum is evaluated with respect to a *point* and that the angular momentum depends upon the location of this point. The components of the angular-momentum vector on the coordinate axes of a coordinate system with its origin as the reference point often are referred to as the angular momentum about the axes. It should be kept in mind, though, that these components ordinarily cannot be determined until the reference point for the angular momentum has been chosen.

The angular momentum associated with the motion in the xy-plane can be expressed as $l_z = xp_y - yp_x$, as shown in the foregoing discussion, and similar expressions apply to the other components; that is,

$$l_x = yp_z - zp_y,$$
$$l_y = zp_x - xp_z, \quad\quad\quad (9\text{--}10)$$
$$l_z = xp_y - yp_x.$$

The magnitude of the total angular momentum then can be expressed as

$$l = \sqrt{l_x^2 + l_y^2 + l_z^2} . \quad\quad\quad (9\text{--}11)$$

As shown in the previous section, this magnitude can also be expressed as

$$l = rp \sin \phi, \quad\quad\quad (9\text{--}12)$$

where r is the magnitude of the radius vector $\mathbf{r}$ from the reference point to the particle, p is the magnitude of the momentum $\mathbf{p}$, and ϕ is the angle between the vectors $\mathbf{r}$ and $\mathbf{p}$ (Fig. 9–22).

According to Eq. (9–10), the components of the angular momentum of the particle are expressed in terms of certain products of the components of the position vector $\mathbf{r}$ and the momentum vector $\mathbf{p}$. The angular-momentum vector then is uniquely determined by the position vector $\mathbf{r}$ and the momentum vector $\mathbf{p}$. The three relations in Eq. (9–10) can be conveniently condensed into the one vector relation

$$\mathbf{l} = \mathbf{r} \times \mathbf{p}. \quad\quad\quad (9\text{--}13)$$

As we have seen, this vector has the magnitude $rp \sin \phi$, as given by Eq. (9–12). With regard to the direction of $\mathbf{l} = \mathbf{r} \times \mathbf{p}$, we refer to the discussion of the special case of plane motion (Fig. 9–19).

In a completely analogous manner, we can obtain the angular-momentum vectors $\mathbf{l}$ of the other particles in the system. Since the angular-momentum components that represent motions in a plane can be summed, we can characterize the total angular momentum of a system of particles by the components $L_x = \sum l_x$, $L_y = \sum l_y$, and $L_z = \sum l_z$, and these components define the total angular-momentum vector $\mathbf{L}$ of the system of particles. This vector is then the vector sum of the individual angular-momentum vectors:

$$\mathbf{L} = \sum \mathbf{l} = \mathbf{l}_1 + \mathbf{l}_2 + \cdots. \quad\quad\quad (9\text{--}14)$$

What we have done so far is to generalize the definition of the angular-momentum concept to include motion of particles which do not all move in the same plane. This definition is a natural extension of angular momentum of particles in a plane. However, we recall that the introduction of the angular momentum in a plane was motivated by the observed conservation of angular momentum of a particle system under the influence of a central force. We must now examine the total vector angular momentum in this respect, and investigate what happens to the total angular momentum when the particles not only interact among themselves with central forces, but also are acted upon by central forces toward the origin O. We observe that if forces are central, their *force components* on the coordinate planes *are also central*. (After all, if a force points toward O, the force components on the coordinate planes also point toward O.) In other words, the problem then can be reduced to the familiar one in which particles move in planes under the influence of central forces. We have noted in the previous section that, under such conditions, in each of the coordinate planes, the components of the total angular momentum remain constant. Consequently, the total angular-momentum vector of the system of particles also remains constant.

EXAMPLE. A particle that moves in space has the momentum components $p_x = -1$, $p_y = -2$ and $p_z = 4$ kgm·m/sec as it passes the point $x = 1$, $y = 2$, $z = -3$ m. (a) Determine the angular momentum of the particle with respect to the origin. (b) What is the perpendicular distance (the lever arm) from the line of motion of the particle at that point to the origin? (c) What is the angle between the directions of the position vector **r** and the momentum vector **p**?

Using Eq. (9–10) for the components of the angular momentum, we obtain

$$l_x = 2 \cdot 4 - (-3)(-2) = 2,$$

$$l_y = (-3)(-1) - 1 \cdot 4 = -1,$$

$$l_z = 1 \cdot (-2) - 2 \cdot (-1) = 0.$$

The magnitude of the angular momentum is then

$$l = \sqrt{2^2 + 1^2 + 0^2} = \sqrt{5} \text{ kgm·m}^2/\text{sec}.$$

This magnitude can also be expressed as $l = pD$, where D is the lever arm of the momentum, and p is the magnitude of the momentum, which is expressed as

$$p = \sqrt{1^2 + 2^2 + 4^2} = \sqrt{21} \text{ kgm·m/sec}.$$

Therefore, the lever arm is

$$D = \frac{l}{p} = \frac{\sqrt{5}}{\sqrt{21}} \simeq 0.49 \text{ m}.$$

The magnitude of the angular momentum can also be expressed as $l = rp \sin \phi$, where ϕ is the angle between $\mathbf{r}$ and $\mathbf{p}$. The magnitude of the position vector is

$$r = \sqrt{1^2 + 2^2 + 3^2} = \sqrt{14}$$

and we obtain

$$\sin \phi = \frac{\sqrt{5}}{\sqrt{14} \cdot \sqrt{21}} \simeq 0.13 \quad \text{or} \quad \phi \simeq 7.5°.$$

9–4 Spin and orbital angular momentum. Thus far, the essential result that we have obtained in connection with angular momentum is the following. If a system of particles, including a rigid body, moves in space under the influence of an external force, the total vector angular momentum of the system with respect to the force center is constant, provided that the internal interactions among the particles are central. In this section, nothing basically new will be added to this result. We shall merely discuss the fact that the total angular momentum can be considered as the sum of two parts, one part which is attributed to the motion of the center of mass of the system, and the other part that accounts for the motion with respect to the center of mass. This separation often is quite convenient, particularly when we deal with the motion of spinning rigid bodies, in which case the separate angular-momentum contributions from the translation and from the rotation of the body are easily found. Also, it should be mentioned that on the atomic and subatomic scales there often is a "spin" angular momentum associated with a particle, and this contribution must be considered in a determination of the total angular momentum of the particle.

In order to prove that the total angular momentum can be decomposed into the two parts as mentioned, we determine the total angular momentum of a collection of particles with respect to a fixed point, which we choose as the origin of the coordinate system. Let one of these particles have a position $\mathbf{r}$, specified by (x, y, z), and a momentum $\mathbf{p}$, specified by (p_x, p_y, p_z). The center of mass of the whole particle system has the position vector $\mathbf{R}$, specified by (X, Y, Z), and a velocity $\mathbf{V}$, specified by (V_x, V_y, V_z). The z-component of the angular momentum of a particle in the system, according to Eq. (9–10), is $l_z = xp_y - yp_x$, and the z-component of the total angular momentum is obtained by summing over all the particles, so that $L_z = \sum l_z$.

We can set $x = X + x^*$, where x^* is the x-coordinate of the particle, as measured from the center of mass. Similarly, we have $p_y = mV_y + p_y^*$, where p_y^* is the momentum with respect to the center of mass. The other components of $\mathbf{p}$ and $\mathbf{r}$ are expressed in the same manner. For the z-component of the angular momentum of one of the particles, we then obtain

$$l_z = (X + x^*)(mV_y + p_y^*) - (Y + y^*)(mV_x + p_x^*)$$

$$= (XmV_y - YmV_x) + \underbrace{(x^*p_y^* - y^*p_x^*)}_{l_z^*}$$

$$+ (Xp_y^* - Yp_x^*) + (V_ymx^* - V_xmy^*).$$

If now we sum over all the particles in the system, the first group of terms gives $XP_y - YP_x$, where P_x and P_y are the components of the total momentum $\mathbf{P} = \sum \mathbf{p}$. The second term gives the total angular-momentum component $L_z^* = \sum l_z^*$, with respect to the center of mass. The remaining terms add to zero since $\sum p_y^* = \sum p_x^* = 0$, and similarly, $\sum mx^* = \sum my^* = 0$. The z-component of the total angular momentum is then

$$L_z = L_z^* + (XP_y - YP_x) = L_z^* + (\mathbf{R} \times \mathbf{P})_z. \qquad (9\text{--}15)$$

The x- and y-components of the angular momentum are then similarly obtained, and the result is summarized concisely by the vector relation

$$\mathbf{L} = \mathbf{L}^* + \mathbf{R} \times \mathbf{P}. \qquad (9\text{--}16)$$

Particularly, when we deal with motion of rigid bodies, the contribution $\mathbf{R} \times \mathbf{P}$ from the translational motion is called the *orbital angular momentum* and the contribution $\mathbf{L}^*$ resulting from the rotation of the body is called the *spin angular momentum*.

Equation (9–16) then states that the total angular momentum of a system of particles or of a rigid body is simply the vector sum of the orbital angular momentum and the spin angular momentum. This summation is illustrated schematically in Fig. 9–23. To obtain this result, we operated with the components of the position and momentum vectors. However, it could have been obtained more directly in terms of vector algebra,

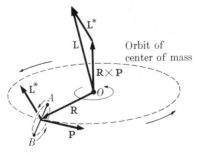

FIG. 9–23. The total angular momentum, with respect to a fixed point O, is the vector sum of the orbital and the spin angular momenta of the system; that is, $\mathbf{L} = \mathbf{L}^* + \mathbf{R} \times \mathbf{P}$.

had we shown that the distributive law $(\mathbf{A} + \mathbf{B}) \times \mathbf{C} = \mathbf{A} \times \mathbf{C} + \mathbf{B} \times \mathbf{C}$ applies also to the vector product. We leave it as an exercise to prove this relation, and then to carry through the foregoing analysis in terms of vector algebra (Problem 9–31).

EXAMPLE 1. The center of mass of a uniform circular disc of radius R and mass M slides with a speed V in an xy-plane along the line $y = 2R$ in the negative x-direction. At the same time, the disc spins with an angular velocity $\omega = V/R$ in the negative direction of rotation (clockwise when viewed from the positive z-axis). What is the total angular momentum of the disc with respect to the origin?

The orbital angular momentum of the disc is $MV(2R)$, since the lever arm is $2R$, with respect to the origin. The spin angular momentum is $L^* = -I_0\omega$, and when we introduce the quantity $I_0 = MR^2/2$, we obtain

$$L^* = -\frac{MR^2}{2}\frac{V}{R} = -\frac{MVR}{2}.$$

The total angular momentum is then

$$L = MVR - \frac{MVR}{2} = \frac{MVR}{2}.$$

EXAMPLE 2. A bar of length R rotates in a horizontal plane, about one of its ends, with a constant angular velocity Ω, as shown in Fig. 9–24. On its other end, this bar carries a "propeller," consisting of another bar that has on its ends two particles, each of mass m and separated by a distance d, as shown. This propeller spins with an angular velocity ω in a plane perpendicular to the first

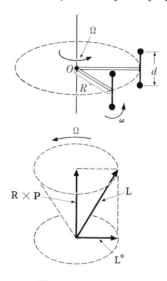

FIGURE 9–24

bar. What is the angular momentum of the propeller with respect to O? The mass of the bars may be neglected.

The spin angular momentum $\mathbf{L}^*$ of the propeller has the magnitude $L^* = m\omega\, d^2/2$ and is directed along the horizontal bar.

The orbital angular momentum $\mathbf{R} \times \mathbf{P}$ of the propeller has the magnitude $2mR^2\,\Omega$ and is directed upward.

The total angular momentum of the propeller is then $\mathbf{L} = \mathbf{L}^* + \mathbf{R} \times \mathbf{P}$, and since $\mathbf{L}^*$ circles around with the first bar and $\mathbf{R} \times \mathbf{P}$ remains fixed, it follows that the arrow which represents $\mathbf{L}$ traces out the surface of a cone that has a vertex at O.

The magnitude of $\mathbf{L}$ is $L = \sqrt{(m\omega\, d^2/2)^2 + (2mR^2\Omega)^2}$.

9–5 Angular impulse and torque. *Single particle.* We have seen that centrally directed impulses and forces do not change the angular momentum of a point mass. This, in fact, was the basis upon which the angular-momentum concept was developed. Now, consider an impulse $\mathbf{J}$ which does have a component in a direction perpendicular to the central or radial direction.

If the impulse is applied to a particle of momentum $\mathbf{p}_1$, the momentum changes to the value $\mathbf{p}_2 = \mathbf{p}_1 + \mathbf{J}$. In order to determine the change of the angular momentum produced by this impulse, we consider first the angular momentum that is associated with the motion in the xy-plane. Thus, if the x- and y-components of the impulse are J_x and J_y, the changes of the momenta in these directions are simply $\Delta p_x = J_x$ and $\Delta p_y = J_y$. According to Eq. (9–10), the change of the z-component of the angular momentum is

$$\Delta l_z = xJ_y - yJ_x$$

if the impulse is *instantaneous*. Similar expressions may be obtained for the changes of the x- and y-components of the angular momentum. The total change of the angular momentum then can be described by the vector

$$\Delta l = \mathbf{G} = \mathbf{r} \times \mathbf{J}. \qquad (9\text{–}17)$$

This net change of the angular momentum is often called the *angular impulse* on the particle, with respect to the chosen reference point.

Many particles. Suppose now that the particle receiving the external impulse is a member of a group of particles which interact only among themselves with central forces. In the absence of the external impulse, the angular momentum and, of course, the momentum remain constant. Hence the changes of the total momentum and the total angular momentum are caused solely by the external impulse. The momentum change is $\Delta \mathbf{P} = \mathbf{J}$ regardless of the point of application of the impulse. The angular-momentum change, on the other hand, does depend on the point of application. If **r** is the position vector of the particle that receives the impulse, the total angular-momentum change, with respect to the origin of **r**, then is

$$\Delta \mathbf{L} = \mathbf{r} \times \mathbf{J}. \tag{9-18}$$

We can regard this total change of the angular momentum as a result of changes of both the orbital and the spin angular momenta of the particle system. If **R** is the position vector of the center of mass, the change of the orbital part is simply $\mathbf{R} \times \Delta \mathbf{P} = \mathbf{R} \times \mathbf{J}$. The remaining part $\Delta \mathbf{L} - \mathbf{R} \times \mathbf{J} = (\mathbf{r} - \mathbf{R}) \times \mathbf{J}$ must be the change of the spin angular momentum of the system. We note that $\mathbf{r} - \mathbf{R} = \mathbf{r}^*$ is the position vector of the point of application of the impulse, with respect to the center of mass of the particle system. Consequently, to obtain the change of the spin angular momentum of the system, we simply multiply the impulse by the lever arm to the center of mass. Expressed in vector form, this is

$$\Delta \mathbf{L}^* = \mathbf{r}^* \times \mathbf{J}. \tag{9-19}$$

EXAMPLE. Three particles connected by bars of negligible mass are located at the corners of an equilateral triangle, as shown in Fig. 9-25. The masses of the particles are all the same, equal to m, and the distances between the particles are d. Particle A is given an impulse parallel to the line that connects C and B. Describe the motion after the impulse, if the system slides on a frictionless surface.

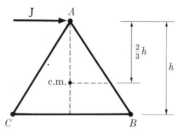

FIGURE 9-25

First, we determine the location of the center of mass, c.m. We find that it is located a distance $\frac{2}{3}h$ from A, as shown, where $h = d\sqrt{3}/2$. After the impulse, the center of mass will move with the velocity

$$V = \frac{J}{3m},$$

and the body will have acquired a spin angular momentum

$$L^* = J\tfrac{2}{3}h = \frac{Jd}{\sqrt{3}}.$$

We can also express the angular momentum in terms of the angular velocity of the triangle by introducing the moment of inertia of the system:

$$I_0 = m_1 r_1^2 + m_2 r_2^2 + m_3 r_3^2,$$

where r_1, r_2, r_3 are the distances from the particles to the center of mass. In this case, these distances are all fixed and the same, $r_1 = \frac{2}{3}h = d/\sqrt{3}$. The moment of inertia is then

$$I_0 = 3m\,\frac{d^2}{3} = md^2,$$

and the angular momentum about the center of mass is

$$L^* = I_0\omega = md^2\omega = \frac{Jd}{\sqrt{3}}.$$

Thus, we obtain

$$\omega = \frac{J}{\sqrt{3}\,md}.$$

Torque. Let us now consider the effect of a continuously acting force, rather than that of an instantaneous impulse. The angular momentum of the particle acted on by the force now changes continuously and the time rate of change of the angular momentum is called the *torque* of the force. If the position vector of a particle is $\mathbf{r}$ and its momentum is $\mathbf{p}$, the angular momentum with respect to the origin of $\mathbf{r}$ is $\mathbf{l} = \mathbf{r} \times \mathbf{p}$. To study the rate of change of the angular momentum, we first study the rate of change of one of the components. The z-component of the angular momentum is $l_z = xp_y - yp_x$ and the rate of change is then

$$\frac{dl_z}{dt} = \frac{dx}{dt}\,p_y + x\,\frac{dp_y}{dt} - \frac{dy}{dt}\,p_x - y\,\frac{dp_x}{dt}.$$

The first and the third terms in this expression cancel each other, since $dx/dt = p_x/m$ and $dy/dt = p_y/m$. The second and fourth terms can be written xF_y and yF_x respectively, and the rate of change of the z-component of the angular momentum then can be written as

$$\frac{dl_z}{dt} = xF_y - yF_x. \tag{9-20}$$

Similar expressions are obtained for the rate of change of the other components. The rate of change of the angular momentum, or the torque, then is a vector $\boldsymbol{\tau}$, with the components of the vector product $\mathbf{r} \times \mathbf{F}$, and we have

$$\boldsymbol{\tau} = \frac{d\mathbf{l}}{dt} = \mathbf{r} \times \mathbf{F}. \tag{9-21}$$

To obtain this result, we operated with the components of the vectors **l**, **r**, and **p**. We could have obtained the same result by operating directly with the vectors, had the relation $d(\mathbf{r} \times \mathbf{p})/dt = \mathbf{r} \times (d\mathbf{p}/dt) + (d\mathbf{r}/dt) \times \mathbf{p}$ been proved valid. We leave it as an exercise to prove this result, and then to apply it in the derivation of the result (9–20) (see Problem 9–39).

The magnitude of the torque then can be expressed as the product of the force and the lever arm of the force, with respect to the reference point $\mathbf{r} = 0$. The lever arm has the magnitude $r \sin \phi$, where ϕ is the angle between the directions of **r** and **F**, and we have

$$\tau = Fd = Fr \sin \phi.$$

Clearly, the magnitude of τ can also be interpreted as the product of the component $F \sin \phi$ of the force perpendicular to **r** and the distance r to the reference point (see Fig. 9–26).

In the case of motion in a plane, we have $l = mr^2\omega$ and the rate of change of the angular momentum becomes

$$\frac{dl}{dt} = mr^2 \frac{d\omega}{dt} + 2m\omega r \frac{dr}{dt} = mr^2\alpha + 2m\omega r \frac{dr}{dt}, \qquad (9\text{--}22)$$

where

$$\alpha = \frac{d\omega}{dt}$$

is the *angular acceleration*. If r is constant, which, for example, is the case when the particle belongs to a rigid body that rotates about a fixed axis, the rate of change of angular momentum is simply $mr^2\alpha$. The second term in Eq. (9–22) represents the change of the angular momentum, which is a result of the change of the lever arm. This change is present

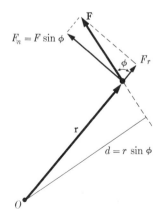

FIG. 9–26. The magnitude of the torque $\tau = \mathbf{r} \times \mathbf{F}$ is $Fr \sin \phi = F_n r = Fd$.

even if the angular velocity of the particle remains constant. We shall further discuss this relation in Chapter 11.

EXAMPLE. A mass m is attached to a string which passes through a hole in a horizontal frictionless table at a point O. Pivoted at O is one corner of a stick which serves to push the mass in a path about O (Fig. 9–27).

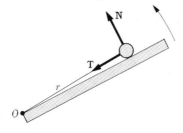

FIGURE 9–27

(a) If the normal force N is maintained at a constant value, and if the length of the string is kept constant, what are the angular acceleration, angular momentum, and angle turned through after t sec?

The torque on the mass is $\tau = Nr$, and so from $\tau = mr^2\alpha$, the angular acceleration is $\alpha = N/mr$ (dr/dt is zero). Since the torque is constant, the rate of change of angular momentum is constant. Therefore, if the system started from rest, the angular momentum is $l = \tau t = Nrt$. The angular velocity is $\omega = \alpha t = (N/mr)t$. Since the angular acceleration is constant, the angle traversed is $\theta = \alpha t^2/2 = Nt^2/2mr$.

(b) Suppose now that the stick rotates at a constant angular velocity ω, and that the mass is allowed to slide out along the length of the stick at a rate dr/dt. What is the normal force?

Here the angular velocity of the mass is constant, and the angular momentum increases only because the mass moves to a larger radius. Since $mr^2\alpha$ is zero, we have

$$Nr = 2mr\omega \frac{dr}{dt}$$

or

$$N = 2m\omega \frac{dr}{dt}.$$

The foregoing result can be applied directly to the total angular momentum of a system of particles or a rigid body acted upon by external forces. The forces on a particular particle in such a system fall into two categories, internal and external forces. Either type, of course, can change the angular momentum of that particle, but only the external forces (or, rather, external torques) can change the angular momentum of the system. The reason for this is that the internal forces are central, and since they are interaction forces, always act in pairs. Consider the angular momentum of the earth-moon system about the sun, for example. (Here we ignore the angular momentum either body has by virtue of rotation about its own axis.) The moon exerts a gravitational force on the earth, and so the angular momentum of the earth about the sun varies. The earth exerts a gravitational force on the moon, and so the moon's angular momentum also varies. But, because the earth-moon and moon-earth gravitational forces are equal and opposite (interaction forces), and have the same line of action (central forces), the torques on these two bodies are equal and opposite and the angular momentum of the *system* remains constant. Similarly, if an external force (torque) were exerted on, say, the earth, this external torque would not be equal to the rate of change of the angular momentum of the earth alone, but would be equal to the rate of change of the angular momentum of the system, earth plus moon. Then, for a system of particles which interact only among themselves, we have

$$\sum \tau = \frac{d\mathbf{L}}{dt},\qquad\qquad(9\text{--}23)$$

where $\mathbf{L}$ is the total *vector* angular momentum of the system, and $\sum \tau$ is the net *vector* torque on the system.

When the external torque is zero, i.e., when the external force is central or zero, the total angular-momentum vector remains constant both in magnitude and direction. If the force is zero, both the total angular momentum and the momentum are conserved, and it follows that orbital and spin angular momenta contributions individually remain constant. Consequently, in a collision that involves a system of particles or a rigid body, we can learn a great deal about the outcome of the collision from these conservation laws.

EXAMPLE. A dumbbell consists of two small balls A and B, each of mass m, attached to the ends of a bar of length d of negligible mass. The dumbbell is at rest on a horizontal, frictionless surface. Another ball C, also of mass m, moves along a line perpendicular to the dumbbell with a speed v_0, and collides with and sticks to B, as shown in Fig. 9–28. Describe the motion of the system after the collision.

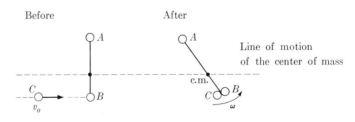

FIGURE 9–28

Here we have an isolated system of particles (no external forces in the plane of motion) and the total momentum, as well as the total angular momentum, remains constant. Conservation of momentum requires that the center of mass of the system move along a straight line with constant speed, which can be obtained from the equation

$$mv_0 = 3mV, \qquad V = \frac{v_0}{3}.$$

After the collision, the center of mass is located a distance $d/3$ from B, and this point will have a pure translational motion. The rest of the system rotates about the center of mass with an angular velocity which can be determined from the conservation of angular momentum. Before the collision, only C contributes to the angular momentum. The lever arm to the center of mass of the system is $d/3$ and the magnitude of the angular momentum is then $l = mv_0\,d/3$. After the collision, the angular momentum is $I_0\omega$, where I_0 is the moment of inertia of the system, with respect to the center of mass. We have

$$I_0 = 2m\left(\frac{d}{3}\right)^2 + m\left(\frac{2d}{3}\right)^2 = \tfrac{2}{3}md^2.$$

The angular velocity is then obtained from $I_0\omega = mv_0\,d/3$; that is,

$$\omega = \frac{v_0}{2d}.$$

Although the formal introduction of angular momentum and torque as vectors follows in a straightforward manner from the motion in a plane, a thorough familiarity with these ideas and the relation $\tau = d\mathbf{l}/dt$ requires a rather careful study of specific examples of motion involving, for example, the mechanics of spinning rigid bodies. We shall return to problems of this kind in Chapter 13.

PROBLEMS

9–1. A 2-kgm mass moves from right to left along the line $y = 0.5$ m, with velocity $v = 10$ m/sec. (a) What is the component of momentum in the θ-direction when the mass is at $x = 0$, $y = 0.5$? $x = 0.5$, $y = 0.5$? $x = 6$, $y = 0.5$? $x = 100$, $y = 0.5$? (b) What is the product $p_\theta r$ at each of these points?

9–2. Refer to Problem 9–1. At the point $x = 1$, $y = 0.5$, the mass is given an impulse which causes it to travel along the line $x = 1$ m with a velocity of 5 m/sec. What are the angular momenta with respect to the origin ($x = 0$, $y = 0$) before and after the impulse? From this, determine the direction of the impulse.

9–3. A particle of 1-kgm mass moves around the perimeter of a 1-m square, as shown in Fig. 9–29. The angular momentum about point O remains constant. Point O is centered 20 cm above the lower side of the square, and the particle has a velocity of 10 m/sec when on this lower side. What impulses must be given to the particle at the corners, A, B, C, and D?

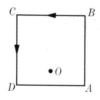

FIGURE 9–29

9–4. Show that the dimension of angular momentum is the product of the dimension of work and the dimension of time. What are the units of angular momentum in the mks, cgs, and English gravitational systems?

9–5. A particle of mass m is moving in a circle of radius R under the action of an attractive force $F = A/R^2$ from a fixed point O (A is a constant). The angular momentum of the particle about O is l. (a) What is the radius of the circular orbit in terms of l, m, and A? (b) Check the dimensions of the result.

9–6. A particle of 3-gm mass is attached to a light thread of length 1 m. The other end of the thread is attached to a fixed peg on a frictionless surface (see Fig. 9–30). The particle is given a velocity of 10 m/sec and passes within 10 cm of the peg, the thread dangling behind. When the particle gets to the end of it, the thread remains stretched and the particle there-

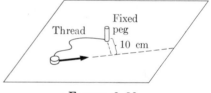

FIGURE 9–30

after moves in a circular path. What is the angular velocity of the particle?

9–7. As shown in Fig. 9–31, a particle of mass m is attached to the end of a string and moves in a circle of radius r on a frictionless horizontal table. The string passes through a frictionless hole in the table and, initially, its other end is held fixed. (a) If, now, the string is pulled so that the radius of the circular orbit decreases, how does the angular velocity change, if it is ω_0 when the radius is r_0? (b) What is the work done when the particle is pulled *slowly* in from a radius r_0 to a radius $r_0/2$? (By a slow pull is meant one for which the radial velocity of the body is at all times negligible in comparison to the tangential velocity.)

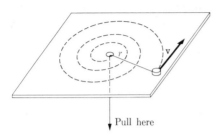

Pull here

FIGURE 9-31

9-8. Consider a situation similar to that discussed in Problem 9-7 but now let the string wind itself around a vertical circular cylinder of R. (a) Is the angular momentum of the particle, with respect to the center of the cylinder, constant in this case? Discuss. (b) If the particle starts with a velocity v_0 when the free length of the string is r_0, what is the angular momentum of the particle with respect to the center of the cylinder when the free length of the string is r? You may, if you wish, consider r to be much larger than R. Discuss the work done on the particle by the string.

9-9. A particle moves along the line $x = 100$ cm with $v_y = 10$ cm/sec. At $t = 0$, the particle is at $y = -100$ cm. (a) What area is swept out by the radius vector in the intervals 0–1 sec, 4–5 sec, 10–11 sec? (b) If the particle has a mass of $m = 3$ gm, what is its angular momentum? (c) What is the angular velocity at $t = 0, 4, 10$ and 20 sec?

9-10. A satellite moves in an elliptic orbit about the earth. When it crosses the minor axis of the ellipse, the speed is v_0. What is the round-trip time if the major and minor axes of the ellipse are $2a$ and $2b$, respectively? (The area of an ellipse is πab.)

9-11. Refer to Fig. 9-10 in the text. Show that the total angular mo-

mentum of the two interacting particles can be expressed as

$$l = \mu \, d^2 \omega,$$

where ω is the angular velocity, $\mu = m_a m_b/(m_a + m_b)$ is the reduced mass, and d is the distance between the particles.

9-12. Refer to Fig. 9-10 in the text. Let the masses of the particles be the same, $m_a = m_b$, and let the relaxed length of the spring be d_0. The system is set in motion by stretching the spring to the length $2d_0$, and then releasing it, so that each particle is given a speed v perpendicular to the spring. (a) What is the angular velocity of the system at the moment when the length of the spring is $3d_0/2$? (b) What then is the radial velocity component of each particle? The spring constant is K.

9-13. Consider a man on a turntable, as shown in Fig. 9-11. He has a weight in each hand. By proper motion of his arms, he is able to turn himself from one angular position to another, starting from rest. Explain how this can be done and how it is consistent with the law of conservation of angular momentum.

9-14. Two skaters, each of mass 50 kgm, approach each other along parallel paths separated by 3 m. The skaters have equal (but oppositely directed) velocities of 10 m/sec. The first skater carries a long light pole, 3 m long, and the second skater grabs the end of it as he passes. (Assume frictionless ice.) (a) Describe, giving pertinent velocities, the motion of the skaters after they are connected by the pole. (b) Suppose one of the skaters then pulls on the pole and manages to reduce his distance to 1 m from the other skater. What then is their motion? (c) Compare the kinetic energy of the system in parts (a) and (b).

9–15. Two particles of masses m_1 and m_2 are connected by a string of length d (neglect the mass of the string) and are lying at rest on a frictionless table with the string stretched between them. The particle m_2 is given an impulse perpendicular to the string, and is thereby given an initial velocity v_0. It is assumed that a central inter-action is provided by the string between the particles. (a) Describe the motion of the bodies after the impulse. (b) What is the tension in the string during this motion?

9–16. Two particles A and B of masses m_a and m_b are lying on a frictionless horizontal table. They are connected by a flexible stretched string that runs through a frictionless small ring O, which is fixed on the table. Particle A is originally a distance r_a from O, and then, at $t = 0$, is given an impulse at right angles to the string such that its velocity becomes v_0. (a) Determine the speed of particle B as a function of the distance $OA = r$. (b) What is the tension in the string as a function of r?

9–17. Determine the moment of inertia, with respect to one end, of a straight uniform bar of length L and mass M (a) approximately, by dividing the bar into three equal parts and treating them as mass points, with the masses concentrated at the centers of the elements, and (b) exactly, by integration.

9–18. What is the moment of inertia of a thin rod of mass M which has been bent into the shape of a circle of radius R? (The moment of inertia is referred to the center of the circle.) Why is this moment of inertia larger than it would be for the same mass of material hammered into a flat disc of radius R?

9–19. What are the radii of gyration of the following bodies: (a) a uniform disc of radius R about its center, (b) a thin uniform rod of length L about one end, (c) a thin uniform rod of length L about its center?

9–20. A body located at a point A at $y = 3$ m, $x = 0$ receives an impulse $J_x = -5$ kgm·m/sec. What is the angular momentum of the body after the impulse, with respect to the origin O? with respect to A? with respect to the point $x = 0$, $y = 6$?

9–21. A body originally at rest at $x = 2$ m, $y = 0$ receives an impulse $J_y = 6$ kgm·m/sec in the y-direction. At a later time, when the body passes point A, $x = 2$ m, $y = 5$ m, it receives another impulse with the components $J_x = -4$ and $J_y = -2$ kgm·m/sec. (a) What is the angular momentum of the body after the second impulse, with respect to the origin? (b) What is the angular momentum after the second impulse, with respect to point A?

9–22. Refer to Fig. 9–18 and show that pd, $p_\theta r$, $xp_y - yp_x$, and $|r| |p| \sin \phi$ are all equivalent.

9–23. A body of mass 10 kgm has a velocity $v = 10$ m/sec directed at an angle of $\theta = 30°$ to the x-axis. At a certain instant, the body is at the point $x = 3$ m, $y = 4$ m. (a) What are the x- and y-components of the body's momentum? (b) Find the angular momentum from each of the four expressions given in Problem 9–22.

9–24. In the text we used the symbolism $x \to y$ to describe the direction of the z-axis in a right-handed coordinate system. Using the same symbolism, express the directions of (a) the x- and y-axes, and (b) the direction of the **l**-vector in terms of the radius vector **r** and the momentum **p**.

9–25. A particle has the momentum components $p_x = 1$, $p_y = 2$, $p_z = 3$

when it passes the point $x = 4$, $y = -5$, $z = 3$ in space. (a) What is the angular momentum of the particle with respect to the origin? (b) What is the perpendicular distance from the line of motion of the particle to the origin? (c) With respect to what point, or points, is the angular momentum zero?

9–26. A particle moves in an xy-plane along the line $x = 5$ with a constant momentum $p_y = +10$ kgm·m/sec. (a) What is the angular momentum of the particle, with respect to the origin $x = 0$, $y = 0$, $z = 0$, when the particle is at $x = 5$ m, $y = 5$ m? Indicate all components of the angular momentum. (b) If, instead, the reference point is taken to be $z = +1$ m, what then are the angular-momentum components in the x-, y- and z-directions? (c) How does the angular momentum change when the reference point is moved from $z = -\infty$ to $z = +\infty$ along the z-axis? Discuss, in a similar manner, the situations in which the reference point is moved along the x- and the y-axes.

9–27. Let $\mathbf{A}$ be a vector along the x-axis, $\mathbf{B}$ be a vector along the y-axis, and $\mathbf{C}$ be a vector along the z-axis. Indicate in a sketch the directions of $\mathbf{A} \times \mathbf{B}$, $\mathbf{B} \times \mathbf{A}$, $\mathbf{C} \times \mathbf{B}$, $-\mathbf{C} \times \mathbf{B}$, $\mathbf{A} \times (\mathbf{B} \times \mathbf{C})$, $\mathbf{C} \times (\mathbf{B} \times \mathbf{C})$, $\mathbf{B} \times (\mathbf{C} \times \mathbf{B})$, and $(\mathbf{B} \times \mathbf{C}) \times \mathbf{B}$.

9–28. A particle moves in a plane $x = x_0$ parallel with the yz-plane. At the point x_0, y_0, z_0, the magnitude of its momentum is p and its direction makes an angle θ with the positive y-axis. (a) What is the magnitude of the angular momentum, with respect to the origin? (b) Discuss the magnitude of the angular momentum as a function of the angle θ.

For what angles is the magnitude of the angular momentum maximum and minimum, and what are the maximum

and minimum values of l? Discuss.

9–29. A unit vector has a magnitude equal to unity. If the unit vectors in the x-, y- and z-directions are denoted by $\mathbf{i}$, $\mathbf{j}$ and $\mathbf{k}$, respectively, prove that $\mathbf{i} \times \mathbf{i} = 0$, $\mathbf{j} \times \mathbf{j} = 0$, $\mathbf{k} \times \mathbf{k} = 0$, $\mathbf{i} \times \mathbf{j} = \mathbf{k}$, $\mathbf{j} \times \mathbf{k} = \mathbf{i}$, $\mathbf{k} \times \mathbf{i} = \mathbf{j}$. From these properties of the unit vectors, show, by direct term-by-term vector multiplication of the vectors $\mathbf{A} = A_x\mathbf{i} + A_y\mathbf{j} + A_z\mathbf{k}$ and $\mathbf{B} = B_x\mathbf{i} + B_y\mathbf{j} + B_z\mathbf{k}$ and by use of the distributive law, that the components of the vector product $\mathbf{C} = \mathbf{A} \times \mathbf{B}$ are $C_x = A_yB_z - B_yA_z$, $C_y = A_zB_x - B_zA_x$, $C_z = A_xB_y - B_xA_y$.

9–30. A line in space goes between two points P_1 ($x_1 = 2$, $y_1 = -2$, $z_1 = 3$) and P_2 ($x_2 = 1$, $y_2 = 3$, $z_2 = -2$). What is the perpendicular distance from this line to the origin? (*Hint.* What is the vector product of the vectors corresponding to P_1P_2 and OP_1?)

9–31. Use the components of the vector product as given in Eq. (9–10) in the text and prove the distributive law $(\mathbf{A} + \mathbf{B}) \times \mathbf{C} = \mathbf{A} \times \mathbf{B} + \mathbf{B} \times \mathbf{C}$ for the vector product. Use this result to prove the relation $\mathbf{L} = \mathbf{L}^* + \mathbf{R} \times \mathbf{P}$ [Eq. (9–16) in the text], by direct operation with vectors.

9–32. A straight, uniform, thin bar of length $d = 2$ m and mass $M = 3$ kgm slides on a horizontal xy-plane, so that its center of mass moves with a speed $V = 0.5$ m/sec along the line $y = 2d = 4$ m in the positive x-direction. The bar spins in a clockwise direction with an angular velocity $\omega = 4$ sec^{-1}. (a) What is the total angular momentum of the bar, with respect to the origin $x = 0$, $y = 0$? (b) With respect to what points is the total angular momentum zero?

9–33. Consider the bar in Problem 9–32. Again the bar spins with the angular velocity $\omega = 4 \sec^{-1}$ in a plane parallel with the xy-plane. However, the center of mass now moves in the yz-plane along the line $y = 2d$ in the positive z-direction, with the speed $V = 0.5$ m/sec. (a) What now is the angular momentum with respect to the origin? (b) Is there any point with respect to which the total angular momentum is zero?

9–34. Particles A, B, and C are acted on by constant forces $\mathbf{F}_a$, $\mathbf{F}_b$, and $\mathbf{F}_c$, respectively, with components as given in the following table.

	F_x	F_y	F_z (newtons)
$\mathbf{F}_a$:	0	3	4
$\mathbf{F}_b$:	2	−2	1
$\mathbf{F}_c$:	0	0	5

The masses of the particles, in kgm, are $m_a = 1$, $m_b = 2$, and $m_c = 1$. The particles start from initial rest positions $(x_a = 3,\ y_a = 0,\ z_a = 0)$, $(x_b = 0,\ y_b = 2,\ z_b = 0)$, $(x_c = 0,\ y_c = 0,\ z_c = 1)$. (a) Describe the motion of the center of mass of the system. (b) What is the total angular momentum of the system as a function of time, with respect to the origin $(x = 0,\ y = 0,\ z = 0)$? What is the angular momentum, with respect to the center of mass?

9–35. A particle with a momentum $\mathbf{p}$ has an angular momentum $\mathbf{l}$ with respect to a fixed point in space. The particle receives an impulse perpendicular to $\mathbf{p}$. Does this mean that the corresponding increment $\Delta\mathbf{l}$ of the angular momentum is perpendicular to $\mathbf{l}$? Can $\Delta\mathbf{l}$ be zero under these conditions? Discuss.

9–36. A body of mass $m = 2$ kgm moves in a circle of radius $R = 0.5$ m in the xy-plane about the origin with a speed equal to $v = 5$ m/sec. It receives an instantaneous impulse, in the

z-direction, of magnitude $J = 6$ n·sec. What is the new angular momentum of the particle? Give both the magnitude and the direction.

9–37. A force has the components $F_x = 2$, $F_y = 3$, and $F_z = -4$ newtons. It is applied at a point $x = 2$, $y = 1$, and $z = 3$ m on a rigid body. What is the torque (magnitude and direction) of the force with respect to the origin? Indicate the direction of the torque vector by giving the angles between the torque and the coordinate axes.

9–38. Two particles A and B, each of mass m, located at $x_a = a$, $y_a = 2a$, $z_a = -2a$ and $x_b = 2a$, $y_b = a$, $z_b = 2a$, are acted upon by a third particle C, located at the origin. A is attracted to, and B is repelled by, C with forces of magnitudes $|F_a| = c/r_a^2$ and $|F_b| = c/r_b^2$, respectively. What is the torque on the system of particles A and B considered as a unit, with respect to their center of mass? Give the magnitude and direction of the torque.

9–39. Operate with the components of the vector product as given in Eq. (9–10) in the text. Prove that $d(\mathbf{r} \times \mathbf{p}) = \mathbf{r} \times d\mathbf{p}/dt + (d\mathbf{r}/dt) \times \mathbf{p}$, and obtain $\boldsymbol{\tau} = d\mathbf{l}/dt = \mathbf{r} \times \mathbf{F}$.

9–40. A horizontal circular track of mass $M = 1.5$ kgm and radius $R = 0.5$ m is mounted on a wheel which can rotate (neglect friction) about its fixed vertical axis, as shown in Fig. 9–32. The mass of the wheel may be neglected. A toy locomotive of mass $m = 0.5$ kgm on the track starts from rest and soon reaches a constant speed $v_0 = 2$ m/sec, with respect to the laboratory system. (a) What is then the angular velocity of the wheel if it starts from rest? Indicate direction. (b) The locomotive slows and finally stops. What is the final angular velocity of the wheel? (c) If, instead of being held in position by a fixed axis, the wheel is lying on a frictionless horizontal surface, what then will be the motion of the system after the locomotive is started? Describe this motion, without a detailed analysis.

FIGURE 9–32

9–41. When two rigid bodies collide, the total angular momentum of the bodies remains constant. Does that mean that the contact forces between the bodies go through the center of mass of the bodies? Discuss.

9–42. Is it possible in a collision between rigid bodies that the spin angular momentum of one body changes, without a change of the spin angular momentum of the other?

9–43. Is it possible in a collision between two extended rigid bodies that, after the collision, both bodies have only rotational kinetic energy

about their individual centers of mass? If so, give an example.

9–44. Two small bodies, each of mass m, are connected by a stiff piece of wire, bent into the shape shown in Fig. 9–33. The system is free to slide

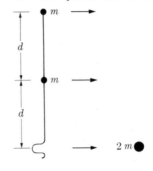

FIGURE 9–33

on a frictionless horizontal surface. The mass of the wire may be neglected. Initially, the bodies have a pure translatory motion, with velocity V. Then, a third body of mass $2m$, which is initially at rest, is caught in the spring clip. (All three masses may be regarded as mass points.) After the third mass is caught, (a) what is the center-of-mass velocity of the system, and (b) what spin angular momentum does the system have, and what is the angular velocity?

CHAPTER 10

EXAMPLES OF FORCES AND MOTION — III

Summary. Starting from observations on the motion of the moon, and continuing with the analysis of Kepler's laws of motion, we obtain Newton's universal law of gravitation. In this preliminary analysis, circular orbits are assumed. Gravitational mass and the properties of gravitational interaction are reviewed (absence of "shielding," velocity independence, etc.). A detailed analysis of Kepler's laws follows, in which the elliptical orbit of a planet is shown to imply an inverse-square-law force. The problem is then turned around, and the possible orbits of a particle in a gravitational field are discussed. As an example, the trajectory of a satellite is determined from its initial conditions. Finally, the problem of a repulsive inverse-square-law force is discussed briefly in terms of the Rutherford-scattering experiment.

The motion of planets and the moon played an important role in the development of the theory of motion and was basic to the formulation of Newton's universal law of gravitation. The sequence of events which led to this important law traced a path which involved many of the world's most profound thinkers and is a beautiful example of physics at work. Similarly, the study of the deflection of charged particles by atomic nuclei (Rutherford scattering) has had a profound influence on the development of scientific thought and has marked the opening of a new era. We have selected these examples of forces and motion for study in the present chapter.

10–1 The universal law of gravitation. *The moon-earth interaction.* Newton's first approach to the universal gravitational force involved, as is recorded in his famous *Principia*, a consideration of the motion of the moon and the motion of an object in the local gravitational field of the earth. Galileo had pointed out that all bodies fall with the same acceleration in the local gravitational field. Newton assumed that this result would be true anywhere, so that if he were able to take an object A up to the location of the moon, it would fall toward the earth with the same acceleration as the moon. Consequently, by comparing the acceleration of the moon and the acceleration of A at the earth's surface, the ratio of the gravitational forces on A at these two positions should be obtainable. Newton found from the observations of the motion of the moon that its acceleration earthward is such that it would fall a distance of about

266

15 ft 1 in. in one minute, if it started from rest. Comparing this value with the corresponding distance of fall in the local gravitational field, he concluded that the ratio of the gravitational force on a body at the earth's surface is about 60^2 times larger than the value that would be obtained at the position of the moon. This ratio is very nearly the same as $(R_2/R_1)^2$, where R_1 is the radius of the earth and R_2 is the earth-moon distance. This result suggests that the gravitational force on a body of mass m is of the form $F \simeq Cm/r^2$, where r is the distance of the body to the center of the earth and C is a constant. The experiments on interaction between a pair of bodies on the laboratory scale have indicated that the force on one is equal and opposite to the force on the other. Thus, if the analogy between the motion of the moon-earth system and the forces and motion in the laboratory is to be complete, we must assume, Newton argued, that the moon also attracts the earth with a force that corresponds to an acceleration of the earth toward the moon. This force then is proportional to the mass of the earth, and therefore if the mass of the earth and the mass of the moon are denoted by m_1 and m_2, respectively, the gravitational law should be of the form

$$F = G \frac{m_1 m_2}{r^2}, \tag{10-1}$$

where G is a constant. Actually, this constant is not only applicable to the moon-earth system but has been proven a universal constant, as we shall see below.

Sun-planet interaction. Analysis of Kepler's laws. The gravitational force law now will be put on firmer ground if we prove, as Newton did, that the law of Eq. (10-1) follows as a consequence of Kepler's description of the experimental facts regarding planetary motion. The following three statements summarize Kepler's three laws of motion:

1. The planets move around the sun in elliptical paths. The sun, in each case, is located at one focus of the ellipse.

2. The radius vector from the sun to a planet sweeps out equal areas in equal time intervals.

3. The square of the time required for a planet to complete its trip around the sun is proportional to the cube of the semimajor axis of the ellipse.

Let us now prove that these laws are consistent with Eq. (10-1). In Chapter 9, we observed that when a body moves under the influence of a central force, angular momentum is conserved. The motion of a body, under these conditions, is characterized by two of the features contained in Kepler's laws: the motion is in a single plane and the radius vector from the force center sweeps out equal areas in equal times (see Fig. 10-1).

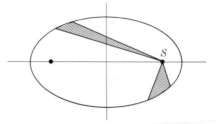

FIG. 10–1. Planets move around the sun in elliptic orbits, with the sun at one focus S. The radius vector sweeps out equal areas in equal times.

The area of an ellipse with the semiaxes a and b is πab. This total area is swept out by the radius vector in the period T of the planet (one year for the earth). But we know from Kepler's law that the area is swept out by the radius vector at a constant rate. Hence, at all times, we have

$$\frac{dA}{dt} = \frac{\pi ab}{T} \qquad (10\text{–}2)$$

for the rate at which the radius vector sweeps out area. The quantity dA/dt, on the other hand, is $r^2\omega/2$, where ω is the angular velocity $d\theta/dt$. Since the angular momentum can be written as $mr^2\omega$, we see that Eq. (10–2) implies constant angular momentum, (see also Eq. 9–5),

$$l = 2m\,\frac{dA}{dt} = \frac{2\pi mab}{T}. \qquad (10\text{–}3)$$

This, in turn, means that the force on the planet is central and directed toward the sun.

Let us now assume that the planetary orbits are circular (elliptic orbits will be considered later). For a planet to traverse a circular path about the sun, there must be a force **F** on the planet, directed toward the sun, that has a magnitude of

$$F = m\omega^2 r = \frac{m4\pi^2 r}{T^2}, \qquad (10\text{–}4)$$

where

$$T = \frac{2\pi r}{v} = \frac{2\pi}{\omega}.$$

The mass of the planet is m, r is the radius of the planet's orbit, and T is the period or time for one revolution about the sun. Under our current assumption of circular orbits, r is a constant. Equation (10–2) then says nothing about how the force varies with distance. The force could, for example, be a spring-type force, or even a constant force, or, aside from the naïvete of the idea, the force could be provided by a giant chain.

Kepler's third law, on the other hand, contains the missing information on the r dependence, since it compares the behavior of planets at various distances from the sun. It says that for all planets the square of the time required for one revolution is proportional to the cube of the semimajor axis (radius, in the present case). That is, we have from experiment

$$T^2 = C_1 r^3, \tag{10-5}$$

where C_1 is a constant that is the same *for all planets*. Expression (10-4) relates the orbit radius and period to the required force, while Eq. (10-5) gives the variation of the period with the orbit radius. Combining the two relations, we obtain $F = m 4\pi^2/C_1 r^2$. Then, for Kepler's laws to hold, the force on a planet must (a) be proportional to its inertial mass, (b) vary as the inverse square of the orbit radius, and (c) be directed toward the sun.

Using the same arguments of the mutuality of the two-body interaction forces, as in the earth-moon discussion, we are led to the general or universal law of gravitation of Eq. (10-1). This law then has been shown to be consistent with observations on falling bodies at the earth's surface, the earth-moon interaction, and planetary motion, and it is assumed to be generally valid. In other words, whenever two bodies with masses m_1 and m_2 are separated by a distance r, they are attracted toward each other with a force as given by Eq. (10-1). When the law is given in this form, it is implied that the dimensions of the interacting objects are small in comparison to r. If the bodies are both spheres, or if one body is a large sphere (for example, the earth) and the other body is small compared with r, Eq. (10-1) still applies, as can be shown simply by the methods of integral calculus (see Appendix C). (Newton's contributions to integral calculus were made after his work on gravitation.)

Determination of G. Recall that, for planetary motion, the relation we obtained from Kepler's laws, $T^2 = C_1 a^3$, was valid for *all* planets. Under our force-law assumption, we have $C_1 = 4\pi^2/Gm_s$, where m_s is the mass of the sun. Therefore, at least for all the planets, G is a constant. From these considerations alone, we cannot determine G, for we have no way of finding the mass of the sun. Similarly, from measurements of g and the radius of the earth, we can find Gm_e, but G or the mass of the earth m_e cannot be obtained separately. Thus, to be able to determine G, we must study the force produced by a known mass. Early investigators (starting around 1750) tried to measure G by studying the influence of a mountain (or some other natural mass) on the period of a pendulum, when the pendulum was placed above or beside the mountain. The total mass and shape of the mountain were estimated by surveys and geological studies. Other similar experiments involved the comparison of the periods of pendulums at the surface of the earth and at the bottom of a mine. Although many of these studies had the measurement of the mass of the earth as their prime objective, a knowledge of this mass gives G, when g is known.

The first measurement of the gravitational force between laboratory-sized objects was made by Cavendish in England in 1797. The principle of the Cavendish experiment is shown in Fig. 10–2. Two bodies A and B were mounted at the ends of a rod, which, in turn, was supported at its midpoint by a very thin wire. Large spheres of lead were placed at positions 1 and 4 and then at positions 2 and 3. The attractive forces between the suspended bodies and the spheres deflected the rod and twisted the wire slightly. The motion of the system as a torsion pendulum served to measure the torque constant of the wire, and so the attractive force between the bodies (A and B) and the lead spheres could be measured. Later, more accurate but entirely similar measurements have been made, for example, in the United States at the National Bureau of Standards. The value of G thus obtained is

$$G = (6.67 \pm 0.005) \cdot 10^{-11} \frac{\text{n} \cdot \text{m}^2}{\text{kgm}^2}. \qquad (10\text{–}6)$$

Once a value for G has been established, the mass of the earth and the mass of the sun may be obtained. In fact, for any planet that has a moon of its own, the mass may be obtained, because only the period and planet-moon distance need be known, and these can readily be measured.

As was mentioned before, the planets exert forces on one another, and their motion, therefore, is not exactly that which would be predicted if they moved only under the influence of the sun. The deviations from elliptic paths are very small but are measurable. These deviations, called

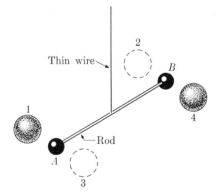

FIG. 10–2. The Cavendish experiment. Bodies A and B are attracted toward lead spheres first placed at 1 and 4, and then at 3 and 2.

perturbations, have afforded many important clues to and alternative measurements of planetary masses. The existence of both Neptune and Pluto was predicted from the perturbations they produced on the motion of nearby planets.

10–2 Properties of the gravitational interaction. In the discussion in Chapter 3 of the local gravitational field, we mentioned that the property of matter which is considered responsible for gravitational force is called the *gravitational mass.* It was pointed out that this property, measured in terms of the weight of a body, was found to be proportional to the inertial mass. The experimental evidence for this result was the fact that all bodies fall with the same acceleration in the local gravitational field. In the development of the general gravitational law, the corresponding experimental evidence for this result is the universality of G; it is the same for all bodies, regardless of their compositions, colors, shapes, etc. Numerous experiments have been designed to determine the possible influence of various factors on the gravitational attraction, but all such experiments, so far, have been negative; the only factor of importance seems to be the mass of the body. Newton himself carried out numerous experiments with pendulums that were designed to test the relation between weight and inertia; in other words, the proportionality between the gravitational and the inertial masses. He compared the periods of pendulums of equal lengths but made of different materials, yet found no difference within the experimental errors.

It should be noted that the gravitational force does not depend on the relative velocities of the interacting bodies. The speed of the planets does not enter into the force law. Neither does the gravitational force depend on the composition of the medium inserted between the interacting bodies, a result which distinguishes gravitational interaction from electrical interaction. We know, for example, that the electric field can be shielded by a conducting screen ("Faraday cage") and a magnetic field can be distorted considerably by a piece of iron. Corresponding phenomena do not exist in the gravitational field. There is apparently no way to "shield" an object from the gravitational field.

One might suspect that a sphere composed of a material like crystalline quartz or wood, having a structure with a definite orientation, would have a different gravitational force field in different directions. No such effect has been observed.

The gravitational field does not depend on temperature. Again, careful experiments have been performed to determine any effects, but the results have been negative.

None of the above or other similar experiments have been able to alter the original assumption that gravitational interaction depends only on mass.

10–3 The gravitational field inside a homogeneous sphere. We have already indicated that the gravitational law, as given by Eq. (10–1), applies only when the dimensions of the interacting objects are small compared with r. If this condition is not fulfilled, the calculation of the interaction force involves summation of the force contributions resulting from the various small elements of the body. A calculation of this type is given in Appendix C for the determination of the gravitational force from a sphere on a small object *outside* the sphere. In this particular case, the result is very simple; the force is the same as it would be if the entire mass of the sphere were concentrated in the center of the sphere. A completely analogous result applies to the force *outside* a spherical shell. However, the situation is entirely different inside the shell and, in fact, it is simple to show that the gravitational force from a shell is zero everywhere inside the shell.

This result is immediately clear for a point P_1 at the center of the shell, since this point is acted on by equal forces in all directions. It is also true for any arbitrary location P_2. To obtain the force on P_2, we can divide the shell into elements dm_1 and dm_2, as shown in Fig. 10–3, and we find that the net force from each such pair is zero, since $dm_1/r_1^2 = dm_2/r_2^2$. (The area of the shell that corresponds to a solid angle element $d\Omega_1$ is proportional to r_1^2.)

Now that this result has been obtained, we can proceed to calculate the gravitational force on an object inside a uniform sphere. With reference to Fig. 10–4, consider a uniform sphere of radius R with a point P located a distance r from the center. From the principle of superposition, the force on P (mass m) can be regarded as the sum of the forces from the spherical shell, between r and R, and the sphere of radius r. We have just proved that the former contribution is zero, and the contribution from the sphere is simply $Gm_r m/r^2$, where m_r is the mass of the sphere of radius r. If the total mass of the sphere is M, we have $m_r = (r/R)^3 M$, and the force on P becomes

$$F_r = -G \frac{r^3}{R^3 r^2} Mm = -\frac{GMm}{R^3} r, \qquad (r < R).$$

In other words, the force on m increases in proportion to its distance from the center of the sphere and reaches the maximum value GMm/R^2 at the surface of the sphere. When r is larger than R, the force on m decreases, of course, as $1/r^2$.

The force inside the sphere is similar to the spring-type force in its dependence on distance and direction, because it acts as a restoring force proportional to the displacement r from the equilibrium position. The equivalent spring constant is $K = GMm/R^3$. Imagine a frictionless tunnel through the center of the earth, into which a body is dropped

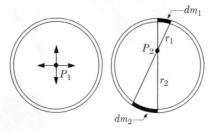

FIG. 10–3. The gravitational force inside a uniform shell is zero.

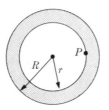

FIG. 10–4. The gravitational force inside a uniform sphere is proportional to the distance from the center of the sphere.

from the surface of the earth. The body then would perform harmonic motion with a period $T = 2\pi\sqrt{m/K} = 2\pi\sqrt{R^3/MG}$ *independent* of the mass of the body. If we introduce the density ρ of the sphere so that $M = (4\pi/3)R^3\rho$, we obtain $T = \sqrt{3\pi/\rho G}$, dependent only on the density and the universal constant G. The density of the earth is about 5.5 gm/cm^3, and with $G = 6.7 \cdot 10^{-8}$ dyne·cm^2/gm^2, we obtain $T \simeq 5 \cdot 10^3$ sec $\simeq 1\frac{1}{2}$ hr. We leave it as an exercise to show that the period of oscillation will be the same for any straight tunnel connecting two arbritrary points on the surface of the earth (Problem 10–11).

10–4 Derivation of the gravitational force law from the elliptic orbit of a single planet. In Sec. 10–1, the derivation of the general law of gravitation from Kepler's laws was based on the assumption of circular orbits. In order to obtain the force law, we had to use the experimental observations for different planets with different radii. We shall now consider the elliptic orbits of the planets. Clearly, r does not remain constant and we should be able to obtain the dependence of the force on r from the mere fact that the orbit is elliptical.

Let us review the mathematical description of an ellipse. In Fig. 10–5 is shown an ellipse with one of its foci at the origin of a coordinate system. The distance from the center of the ellipse to the outer extremity is called the semimajor axis a, and the curve is such that $r + r' = 2a$, where in

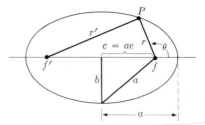

Fig. 10–5. An ellipse. The distance a is the semimajor axis, and b is the semiminor axis. The shape of an ellipse is such that the distance $r + r' = 2a$ for any point P on the curve. Recall that an ellipse can be constructed with the help of a string of length $2a$ with the ends fastened at the focal points. If a pencil is held against the string and is moved around under the constraint of the stretched string it will draw an ellipse.

the figure the foci are at f and f'. The polar equation for an ellipse* is

$$r = \frac{a(1 - e^2)}{1 + e \cos \theta} = \frac{b^2/a}{1 + e \cos \theta}, \qquad (10\text{–}7)$$

where e is the eccentricity and, from the figure, we have

$$\frac{b}{a} = \sqrt{1 - e^2}\,.$$

This description of the ellipse in Eq. (10–7) is in terms of the polar coordinates r, θ, which are particularly convenient to use when we deal with a central force (that the force is central follows from Kepler's second law— see Sec. 10–1). The force then has a component only in the **r**-direction, and the problem is to compute this force from the known trajectory. The polar components of the velocity, $v_\theta = \omega r$ and $v_r = dr/dt$, are indicated in Fig. 10–6. In the case of a circle, when r remains constant, the velocity has only a v_θ-component, and we know that the acceleration resulting from this component in the radial direction is $\omega^2 r$ directed toward the center, where $\omega = d\theta/dt$. Now, when the radius r does vary, we have a velocity component $v_r = dr/dt$ and a contribution of d^2r/dt^2 to the radial acceleration. Consequently, the radial force is

$$F_r = m \frac{d^2r}{dt^2} - m\omega^2 r. \qquad (10\text{–}8)$$

We must now merely combine r from Eq. (10–7) with (10–8) and convince ourselves that, indeed, the force varies as $1/r^2$. Although the problem is straightforward, there is some algebraic work involved.

---

* See George B. Thomas, Jr., *Calculus and Analytic Geometry*, 3rd ed. Chap. 9, Addison-Wesley Publishing Company, Inc., Reading, Massachusetts.

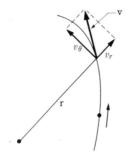

Fig. 10–6. The polar components of velocity.

The second term in Eq. (10–8) can be evaluated immediately. The angular velocity ω certainly varies with r, but we know from Kepler's second law that l, the angular momentum, is constant. We have $l = mr^2\omega = \text{const}$ and $\omega = l/mr^2$, so that the second term in Eq. (10–8) is $m\omega^2 r = l^2/mr^3 = (l^2/m)u^3$, where u is $1/r$. The equation for an ellipse is simpler in terms of u than it is in terms of r. We have $u = (a/b^2)(1 + e\cos\theta)$.

The evaluation of the second term, d^2r/dt^2, requires that we call on our knowledge of calculus. We have $dr/dt = (dr/d\theta)(d\theta/dt) = (dr/d\theta)\omega = (dr/d\theta)(l/m)u^2$, where we have used $\omega = (l/m)u^2$.

Note that $dr/d\theta = d(1/u)/d\theta = -(1/u^2)(du/d\theta)$, and we find that dr/dt is simply $-(l/m)(du/d\theta)$. Differentiating once more with respect to time, we obtain $d^2r/dt^2 = -(l/m)(d^2u/d\theta^2)(d\theta/dt) = -(l/m)^2(d^2u/d\theta^2)u^2$. Therefore, expression (10–8) for the radial force becomes

$$F_r = -\frac{l^2}{m}u^2\left(u + \frac{d^2u}{d\theta^2}\right). \qquad (10\text{–}8\text{a})$$

With $u = (a/b^2)(1 + e\cos\theta)$, we then have $d^2u/d\theta^2 = -(ae/b^2)\cos\theta$ and $u + d^2u/d\theta^2 = a/b^2$. Therefore

$$F_r = -\frac{l^2}{m}\frac{a}{b^2}u^2 = -\frac{l^2}{m}\frac{a}{b^2}\frac{1}{r^2}, \qquad (10\text{–}9)$$

which proves that the force varies as $1/r^2$.

We can proceed to determine the period of the planet. The area of an ellipse is πab, and from Eq. (10–3) we have $T = 2m\pi ab/l$. If in Eq. (10–9) we set $l^2a/mb^2 = K$, that is, $F_r = -K/r^2$, we have

$$b^2 = \frac{l^2}{m}\frac{a}{K}, \qquad (10\text{–}10)$$

and inserting this in the expression for T gives

$$T^2 = \frac{4m\pi^2}{K} a^3. \tag{10-11}$$

According to Kepler's third law, we have $T^2 = (\text{const})a^3$ for *all* planets, and this means that K/m must be the same for any planet of mass m. If we use $F_r = -K/r^2 = -GM_s m/r^2$, we can see that K/m is just GM_s. Kepler's third law implies, therefore, that G is a universal constant. This then completes the derivation of the gravitational law from Kepler's laws.

10–5 Orbits in the gravitational force field. In the previous section we started from a given elliptic trajectory of a body and from it proved that the force on the body was of the $(1/r^2)$-type. If we reverse the problem and seek the trajectory of a body moving in a given gravitational force field, it is clear that one of the possible solutions must be an ellipse. However, other orbits are also possible.

We have already seen in Chapter 7 that the character of the orbit depends essentially on the total mechanical energy involved. We recall that with a potential energy V which is chosen to be zero at infinity, we have $V = -K/r$, and the total mechanical energy is then

$$H = \tfrac{1}{2}mv^2 - \frac{K}{r}, \tag{10-12}$$

where $K = GmM$ (M is the mass of the source of the field and m is the mass of the moving body). As was illustrated in Fig. 7–6, we found that trapped orbits of the body are characterized by $H < 0$, whereas for $H > 0$ the body can escape. We shall leave the detailed mathematical problem of deriving the orbits from the force field for Appendix D, where it is shown that the only trapped orbits are ellipses (or circles) ($H < 0$) and the escape orbits are hyperbolas ($H > 0$) or parabolas ($H = 0$).

A problem of particular interest concerns the determination of the orbit of a satellite projected from a known position in the gravitational force field, with a known velocity. Here we shall consider the case when $H < 0$, that is, when we have an elliptic orbit. A typical elliptic orbit is shown in Fig. 10–7. As the particle passes one of the endpoints B of the minor axis of the ellipse, the distance from the force center is $r = a$ (see Fig. 10–5). Let us denote the speed of the particle at this point by v_a. Then the constant sector velocity of the particle can be expressed as $v_a b/2$, where b is the semiminor axis. Now, since the area of the ellipse is πab, the period of the motion becomes

$$T = \frac{\pi ab}{(v_a b/2)} = \frac{2\pi a}{v_a}. \tag{10-13}$$

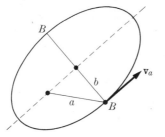

FIG. 10–7. When expressed in terms of $\mathbf{v}_a$ the period of the orbital motion is $T = 2\pi a/v_a$, that is, it is independent of the minor axes.

This result demonstrates the interesting property of the motion that the period, when expressed in terms of v_a, does not depend on the length of the minor axis and the eccentricity of the ellipse. *All* elliptic orbits (including circular orbits), whose major axes are the same, and for which v_a is the same, have the same periods. Using the circular orbit we can, of course, calculate this period by using $mv_a^2/a = K/a^2$, to obtain

$$T = 2\pi\sqrt{m/K}\, a^{3/2}. \tag{10–14}$$

The period depends only on the major axis of the ellipse. [Compare Kepler's third law and also Eq. (10–11).]

The potential energy of the particle at point B, where $r = a$, is $V_a = -K/a$, and the constant total mechanical energy of motion then can be expressed as $H = (-K/a) + (mv_a^2/2)$. Introducing the value of v_a found from (10–12) and (10–13), or directly from $mv_a^2/a = K/a^2$, we then obtain

$$H = -\frac{K}{2a}. \tag{10–15}$$

In other words, the total mechanical energy of motion is determined uniquely by the major axis of the ellipse. Conversely, the lengths of the major axes of all elliptic orbits with the same total mechanical energy are the same and are equal to

$$a = -\frac{K}{2H}. \tag{10–16}$$

(Recall that H is negative for trapped orbits, so that $-K/2H$ is a positive quantity.)

To obtain the minor axis of an elliptic orbit, we note that the constant angular momentum is $l = mv_ab$, which gives $b = l/mv_a$. Introducing $v_a = \sqrt{K/ma} = \sqrt{-2H/m}$, we obtain

$$b = \frac{l}{\sqrt{-2Hm}}. \tag{10–17}$$

Thus we have determined the basic properties of the elliptic orbit in terms of the two constants of motion, the total mechanical energy H, and the angular momentum l. These are easily obtained from the initial conditions of the particle. For example, if, as in Fig. 10–8, a particle is projected from a point P with a speed v_1 in a direction which makes an angle ϕ_1 with the radius vector r_1 from the force center (e.g., the earth), we have

$$H = \frac{-K}{r_1} + \frac{mv_1^2}{2} \quad \text{and} \quad l = mv_1 r_1 \sin \phi_1. \quad (10\text{–}18)$$

It remains to determine the orientation of the axes of the ellipse. This can be done by using the expression (10–7) for the ellipse. Measuring the angle θ_1 as shown in Fig. 10–8, we obtain

$$r_1 = \frac{b^2/a}{1 + e \cos \theta_1} \quad \text{or} \quad \cos \theta_1 = \frac{b^2}{ar_1} - 1. \quad (10\text{–}19)$$

Thus, from given initial values of v_1, r_1 and ϕ_1, we obtain the constants of motion l and H from Eq. (10–18), the major and minor axes of the ellipse from Eqs. (10–16) and (10–17), and finally the orientation of the ellipse from Eq. (10–19) (Problem 10–17).

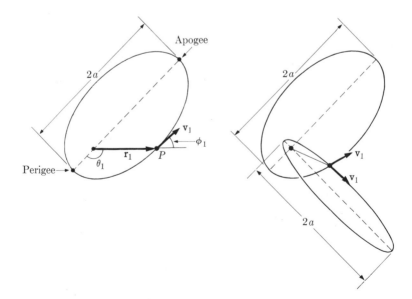

FIG. 10–8. The lengths of the major axes depend only on the magnitude and not on the direction of the initial velocity.

10–6 Rutherford scattering. In the previous section we discussed the motion of a particle under the influence of an attractive force which decreases with distance according to the inverse-square law. Certain aspects of the corresponding problem involving the repulsion of two equally charged particles will now be considered.

By 1910, the atomic nature of matter was well established. Atomic weights were known (from chemistry), and atoms were known to have dimensions of the order of 10^{-8} cm (from both chemistry and the kinetic theory of gases). The mass and charge of the electron had been measured, and electrons were known to be one of the constituents of atoms. There was some evidence that the number of electrons in an atom is about half the atomic weight of that atom. Atomic weights, it should be recalled, are based on the assignment of 16 for oxygen and 1 for hydrogen, the lightest of all atoms. The radioactive decay of atoms was known, and the emitted rays were called α-, β-, and γ-rays. We shall here be concerned with only the α-ray, which is known to have a positive charge equal to twice that of an electron, and to have a mass equal to about four times that of a hydrogen atom.

There were, of course, many unanswered questions about atoms. There still are. In 1910 some of the most striking questions were the following:

(a) Atoms are ordinarily electrically neutral. Electrons, the only identified and studied constituent of atoms, were known to be negatively charged. What, in an atom, carried the positive charge?

(b) The mass of an electron was known to be about 2000 times smaller than the mass of the hydrogen atom. What, in an atom, was responsible for its relatively large mass?

(c) How were the electrons, the positive charge, and the large mass distributed within an atom? Did the electrons occupy definite fixed positions? Was the atom a homogeneous pudding of charge and mass? In short, what was a satisfactory *model* for an atom?

Over a period of several years Professor Ernest Rutherford and his co-workers and students at the University of Manchester, in England, had been investigating the radioactive decay of atoms and the emitted α-, β-, and γ-rays. One of their experiments involved an arrangement such as that shown schematically in Fig. 10–9. Most of the particles, it was found, were deflected only a little in passing through the foil. Occasionally, however, a particle was found to have deflected through a very large angle, and some were even scattered backward through an angle θ near 180°.

It should be clear from Chapters 4 and 5 that a heavy particle that collides elastically with a light one cannot be deflected through a large angle. The light particle is simply pushed away, and the heavy one continues its forward motion with very little deflection. Hence, if the

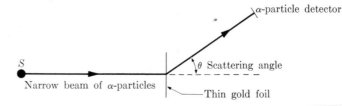

FIG. 10–9. The scattering of α-particles. A narrow beam of α-particles, originating from the radioactive material S, passes through a thin gold foil. The path of some of the α-particles is deflected, and by means of the α-particle detector, the scattered particles are detected.

α-particles are deflected through a large angle, they sometimes collide with something very heavy, presumably the massive parts of the atom we have mentioned.

If the atom were a homogeneous pudding of mass and charge, certainly the electric force would be small everywhere, for positive and negative charges have effects that tend to cancel. Rutherford then argued that the positive charge must somehow be separated from the negative charge, and as an atomic model he adopted a relatively small yet massive, positively charged *nucleus*, surrounded by the atomic electrons. The electric force outside the atom was small but *inside* the atom, inside the shell of atomic electrons, the force was large. Rutherford then proceeded to calculate the scattering law to be expected from this atomic model.

The force between the gold nucleus and the α-particle was assumed to be correctly described by Coulomb's law. To be sure, Coulomb's law (and newtonian mechanics as well) had never been shown to be valid at the small distances involved in this problem. But these were certainly the best and only reasonable assumptions to make. Later investigations have shown that Coulomb's law *is* valid at atomic distances, but that generally newtonian mechanics is not. Accidentally, Rutherford scattering is one of a very few atomic processes which can be correctly treated with newtonian mechanics.

The coulomb or electric force, we recall, is a (K/r^2)-type force which for particles of like electric charge is repulsive. The problem, it turns out, is entirely similar to the planetary motion problem discussed in Sec. 10–5. But here the total mechanical energy of the α-particle is always positive, and the α-particle describes a hyperbolic rather than an elliptic path. We could adopt the results of our planetary motion discussion in this problem, but a direct approach is simpler and more instructive.

Clearly, the deflection of the α-particle depends upon how far away from the nucleus it passes. If it passes far from the nucleus, the scattering

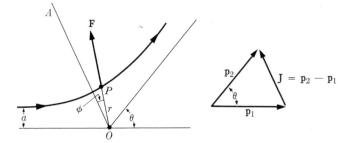

Fig. 10–10. The α-particle, if it were uncharged, would pass the nucleus at a distance a. The α-particle *is* charged, and is therefore repelled by the nucleus and scattered through the angle θ. The trajectory is symmetrical about the line OA. The distance a is called the impact parameter.

angle will be small, and if it passes close to the nucleus, the scattering angle should be large. We shall therefore try to establish a relation between the scattering angle and the impact parameter or characteristic distance a, as shown in Fig. 10–10. We shall assume the scattering nucleus to have a mass much larger than that of the α-particle, and, as we have seen before, under these conditions the nucleus will acquire only a small kinetic energy. We can therefore regard the kinetic energy of the α-particle to be the same after the collision as it was before. Further, since the force between the nucleus and the α-particle is a central force, the angular momentum of the system must remain constant, and because we have taken the mass of the nucleus to be much larger than the mass of the α-particle, the angular momentum of the α-particle about the nucleus can be considered constant. As the α-particle approaches the nucleus from the left, the force on it, which is always directed radially away from the nucleus, becomes increasingly large. The α-particle continuously loses kinetic energy and gains potential energy, but the angular momentum remains constant. When the α-particle moves away from the nucleus, it regains its original kinetic energy. The final and initial momenta of the α-particle are therefore the same in magnitude, and the net effect of the encounter with the nucleus is a change in direction of the α-particle. The impulse $\mathbf{J} = \mathbf{p}_2 - \mathbf{p}_1$ has a magnitude of $J = 2p \sin \theta/2$. The impulse $\mathbf{J}$ arises from the component of the coulomb, or electric, force directed along OA, since the impulse contributions of the other components cancel one another. The force component along OA is

$$F_a = F \cos \phi = \frac{Kq_\alpha q_n}{r^2} \cos \phi,$$

where q_α and q_n are the charges on the α-particle and nucleus, respectively.

The impulse, of course, is the time integral of F_a extending from long before to long after the nuclear encounter:

$$J = \int \frac{Kq_\alpha q_n}{r^2} \cos \phi \, dt. \tag{10–20}$$

This integral cannot be evaluated directly, because r and ϕ both vary with t in a manner as yet unknown. The angular momentum, $l = pa = mr^2\omega$, however, is known to be constant. Since l can be written as $m_\alpha r^2 (d\phi/dt)$, we have

$$J = \int_{-(\pi-\theta)/2}^{(\pi-\theta)/2} \frac{Kq_\alpha q_n}{l} m_\alpha \cos \phi \, d\phi. \tag{10–21}$$

The above integration can now be carried out because nothing except $\cos \phi$ depends on ϕ. The integration limits correspond to ϕ long before and long after the collision. When the indicated integration is performed, we find that

$$J = \frac{2Kq_\alpha q_n}{m_\alpha v a} m_\alpha \cos \frac{\theta}{2}, \tag{10–22}$$

where $m_\alpha v a$ is the constant angular momentum of the α-particle. Since we know that J can be written as $J = 2p \sin \theta/2$, we have

$$\tan \frac{\theta}{2} = \frac{Kq_\alpha q_n}{m_\alpha v^2 a}, \tag{10–23}$$

where $v = p/m_\alpha$ is the velocity of the α-particles. This is the relation that we sought between the scattering angle and the distance a. When a is large the scattering angle is small, because the force on the α-particle is small as it passes the nucleus.

The relation (10–23) cannot be compared directly with experimental results because when an α-particle impinges on a gold foil, for example, one has no way of knowing in advance what distance a will characterize its collision. The α-particles cannot be "aimed" toward a particular nucleus. Rather, a certain area A of the foil is uniformly bombarded with α-particles. Suppose there were just one gold nucleus in the area A of the foil. Then if the foil were uniformly bombarded with 1000 α-particles, we would expect $1000\pi a^2/A$ to pass within a distance a of the gold nucleus. Similarly, we would expect $1000 \cdot 2\pi a \, da/A$ to pass within a and $a + da$ of the gold nucleus. If there were N gold nuclei in the area A of foil, we would expect $1000N2\pi a \, da/A = 1000n2\pi a \, da$ α-particles to pass within a and $a + da$ of *some* nucleus. Here $n = N/A$ is the number of gold nuclei per unit area of foil. In other words, $2\pi n a \, da$ is the fraction of α-particles that will pass within a and $a + da$ of some nucleus of the foil.

From expression (10–23) we can predict the scattering angle θ for a given impact parameter a. Similarly, we can predict a scattering angle $\theta + d\theta$ for an impact parameter $a + da$. All the α-particles with impact parameters between a and $a + da$ will have scattering angles between θ and $\theta + d\theta$. Therefore, since $2\pi na\, da$ is the fraction of α-particles for which the impact parameter is between a and $a + da$, $2\pi na\, da$ expressed in terms of θ and $d\theta$, rather than of a and da, represents the fraction of α-particles that will be scattered through an angle between θ and $\theta + d\theta$. We have assumed here that the foil is so thin that there is a negligible chance that an α-particle will be scattered through an appreciable angle by more than one nucleus. We then have for the fraction f:

$$f = \pi n \left(\frac{K q_\alpha q_n}{m_\alpha v^2} \right)^2 \frac{\cos \theta/2}{\sin^3 \theta/2}\, d\theta. \qquad (10\text{–}24)$$

Practically, a detector of α-particles was used that covered a given *solid angle*. Since the element of solid angle is $2\pi \sin \theta\, d\theta = d\Omega$, the fraction f of particles scattered through the angle θ into the solid angle $d\Omega$ is

$$f = \frac{n}{4} \left(\frac{K q_\alpha q_n}{m_\alpha v^2} \right)^2 \frac{d\Omega}{\sin^4 \theta/2}. \qquad (10\text{–}25)$$

This is the expression found by Rutherford and is the one with which he compared his experimental results. The dependence of f on the scattering angle θ, the number of atoms n per unit area of foil, and the velocity v of the α-particles were all measured experimentally and the values were found to agree with those predicted. The dependence of f on the nuclear charge q_n could not be checked directly, since at that time there existed no independent measurements of nuclear charge. Foils of various elements were used, however, and it was found that the nuclear charge (measured in units of charge on the electron), as deduced from experiment and from the predictions (10–25) of the assumed atomic model, was approximately equal to one-half the atomic weight. Recall that there was some previous evidence that the number of electrons in an atom was approximately equal to one-half the atomic weight. A few years later it was shown that both the nuclear charge and the number of electrons in an atom were equal to the *atomic number*, which, for most atoms, is approximately half the atomic weight.

One further and most significant deduction from the experimental results and proposed model concerned the size of the nucleus (see Problem 10–19).

Problems

10-1. From the value of the gravitational constant G, the local gravitational acceleration g, and the radius of the earth, determine the average mass density of the earth.

10-2. With what accuracy would you have to measure the period of a pendulum if you were to detect a variation of g at two stations 10 m apart in elevation?

10-3. Indicate, at least in principle, how you can "weigh" the earth by comparing the period of a pendulum when it is placed on the side of a mountain of known mass with the period when it is placed on the top of the mountain. This method was used by early investigators for the determination of the gravitational constant G.

10-4. Jupiter has twelve known moons, four of which were discovered by Galileo, and the last of which was discovered in 1951. The orbit radii and periods of the first four are given below.

r, miles	T, days
112,000	0.498
262,000	1.769
417,000	3.551
666,000	7.155

(a) Do these four satellites of Jupiter obey Kepler's third law? (b) Given the above data and the value of G, find the mass of Jupiter. (c) Jupiter's diameter is 88,770 mi. What is its average density?

10-5. Two lead spheres, each of 1-m radius, are in contact. (a) What is their mutual attractive force? (b) What is their potential energy? (c) What velocity would they have at the instant of contact if they started very far apart in free space and "fell" toward each other?

10-6. Prove that the period of a satellite, moving around and close to the surface of a planet, depends only on the mass density of the planet and not upon its radius. What is the period if $\rho = 5 \,\mathrm{gm/cm^3}$?

10-7. If a man-made satellite is to travel in a circle 200 mi above the earth's surface, what must be its velocity? How often will it circle the earth? If the satellite passes overhead, what is the interval before it disappears below the horizon?

10-8. At what point between the earth and the sun do the gravitational forces of these two bodies cancel? Is there any point where the potential energies are equal? Do gravitational potential energies ever cancel?

10-9. The perigee (point of closest approach) of a satellite is 200 mi above earth, and the apogee (point of farthest distance) is 1500 mi above earth. (a) What is the semimajor axis of the satellite's orbit? (b) What is the eccentricity of its orbit? (c) If the satellite's weight is 30 lb, what is its total energy? (d) What is its velocity at the apogee? (e) What is its velocity at the perigee? (f) What is its angular momentum?

10-10. Some comets, at least, are parts of the solar system and have periods of roughly 100 years. Generally, comets have rather eccentric orbits. Sketch a typical comet orbit for an eccentricity of 0.8, and include the approximate orbits of the planets. Why is it usually very difficult to predict exactly when such a comet will closely approach the earth?

10-11. Refer to the discussion in Sec. 10-3. Imagine a straight frictionless tunnel through the center of the earth, between two arbitrary points on the surface of the earth. Consider a body that has been released from rest from one of the endpoints in the tunnel. Show that the motion of the body is harmonic and that the period will be the same in any tunnel, independent of the location of the endpoints. In the case of a tunnel through the center of the earth, determine the speed of the body as it passes the center.

10–12. Early investigators tried to determine the gravitational constant G by comparing the periods of two identical pendulums, one at the surface of the earth and one at the bottom of a mine of known depth. Indicate how you would proceed to find the gravitational constant G. What additional data do you need?

10–13. The orbits of two earth satellites A and B are ellipses, with major axes R and $4R$ respectively. (a) What is the ratio between their total mechanical energies? (b) What is the ratio between their periods? (c) What can you say about the ratio between their angular momenta?

10–14. Does the escape velocity of a particle depend upon the direction in which it is projected from the earth? Discuss.

10–15. Consider a projectile a distance $r = 2R$ from the center of the earth (R = earth radius). The projectile is sent off in a direction perpendicular to the radius. Indicate schematically in a diagram the nature of the orbits as the initial speed of the satellite is varied from zero to infinity. Indicate the ranges of speeds that are characteristic of elliptic, parabolic, and hyperbolic trajectories.

10–16. Carry through the same analysis as in the previous problem, but choose an angle of 120° between $\mathbf{v}$ and $\mathbf{r}$.

10–17. A man-made satellite is projected into a circular orbit around the earth at a distance of 200 mi above the

earth's surface. Imagine that another identical satellite is projected from the same position with the same speed, but at an angle which deviates 20° outward from the given circular orbit (the angle between $\mathbf{v}$ and $\mathbf{r}$ is 70°). Determine this orbit and its major and minor axes. Find the locations of the apogee and perigee with respect to the initial point. Each satellite is of 100-kgm mass.

10–18. Why, in Rutherford scattering, is the trajectory of the α-particle symmetrical about the line OA?

10–19. Some of Rutherford's original experiments were carried out with gold foil and α-particles with an energy of about 4 Mev (4 million electron volts). (An energy of one electron volt corresponds to an energy of about $1.6 \cdot 10^{-19}$ joule.) From the observation that some α-particles were scattered backward (through $\theta = 180°$), find an upper limit to the radius of the nucleus of gold. What evidence exists that this large-angle scattering does not arise from some new nonelectric-type force? (One of Rutherford's original articles can be found in *Philosophical Magazine* **6**, 21, 1911.)

10–20. Both Rutherford scattering and planetary motion involve motion of particles under the influence of an r^{-2}-law. It might be expected that the motion of electrons about the nucleus of an atom would be similar to the motion of the planets around the sun. What would be the energy of an electron if it were 10^{-8} cm from the nucleus of a hydrogen atom?

10–21. (a) What must be the impact parameter in order that a 4-Mev α-particle be scattered through 90° by a gold nucleus? (b) How many nuclei should there be, per cm^2 of foil, in order that one α-particle in 10^4 be scattered through *more* than 90°? How thick is this foil, in cm?

CHAPTER 11

MOVING COORDINATE SYSTEMS AND INERTIAL FORCES

Summary. Many physical phenomena are advantageously described and analyzed with respect to a moving coordinate system. As an important example of the use of a coordinate system moving at a constant velocity, we discuss a two-body interaction with respect to the center-of-mass coordinate system. The relations between interaction forces and motion (the ordinary laws of motion), which we have obtained and studied so far in a coordinate system at rest, are applicable also in coordinate systems that move at constant velocities (inertial frames of reference). However, in accelerated or rotating coordinate systems, inertial forces must be introduced so that the results obtained will be consistent with those in the inertial frames of reference. The use of inertial forces is illustrated in several examples which include problems of planetary, lunar, and tidal motion. Einstein's principle of equivalence is treated briefly.

The starting point of mechanics, was, as we have seen, the contention put forth by Galileo that a body which does not interact with other bodies moves at constant (or zero) velocity. From this basic contention, we saw how the various conservation laws and the force concept evolved. In all of our considerations, there was an implicit assumption that we, as observers, and our coordinate systems were at rest. There are many situations in nature in which it is more natural and, indeed, computationally and conceptually easier for us to consider a problem from the standpoint of a coordinate system in motion. In particular, when a coordinate system moves with the velocity of the center of mass of a group of interacting bodies, a problem is far less complex than it is when the coordinate system is at rest. For this reason, coordinate systems that move with constant velocities will be discussed first in this chapter. (Recall that if a group of particles interact only among themselves, the center of mass must move at constant velocity.) We shall find that the laws of motion in a coordinate system moving at constant velocity are the same as in a coordinate system at rest.

Consider now, however, the altered situation that obtains when motion is described and analyzed in an accelerated coordinate system. We need only imagine a few simple experiments that can be carried out in an accelerating car, in a car traveling over a bumpy road, or on a rapidly rotating merry-go-round to become convinced that the basic laws of mechanics are in need of revision when motion is described with reference to accelerating or rotating coordinate systems.

A ball placed on the level floor of a car moving with constant velocity remains at rest (in a coordinate system attached to the car) but then suddenly rolls to the front (when the car decelerates), to the rear (when the car accelerates), or starts to bounce (when the car hits a bump).

A puck sliding on the frictionless surface of a rotating merry-go-round moves along a straight line, with respect to a coordinate system S attached to the ground. But with respect to a coordinate system S' rotating with the merry-go-round, the puck traverses an odd spirallike path. Furthermore, we find that even if the puck is at rest with respect to S', a net interaction force directed toward the center of the merry-go-round must be applied on the puck. This fact is not consistent with the laws of motion familiar from a coordinate system at rest, in which the net interaction force on a body at rest must be zero.

The laws of mechanics formulated in terms of interaction forces, then, are not directly usable in their original forms when applied to accelerating or rotating coordinate systems. Why worry, one may ask, about how strange these phenomena may seem relative to accelerated and rotating coordinate systems, so long as we can predict with confidence the results of experiments when we refer them to a coordinate system at rest? Here, we need only recall the fact that the earth revolves on its own axis and rotates about the sun, which, in turn, rotates about the galactic center together with the 10^{11} or so other stars in our galaxy. Whether we like it or not, we are on a most complex rotating coordinate system (Fig. 11–1) and, as we shall see, there are interesting and important observable consequences. This, of course, brings up the delicate question of just what was meant, in our previous discussions, when observers on the earth were glibly assumed to be at rest. When we consider all these rotations, is it possible for an observer ever to be at rest? If so, in relation to what is he at rest?

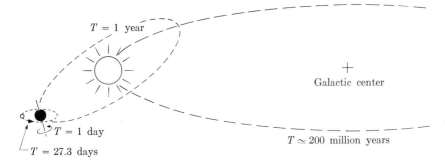

Fig. 11–1. A coordinate system fixed to the surface of the earth is by no means at rest. (The sun is about 30,000 light-years from the galactic center.)

The answers to these questions are not known, or at least have not gained general acceptance. As a practical matter, however, the effects of such rotations are often small. For the purposes of our collision experiments with pucks and cars, for example, the effect of the earth's rotation had consequences far smaller than were measurable. From such experiments, we derived the laws of mechanics (Newton's laws) and we investigated the properties of various interaction forces. If, in another coordinate system, these laws of motion are applicable for correct prediction of motion without introducing forces other than interaction forces, this coordinate system is called an *inertial frame of reference*. For example, a coordinate system rotating with the earth is an inertial frame for the purposes of the collision experiments referred to above, but it is not an inertial frame upon which to base a discussion of moon or satellite motion. (Recall that the moon rotates around the earth every 27.3 days, yet rises about every 24 hours—an effect of the earth's rotation.) For such considerations, therefore, we might choose a coordinate system which is centered on the earth and has axes fixed relative to the stars. But even this is not an inertial frame for a discussion of planetary motion, for the origin of our coordinate system circles the sun once a year. Thus, for planetary motion we find that an inertial frame must be centered at the sun. Perhaps the ultimate inertial frame is fixed relative to the center of mass of all the stars in the universe.

11–1 Motion with respect to a coordinate system which moves at constant velocity. A coordinate system S is at rest and another system S' moves at constant velocity relative to S. What will be the relation between the descriptions of the motion of an object with respect to S and S'? Imagine, for concreteness, that the coordinate system S is marked off on a large piece of glass, and that the coordinate system S' is marked off on the top of a car that can roll under the glass. To avoid unessential complication, let us assume that the coordinate axes of S and of S' are parallel, that the velocity V_x of S' is directed along the x-axis of S, and that at time $t = 0$ the two coordinate systems coincide. From Fig. 11–2, for the coordinates of a point P, we have

$$x' = x - V_x t, \qquad y' = y. \tag{11–1}$$

If P moves with a velocity $\mathbf{v}$ (components v_x and v_y) with respect to S, the velocity components with respect to S' are

$$v_x' = v_x - V_x, \qquad v_y' = v_y. \tag{11–2}$$

Thus the momenta of a particle of mass m, as assigned by the two coordinate systems, are related by

$$p_x' = p_x - mV_x, \qquad p_y' = p_y. \tag{11–3}$$

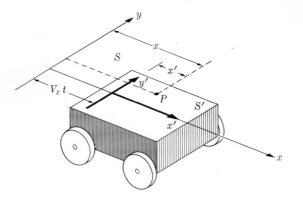

FIG. 11–2. The coordinate system S is at rest and the coordinate system S' moves along x with a velocity V_x. At $t = 0$ the axes coincide; but at time t, S' has moved a distance $X = V_x t$ along x.

(We have tacitly assumed here that mass, length, and time measurements are all unaffected by the motion of S'. That this is not a justified assumption when V_x is very large has been pointed out and, in effect, we are assuming here that V_x is much less than the velocity of light.) The relations (11–1) and (11–2) are called galilean transformations, for Galileo was one of the first, if not the first, to describe correctly motion as viewed from a moving coordinate system.

On the basis of Eq. (11–3), what now is the relation between the forces as measured with respect to S and S'? According to S, the force is of course dp/dt and, correspondingly, the force according to S' is dp'/dt. But, from (11–3), we see that dp'_x/dt and dp_x/dt are equal, since m and V_x are both constant. Further, dp'_y/dt and dp_y/dt are equal, and we therefore conclude that the forces with respect to both S' and S are the same:

$$F'_x = F_x, \qquad F'_y = F_y, \tag{11–4}$$

If S is an inertial frame of reference, all coordinate systems moving with constant velocities with respect to S are also inertial frames of reference.

EXAMPLE 1. One of Galileo's examples, and one that is instructive for us as well, concerns the motion of an object dropped from the mast of a moving ship. According to an observer on the ship, the object falls straight down and lands at the base of the mast. He is in an inertial frame (assuming that the ship's velocity v_0 is constant and that there is no rolling or pitching), and the velocity of the object in the x'-direction is zero at the top of the mast and zero also while the object is in flight. An observer on the shore, on the other hand, would say that the object was released from the moving ship and so had an initial velocity v_0 in the x-direction. The path of the object is therefore a parabola ($y = h - gt^2/2$, $x = v_0 t$), and that the object lands at the base of the mast is just a consequence of the fact that both the ship and the dropped object had the same constant velocities v_0 in the x-direction.

EXAMPLE 2. A gun is placed on a train going northward with a velocity v_0 along a horizontal straight track, as shown in Fig. 11–3. The muzzle velocity of the shots fired from the gun is v. If the gun is set at an angle θ' with respect to the direction of the track, what then is the direction of the trajectory of a projectile shot horizontally from the gun?

The velocity components with respect to the moving coordinate system are $v_x' = v \cos \theta'$ and $v_y' = v \sin \theta'$, respectively. The corresponding velocity components with respect to the fixed system are $v_x = v \cos \theta' + V_0$ and $v_y = v_y' = v \sin \theta'$. In other words, the angle θ between the trajectory and the x-axis is obtained from

$$\tan \theta = \frac{v_y}{v_x} = \frac{v \sin \theta'}{v \cos \theta' + V_0} = \frac{\sin \theta'}{\cos \theta' + \beta},$$

where β is V_0/v.

11–2 Motion with respect to the center of mass. In the previous section, we concluded that the force on a body with reference to a coordinate system moving at constant velocity is the same as the force as measured in a coordinate system at rest. Further, we found how the coordinates, velocities, and momenta are related according to the two systems. In this section, we shall discuss the special and important case of the coordinate system S' moving with the constant center-of-mass velocity of a group of particles which interact only among themselves. The coordinate system moving with the center of mass, with its origin at the center of mass, is often called the *center-of-mass system* (C-system), and the coordinate system at rest is called the *laboratory system* (L-system).

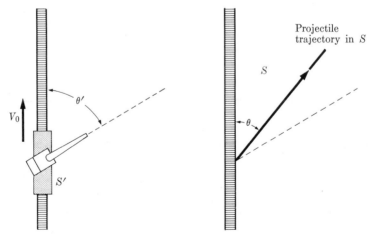

FIGURE 11–3

The total momentum with respect to the center of mass. We shall consider just two particles which interact with only each other. The extension to systems of many particles is straightforward.

From our previous work we know that the coordinate and velocity of the center of mass are

$$X = \frac{m_a x_a + m_b x_b}{m_a + m_b} \quad \text{and} \quad V_x = \frac{m_a v_{ax} + m_b v_{bx}}{m_a + m_b}. \quad (11\text{-}5)$$

The coordinates x_a^* and x_b^* of A and B, with respect to the C-system, are then $x_a^* = x_a - X$ and $x_b^* = x_b - X$. The coordinate of the center of mass in the C-system clearly is $X^* = 0$, and we have

$$m_a x_a^* + m_b x_b^* = 0. \quad (11\text{-}5\text{a})$$

Similarly, we have $V_x^* = 0$ and

$$m_a v_{ax}^* + m_b v_{bx}^* = 0. \quad (11\text{-}5\text{b})$$

Entirely analogous expressions are obtained for the y- and z-components. We can obtain Eq. (11-5b) also in the following way. According to the C-system, body A will have a velocity $v_{ax}^* = v_{ax} - V_x$ and body B will have a velocity $v_{bx}^* = v_{bx} - V_x$. The total momentum with respect to the C-system is then

$$p_{ax}^* + p_{bx}^* = m_a(v_{ax} - V_x) + m_b(v_{bx} - V_x)$$
$$= m_a v_{ax} + m_b v_{bx} - (m_a + m_b)V_x = 0,$$

because the last term, from (11-5), is equal to the sum of the first two. Again, entirely similar relations hold for the y- and z-components, and we conclude that *the net momentum with respect to the center of mass is zero.*

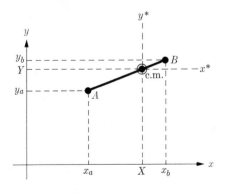

FIGURE 11-4

That is,

$$\mathbf{p}^* = \mathbf{p}_a^* + \mathbf{p}_b^* = 0. \tag{11-6}$$

The individual momenta $\mathbf{p}_a^*$ and $\mathbf{p}_b^*$ are always equal and opposite, and if the bodies are destined to collide, they will approach each other along the same straight line, when viewed from their center of mass. Similarly, after the two bodies collide, they must leave the collision center along a straight line. In general, these straight lines before and after a collision will not coincide, as illustrated in Fig. 11–5.

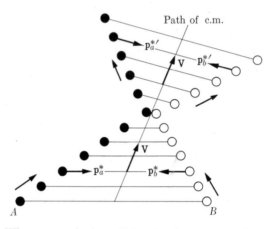

FIG. 11–5. When a two-body collision is viewed from the center of mass, the bodies have equal and opposite momenta $\mathbf{p}_a^* = -\mathbf{p}_b^*$. The motion is along the lines that connect the bodies.

Total kinetic energy. The total kinetic energy with respect to the C-system is, of course, $E^* = m_a v_a^{*2}/2 + m_b v_b^{*2}/2$. How is E^* related to $E = m_a v_a^2/2 + m_b v_b^2/2$, the kinetic energy according to the L-system? Again we shall consider just two particles, since the extension to three or more involves nothing essentially different. For the x-components of velocity, we have

$$\tfrac{1}{2}m_a v_{ax}^2 + \tfrac{1}{2}m_b v_{bx}^2 = \tfrac{1}{2}m_a(v_{ax}^* + V_x)^2 + \tfrac{1}{2}m_b(v_{bx}^* + V_x)^2$$

$$= \tfrac{1}{2}m_a(v_{ax}^{*2} + V_x^2 + 2v_{ax}^* V_x) + \tfrac{1}{2}m_b(v_{bx}^{*2} + V_x^2 + 2v_{bx}^* V_x)$$

$$= (\tfrac{1}{2}m_a v_{ax}^{*2} + \tfrac{1}{2}m_b v_{bx}^{*2}) + \tfrac{1}{2}(m_a + m_b)V_x^2 + V_x(m_a v_{ax}^* + m_b v_{bx}^*).$$

According to Eq. (11–5b), the last term is zero.

Similar expressions obtain for the y- and z-components of velocity and by addition, using $v^2 = v_x^2 + v_y^2 + v_z^2$, we obtain

$$E = \tfrac{1}{2}MV^2 + E^*, \tag{11-7}$$

where $M = m_a + m_b$ is the total mass of the system. In other words, the kinetic energy according to the L-system is simply the sum of the (translational) kinetic energy $MV^2/2$ of the center of mass and the kinetic energy E^* according to the C-system. The result in Eq. (11–7) applies to an arbitrary number of particles, as can be shown in a manner completely analogous to the foregoing derivation for two particles (see Problem 11–9).

In a *perfectly elastic collision*, the total kinetic energy of the system before the collision is the same as the total kinetic energy after the collision. From the conservation of total momentum, it follows that the velocity of the center of mass, and consequently $MV^2/2$, remains constant. Therefore, in the perfectly elastic collision, the kinetic energy with respect to the center of mass also is the same before and after the collision, $E^* = E^{*\prime}$. In the case of two colliding particles A and B, the kinetic energy with respect to the center of mass is $E^* = (p_a^{*2}/2m_a) + (p_b^{*2}/2m_b)$, and since we have $p_a^{*2} = p_b^{*2}$ this energy can be expressed as $E^* = p_a^{*2}/2\mu$, where $\mu = m_a m_b/(m_a + m_b)$ is the reduced mass of the system. Then, since $E^* = E^{*\prime}$, it follows that the magnitude of the momentum of particle A with respect to the C-system is the same before and after the collision, $p_a^* = p_a^{*\prime}$. Similarly, we obtain $p_b^* = p_b^{*\prime}$. In other words, in a perfectly elastic two-particle collision described with respect to the C-system, the magnitude of the momentum and the velocity of each particle is the same before and after the collision. The total effect of the perfectly elastic collision in the C-system is therefore merely a change in the direction of motion of the colliding particles.

In a *perfectly inelastic collision*, on the other hand, the particles stick together after the collision, so that the kinetic energy with respect to the center of mass is zero, $E^{*\prime} = 0$. However, the velocity of the center of mass, and consequently the translational kinetic energy $MV^2/2$, after the collision is the same as before. Thus, in a perfectly inelastic collision the initial kinetic energy $E = (MV^2/2) + E^*$ is reduced to $E' = MV^2/2$; that is, the initial kinetic energy, with respect to the center of mass, is lost in the collision. It is clear, though, that no collision can reduce the kinetic energy in the L-system to a value less than $MV^2/2$.

The relative velocity is $\mathbf{v}_a - \mathbf{v}_b$ between two particles A and B moving in space. If we introduce the center-of-mass velocity $\mathbf{V}$ of the particles, we have $\mathbf{v}_a^* = \mathbf{v}_a - \mathbf{V}$ and $\mathbf{v}_b^* = \mathbf{v}_b - \mathbf{V}$. It follows that the relative velocity $\mathbf{v}_a^* - \mathbf{v}_b^*$ in the L-system is the same as the relative velocity in the C-system:

$$\mathbf{v}_a - \mathbf{v}_b = \mathbf{v}_a^* - \mathbf{v}_b^*.$$

In a perfectly elastic collision, as we have seen, the magnitudes of the relative velocities in the C-system are the same before and after collision (the collision merely changes the direction of the straight-line motion of the colliding particles, but does not change the magnitudes of the velocities). Consequently, in a perfectly elastic collision, the magnitudes of the relative velocities, also with respect to the L-system, remain constant, and $|\mathbf{v}_a - \mathbf{v}_b| = |\mathbf{v}_a^* - \mathbf{v}_b^*|$.

EXAMPLE. Body A of mass 2 kgm approaches the origin with a speed 3 m/sec in the negative y-direction, and body B of mass 4 kgm approaches the origin with a speed 2 m/sec in the negative x-direction. The bodies collide at the origin and their relative velocity is decreased by a factor of two as a result of the collision. According to a coordinate system at rest, what is the final total kinetic energy?

The two components and the magnitude of the center-of-mass velocity are given by

$$V_x = \frac{2 \cdot 0 - 4 \cdot 2}{2 + 4} = -\tfrac{4}{3} \text{ m/sec}, \qquad V_y = \frac{-2 \cdot 3 + 4 \cdot 0}{2 + 4} = -1 \text{ m/sec},$$

$$|\mathbf{V}| = \sqrt{V_x^2 + V_y^2} = \tfrac{5}{3} \text{ m/sec}.$$

The velocities, with respect to the C-system, are therefore

$$v_{ax}^* = 0 - (-\tfrac{4}{3}) = \tfrac{4}{3} \text{ m/sec}, \qquad v_{bx}^* = -2 - (-\tfrac{4}{3}) = -\tfrac{2}{3} \text{ m/sec},$$

$$v_{ay}^* = -3 - (-1) = -2 \text{ m/sec}, \qquad v_{by}^* = 0 - (-1) = 1 \text{ m/sec},$$

$$|\mathbf{v}_a^*| = \sqrt{\tfrac{52}{9}} \text{ m/sec}, \qquad |\mathbf{v}_b^*| = \sqrt{\tfrac{13}{9}} \text{ m/sec}.$$

The kinetic energy in the center of mass before the collision is

$$E^* = \tfrac{1}{2} m_a v_a^{*2} + \tfrac{1}{2} m_b v_b^{*2} = \tfrac{26}{3} \text{ joules}.$$

As a result of the collision the magnitude of the relative velocity as well as the magnitudes of the velocities in the C-system of each of the bodies will be reduced by a factor of two. Therefore the kinetic energy in the C-system will be reduced by a factor of four:

$$E^{*\prime} = \frac{E^*}{4} = \tfrac{13}{6} \text{ joules}.$$

The kinetic energy in the L-system therefore is given by

$$E = \tfrac{1}{2} M V^2 + E^* = \tfrac{1}{2} \cdot 6 \cdot \tfrac{25}{9} + \tfrac{26}{3} = 17 \text{ joules} \qquad \text{(before)},$$

$$E' = \tfrac{1}{2} M V^2 + E^{*\prime} = \tfrac{1}{2} \cdot 6 \cdot \tfrac{25}{9} + \tfrac{13}{6} = 10.5 \text{ joules} \qquad \text{(after)}.$$

Alternatively, we could have found the kinetic energy, $E = m_a v_a^2/2 + m_b v_b^2/2$ = 17 joules directly, and subtracted from it $M V^2/2 = 25/3$ joules to get $E^* = 26/3$ joules. Then, knowing that the kinetic energy according to the moving observer would be reduced by a factor four, we would have obtained $E^{*\prime} = 13/6$ joules and $E' = M V^2/2 + E^{*\prime} = 10.5$ joules.

11-3 Motion with respect to an accelerated coordinate system. We can conclude from the previous section that essentially nothing new arises when we consider motion relative to a coordinate system moving at constant velocity. Bodies moving at constant velocity, according to a coordinate system at rest, move with a different but, nonetheless, constant velocity according to a moving coordinate system. Further, momentum changes and forces are the same according to either system.

Essentially new features do arise, however, when the moving coordinate system is accelerated. That this must be so is obvious from the following simple argument. When a body has a velocity $\mathbf{v}$ with respect to a coordinate system S at rest, it has a velocity $\mathbf{v}' = \mathbf{v} - \mathbf{V}$ with respect to a coordinate system S' moving with a velocity $\mathbf{V}$. The momentum with respect to S' is then $m\mathbf{v}' = m\mathbf{v} - m\mathbf{V}$. If $\mathbf{V}$ changes (if S' is accelerated), the body's momentum will have changed according to S' and therefore there must be a force on the body; according to S, however, there is a force on the body only when its momentum, relative to S, changes. This momentum $m\mathbf{v}$, of course, has nothing to do with the acceleration of S'.

Let us consider a simple case in which the acceleration of S' is in the x-direction. From Fig. 11–2 and the discussion of it, we have for the momenta with respect to S' and S,

$$p'_x = p_x - mV_x, \qquad p'_y = p_y. \tag{11–8}$$

As before, the relation between the forces in the two systems, by definition, are the rates of change of the momenta. Since now V_x is not constant, we have

$$F'_x = F_x - mA_x, \qquad F'_y = F_y, \tag{11–9}$$

where $A_x = dV_x/dt$ is the acceleration of the coordinate system S'. Recall now that $dp_x/dt = F_x$, the x-component of the force in the coordinate system S, is a force attributable to the presence of some other body. The force may be contact, gravitational, electric, etc., and is an *interaction* force. The force $F'_x = dp'_x/dt$ according to S', however, consists of two parts, the first of which is F_x, the same interaction force as observed by S, and the second of which is $F_{ix} = -mA_x$.

This new type of force clearly is *not* an interaction force. It is called an *inertial force* and arises because of the acceleration of the coordinate system S'. An accelerated coordinate system is not an inertial frame. Inertial forces occur only in accelerated and rotating coordinate systems, never in inertial frames. We have then

$$F'_x = F_x + F_{ix}, \tag{11–10}$$

$$F_{ix} = -mA_x. \tag{11–11}$$

That is, if the motion of a body is to be correctly predicted with respect to an observer in an accelerated coordinate system S', not only interaction forces (gravity, contact, etc.) but also the inertial force $F_{ix} = -mA_x$ must be introduced. Only then will the observed rates of change of momentum be consistent with the known forces. The acceleration A_x of the coordinate system S' must be known, of course.

In general, inertial forces are distinctly different from interaction forces, in that interaction forces occur in pairs; that is, there is always a reaction force on some other body. This is not the case with inertial forces.

Before we discuss a few examples of motion and forces in accelerated coordinate systems, let us extend our one-dimensional considerations to the more general case wherein the direction and magnitude of the acceleration of S' are not necessarily constant.

The position $\mathbf{r}'$ of P, according to S', is $\mathbf{r}' = \mathbf{r} - \mathbf{R}$. The velocities in the two coordinate systems are therefore related by $\mathbf{v}' = \mathbf{v} - \mathbf{V}$, so that for the momentum we have

$$\mathbf{p}' = \mathbf{p} - m\mathbf{V}. \tag{11-12}$$

As before, the force as assigned by S' is obtained from the time rate of momentum change and, in complete analogy with our previous discussion, we have

$$\mathbf{F}' = \mathbf{F} + \mathbf{F}_i, \tag{11-13}$$

where $\mathbf{F}_i = -m\mathbf{A}$ and $\mathbf{A}$ is the vector acceleration of the coordinate system S'. Note carefully that $\mathbf{A}$ is the *translational* acceleration of the coordinate system; that is, the coordinate axes of S' are always parallel with those of S. A rotation of S' introduces additional inertial forces, as will be shown shortly. Since $\mathbf{A}$ is not necessarily constant, it follows that the inertial force $\mathbf{F}_i = -m\mathbf{A}$ may vary with time.

EXAMPLE 1. A boy who is holding a suitcase stands in an elevator. The elevator has an acceleration $\mathbf{A}$, which may be directed upward ($\mathbf{A}$ positive) or downward ($\mathbf{A}$ negative). What force does the suitcase exert on the boy's hand? We shall consider the problem from two points of view.

According to S: With respect to the coordinate system S attached to the ground, the suitcase, as well as the boy and the elevator, is accelerated and so the net interaction force $F - mg$ (contact and gravity) must equal the observed rate of change of momentum mA; that is,

$$F - mg = mA \qquad \text{or} \qquad F = m(g + A).$$

If A is positive (elevator accelerated upward) the contact force on the suitcase from the boy's hand is larger than the weight of the suitcase, and so the suitcase feels heavier. On the other hand, when A is negative (elevator accelerated down-

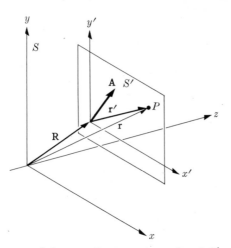

FIG. 11–6. The axes of the coordinate systems S and S' are always parallel, but the origin of S' has an acceleration **A**.

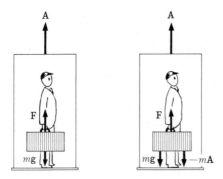

FIG. 11–7. With respect to a coordinate system at rest, the rate of change of momentum of the suitcase is mA so that there is a net force $F - mg = mA$ on it. With respect to a coordinate system in the elevator, the suitcase is in equilibrium under the influence of three forces, the two interaction forces **F** and $m\mathbf{g}$ and the inertial force $\mathbf{F}_i = -m\mathbf{A}$.

ward) the suitcase feels lighter and, in fact, when A is $-g$, the suitcase exerts no force on the boy's hand. The elevator, boy, and suitcase are all in free-fall motion.

According to S': With respect to a coordinate system on the elevator, the suitcase is at rest relative to that system, and so it is concluded that the suitcase is in equilibrium. But it is in equilibrium under the influence of the two inter-action forces, the force of the boy's hand **F**, and the weight $m\mathbf{g}$, and the inertial force $\mathbf{F}_i = -m\mathbf{A}$. Since the acceleration according to S' is zero, we have

$$F - mg - mA = 0 \quad \text{or} \quad F = m(g + A).$$

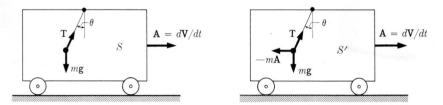

Fig. 11–8. A weight of mass m hangs from the roof inside an accelerating car. According to S, the mass is accelerated toward the right, and so must have a net force on it. According to S', the mass is not accelerated, and so is in equilibrium under the forces $m\mathbf{g}$, $\mathbf{T}$, and the inertial force $-m\mathbf{A}$. Of course, both S and S' predict the same angle θ.

In other words, the apparent weight of an object in an accelerated elevator is $m(g + A)$, and to an observer in the coordinate system on the elevator, there is no way of distinguishing whether the apparent weight of objects arises from gravitational force or from a uniform acceleration of the coordinate system.

EXAMPLE 2. A weight is hung by a string from the ceiling of an accelerating car. At what equilibrium angle will the weight hang?

According to S: The observer describing the motion with respect to ground reasons that the mass m is in equilibrium in the y-direction, and accelerates in the x-direction under the influence of two interaction forces, the tension in the string, here denoted by $\mathbf{T}$, and the weight, $m\mathbf{g}$. Therefore,

$$T \cos \theta - mg = 0, \qquad T = \frac{mg}{\cos \theta}$$

and

$$T \sin \theta = mA.$$

For the angle θ, then,

$$\tan \theta = \frac{A}{g}.$$

The mass must be to the left of the center of the car, for only then will T have a component in the $+x$-direction.

According to S': It is asserted by a person at rest in the car's coordinate system S' that the mass must be in equilibrium for, relative to him, it is at rest. We assume, of course, that the person in S' knows he and his car are accelerated. The interaction forces are the tension in the string and the weight, as before, and the inertial force is $-m\mathbf{A}$. Therefore, according to S',

$$T \cos \theta - mg = 0, \qquad -mA + T \sin \theta = 0,$$

and so for the angle θ, as before,

$$\tan \theta = \frac{A}{g}.$$

The reader should note carefully that, while the algebraic steps used in the two methods of analysis appear to be similar, the reasoning is quite different.

We have seen that in the analysis of motion with respect to an accelerated coordinate system we can account for this acceleration and thus consider the coordinate system to be at rest by introducing an inertial force $-m\mathbf{A}$ on any body of mass m whose motion we wish to study. If $\mathbf{A}$ is a constant acceleration, the inertial force is proportional to the inertial mass of the object being studied, and so is entirely like a local gravitational force (assuming, of course, that the inertial and gravitational masses are identical). This important fact will be discussed in a later section. For the moment, note that when a coordinate system has a constant acceleration, the inertial force $-m\mathbf{A}$, because it is like gravitational force, may be treated and thought of in the same manner. In other words, all the familiar procedures of, for example, the work-energy and potential-energy concepts may be carried over intact.

EXAMPLE. A light rod of length $2r$ is mounted on a vertical shaft which, in turn, is mounted on a car that has a constant acceleration $\mathbf{A}$ to the right, as shown in Fig. 11–9. The rod has a pivot at its center that enables it to rotate freely in a horizontal plane. On the ends of the rod are attached masses m and M, as shown. What is the motion of the rod with respect to a moving coordinate system attached to the car?

Gravitational forces are of no consequence so far as motion in the horizontal plane is concerned. Both masses, however, are subject to inertial forces mA and MA, directed toward the left. If the mass of M and that of m are equal, there is no tendency for the rod to rotate. If the masses are unequal, the larger mass will move toward the left (toward the negative x-axis).

More generally, the rod swings as a pendulum about the negative x-axis. When the rod makes an angle θ with the negative x-axis, there is a torque $\tau = -(M - m)Ar \sin \theta$, or $-(M - m)Ar\theta$ for small θ. This torque must

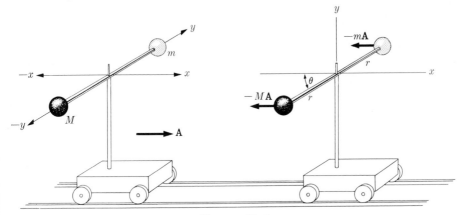

FIGURE 11–9

be equal to the rate of change of angular momentum; that is, $I_0 d^2\theta/dt^2 = -(M - m)Ar\theta$, and since $I_0 = Mr^2 + mr^2$, the rod swings back and forth, about $\theta = 0$, with a period of

$$T = 2\pi \sqrt{\frac{Mr^2 + mr^2}{(M - m)rA}}.$$

The system has a potential energy $(M - m)Ar(1 - \cos\theta)$, and if it is released from θ_0, the kinetic energy at $\theta = 0$ will be

$$E = (M - m)Ar(1 - \cos\theta_0).$$

11–4 Inertial forces in planetary and lunar motions. *Gravitational force on the moon.* While the moon is about 390 times as far from the sun as it is from the earth, the mass of the earth is only $1/330,000$ of that of the sun. Consequently, the sun's gravitational force on the moon is 2.2 times the earth's gravitational force on the moon. Why, under these conditions, does not the moon fall into the sun?

An observer, in a coordinate system S fixed relative to the sun and with axes directions fixed relative to the stars, *does* see the moon falling toward the sun, in the same sense that he sees the earth falling toward the sun. That is, an observer on the sun sees that the moon, like the earth, travels in an approximately circular path about the sun, and the gravitational force on the moon from the sun is just sufficient to keep the moon in this circular orbit. There are, to be sure, very tiny wiggles in the moon's path caused by the moon's motion around the earth, but the moon's gross motion is very nearly the same as that of the earth.

An observer, in a coordinate system S' fixed relative to the earth but with axes directions still fixed relative to the stars, sees things rather differently. To him, the gross motion of the moon is the orbit around earth every 27.3 days. We have seen in Chapter 10 that the moon's behavior is well predicted when the large force exerted on it by the sun is ignored. How can this be?

In our previous discussion of lunar motion, we ignored both the force the sun exerts on the moon and the fact that a coordinate system attached to the earth is accelerated. Inertial forces should have been included. Apparently, however, the two ignored forces canceled, and we shall show that, indeed, this was the case.

The earth is continuously accelerated toward the sun. If this acceleration is $\mathbf{A}$, we must assume that there is an inertial force $\mathbf{F}_i = -m_m \mathbf{A}$ on the moon. Here $\mathbf{A}$ is the acceleration of the coordinate system at the earth's center. This acceleration is directed along the earth-sun line. The inertial force $\mathbf{F}_i$ on the moon is not directed exactly away from the sun because, except during an eclipse, the sun, earth, and moon are not along the same line. Of course, the inertial force on the moon is very

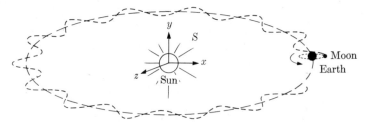

FIG. 11-10. The moon moves around the sun in an orbit almost the same as the earth's orbit. The moon-earth distance is only 0.4% of the earth-sun distance, and in the figure, the wiggles in the moon's orbit are greatly exaggerated.

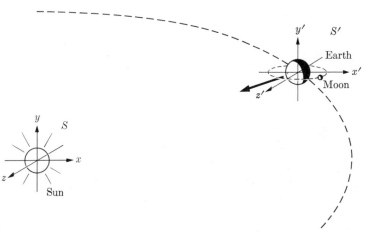

FIG. 11-11. A coordinate system S' attached to the earth is *not* an inertial frame since the earth is continuously accelerated toward the sun. (Note carefully that the coordinate axes of S and S' remain parallel. It is the origin of S' that is accelerated.)

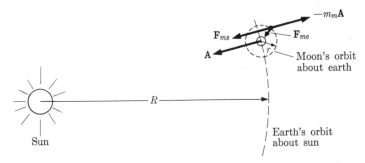

FIG. 11-12. The acceleration $\mathbf{A}$ is directed toward the sun from the earth's center, and therefore the inertial force $-m_m\mathbf{A}$ on the moon is directed almost, but not exactly, away from the sun.

nearly directed away from the sun because the earth-sun distance is so much greater than the moon-earth distance. The magnitude of the inertial force is $m_m\omega^2 R$, where ω is the earth's angular velocity about the sun and R is the earth-sun distance. Here we have assumed the orbit of the earth to be circular.

There are two interaction forces on the moon, the gravitational force of the sun and the gravitational force of the earth. The gravitational force of the sun is, of course, directed toward the sun. If we neglect the small difference between the moon-sun and earth-sun distances, the sun's gravitational force is

$$F_{ms} = \frac{Gm_m m_s}{R^2}.$$

The inertial force $m_m\omega^2 R$ and the attractive force of the sun are, to a very good approximation, oppositely directed and equal in magnitude. Therefore, in the force equation of S',

$$\mathbf{F'} = \mathbf{F}_{me} + \mathbf{F}_{ms} + \mathbf{F}_i,$$

these two terms cancel, and we have

$$F' = G \frac{m_m m_e}{r^2},$$

where the force is directed toward the earth. In other words, to a very good approximation, a coordinate system fixed relative to the earth, but with axes directions fixed relative to the stars, is an inertial frame for a discussion of lunar motion, for the gravitational force of the sun on the moon almost exactly cancels the inertial force that results from the earth's acceleration toward the sun.

The tides. The origin of the tides, like so many of nature's "mechanical" phenomena, was first explained by Newton. Stated simply, the observational facts about the tides are:

(1) The level of the surface of the oceans rises and falls periodically.

(2) On the average, there are two high and two low tides each day, and the average time between two high tides is 12 hours and 25 minutes.

(3) The magnitudes of the tides vary over the surface of the earth, and vary also with time. In many places, the magnitudes of the tides alternate. One high tide will be somewhat higher than the one that follows it. Occasionally, there are especially high (spring) tides and especially low (neap) tides.

It was long suspected that in some way the moon influenced the tides, because the average time that it took for the moon's *apparent* motion about the earth was seen to be 24 hours and 50 minutes, just the same as the time between alternate high tides (see Fig. 11–13). Further, spring tides were known to occur at the time of new and full moons, while neap tides were known to occur at the time of first- and third-quarter moons. This suspicion, it turns out, is entirely valid, as is the popular conjecture that the gravitational force of the moon "heaps up" the water on one side of the earth. The difficulty, the yet-to-be-explained fact, is that there are *two* high tides a day. Evidently the water is "heaped up" on the sides of the earth both toward and away from the moon. There is an additional "heaping up" of water attributable to the sun, but for now we shall consider only the moon's tidal effects and the earth-moon system.

We can see, from the following simple qualitative argument, the basic cause for the two "heaps" of water. Under our assumptions, the moon is in free fall toward the earth and the earth is in free fall toward the moon. From the point of view of an observer at rest, the fact that the earth and moon are in orbits about each other is of no consequence. The interaction forces do not depend upon velocity, and for an observer at rest there are no inertial forces. If the gravitational field in which the earth falls were uniform, all mass elements, including the water on the earth, would be

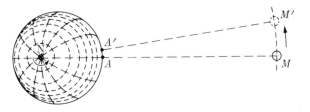

Fig. 11–13. The moon rotates around the earth once every 27.3 days and, of course, the earth turns on its own axis once a day. An observer at A, at the time shown, sees the moon on the meridian. In 24 hours the observer will have turned with the earth and returned to A, but by now the moon has moved toward M'. Fifty minutes later the observer will find the moon at M', which is now on his meridian again. (The meridian is a great circle on the celestial sphere, and passes through the North and South Poles and the observer's zenith.)

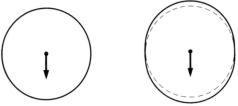

Fig. 11–14. If the earth fell toward the moon in a uniform gravitational field, the water would maintain a spherical shape. But because the gravitational field of the moon grows weaker with distance, the spherical shape is distorted.

subject to the same external force and fall with the same acceleration, and the water on the earth's surface would maintain a spherical shape. The moon's gravitational field is not uniform, however, there being a somewhat greater force on the elements of water nearer the moon and a somewhat lesser force on the elements of water away from the moon. A more detailed discussion of the two heaps or bulges of water follows.

While we ordinarily say that the moon rotates about the earth, we should more properly say that the earth and moon rotate about their common center of mass. The mass m_e of the earth is about 81 times the mass m_m of the moon. Thus the center of mass lies at $r_1 = rm_m/(m_m + m_e) \approx r/82$ from the center of the earth, where r is the earth-moon distance. Since the distance to the moon is about 60 earth radii, the center of mass is inside the earth, only $3R/4$ from the center. For most qualitative discussions, the displacement of the earth-moon center of mass from the earth's center is of no consequence. However, in the study of tidal motion, this displacement is of prime importance, since the earth actually rotates about the center of mass. Thus, a coordinate system attached to the earth, even with the directions of the coordinate axes fixed in space, is accelerated and so is not an inertial frame. For the sake of clarity, we depict in Fig. 11–15 the earth and an attached coordinate system rotating about an exterior point P. It should be noted carefully that here we are *not* concerned with the rotation of the earth on its own axis. The coordinate system has axes whose directions are fixed in space, with the y'-axis, for example, always pointing toward a distant star. This coordinate system clearly is accelerated toward the point P, and the magnitude of the acceleration is

$$A = \omega^2 r_1,$$

where r_1, the radius of the circle on which the coordinate system moves, is the distance from the earth's center to the center of mass at P. The quantity $\omega = 2\pi/T$ is the angular velocity of the moon and earth about their center of mass and T is 27.3 days. As a consequence of the acceleration, there is an inertial force $\mathbf{F}_i = -m\mathbf{A}$ on any mass whose motion we discuss with respect to this accelerated coordinate system. At the center of mass of the earth, this inertial force is exactly compensated by the gravitational force of the moon, but this cancellation is not complete at other points. Point C in Fig. 11–16, for example, is somewhat nearer the moon than is the earth's center at O, and so the gravitational force $\mathbf{F}_m$ on a mass m at that point is somewhat larger than the inertial force $\mathbf{F}_i$. Point D, on the other hand, is somewhat farther from the moon than point O, and so the inertial force is the larger. At other points on the earth's surface, similar situations hold but then the inertial and gravitational forces are not even collinear. In short, the resultant force $\mathbf{f}$ of the two forces $\mathbf{F}_i$ and $\mathbf{F}_m$ is zero only at the earth's center. The resultant tends to be directed moonward on the side of the earth toward the moon, and tends away from the moon on the opposite side of the earth. A fluid in equilibrium has a surface which

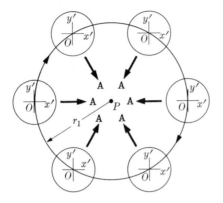

FIG. 11–15. A coordinate system, attached to the earth with axes directions fixed in space, is accelerated. The acceleration here is directed toward P and has a magnitude $4\pi^2 r_1/T^2 = \omega^2 r_1$. In the case of the earth-moon system, the point P lies within the earth's surface, and in the case of the earth-sun system, P lies much farther from the earth than it is possible to indicate in the diagram.

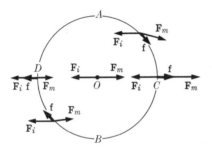

FIG. 11–16. Origin of the tidal force of the moon. The gravitational force of the moon is $\mathbf{F}_m$, and $\mathbf{F}_i$ is the inertial force that results from the earth's rotation about the moon-earth center of mass. These two forces cancel only at the earth's center. At other points, $\mathbf{F}_i$ and $\mathbf{F}_m$ have a resultant $\mathbf{f}$.

forms an equipotential-energy surface. Hence the surface of water in a pail is a horizontal plane, and the surface of the oceans, tidal effects ignored, is spherical. Now we have seen that the *net* force (earth's gravitational force included) on a 1-gm mass at point C or D is somewhat *less* than it is at A or B (see Fig. 11–17). An equipotential-energy surface is therefore *farther* from the center of the earth at C and D than it is at A and B. Since, as mentioned above, a water surface coincides with an equipotential-energy surface, there is a bulge of water at C and also at D. As the earth turns on its own axis, in effect it turns under these bulges of water, and so there is a high tide at a given place on the earth twice a day. Note also that because the earth's axis is not perpendicular to the plane of the moon's orbit, the two high tides are not of equal magnitude.

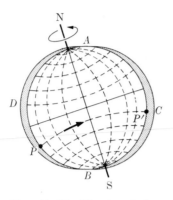

Moon

FIG. 11–17. The two bulges of water (greatly exaggerated) result from the moon's gravitational force and from the moon's rotation about the earth. At the time shown, there would be high tides at P and P'. About 12 hours later (actually 12 hours, 25 minutes), P will have advanced as a result of the earth's rotation to P' where there is a somewhat higher high tide.

While the force that the sun exerts on the earth is about 180 times the force that the moon exerts on the earth, the tide-raising force of the sun is only about one-half that of the moon. This is because the sun is much farther from the earth than is the moon and the *difference* in the sun's force at various places on the earth is smaller than that of the moon. When the moon is new or full, the earth, sun, and moon all lie more or less along the same line. (When the moon is new, it lies between the earth and the sun, and when the moon is full, the earth lies between the moon and the sun.) At these times, therefore, the moon- and sun-produced tides are in phase and aid each other in producing an especially high (spring) tide. When the moon is in its first or third quarter, on the other hand, it lies along a line more or less perpendicular to the earth-sun line, and at these times the moon- and sun-produced tides are in opposition, resulting in low (neap) tides.

The detailed behavior of the tides is enormously complicated by the inertia of the water and by the fact that ocean waters must flow over the ocean floor and between and around the land masses. The high tides, therefore, do not keep up with the position of the tide-raising forces, but lag behind by times which range up to several hours.

The principle of equivalence. In our previous discussions, we have noted that the effect of a constant acceleration is in all respects the same as the effect of a uniform gravitational field. This almost incidental observation, it turns out, has some very interesting and important consequences.

Before we discuss this matter further, we should take particular note of the fact that the mass which enters the inertial-force term $-m\mathbf{A}$ is inherently the *inertial mass*, a mass which, in principle, arises from experiments such as those with the colliding cars and colliding pucks in which the inertia of bodies are compared. The mass that enters the gravitational force on the other hand, is the *gravitational* mass, one which, in principle, arises from experiments such as weight measurements in which the gravitational forces on bodies are compared. As we discussed in Chapter 3, the mass scales which evolve from these two very different mass concepts are equivalent, at least to the limits of all experiments that bear on the matter. Baron Roland Eötvös, a Hungarian who investigated many aspects of the gravitational force of the earth, in about 1909 performed a series of very careful experiments which showed, in effect, that the ratio of gravitational to inertial mass was the same, to within one part in 10^8, for all the substances he tried.

In the general theory of relativity, Einstein postulated that gravitational and inertial masses are *strictly* proportional. For example, an observer in the elevator of Fig. 11-7 could not, according to Einstein's postulate, *even in principle* tell whether the apparent weight of his suitcase arose from a uniform gravitational field, from a uniform acceleration, or from a combination of the two. Under Einstein's postulate of equivalence, the hypothetical observer would be free to make whatever type of physical measurement he chose, yet he would not be able to detect a difference between the effects of gravity and uniform acceleration. His measurement could involve mechanical, electrical, magnetic, nuclear, or any other type of phenomena. (An observer looking out a window, of course, is not within the spirit of the postulate.)

The equivalence postulate, suggested by the results of experiments in mechanics, leads to the surprising prediction that light should be bent in a gravitational field. The argument is not difficult, and we shall discuss it here both because of its importance and interesting consequence and also because it is such a beautiful example of the delicate connection of one branch of enquiry to another.

Imagine first an isolated elevator moving with a constant velocity V_0 in the direction indicated in Fig. 11-18. An observer outside the elevator sees a horizontal light beam enter the elevator at P_1 and leave at P_2. During the time Δt when the front of the light beam was passing through the elevator, the elevator moved a distance $V_0 \Delta t$. An observer in the elevator, on the other hand, concludes correctly that, according to him, the light beam was traveling in an inclined direction, and so P_1 and P_2, the entry and exit points, are at unequal distances above the floor. According to both observers, the light nonetheless traveled in a straight-line path. .

Imagine now that the elevator is accelerated, but still isolated in space. Let the velocity of the elevator be zero when the front of the light beam enters. Then the elevator will have moved a distance $A(\Delta t)^2/2$ when the front of the light beam leaves. The observer outside the elevator still

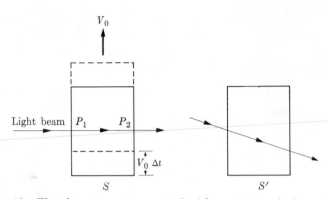

FIG. 11–18. The elevator moves upward with constant velocity. According to both S and S', the light beam travels in a straight line.

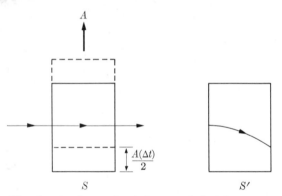

FIG. 11–19. The elevator is accelerated upward, but has zero velocity when the light beam enters the elevator. An observer on the elevator sees the light beam bent downward.

sees the light beam travel horizontally, but the observer in the elevator now sees the light beam curve down toward the floor. The beam, according to the accelerated observer, no longer travels in a straight line, but is bent. Recall now that, according to the equivalence postulate, the observer on the elevator could not, even in principle, distinguish between a uniform acceleration and a gravitational field regardless of the type of experiment or phenomenon involved. Then, since a light beam "falls" in an isolated accelerating elevator, it should also fall in an elevator at rest in the presence of a gravitational field.

Of course, this argument does not *prove* that light beams are bent by gravitational fields. But if experiments did show that light beams were not bent, the contention of Einstein, stated above, would thereby be disproved. In the gravitational field of the earth, a light beam should evidently "fall" just like any material object, the distance of fall in a

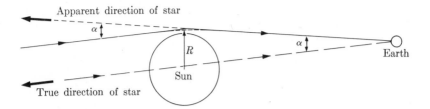

Fig. 11–20. Light from a star is deflected through an angle α by the sun's gravitational field. To an observer on the earth the star is apparently "moved over" through an angle α. Einstein's value for α is $2Gm_s/Rc^2$, where G is the gravitational constant, m_s is the mass of the sun, R is the distance of closest approach to the sun's center, and c is the velocity of light.

time t being $gt^2/2$. In this sense, light would have mass. But the velocity of light is so large ($3 \cdot 10^8$ m/sec) and flight times are so short that this bending of light by the earth has never been measured. In one of his very early papers on relativity, Einstein predicted the amount of bending of the light from a star when it passes close to the sun. Even here the bending is very small, and its accurate measurement has challenged astronomers for many years. The measurements must be made during the time and at the place of a total eclipse of the sun, for otherwise the stars cannot be seen or photographed in the light from the sun that is scattered by the earth's atmosphere. A similar set of measurements must then be made (several months later) on the same stars at night. The two sets of measurements are then compared. The angular position of the stars should, according to the equivalence postulate (general relativity), be shifted by about 0.87 sec of arc. To date, the measurements (made in 1922, 1929, and 1951) are in fair agreement with the postulate, but the matter cannot, as yet, be considered definitely settled.

11–5 Motion with respect to a rotating coordinate system. Until now, we have carefully avoided coordinate systems whose axes rotate. In several examples, the coordinate systems translated in a circular path, but the *directions* of the axes were always fixed. To be sure, any coordinate system attached to the earth's surface rotates, since the earth rotates. For example, the direction of the edge of this page points toward a fixed place on the celestial sphere now, but in ten minutes (even if the book is not moved) its direction will differ by as much as $2\frac{1}{2}°$. For most purposes, as we shall see, the effect of the earth's rotation on laboratory experiments is very small.

That essential complications arise when a coordinate system rotates can be demonstrated with a simple thought experiment. Imagine a merry-go-round, above which is mounted a horizontal track, as shown

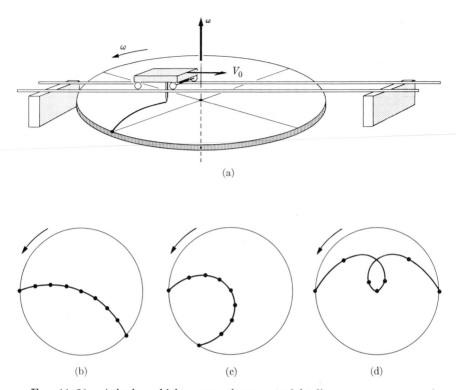

FIG. 11–21.   A body, which moves along a straight line at constant speed with respect to a fixed coordinate system, traces curved paths as shown in (a) and (b), when the coordinate system is rotating. When the angular velocity ω of the merry-go-round increases, the path becomes as shown in (c), and when it increases still further, the path becomes as shown in (d).

in Fig. 11–21.   A stylus is affixed to a car which moves on the track at a constant speed V_0 with respect to a fixed coordinate system. As the merry-go-round rotates counterclockwise with angular velocity ω, the stylus traces a curved path as shown in parts (a) and (b) of the figure. When ω increases, the path becomes as shown in (c), and when it increases still further, the path becomes as shown in (d). Note that the paths are rather complicated and that the velocity according to S', as indicated by the spacing of the dots, is by no means constant either in magnitude or direction.   In the rotating coordinate system S', we conclude that there must be inertial forces on the object.   It is now our purpose to determine what these inertial forces are.

The velocity according to S' and S.   As a first step toward our goal of determining the inertial forces involved in our thought experiment, let us see how the velocities according to S and according to S' are related.

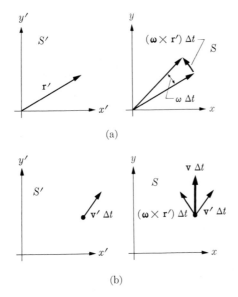

(a)

(b)

FIG. 11–22. In (a) a body is at rest in the coordinate system S' and so has a velocity $\boldsymbol{\omega} \times \mathbf{r}'$ in the coordinate system S. In (b) the body has a velocity $\mathbf{v}'$ in the coordinate system S'.

A body at rest in S' at a distance r' from the center will travel in a circle of radius r' and with a speed $\omega r'$ according to S. If we regard $\boldsymbol{\omega}$ as a vector quantity ($\boldsymbol{\omega}$ is directed *outward* from the paper in Fig. 11–22), we can express this velocity according to S concisely by $\mathbf{v} = \boldsymbol{\omega} \times \mathbf{r}'$, where $\mathbf{r}'$ is the position vector according to S'. An object at rest according to S' has a velocity of $\boldsymbol{\omega} \times \mathbf{r}'$ according to S, and if an object has a velocity $\mathbf{v}'$ according to S', its velocity according to S is simply

$$\mathbf{v} = \mathbf{v}' + \boldsymbol{\omega} \times \mathbf{r}'. \qquad (11\text{–}14)$$

That this is so can be seen easily as follows. With reference to Fig. 11–22(b), during a time Δt, the body moves through $\mathbf{v}' \, \Delta t$ according to S'. But also, during Δt, the coordinate system S' has rotated through an angle $\omega \, \Delta t$ so that the vector displacement $\mathbf{v} \, \Delta t$ according to S is the vector sum $\mathbf{v}' \, \Delta t + (\boldsymbol{\omega} \times \mathbf{r}') \, \Delta t$. The velocity according to S is therefore as given above by expression (11–14). Alternatively, the velocity according to S' is

$$\mathbf{v}' = \mathbf{v} - \boldsymbol{\omega} \times \mathbf{r}', \qquad (11\text{–}15)$$

for, on a body at rest in the coordinate system S, the effect of a rotation is to produce a clockwise movement (when $\boldsymbol{\omega}$ is counterclockwise) *according to S'.*

We can obtain the important relation between the velocities $\mathbf{v}$ and $\mathbf{v}'$ in an alternate way. Imagine the two coordinate systems, S and S', at a time such that S' has rotated through an angle $\theta = \omega t$. A point P that has the coordinates (x, y) in S has the coordinates (x', y') in S', where x' and y' are given by

$$x' = x \cos \theta + y \sin \theta \quad \text{and} \quad y' = y \cos \theta - x \sin \theta. \quad (11\text{–}16)$$

These expressions, which are evident from Fig. 11–23, may be differentiated with respect to the time t. The angle θ must be considered as changing, of course, and $d\theta/dt$ is ω. When these differentiations are carried out, we obtain

$$v'_x = v_x \cos \theta + v_y \sin \theta + \omega y' \quad \text{and} \quad v'_y = v_y \cos \theta - v_x \sin \theta - \omega x'$$

$$(11\text{–}17)$$

for the two components of the vector velocity $\mathbf{v}'$. That the above expressions agree with (11–15) is evident because $v_x \cos \theta + v_y \sin \theta$ is the x'-component of the vector $\mathbf{v}$ and $\omega y'$ is the x'-component of the vector $-\boldsymbol{\omega} \times \mathbf{r}'$. Similarly, $v_y \cos \theta - v_x \sin \theta$ is the y'-component of the vector $\mathbf{v}$ and $-\omega x'$ is the y'-component of the vector $-\boldsymbol{\omega} \times \mathbf{r}'$. The details of this demonstration will be presented as a problem at the end of this chapter.

EXAMPLE. With reference to Fig. 11–21, let the car cross the merry-go-round in 8 sec, and let the diameter of the merry-go-round be 96 ft. Then the velocity according to S is $96/8 = 12$ ft/sec directed along the y-axis. The merry-go-round rotates once every 8 sec, so its angular velocity is $\omega = 2\pi/8 = (\pi/4)$ rad/sec directed along the z-axis (outward from the page). What is the velocity of the car according to S' at $t = 0$ and at $t = 1$ sec?

The velocity according to S' is $\mathbf{v}' = \mathbf{v} - \boldsymbol{\omega} \times \mathbf{r}'$. As is shown in Fig. 11–24, at $t = 0$, $\mathbf{v}$ is directed along the y'-axis and has a magnitude of 12 ft/sec. The position vector $\mathbf{r}'$ extends from the origin to the point P_0, and has a magnitude of 48 ft, the radius of the merry-go-round. Therefore, the vector $\boldsymbol{\omega} \times \mathbf{r}'$ has the direction indicated and a magnitude of $(\pi/4)48 = 12\pi$ ft/sec. The velocity $\mathbf{v}' = \mathbf{v} - \boldsymbol{\omega} \times \mathbf{r}'$ has a magnitude of

$$v' = \sqrt{12^2 + (12\pi)^2} = 12\sqrt{1 + \pi^2} = 39.5 \text{ ft/sec,}$$

and the angle θ_0 is given by

$$\tan \theta_0 = \frac{12}{12\pi}, \qquad \theta_0 = 17.7°.$$

At $t = 1$ sec, the car has moved to point P_1 which is $48 - 12 = 36$ ft from the origin, and $\mathbf{r}'$ extends from the origin to P_1, the coordinate system having rotated 45°. The velocity $\mathbf{v}$ still has a magnitude of 12 ft/sec, but now is directed along the broken line shown in the figure. The vector $-\boldsymbol{\omega} \times \mathbf{r}'$ has

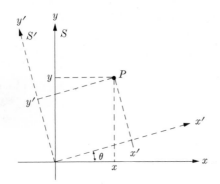

Fig. 11–23. The coordinate system S' is rotated through an angle $\theta = \omega t$.

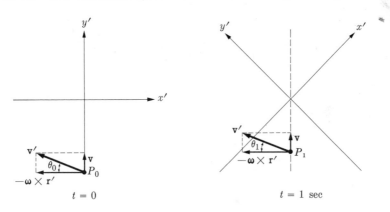

Fig. 11–24. Velocity $\mathbf{v}'$ according to S' at $t = 0$ and at $t = 1$ sec for the motion illustrated in Fig. 11–21.

a magnitude $(\pi/4)36 = 9\pi$ ft/sec, and is directed perpendicular to the broken line. The velocity according to S' therefore has a magnitude of

$$v' = \sqrt{12^2 + (9\pi)^2} = 30.6 \text{ ft/sec}$$

and the angle θ_1 is given by

$$\tan \theta_1 = \frac{12}{9\pi}, \qquad \theta_1 = 23°.$$

The acceleration according to S' and S. It should be perfectly clear by now that when the motion of a body is described with reference to the rotating coordinate system S', the rotation itself will produce rates of change of the velocity and the momentum of the body. As a result we will have inertial forces on the body in S'. We can determine these inertial forces if we can find the manner in which the accelerations in the two coordinate systems S and S' are related. Certainly, the mass times the acceleration, $m\mathbf{a}$ according to S, must be equal to the interaction forces, while $m\mathbf{a}'$ according to S' must be equal to the net force, that is, interaction forces plus inertial forces.

The relation between the accelerations can be found easily from the expressions that we have developed to relate the velocity components. Hence, if we simply differentiate and rearrange the two expressions (11–17), we obtain

$$a'_x = a_x \cos \theta + a_y \sin \theta - 2\omega v'_y + \omega^2 x', \qquad (11\text{--}18a)$$

$$a'_y = a_y \cos \theta - a_x \sin \theta + 2\omega v'_x + \omega^2 y' \qquad (11\text{--}18b)$$

for the two components of the acceleration $\mathbf{a}'$, according to S'. The first two terms on the right of (11–18a) constitute the x'-component of the vector $\mathbf{a}$, while $-2\omega v'_y$ is the x'-component of the vector $-2\boldsymbol{\omega} \times \mathbf{v}'$. The last term, $\omega^2 x'$, is the x'-component of the vector $\omega^2 \mathbf{r}'$. Similarly, the first two terms of (11–18b) constitute the y'-component of the vector $\mathbf{a}$, $2\omega v'_x$ is the y'-component of $-2\boldsymbol{\omega} \times \mathbf{v}'$, and $\omega^2 y'$ is the y'-component of the vector $\omega^2 \mathbf{r}'$. Expressions (11–18a, b) can therefore be written in vector form as

$$\mathbf{a}' = \mathbf{a} - 2\boldsymbol{\omega} \times \mathbf{v}' + \omega^2 \mathbf{r}'. \qquad (11\text{--}19)$$

This derivation has been carried out for motion in the xy-plane. When the motion also has a z-component, we note that v'_z and a'_z are parallel with the axis of rotation and hence are not influenced by the rotation. Equation (11–19) then can be applied to an arbitrary motion if in the third term we replace $\mathbf{r}'$ by the vector component in the xy-plane. The magnitude of this component is $r \sin \phi$, where ϕ is the angle between $\mathbf{r}'$ and $\boldsymbol{\omega}$. Therefore we obtain both the correct magnitude and direction if $\omega^2 \mathbf{r}'$ is replaced by $-\boldsymbol{\omega} \times (\boldsymbol{\omega} \times \mathbf{r}')$. That is, the general relation between $\mathbf{a}$ and $\mathbf{a}'$ is

$$\mathbf{a}' = \mathbf{a} - 2\boldsymbol{\omega} \times \mathbf{v}' - \boldsymbol{\omega} \times (\boldsymbol{\omega} \times \mathbf{r}'). \qquad (11\text{--}19a)$$

Before we go on to discuss the inertial forces, let us consider a somewhat more physical method of arriving at the relationship between the accelerations $\mathbf{a}$ and $\mathbf{a}'$.

Consider an arbitrary vector $\mathbf{A}$ in the xy-plane. $\mathbf{A}$ may be a position vector, a displacement vector, a velocity vector, etc. If $\mathbf{A}$ is a constant according to S', it will *not* be a constant according to S because the direction of $\mathbf{A}$, according to S, will be changing continuously (Fig. 11–25). If the coordinate axes rotate through an angle $\Delta\theta = \omega \Delta t$, the direction of $\mathbf{A}$ will have changed by an angle $\Delta\theta$ according to S, even though $\mathbf{A}$ does not change direction according to S'. Because according to S the direction of $\mathbf{A}$ changed, $\mathbf{A}$ itself will have changed by an amount $|\mathbf{A}|\omega\,\Delta t$, the change being directed *perpendicular* to $\mathbf{A}$. To S, it will thus appear that $\mathbf{A}$ had a time derivative $(d\mathbf{A}/dt)_S = \boldsymbol{\omega} \times \mathbf{A}$. According to S', of course, $(d\mathbf{A}/dt)_{S'}$ is zero, in keeping with our initial assumption.

If, during the time interval Δt, vector $\mathbf{A}$ changes according to S' by an amount $\Delta\mathbf{A}$, the change in $\mathbf{A}$ according to S will be $\Delta\mathbf{A} + \boldsymbol{\omega} \times \mathbf{A}\,\Delta t$ (Fig. 11–26). The time rate of change is then

$$\left(\frac{d\mathbf{A}}{dt}\right)_S = \left(\frac{d\mathbf{A}}{dt}\right)_{S'} + \boldsymbol{\omega} \times \mathbf{A}$$

according to S. In other words, the vector $\mathbf{A}$ with respect to S changes for two reasons. First, it changes direction even if it is constant in the rotating system. This is the origin of the $\boldsymbol{\omega} \times \mathbf{A}$ term. Second, if ω is zero (coordinate system S' not in rotation), both S and S' must agree on the rate of change of $\mathbf{A}$. This is the essence of the $(d\mathbf{A}/dt)_{S'}$ term.

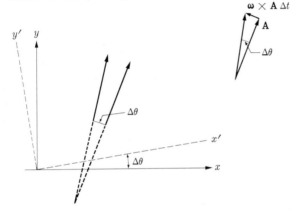

FIG. 11–25. When the coordinate system S' rotates through $\Delta\theta$, a constant vector in the coordinate system S' rotates through $\Delta\theta$, according to S.

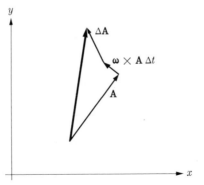

FIG. 11–26. When $\mathbf{A}$ changes by $\Delta\mathbf{A}$ according to S', it changes by $\Delta\mathbf{A} + \boldsymbol{\omega} \times \mathbf{A}$ according to S.

We can apply this useful relation directly to the position vector $\mathbf{r} = \mathbf{r}'$ of a particle. Then we have directly $\mathbf{v} = \mathbf{v}' + \boldsymbol{\omega} \times \mathbf{r}'$, in agreement with our previous findings. So far as the acceleration is concerned, we need only apply the relation again to the velocity, $\mathbf{v} = \mathbf{v}' + \boldsymbol{\omega} \times \mathbf{r}'$. Here we shall get four terms, for we must differentiate $\mathbf{v}' + \boldsymbol{\omega} \times \mathbf{r}'$ to obtain $\mathbf{a}' + \boldsymbol{\omega} \times \mathbf{v}'$, and then add $\boldsymbol{\omega} \times \mathbf{v}$ to obtain $\boldsymbol{\omega} \times \mathbf{v}' + \boldsymbol{\omega} \times (\boldsymbol{\omega} \times \mathbf{r}')$. When we add the two like terms, we have $\mathbf{a} = \mathbf{a}' + 2\boldsymbol{\omega} \times \mathbf{v}' + \boldsymbol{\omega} \times (\boldsymbol{\omega} \times \mathbf{r}')$, and this is also in agreement with our previous findings.

The inertial forces. Now that we have found how the accelerations $\mathbf{a}$ and $\mathbf{a}'$ (according to S and S', respectively) are related, we can proceed to find the inertial forces. If we multiply expression (11–19) by the mass of the object we wish to consider, we have

$$m\mathbf{a} = m\mathbf{a}' + 2m(\boldsymbol{\omega} \times \mathbf{v}') + m\boldsymbol{\omega} \times (\boldsymbol{\omega} \times \mathbf{r}')$$

or, when this is rearranged,

$$\mathbf{F}' = \mathbf{F} - 2m(\boldsymbol{\omega} \times \mathbf{v}') - m\boldsymbol{\omega} \times (\boldsymbol{\omega} \times \mathbf{r}'). \qquad (11\text{–}20)$$

On the left, we have $\mathbf{F}' = m\mathbf{a}' = d\mathbf{p}'/dt$, the force as assigned by an observer S' in a rotating coordinate system. On the right, we have $\mathbf{F}$, the force according to an observer at rest in an inertial frame. This latter force, as we have emphasized before, is an *interaction* force or a net interaction force. The two remaining terms in (11–20) are the *inertial forces:*

$$\mathbf{F}'_i = -2m(\boldsymbol{\omega} \times \mathbf{v}') - m\boldsymbol{\omega} \times (\boldsymbol{\omega} \times \mathbf{r}'). \qquad (11\text{–}21)$$

Clearly, when $\boldsymbol{\omega}$ is zero, S' is not rotating, and so S' and S must agree on the forces. That this is indeed the case is clear from (11–20) because the inertial forces both go to zero when $\boldsymbol{\omega}$ goes to zero.

The second of the inertial-force terms, $-m\boldsymbol{\omega} \times (\boldsymbol{\omega} \times \mathbf{r}')$ (which can be written $m\omega^2\mathbf{r}'$ when motion is confined to a plane perpendicular to $\boldsymbol{\omega}$), has a very simple and readily understandable significance. An object at rest on a rotating platform is, according to an observer at rest, moving in a circular path and is therefore accelerated toward the center of the circle (Fig. 11–27). The force responsible for this acceleration may be supplied by a block attached to the platform, a string in which there is tension, or any other interaction force. This interaction force must be equal to $m\omega^2r'$ and directed *inward*, for the acceleration is toward the center of the circle.

With respect to the rotating coordinate system, on the other hand, the mass is at rest and so is in equilibrium. The *net* force $\mathbf{F}'$ then must be zero. The first inertial-force term is zero because $v' = 0$. The second

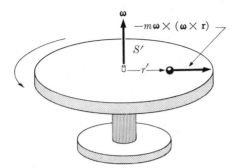

FIG. 11-27. The mass m is at rest according to S', and the centrifugal force is directed outward.

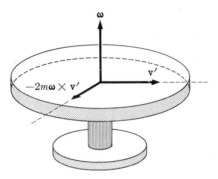

FIG. 11-28. The coriolis force is perpendicular to $\boldsymbol{\omega}$ and to $\mathbf{v}$.

inertial-force term, $-m\boldsymbol{\omega} \times (\boldsymbol{\omega} \times \mathbf{r}')$, has a magnitude of $m\omega^2 r'$ and is directed *outward*. Therefore, in order for the object to be in equilibrium in S', there must be an interaction force of magnitude $m\omega^2 r'$ directed inward. Thus, we see that the interaction forces agree in S and S'.

The inertial force $-m\boldsymbol{\omega} \times (\boldsymbol{\omega} \times \mathbf{r}')$, which for plane motion is $m\omega^2 \mathbf{r}'$, exists *only* in S', and is called the *centrifugal force*. It is always directed outward, is always perpendicular to the axis of rotation, and is proportional to ω^2 and to the perpendicular distance to the axis.

While the centrifugal force $-m\boldsymbol{\omega} \times (\boldsymbol{\omega} \times \mathbf{r}')$ depends upon position $\mathbf{r}'$ but not upon velocity $\mathbf{v}'$, the first inertial-force term in (11-21), $-2m\boldsymbol{\omega} \times \mathbf{v}'$, called the *coriolis force*, depends upon velocity in S' but *not* upon position. Recall our discussion of the path of the car that moves on a track above the surface of a merry-go-round. According to the coordinate system S, the path of a force-free mass is, of course, a straight line. But according to S', the coordinate system on the merry-go-round, the path is curved. The coriolis force is perpendicular to $\boldsymbol{\omega}$ and perpendicular to $\mathbf{v}'$, and for the case shown in Fig. 11-28 tends to curve the trajectory toward the right. In fact, on the surface of the platform, the coriolis force tends always to deflect a moving mass to the right, or clockwise.

It is important that the reader be aware that the curved path, when viewed from a coordinate system at rest, arises for purely geometric reasons. A pencil that is pushed at a constant speed across a stationary piece of paper will trace a straight line. But if the paper is rotating, the line will be curved. The inertial forces, centrifugal and coriolis, apply *only* in the description of motion with respect to rotating coordinate systems.

EXAMPLE 1. A body is at rest according to S. According to S', which is a rotating coordinate system, the same body rotates with an angular velocity ω and has the speed $\omega r'$. Since the acceleration of a body traveling in a circular path is $\omega^2 r'$ directed toward the center of rotation, there must be a net force $m\omega^2 r'$ on the body, directed toward the center. To see that this conclusion is consistent with the expressions for the inertial forces in S', we note that the centrifugal force is $m\omega^2 r'$, directed away from the center, and the coriolis force is $2m\omega^2 r'$, directed toward the center. The total inertial force, centrifugal plus coriolis, is therefore

$$\mathbf{F}'_i = -2m(\boldsymbol{\omega} \times \mathbf{v}') - m\boldsymbol{\omega} \times (\boldsymbol{\omega} \times \mathbf{r}')$$

$$= -2m\omega^2\mathbf{r}' + m\omega^2\mathbf{r}' = -m\omega^2\mathbf{r}'.$$

The mass times the acceleration, according to S', must be the net force, i.e., interaction forces plus inertial forces. The mass times acceleration is $-m\omega^2\mathbf{r}'$, and since the inertial forces alone are $-m\omega^2\mathbf{r}'$, no interaction forces are necessary. Of course, this same conclusion is reached in S, since relative to S the body is at rest.

EXAMPLE 2. A particle of mass m which is at rest on a frictionless horizontal surface is pushed by a stick of length L, pivoted at one end. The stick rotates about the pivot at a constant angular velocity ω, and the particle is initially just slightly to one side of the axis. What is the contact force F that is exerted on the particle by the stick, and what is the kinetic energy of the particle when it leaves the end of the stick? (Assume sliding without friction.)

Let us take the x'-axis to be along the length of the stick, as shown in Fig. 11–29. Then, according to the coordinate system S' which moves with the stick, the centrifugal force is $m\omega^2 x'$ directed *outward*, and the coriolis force is $2m\omega v'_x$ directed perpendicular to the stick as shown. According to S', the particle is in equilibrium in the y'-direction so that the net force in the y'-direction must be zero. Therefore, if the contact force on the particle is F, we have $F - 2m\omega v'_x = 0$ or $F = 2m\omega v'_x$.

In the analysis according to the coordinate system S at rest, one reasons as follows. The distance x' measures the radial distance of the mass from the axis. The angular momentum is therefore $l = mx'^2\omega$. The torque, or rate of change of angular momentum, is

$$\tau = \frac{dp}{dt} = 2mx'\omega v'_x,$$

but since the torque must be $\tau = F_{x'}$, the force F must be $2m\omega v'_x$. *The interaction forces in S and S' agree.*

The centrifugal force is $m\omega^2 x'$ directed outward, and so as the particle moves from $x' = 0$ to $x' = L$, the work done on it is

$$W = \int_0^L m\omega^2 x' \, dx' = \frac{mL^2}{2}\, \omega^2.$$

Thus, the kinetic energy according to S' is $mL^2\omega^2/2$. Since the kinetic energy is also $mv'^2_x/2$, we get $v'_x = \omega L$ at $x' = L$.

According to S, $v'_x = \omega L$ is a radial velocity and, in addition, the mass has a tangential velocity equal to the velocity of the end of the stick. This tangential velocity is also ωL, so that the speed of the mass with respect to S is $\omega L\sqrt{2}$, and the kinetic energy according to S is $m\omega^2 L^2$. In problems of this kind the motion in S' is often simpler than in S.

In the present example, the trajectory of the particle is simply a straight line in S', but a rather complicated spiral in S. This point is illustrated further in the next example.

EXAMPLE 3. An interesting demonstration of motion in a rotating coordinate system is the following. A small car moves on a straight track on a horizontal table which can rotate about a vertical axis. The car is attached to the midpoint of a spring which is held stretched between the endpoints of the track, as shown in Fig. 11–30. The equilibrium position of the car is at the axis of rotation. When the table does not rotate, the period of oscillation of the car is T_0. What is the period of oscillation when the table rotates with an angular velocity ω?

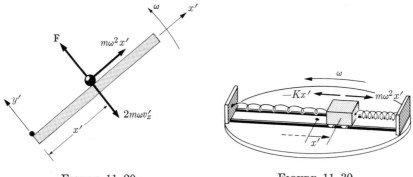

FIGURE 11–29   FIGURE 11–30

We shall study the motion with respect to a coordinate system S' attached to the rotating table. At a distance x' from the equilibrium position we then have two forces acting on the car, the spring interaction force $-Kx'$ and the inertial (centrifugal) force $m\omega^2 x'$, where K is the spring constant and m is the mass of the car. The equation of motion is then

$$m\,\frac{d^2 x'}{dt^2} \;=\; -Kx + m\omega^2 x' \;=\; -(K - m\omega^2)x'.$$

In other words, the centrifugal force reduces the restoring force, and the effective spring constant is $K - m\omega^2$. The period of oscillation is then

$$T \;=\; 2\pi\sqrt{\frac{m}{K - m\omega^2}} \;=\; \frac{T_0}{\sqrt{\omega_0^2 - \omega^2}},$$

where $\omega_0 = \sqrt{K/m}$. It is clear that when $\omega > \omega_0$ the car does not oscillate but has a positive acceleration at all times and moves outward from the axis of rotation.

The effect of the earth's rotation. We now have seen that there are two inertial forces that arise in a rotating coordinate system. The coriolis force depends upon the velocity of a body but not upon its position, while the centrifugal force depends upon the position of a body but not upon its velocity. Centrifugal force has an easily evaluated effect on the motion of bodies on the earth's surface, and we shall therefore consider it first.

The centrifugal force has a magnitude $m\omega^2 r'$, where r' is the distance from the axis of rotation to the mass m; it is directed away from the rotation axis. At a latitude λ therefore, where r' is $R\cos\lambda$, the centrifugal force is $m\omega^2 R\cos\lambda$. In addition to the centrifugal force, there is, of course, the gravitational force which, if the earth is assumed to be a uniform sphere, is directed toward its geometric center. When the weight of a body is measured, the gravitational and centrifugal forces both contribute, and the net weight is their vector sum. At the equator, where $\cos\lambda = 1$, the centrifugal acceleration is $\omega^2 R = (7.3 \cdot 10^{-5})^2 (6.4 \cdot 10^6) = 0.034\ \text{m/sec}^2$, or about 0.35% of g. At other latitudes, the centrifugal contribution is even smaller. From Fig. 11–31, we can see that the measured g is

$$g \simeq g' - \omega^2 R \cos^2 \lambda, \tag{11-22}$$

where g' is the contribution from only the gravitational force. The measured values of g on the earth's surface vary with latitude. However, there is additional variation attributable to the fact that the earth is not a sphere, but is rather in the shape of an oblate sphere with its poles pushed together somewhat.

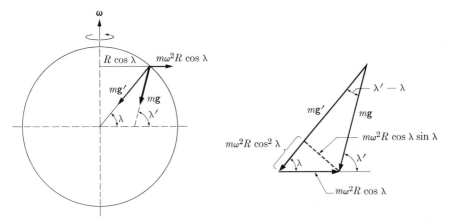

FIG. 11–31. The weight of a body and direction of a plumb bob are both affected by the centrifugal force.

The centrifugal force also causes a plumb bob to indicate other than a "true" vertical. A plumb bob lines up with $m\mathbf{g}$, not $m\mathbf{g}'$, and the angle of deviation, which has its maximum value at $\lambda = 45°$, is given by

$$\lambda' - \lambda \simeq \frac{m\omega^2 R \cos \lambda \sin \lambda}{mg} = \frac{\omega^2 R \sin 2\lambda}{2g}. \tag{11–23}$$

The maximum deviation is about 0.1°.

The centrifugal force increases as the distance from earth increases, and in the equatorial plane at about 26,000 mi from the earth's center, it becomes equal to the gravitational force $Gm_e m/r^2$. A satellite at this distance would be in equilibrium under the centrifugal and gravitational forces and would, for an observer at the equator, remain always in the same position overhead. (There would be no coriolis force because according to a coordinate system attached to the earth the satellite would have no velocity.) Viewed from a coordinate system that does not rotate with the earth, the satellite would be in an ordinary orbit which would be in the equatorial plane. The time for one earth traversal would be one day. Ordinarily, astronomical calculations are made from the viewpoint of a coordinate system S fixed in space, and for observational purposes, the results are transformed to the earth's rotating coordinate system S' later. This procedure is usually less cumbersome and less complicated than solving the problem from S' in which the coriolis- and centrifugal-force terms must be included.

The effect of the coriolis force on the motion of objects on the surface of the earth is usually very small. Since the angular velocity of the earth is $\omega = 2\pi/T = 7.3 \cdot 10^{-5}$ rad/sec, the velocity of an object must be at least $v = g/2\omega = 1.4 \cdot 10^5$ m/sec, in order that the coriolis acceleration be equal to g. On the other hand, when flight times are long, as they are for long-range projectiles and winds, even these relatively small accelerations are effective in producing large deflections.

Let us consider motion in a horizontal plane at some latitude in the Northern Hemisphere. The angular velocity vector $\boldsymbol{\omega}$ is directed outward from the ground, and as shown in Fig. 11–32, the coriolis force always deflects to the right a body that is moving in the horizontal plane. In the Southern Hemisphere, the angular velocity vector is directed into the ground, and the coriolis force deflects a body to the left. In general, the coriolis force has components normal to the horizontal plane also. In fact, the coriolis force on a particle moving *on* the equator is entirely normal to the horizontal, being directed upward when the particle moves west to east, and downward when it moves east to west. A particle moving perpendicularly across the equator is subject to no coriolis force because $\boldsymbol{\omega}$ and $\mathbf{v}'$ are then parallel and $\boldsymbol{\omega} \times \mathbf{v}'$ is zero.

EXAMPLE. A mass m is dropped from a height h on the rotating earth. If the earth were not rotating, the mass would fall along the direction of a plumb bob. However, the earth does rotate, and so the coriolis force will deflect the body slightly. To keep our considerations simple, let us consider a body dropped from a point on the equator. We assume that the effect of the centrifugal force has been included in the value we use for g, the gravitational acceleration.

The coriolis force, as shown in Fig. 11–33, is directed toward the East and, for a body falling straight down with velocity v, has a magnitude $2m\omega v$. The coriolis force here is very small, and its effect on the velocity is so slight that we may calculate the deflection as follows. The velocity v for a body dropped from h is gt. The coriolis force is therefore $F = 2m\omega gt$. The acceleration toward the East, dv_e/dt, is

$$\frac{dv_e}{dt} = 2\omega gt,$$

and for v_e, the velocity east, we have

$$v_e = \omega gt^2 \qquad \text{or} \qquad \frac{dx}{dt} = \omega gt^2.$$

The eastern deflection in a time t is then

$$x = \frac{\omega gt^3}{3}.$$

Since the time of fall is $t = \sqrt{2h/g}$, for the deflection we have

$$x = \frac{\omega g}{3} \left(\frac{2h}{g}\right)^{3/2}.$$

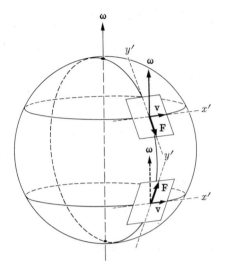

FIG. 11-32. In the Northern Hemisphere, the coriolis force deflects particles moving in a horizontal plane to the right. In the Southern Hemisphere the corresponding deflection is to the left. Note carefully that only the component of the coriolis force in the $x'y'$-plane is indicated in each case.

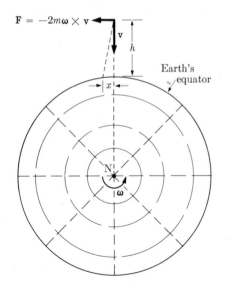

FIG. 11-33. Earth viewed from the North Pole. A body is dropped from a height h at the equator. The angular velocity of the earth is directed outward from this page, and the coriolis force deflects the falling body toward the *East*.

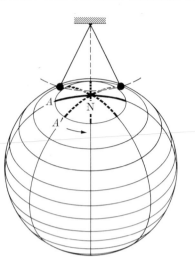

Fig. 11–34. In a coordinate system rotating with the earth, the plane of a Foucault pendulum rotates 360° in one day.

For a body dropped from $h = 100$ ft at the equator, x is only about 0.14 inch. The deflection is even less at higher latitudes and is zero at the Poles.

The problem can also be solved from the point of view of an observer in a fixed coordinate system (Problem 11–37). Qualitatively, the eastern deflection of a falling object, in this case, results from the fact that a body dropped, say, from the top of a high pole at the equator has the same angular velocity as at the base of the pole, but has a slightly higher velocity toward the East. The top of the pole is farther from the center of the earth than is the base.

The Foucault pendulum. The Foucault pendulum provides one of a very few laboratory demonstrations of the earth's rotation. Imagine a pendulum suspended over the earth's North Pole (Fig. 11–34). When the pendulum is started, it will, if the suspension has been carefully designed and prepared, continue to move in a plane that is fixed relative to the stars. The earth rotates under the pendulum once a day, and so when viewed by an observer on the earth, the pendulum's plane of motion appears to rotate. At latitudes other than ±90° (the Poles) the plane of a Foucault pendulum rotates, but the angular velocity is not ω, as it is at the Poles. It is only $\omega \sin \lambda$, where ω is the angular velocity of the earth and λ is the latitude. At a latitude of 30°, the plane rotates once in 48 hours, and at Boston, Massachusetts, ($\lambda = 42°$), the plane rotates once in about 36 hours.

PROBLEMS

11-1. The origin of a coordinate system S' moves with a constant speed $V = 2$ m/sec along the x-axis of a coordinate system S. At $t = 0$, the origins of S' and S coincide. What are the coordinates (x', y') in S' of a point $x = 4$ m, $y = 5$ m in S, at $t = 1$ sec and $t = 3$ sec?

11-2. A boy walks from one side of a slowly moving train to the other in 3 sec. The train is 9 ft wide and is moving along a straight level track at 6 ft/sec. (a) Make a sketch of the boy's path relative to the ground. (b) How far did the boy travel? What was his velocity relative to the ground?

11-3. Refer to Problem 11-2. If the weight of the boy is 96 lb, what is his kinetic energy relative to the coordinate system S' attached to the train and relative to the coordinate system S attached to the ground, when the boy walks with a speed of 3 ft/sec (a) across the train? (b) toward the front? (c) toward the rear of the train? (d) With what speed and in what direction should the boy move in order that the kinetic energy, with respect to S, be zero.

11-4. In our study of projectile motion (Chapter 4), we showed that for maximum range, a projectile should be ejected at an angle of 45° to the horizontal. Suppose a projectile (initial speed v_0) is fired from the rear of a fast-moving train (speed V_0) toward the engine. Observer A says that the motion of the train is immaterial; the angle at which the gun barrel should be set for maximum range is still 45°. Observer B says that this is nonsense; the speed of the train must be considered and the barrel angle should be greater than 45°. Who is right, and why?

11-5. A body moves with a speed of 200 m/sec in a direction making an angle of 30° with the x-axis in a fixed coordinate system. What is the corresponding angle when measured with respect to a coordinate system moving with a speed of 100 m/sec in the x-direction?

11-6. An elevator moves upward at a constant speed of 10 ft/sec. A passenger drops a coin from a height of 3 ft above the elevator floor. Find the time elapsed before the coin strikes the floor. Solve the problem first with respect to the coordinate system moving with the elevator, and then with respect to a coordinate system attached to the building.

11-7. A body of mass m_a travels along a straight line on a frictionless surface with a velocity v_a. It collides perfectly elastically with a body of mass m_b that is initially at rest. Assume a one-dimensional collision. (a) What is the center-of-mass velocity? (b) What are the initial velocities and momenta of bodies m_a and m_b according to S', the coordinate system that moves with the velocity of the center of mass? (c) What are the final velocities according to S'? (d) What are the final velocities according to S, the coordinate system at rest? (e) What is the final kinetic energy of each of the bodies according to S' and according to S?

11-8. A body A of mass $m_a = 10$ kgm travels in the positive x-direction with a speed $v_a = 5$ m/sec. Another body B of mass $m_b = 20$ kgm travels along a line which makes an angle of 45° with the positive x-axis with a speed $v_b = 5$ m/sec. (a) Indicate in a vector diagram, drawn to scale, the total momentum vector and the momentum vectors $\mathbf{p}_a^*$ and $\mathbf{p}_b^*$ of the bodies with respect to the center of mass. Convince yourself that these vectors are equal in magnitude and opposite in direction. (b) Determine analytically the magnitude and direction of the total momentum, the velocity of the center of mass, and the momenta and velocities of A and B with respect to the center of mass. (c) What is the total kinetic energy of the system with respect to the center of mass, and what is the kinetic energy with respect to the laboratory system?

11–9. Refer to Problem 11–8. Suppose that bodies A and B collide at the origin and that the collision is perfectly inelastic. What then is the energy lost in the collision?

11–10. In the text, the energy relation $E = MV^2/2 + E^*$ was obtained for the special case of two particles. Extend the analysis in the text and prove that this energy relation applies to an arbitrary number of particles.

11–11. A body B of mass m is originally at rest and free to move in a plane without friction. Another body A, also of mass m, collides with B. After the collision, the motion of the bodies is not along the same line as before. Show, both analytically and geometrically by means of a vector diagram, that the angle between the trajectories of the bodies after the collision makes an angle of 90° if the collision is perfectly elastic.

11–12. Consider again the perfectly elastic collision of the previous problem, but now let the masses M and m be different. (M is originally at rest.) Show that if the incident mass m is deviated by an angle ϕ when measured in the center-of-mass system, the magnitude of its velocity in the laboratory system after the collision is

$$v' = \frac{\sqrt{M^2 + m^2 + 2Mm\cos\phi}}{m + M} v,$$

where v is the speed before the collision.

11–13. In the previous problem the angle ϕ was measured in the C-system. If the corresponding angle in the L-system is θ, show that in the perfectly elastic collision

$$\cot\theta = \frac{\cos\phi + m/M}{\sin\phi}.$$

11–14. An elevator moves upward at a constant acceleration of 10 ft/sec². Three seconds after the elevator starts to accelerate from rest, a passenger drops a coin from a height of 3 ft above the elevator floor. Find the time elapsed before the coin strikes the floor. Solve the problem first from the viewpoint of an observer in a coordinate system at rest, and then from the viewpoint of a passenger in the coordinate system on the elevator.

11–15. A train starts from rest and accelerates at 10 ft/sec² in the positive x-direction. Three seconds after the train starts, a passenger drops a coin from a height of 3 ft above the train's floor. (a) In the coordinate system S' attached to the train, what is the direction of the inertial force on the coin? (b) Using the coordinate system S', find the time it takes for the coin to strike the floor, and find how far the coin moves toward the front or rear of the train during its fall. (c) Solve the problem from the viewpoint of an observer in a coordinate system attached to the ground.

11–16. An elevator moving downward with a speed of 10 ft/sec is brought to a stop in a distance of 6 inches. A person standing on a weight scale in the elevator notes that the scale reading changes during the deceleration period. If the apparent deceleration is constant, by what factor is the weight, as read from the scale, changed?

11-17. A mass m on a horizontal frictionless table is attached to one end of a spring as shown in Fig. 11-35. The spring constant is K. The table is set in motion with a constant acceleration $\mathbf{a}$ in the horizontal direction. (a) In the coordinate system S' attached to the table, what are the interaction forces and inertial forces on m? (b) What is the maximum compression of the spring caused by the acceleration? (c) What is the subsequent motion of m with respect to the table? (d) If the mass of the table is also m, determine the force required to keep the table at constant acceleration.

11-18. A horizontal bar of length L and of negligible weight can rotate about a vertical shaft through its center, as indicated in Fig. 11-36. The bar is always held horizontal by the bearing at the shaft. Two small balls of masses m and $3m$ are fastened at the ends of the bar, as shown. Both the platform which supports the shaft and the bar are originally at rest. The platform is then given a constant horizontal acceleration $\mathbf{a}$ normal to the bar, as indicated. (a) Determine the magnitudes and directions of the inertial forces on the two balls. (b) What is the initial angular acceleration of the bar caused by the motion of the platform? (c) What is the angular velocity of the bar when it has moved through an angle of 30°? (d) What is the period of small oscillation of the masses about their equilibrium position?

11-19. A plumb bob of length l is hung from the ceiling of a car, and the car is free to slide down a frictionless inclined plane. The inclination angle of the plane is θ. (a) Indicate in a diagram all the interaction forces and the inertial forces on the bob (in the coordinate system S' moving with the car). (b) If we assume that the pendulum makes an angle α with the normal to the plane, what are the components of all the forces on the plane? (c) What is the equilibrium angle of the pendulum? (d) What then is the tension in the string? (e) If the car is released from rest with the

FIGURE 11-35

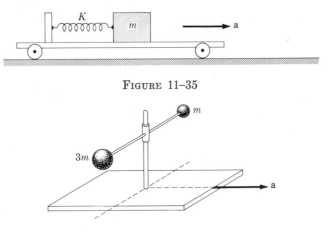

FIGURE 11-36

pendulum hanging vertically, what will be the subsequent motion of the pendulum? (f) What will be the period of the oscillations (assumed small) of the pendulum, and the amplitude of oscillation?

11-20. By how much does the force of the moon on a mass m on the earth's surface vary with the position of m on the earth?

11-21. Imagine an earth satellite consisting of two equal masses mounted on opposite ends of a massless rod of length l. If the satellite is in a circular orbit of radius R, and if the rod axis makes an angle θ with a line to the earth's center, what is the torque on the satellite? What is the period of the small-amplitude simple harmonic motion? How does the period compare with the period of the satellite's rotation about the earth?

11-22. How far does light fall in traveling the length of a football field?

11-23. Estimate the order of magnitude of the deflection of a light beam which grazes the sun, using a rough value of g and a rough value for the time the light is near the sun.

11-24. Is it possible that light can, like a planet or satellite, circle around a massive star? What properties must such a star have?

11-25. An earth satellite traverses a circular path at a height h above the earth's surface. (a) What is the earth's gravitational force on an object of mass m that is within the satellite? (b) What is the inertial force on the object? (c) Must these two forces always be equal in magnitude and oppositely directed?

11-26. A merry-go-round is mounted on the back of a truck which moves at velocity V_0 along a straight road. When the angular velocity ω of the merry-go-round is very small, a child

on the merry-go-round at R from the center moves back and forth in a path somewhat like a sine wave with respect to the coordinate system fixed on the road. When the angular velocity of the merry-go-round is very large, the child appears to move in a path which loops itself. (a) At what value of ω will this looping feature cease? (b) What is the child's velocity when he crosses the center line of the truck?

11-27. A stone becomes lodged in the tread of a 2-ft diameter tire of a truck that is traveling at 60 mi/hr. Draw a vector diagram which shows the initial value of the stone's velocity, if the stone were to break free of the tire at each of eight equally spaced points on the tire.

11-28. A merry-go-round 48 ft in radius rotates once every 8 sec. An object slides along its frictionless surface at 12 ft/sec according to a coordinate system at rest, and passes within 12 ft of the center. Sketch the path of the object according to S'. Include the paths if the merry-go-round rotates once every 16 sec and once each sec.

11-29. How fast should a cylindrical space vehicle 40 ft in diameter spin on its axis in order that a passenger has his normal weight?

11-30. Refer to the derivation of the acceleration $\mathbf{a}'$ in the rotating coordinate system. (a) Derive the expressions for x' and y' from Fig. 11-23. (b) Differentiate x' and y' once to obtain expressions for v_x' and v_y'. Check your results against the vector form, $\mathbf{v}' = \mathbf{v} - \boldsymbol{\omega} \times \mathbf{r}'$. (c) Differentiate v_x' and v_y', and obtain expressions for a_x' and a_y'. Check your results against the vector form, $\mathbf{a}' = \mathbf{a} - 2\boldsymbol{\omega} \times \mathbf{v}' - \boldsymbol{\omega} \times (\boldsymbol{\omega} \times \mathbf{r}')$.

11-31. At the equator, what velocity must an object have in order that its weight and the coriolis force are equal?

11-32. If the centrifugal force at the equator were equal to mg, what would be the corresponding length of one "day"? How would the apparent weights of objects vary with latitude?

11-33. What are the conditions under which the centrifugal and coriolis forces will be comparable in magnitude?

11-34. What is the centrifugal force which results from the earth's rotation about the sun? How does it compare with the centrifugal force which results from the earth's rotation on its axis?

11-35. A locomotive weighing 50 tons travels northward through Boston on a straight track with a speed of $v' = 90$ mi/hr. What is the side thrust from the track on the locomotive due to the rotation of the earth?

11-36. Use the coriolis force to determine the deflection toward the East of a body that is dropped at an arbitrary latitude from height h.

11-37. An object is dropped from a height h at the earth's equator. How far is the object deflected toward the East? Solve the problem with respect to a fixed (nonrotating) coordinate system. (*Hint.* Angular momentum must be conserved.)

11-38. A circular track of radius R rotates about its vertical axis with a constant angular velocity ω (Fig. 11-37). A particle of mass m can slide on the track (frictionless). When the angular velocity ω is smaller than a critical value ω_1, it is possible that the particle will describe oscillations about the lowest point of the track.

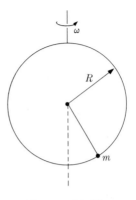

FIGURE 11-37

(a) Determine this critical angular velocity. (b) If $\omega > \omega_1$, describe the nature of the motion and possible equilibrium positions.

11-39. In Chapter 10, we considered an example in which a particle moved under the influence of gravity in an imaginary frictionless tunnel through the center of the earth. We did not, at that time, consider the effect of the earth's spin. We shall now include the effect of this spin on the motion of the particle. Consider the tunnel in the equatorial plane, and determine the motion of the particle with respect to a coordinate system attached to the earth. (a) What is the total force component (interaction and inertial forces) on the particle in the direction of the tunnel? What is the nature of the resulting motion? (b) What is the time required for the particle to travel from one end of the tunnel to the other? (c) Determine the maximum value and the direction of the force from the side wall of the tunnel on the particle.

CHAPTER 12

EXAMPLES OF FORCES AND MOTION—IV

Summary. In this chapter the equations of motion for a system of particles are applied to the study of rigid-body motion. This motion can be described as a superposition of a translation and a rotation. A unique specification of the motion requires, in general, six independent coordinates that express, for example, the position of the center of mass and the orientation of the body with respect to the center of mass. Separate equations are derived to relate the motion of the center of mass and the rotation of the center of mass to the external force and the torque that act on the body. These equations are discussed, and it is shown that an arbitrary force system can be reduced to a resultant force (acting through the center of mass) and a force couple. In the following detailed quantitative study of specific examples, we consider only motion in a plane. The work-energy principle is discussed and applied to some specific problems, among which we study the influence of impulses on rigid bodies, collisions, rolling, and the rotation of a body about a fixed axis. Finally, some examples of statics are given.

In previous chapters we have, from time to time, discussed examples of rigid-body motion to illustrate the laws of motion as applied to a system of particles. For example, we have considered the translational motion and certain aspects of the rotation of a rigid body. In this chapter, we shall discuss rigid-body motion in a more systematic manner.

A rigid body may be defined formally as a collection of particles that are located at fixed distances from one another. Strictly speaking, no object is a rigid body, since all real materials are compressible and are always, to some extent, deformed when under the influence of forces. In fact, even when there is no force acting on a body, the atoms and molecules that comprise the body are not in fixed positions relative to one another, but are in continuous thermal motion. Nevertheless, so far as the "gross motion" of the body is concerned, the rigid-body assumption is satisfactory for many purposes.

12–1 The kinematics of a rigid body. A complete description of the motion of an arbitrary system of particles requires that the location of each particle in the system be specified as a function of time. In the special case of a rigid body, in which the *distances between the particles are fixed*, the positions of only three noncollinear points must be considered.

330

If we specify the location of just one point, say P_1 of Fig. 12–1, the body is free to rotate about that point, thus the orientation of the body is not established. If we specify two points, say P_1 and P_2, the body is still free to rotate about the line that connects these points. However, if a third noncollinear point P_3 is specified, all ambiguity is removed and the location and orientation of the rigid body, and consequently the

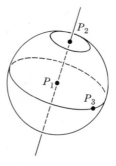

FIGURE 12–1

positions of all particles of the body, are completely determined. It would seem that since three numbers, the three coordinates x, y, and z, are required to specify one point, a total of nine coordinates would be required to specify the location and orientation of a rigid body. However, these nine coordinates are not independent but are related by three equations of the form

$$(x_1 - x_2)^2 + (y_1 - y_2)^2 + (z_1 - z_2)^2 = d_{12}^2,$$

where d_{12}^2 is the constant distance between P_1 and P_2. Therefore only six independent numbers are required to specify the location and orientation of a rigid body. These six numbers are sometimes called the six degrees of freedom of the body. They need not be six rectangular coordinates; they usually are three rectangular coordinates that specify the center-of-mass location and three angles. Two of the angles, for example, determine the direction of an axis such as P_1P_2, and the third angle determines orientation about this axis.

If the angles are constant, so that the orientation of the body remains the same, the motion is a pure *translation*. All particles of the body then move along parallel paths, as illustrated schematically in Fig. 12–2. In a pure *rotation*, on the other hand, the coordinates of the center of mass are constant and only the angles vary with time. These two types of motion

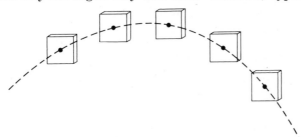

FIG. 12–2. Translation of a rigid body.

are basic, since any arbitrary motion of a rigid body can be produced by
superposition of a pure translation and a rotation. For example, if we
wish to bring a body from an initial to a final position and orientation,
we can translate the body until the center of mass reaches the final des-
tination, and then rotate the body about the center of mass to the final
orientation.

12–2 Equations of motion. The general problem of rigid-body motion
is to determine the location and the orientation of a body, as functions of
time, in terms of the external forces on the body. In the general case, there
will be six unknown coordinates, and six equations of motion are required
for the solution of the problem. Formally, these equations are obtained
from the equations for the rates of change of the total momentum and
angular momentum of the body. Just as for the motion of a collection of
particles (see Chapters 4 and 9), we obtain, for the motion of a rigid body,
the vector equations

$$\frac{d\mathbf{P}}{dt} = \mathbf{F} \tag{12-1}$$

and

$$\frac{d\mathbf{L}^*}{dt} = \boldsymbol{\tau}^*, \tag{12-2}$$

where $\mathbf{P} = M\mathbf{V}$ is the total momentum, expressed as the product of the
total mass M and the center-of-mass velocity $\mathbf{V}$, $\mathbf{F}$ is the resultant of the external forces on the body, $\mathbf{L}^*$ is the spin angular momentum, and $\boldsymbol{\tau}^*$ is the
resultant torque with respect to the center of mass. Each of these vector
equations represents three equations for the components of the vectors
involved, $M\,dV_x/dt = F_x$, $dL_x^*/dt = \tau_x^*$, and so on, and we then have the
required six equations to solve the problem of rigid-body motion. The
general solution to these equations is difficult to obtain, and only special
cases of rigid-body motion are well known.

However, certain general features of the motion are immediately apparent from the basic equations (12–1) and (12–2). From the first equation, it follows that the motion of the center of mass of the body depends
only on the magnitude and direction of the resultant external force, but
not on the point of application of the force. From the second equation,
we see, for example, that if the resultant external force goes through the
center of mass so that $\tau^* = 0$, the spin angular momentum of the body
remains constant. The (uniform) gravitational force is a typical example
of such a force.

These results are illustrated schematically in Fig. 12–3, which shows
a bar that slides over a frictionless horizontal plane under the influence
of a constant force $\mathbf{F}_0$. In (a), the force is applied at the center of mass.

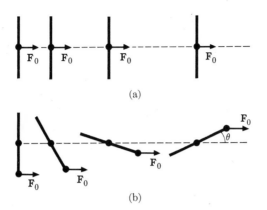

(a)

(b)

FIG. 12–3. The motion of a bar under the influence of a constant force. The center of mass moves along a straight line, and is independent of the point of application of the force.

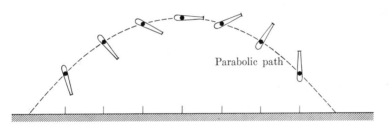

Parabolic path

FIG. 12–4. The center of mass of a rigid body under the influence of gravitational force alone moves along the familiar parabolic path and the angular momentum with respect to the center of mass remains constant, since the torque of the gravitational force with respect to the center of mass is zero.

The torque, with respect to the center of mass, is then zero; when the angular momentum is initially zero, it will remain so. The bar acquires a pure translational motion with constant acceleration. In (b), the force is applied at one end of the bar. The motion of the center of mass is the same as before. However, now the bar both rotates and translates. When the motion is started, the lever arm, with respect to the center of mass, is $d/2$, where d is the length of the bar. As the bar rotates, the lever arm decreases and eventually becomes zero. The inertia of the bar carries it through this zero position, and the torque changes sign. This, in turn, gives the bar an angular acceleration in the opposite direction. The motion, in other words, is like that of a pendulum.

In the example shown in Fig. 12–4, a baseball bat is moving through the air under the influence of the gravitational force. The center of mass then will describe the well-known parabolic path that is characteristic for projectile motion. The resultant force of gravity (in a uniform field) goes through the center of mass of the body, so that the external torque is zero with respect to the center of mass. Consequently, the spin angular momentum of the bat remains constant throughout the motion.

Equivalence of force systems. If we attempt to determine the forces on a rigid body from the known motion, we find that there are many different combinations of external forces that will produce the same motion. The center-of-mass motion (see Chapter 4) depends only upon the magnitude and direction of the external-force resultant, but not upon the point of application. Similarly, the same rates of change of angular momentum can be produced by many force combinations that have the same torques. In order to produce given rates of change of both momentum and angular momentum by different force systems, these systems must necessarily have the same resultant force and torque. If there is only one external force, we note that its point of application can be moved along the line of action of the force without changing the force and torque. Similarly, when there are several forces that act on a rigid body, these forces can be moved along their lines of action, and if these lines intersect, the individual forces can be replaced by a resultant that passes through the point of intersection, as illustrated in Fig. 12–5. The force resultant applied at this point then is equivalent to the force system in both its translatory and rotational effects. Thus, if the force resultant obtained in this manner goes through the center of mass of the body, the force system will produce only a translational motion of the body.

Two equal and opposite forces that act upon a body produce a resultant force of zero, and the center of mass of the body does not accelerate. How-

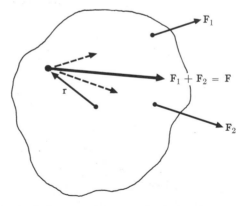

FIG. 12–5. The force resultant $\mathbf{F} = \mathbf{F}_1 + \mathbf{F}_2$, applied at the point of intersection of the lines of action of $\mathbf{F}_1$ and $\mathbf{F}_2$, produces the same initial motion as the original force system $\mathbf{F}_1, \mathbf{F}_2$.

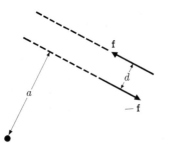

FIG. 12–6. A couple. The magnitude of the torque of the couple is $f(a + d) - fa = fd$.

ever, if the lines of action of the forces are not the same, a torque is produced and the body is given an angular acceleration. A force arrangement of this kind is called a *force couple*. In Fig. 12–6, the forces in the couple are denoted by $\mathbf{f}$ and $-\mathbf{f}$, and d is the perpendicular distance between the lines of action of the forces. If the position vectors of the points of application of the forces are $\mathbf{r}_2$ and $\mathbf{r}_1$, the torque produced by the couple with respect to the origin is $\boldsymbol{\tau} = \mathbf{r}_2 \times \mathbf{f} - \mathbf{r}_1 \times \mathbf{f} = (\mathbf{r}_2 - \mathbf{r}_1) \times \mathbf{f}$. The vector $\mathbf{r}_2 - \mathbf{r}_1$ lies in the plane of the force couple and the magnitude of $\boldsymbol{\tau} = (\mathbf{r}_2 - \mathbf{r}_1) \times \mathbf{f}$ is simply fd. The direction of $\boldsymbol{\tau}$, of course, is perpendicular to the plane of the force couple. Figure 12–6 illustrates a case in which the reference point is in the plane of the force couple.

When a rigid body is acted upon by a system of external forces, we have seen that there are two essential effects. On the one hand, the vector sum $\mathbf{F}$ of the forces effects a center-of-mass acceleration and, on the other hand, the vector sum of the torques with respect to the center of mass effects a rate of change of the spin angular momentum.

If the torques of the external forces add to zero with respect to the center of mass, we can replace these forces by a single force that acts through the center of mass of the body. This single force must, of course, be equal to the vector sum of the external forces.

On the other hand, if the vector sum of the external forces is zero but the resultant torque is different from zero, we can replace the external-force system by a force couple. Similarly, an arbitrary force system, with a resultant force as well as a resultant torque, can be replaced by an equivalent system. In this equivalent system, the resultant force goes through the center of mass and there is a force couple with a torque equal to the external resultant torque *with respect to the center of mass*. The single force then produces the required center-of-mass acceleration, but has no effect on the spin angular momentum; the couple produces the required rate of change of spin angular momentum, but has no effect on the center-of-mass motion.

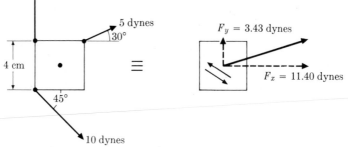

FIGURE 12–7

EXAMPLE. A square plate that has a side length of 4 cm is subject to the forces shown in Fig. 12–7. Reduce this force system to a single force through the center of mass and a force couple.

The x- and y-components of the net force are

$$F_x = 0 + 5\cos 30° + 10\cos 45° \simeq 11.40 \text{ dynes},$$

$$F_y = 8 + 5\sin 30° - 10\sin 45° \simeq 3.43 \text{ dynes}.$$

The net torque about the center of mass is

$$\tau^* = -2 \cdot 8 - 2 \cdot 5\cos 30° + 2 \cdot 5\sin 30°$$
$$+ 2 \cdot 10\cos 45° + 2 \cdot 10\sin 45°$$
$$\simeq 8.58 \text{ dynes·cm}.$$

The required force is specified by the components F_x and F_y. Any couple that has a moment of 8.58 dynes·cm will suffice. Figure 12–7 shows such a couple, where each of the two forces is 8.58 dynes·cm, and they are separated by 1 cm.

12–3 Motion in a plane. Because of the complexity of the general problem of rigid-body motion, a more detailed study of the equations of motion, (12–1) and (12–2), will be limited here to special types of motion in a plane. In such motion, all the parts of a body move along paths which are all parallel to a given plane, say the xy-plane. The position and orientation of the body are then specified uniquely by the two coordinates of the center of mass (X, Y) and one angle θ, which determines the orientation of the body in the plane with respect to a fixed axis in the plane. The angular velocity of the body is then $\omega = d\theta/dt$ and, as we have shown in Chapter 9, the corresponding spin angular momentum component in the z-direction is $L_z^* = I_0\omega$, where I_0 is the moment of inertia with respect to the center of mass. In Chapter 9 we demonstrated the calculation of the moment of inertia, $I_0 = \int r^2\, dm$, and the results of these calculations

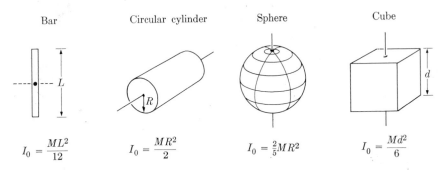

Bar   Circular cylinder   Sphere   Cube

$$I_0 = \frac{ML^2}{12} \qquad I_0 = \frac{MR^2}{2} \qquad I_0 = \tfrac{2}{5}MR^2 \qquad I_0 = \frac{Md^2}{6}$$

FIG. 12–8. The moments of inertia of some familiar bodies.

are included in Fig. 12–8, where the moments of inertia of some simple bodies are given.

The equations of motion from which the three coordinates X, Y, and θ can be determined are then, from Eqs. (12–1) and (12–2),

$$\frac{dP_x}{dt} = F_x, \qquad \frac{dP_y}{dt} = F_y, \qquad \text{and} \qquad I_0\frac{d\omega}{dt} = \tau_z^*, \qquad (12\text{–}3)$$

where $P_x = MV_x = M(dX/dt)$, $P_y = MV_y = M(dY/dt)$, and $\omega = d\theta/dt$.

EXAMPLE. A uniform cylindrical disc of radius R and mass M is pulled over a horizontal frictionless surface by a constant force F. The force is applied by means of a string wound around the cylinder, as shown in Fig. 12–9. Determine the motion of the disc if it starts from rest at $t = 0$.

The x-axis is chosen to be in the direction of the force. The equations of motion are then

$$M\frac{dV_x}{dt} = F$$

and

$$I_0\frac{d\omega}{dt} = FR,$$

where V_x is the velocity of the center of mass and ω is the angular velocity.

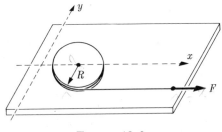

FIGURE 12–9

From these equations, we obtain

$$\frac{dX}{dt} = V_x = \frac{F}{M}t, \qquad \frac{d\theta}{dt} = \omega = \frac{FR}{I_0}t$$

and

$$X = \frac{F}{M}\frac{t^2}{2}, \qquad \theta = \frac{FR}{I_0}\frac{t^2}{2},$$

where X is the coordinate of the center of mass.

If the center of mass of the disc is held fixed by a vertical axis, the center of mass remains at rest and only rotational motion is obtained. In addition to the force of the string, there will be an equal and opposite force at the axis on the disc. The torque of this latter force clearly is zero, since its line of action goes through the axis of rotation.

The kinetic energy. As is the case with any arbitrary collection of particles, the total kinetic energy of a rigid body can be expressed as

$$E = \tfrac{1}{2}MV^2 + E^*, \tag{12-4}$$

where M is the total mass of the body and V is the center-of-mass velocity. The first term is associated with the motion of the center of mass of the body, and the second term with the motion relative to the center of mass. In the case of a rigid body, this latter motion is a rotation, and if it takes place in the xy-plane, the axis of rotation is in the z-direction. The rotational kinetic energy can be expressed in terms of the moment of inertia about this axis as follows. A mass element dm, located a perpendicular distance r from the center-of-mass axis, has the velocity $v = \omega r$ with respect to the center of mass, where $\omega = d\theta/dt$ is the angular velocity of the body. The kinetic energy of this mass element is then $\tfrac{1}{2}(\omega r)^2\, dm$, and the total kinetic energy of rotation is

$$E^* = \tfrac{1}{2}\omega^2 \int r^2\, dm = \tfrac{1}{2}I_0\omega^2, \tag{12-5}$$

where $I_0 = \int r^2\, dm$ is the moment of inertia of the body with respect to the center-of-mass axis perpendicular to the plane of motion.

The total kinetic energy of a rigid body moving in a plane can then be expressed as

$$E = \tfrac{1}{2}MV^2 + \tfrac{1}{2}I_0\omega^2. \tag{12-6}$$

The work-energy relation. Suppose that the external force system has been reduced to a force resultant $\mathbf{F}$ applied at the center of mass and a force couple that produces the resultant torque. When the center of mass is displaced a distance $d\mathbf{R}$, the work done by the resultant force is

$$\mathbf{F} \cdot d\mathbf{R} = d\mathbf{R} \cdot \left(\frac{d\mathbf{P}}{dt}\right) = \mathbf{V} \cdot d\mathbf{P} = d\left(\frac{MV^2}{2}\right).$$

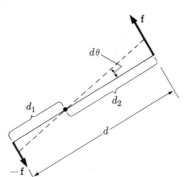

FIG. 12–10. When the body rotates through an angle $d\theta$ in the plane of the force couple, the work done by the couple is $fd_2\, d\theta + fd_1\, d\theta = (fd)d\theta = \tau^*d\theta$.

In other words, the work of the force **F** in this displacement of the center of mass equals the increase of the translational kinetic energy,

$$dE_t = d(\tfrac{1}{2}MV^2) = \mathbf{F}\cdot d\mathbf{R} = F_R\, dR. \tag{12–7}$$

Clearly, a force couple does not contribute any work in a pure translation of the body, since the forces involved are equal and opposite. However, if the body is rotated through an angle $d\theta$ in the plane of the force couple, the perpendicular line between the forces in the couple is also rotated through an angle $d\theta$. Then, the work done by the forces in the couple is $fd_1\, d\theta + fd_2\, d\theta = (fd)\, d\theta = \tau^*\, d\theta$, where $d_1 + d_2 = d$ and $\tau^* = fd$, as indicated in Fig. 12–10. Since $\tau^* = I_0\,(d\omega/dt)$ [Eq. (12–3)], the work done by the torque can be expressed as $\tau^*\, d\theta = I_0(d\omega/dt)\, d\theta = I_0\omega\, d\omega = d(I_0\omega^2/2)$. In other words, the work done by the force couple equals the increase of the kinetic energy with respect to the center of mass:

$$dE^* = d(\tfrac{1}{2}I_0\omega^2) = \tau^*\, d\theta. \tag{12–8}$$

The net changes, of $MV^2/2$ and $I_0\omega^2/2$ are obtained by integration of Eqs. (12–7) and (12–8).

$$(E_t)_2 - (E_t)_1 = \int_1^2 F_R\, dR \quad \text{and} \quad (E^*)_2 - (E^*)_1 = \int_1^2 \tau^*\, d\theta. \tag{12–9}$$

The change of the total kinetic energy then is the sum of the individual contributions in Eqs. (12–7) and (12–8). This change of the total kinetic energy also can be expressed as the sum of the work contributions from the individual forces acting upon the rigid body. Consider one of the external forces $\mathbf{F}_1$ applied at a point a distance $\mathbf{r}_1^*$ from the center of mass

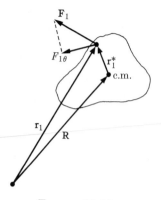

FIGURE 12–11

(see Fig. 12–11). As the body rotates through an angle $d\theta$, the point of application of the force $\mathbf{F}_1$ moves a distance $ds_1 = r_1^* \, d\theta$ perpendicular to $\mathbf{r}_1^*$. We denote this displacement by the vector $d\mathbf{r}_1^*$. If, in addition, the body is given a translational displacement $d\mathbf{R}$, the total displacement of the point of application of $\mathbf{F}_1$ is $d\mathbf{R}_1 = d\mathbf{R} + d\mathbf{r}_1^*$. The work of $\mathbf{F}_1$ is then $\mathbf{F}_1 \cdot d\mathbf{r}_1 = \mathbf{F}_1 \cdot (d\mathbf{R} + d\mathbf{r}_1^*) = \mathbf{F} \cdot d\mathbf{R} + \mathbf{F}_1 \cdot d\mathbf{r}_1^* = F_{1R} \, dR + F_\theta r_1^* \, d\theta$, where F_{1R} is the force component in the direction of the displacement $d\mathbf{R}$ and F_θ is the force component perpendicular to $\mathbf{r}_1^*$. As we have seen, the contribution $F_{1R} \, dR$ serves to increase the translational kinetic energy of the body. The second contribution $F_{1\theta} r_1^* \, d\theta$ can be expressed as $\tau_1^* \, d\theta$, since $\tau_1^* = F_{1\theta} r_1^*$ is the torque with respect to the center of mass, and we found in the foregoing discussion that this part produces an increase of E^*. Thus, the total kinetic-energy contribution by $\mathbf{F}_1$ is $dE_1 = \mathbf{F}_1 \cdot d\mathbf{r}_1$, and when we add the analogous contributions from the remaining external forces we can express the change of the total kinetic energy of the body as

$$dE = dE_t + dE^* = \mathbf{F}_1 \cdot d\mathbf{r}_1 + \mathbf{F}_2 \cdot d\mathbf{r}_2 + \cdots. \qquad (12\text{–}10)$$

These work-energy relations will be applied in numerous examples in our forthcoming discussions.

EXAMPLE 1. In the example of the motion of the disc illustrated in Fig. 12–9, the work FX is converted into translational kinetic energy, where X is the displacement of the center of mass and F is the external force. That is,

$$FX = \frac{MV^2}{2} \quad \text{or} \quad V = \sqrt{\frac{2FX}{M}}. \qquad (12\text{–}11)$$

Similarly, for the rotational kinetic energy we obtain

$$\tau^* \theta = FR\theta = \frac{I_0 \omega^2}{2} \quad \text{or} \quad \omega = \sqrt{\frac{2FR\theta}{I_0}}, \qquad (12\text{–}12)$$

where θ is the total angle of rotation of the disc when the center of mass has moved a distance X.

This method of calculating the kinetic energy from the known external force and torque corresponds to the two equations (12–7) and (12–8) in the text. We can also use Eq. (12–10) for the calculation of the total kinetic energy of the body. Then we must know the total displacement of the point of application of the external force. *In this case*, total displacement comprises the center-of-mass displacement X plus the displacement $R\theta$ produced by the rotation of the body through the angle θ. The total work is then $F(X + R\theta)$, and this work must equal the total kinetic energy of the body at the position X. We see that this result is consistent with the expressions (12–11) and (12–12), from which we obtain the total kinetic energy $(MV^2/2) + (I_0\omega^2/2) = FX + FR\theta$.

It is left as an exercise to show that the expressions for the kinetic energy, obtained by the use of the work-energy relation, are consistent with those obtained when we use the expressions for the center-of-mass velocity and the angular velocity obtained in the previous discussion of this example (see Fig. 12–9).

EXAMPLE 2. A string is wound around a cylinder of radius R, and the end of the string is held fixed, as shown in Fig. 12–12. What will be the subsequent motion of this "Yo-yo" if it is held at rest and then released?

Consider first the translatory motion of the center of mass. There are two external forces on the cylinder, the tension in the string and the weight Mg. We have

$$Mg - T = M\frac{dV}{dt},$$

where V is the center-of-mass velocity in the positive downward direction.

For the rotational motion about the center of mass, we have

$$Tr = I\frac{d\omega}{dt},$$

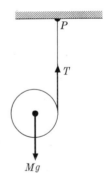

where Tr is the torque, $I_0 = Mr^2/2$ is the moment   FIGURE 12–12
of inertia about the center of mass of the cylinder and ω is the angular velocity. We have $V = r\omega$ and therefore $r(d\omega/dt) = dV/dt$. If we combine the translational and rotational relations and eliminate T, we have

$$\frac{dV}{dt} = \frac{g}{1 + I/Mr^2}.$$

The acceleration is uniform and its magnitude is $2g/3$, since I is $Mr^2/2$. From this equation, we can determine the velocity of the center of mass as a function of time. However, it is interesting to determine the velocity as a function of

position directly from the work-energy relation. The system under consideration is the cylinder and the string. The force on the string at its point of suspension does not do any work and therefore the total work by the external forces
is the work of the gravitational force only. When the center of mass has fallen
a distance y, the work done is Mgy. If the velocity of the center of mass is V at
that point, the angular velocity is $\omega = V/r$ and the total kinetic energy then is

$$E = \frac{MV^2}{2} + \frac{I_0\omega^2}{2} = \frac{3}{2}\frac{MV^2}{2}.$$

From this, we obtain $3MV^2/4 = Mgy$.

The influence of an instantaneous impulse. The motion of a rigid body
under the influence of continuously acting forces can be rather complicated. In order to gain an understanding of the essentials of such motion,
it is often valuable to consider the idealized case when an instantaneous
impulse rather than a continuously acting force is applied on the body.
As we recall, an instantaneous impulse transfers momentum to a body in
zero time, a situation which requires, of course, that the force be infinitely
large, so that the product $\mathbf{J} = \mathbf{F}\,\Delta t$ will be different from zero when
$\Delta t = 0$. In this idealized situation, the position of the body does not
change during the impulse. Consequently the angular impulse with respect
to $\mathbf{r} = 0$ is simply $\mathbf{r} \times \mathbf{J}$, where $\mathbf{r}$ is the position vector of the point of
application of the impulse $\mathbf{J}$.

EXAMPLE 1. A straight bar, at rest on a frictionless horizontal surface, receives
an instantaneous impulse $\mathbf{J}$ perpendicular to the bar. Determine the angular
momentum and total kinetic energy transferred to the bar if the impulse is
applied (a) at the center of mass of the bar and (b) at one end of the bar.
The mass of the bar is $M = 15$ kgm, its length is $d = 2$ m,
and the magnitude of the impulse is $J = 7.5$ n·sec.

The velocity of the center of mass after the impulse is

$$V = \frac{J}{M} = \frac{7.5}{15} = 0.5 \text{ m/sec.}$$

The translational velocity is independent of whether the
impulse is applied at the end of the bar or at its center of   FIGURE 12–13
mass.

(a) If the impulse is delivered at the center of mass, no angular momentum
with respect to the center of mass is transferred. The motion of the bar after
the impulse is then a pure translation, and the kinetic energy is simply

$$E = \tfrac{1}{2}MV^2 = \tfrac{1}{2}M\left(\frac{J}{M}\right)^2 = \frac{1}{2}\frac{J^2}{M} = \frac{15}{8} \text{ joules.}$$

(b) When the impulse is applied at one end of the bar, the lever arm with respect to the center of mass is $d/2 = 1$ m, and the angular momentum with respect to the center of mass after the impulse then is

$$I_0\omega = J\frac{d}{2} = 7.5 \text{ joule·sec.}$$

With $I_0 = Md^2/12$, we obtain

$$\omega = \frac{Jd}{2} \cdot \frac{12}{Md^2} = \frac{6J}{Md} = \frac{6 \cdot 7.5}{15 \cdot 2} = \frac{3}{2} \sec^{-1}.$$

The kinetic energy of rotation of the bar after the impulse is then

$$E^* = \tfrac{1}{2}I_0\omega^2 = \frac{1}{2}\frac{Md^2}{12} \cdot \frac{36J^2}{M^2 d^2} = \frac{3}{2}\frac{J^2}{M},$$

or three times as large as the translational kinetic energy. The total kinetic energy is then

$$E = E^* + \tfrac{1}{2}MV^2 = \tfrac{1}{2}I_0\omega^2 + \tfrac{1}{2}MV^2 = 2\frac{J^2}{M} = 7.5 \text{ joules.}$$

EXAMPLE 2. A straight uniform bar of mass M and length L is hung from a fixed horizontal axis, as shown in Fig. 12–14. An instantaneous horizontal impulse is delivered at B. What is the impulse from the axis at A?

Assume the contact impulse at the axis, $\mathbf{J}_a$, to be directed as shown. (Why is there no vertical component of $\mathbf{J}_a$?) For the translatory motion, we then have

$$J_a + J = MV,$$

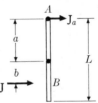

FIGURE 12–14

where V is the velocity of the center of mass immediately after the impulse. Similarly, for the rotational motion about the center of mass, we have

$$Jb - J_a a = I_0\omega = \frac{I_0 V}{a},$$

where I_0 is the moment of inertia about the center of mass and $\omega = V/a$ is the angular velocity immediately after the impulse. If $k_0 = \sqrt{I_0/M}$ is the radius of gyration referred to the center of mass, we have, by eliminating V from the above two expressions,

$$J_a = J\frac{b - (k_0^2/a)}{a + (k_0^2/a)}.$$

The axis impulse is to the right if b is greater than k_0^2/a and to the left (negative) if b is less than k_0^2/a. If b is equal to k_0^2/a, the axis impulse is zero. In this case, point B is called *the center of percussion, referred here to an axis at A.* In the case of a uniform bar of length L, the center of percussion is a distance $L/6$ from the center of mass. If a baseball is hit at the center of percussion of a baseball bat (referred to the point at which the bat is gripped) there will be no "sting." Well-designed hammers, axes, and sledge hammers do not sting because the head and grip location, center of mass, and radius of gyration are related in accordance with the above ideas.

Collisions between rigid bodies. The impulse on a rigid body, considered in the foregoing examples, often results from a collision. When two rigid bodies collide, say two straight bars, they usually exchange momentum as well as angular momentum. In this exchange, the *total momentum* and (if the interaction force between the bodies is central) the *total angular momentum* are conserved. When we calculate the angular momentum we can use any arbitrary fixed point in space as a reference point.

The total kinetic energy of the system, of course, may or may not be conserved in the collision.

EXAMPLE. A bar of mass M and length d initially is in pure translatory motion with a center-of-mass velocity **V**. It collides with and sticks to a second identical bar which is initially at rest, as shown in Fig. 12–15. What is the subsequent motion of the composite bar?

Before the collision, the center-of-mass velocity of the system was **V**/2, and this must remain unchanged. Hence the center of mass of the composite bar moves with a velocity **V**′ = **V**/2.

The angular momentum before the collision was contributed entirely by the translatory motion of the first bar. If taken about the point P, this angular momentum is $MVd/2$. After the collision, the system has a spin angular momentum

$$L = I_0\omega = 2M\frac{d^2}{3}\omega' = MV\frac{d}{2},$$

since the angular momentum about P (or any other fixed point) must remain

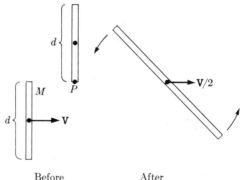

Before   After

FIGURE 12–15

constant. The angular velocity and center-of-mass velocity are therefore

$$\omega' = \frac{3}{4}\frac{V}{d} \quad \text{and} \quad \mathbf{V}' = \frac{\mathbf{V}}{2}.$$

These two relationships completely describe the motion.

The initial kinetic energy was $MV^2/2$. The final kinetic energy is partially translatory ($MV^2/4$) and partially rotational ($I_0\omega'^2/2$). The rotational part is $E^* = (2M\,d^2/3)(\omega'^2/2) = 3MV^2/16$, and so the total kinetic energy after the collision is $7MV^2/16$.

Rolling. An exaggerated picture of the rolling mechanism is presented by the rolling of a cogwheel on a cog track. The cogs can be regarded as a very enlarged representation of the contact surface between the body and the plane. If the body rolls with a constant speed, there will be no horizontal component of the contact force between the surfaces in contact, as indicated in Fig. 12–16(a). However, when the wheel is accelerated, the cogs are pressed together, and the wheel—or any rolling body, for that matter—can be considered to receive a horizontal impulse each time two cogs meet. The direction of these impulses depends upon the manner in which the wheel is driven.

When the wheel is driven by a torque, as is the case with an automobile wheel [Fig. 12–16(b)], the horizontal component of the *contact force at the ground* provides the momentum transfer in the forward direction. (The corresponding force on the ground is directed to the rear.) This horizontal contact force is the same as the *static* friction force which we discussed in Chapter 4. Consequently, the maximum acceleration which can be given to a cylinder or a wheel driven by a torque is $a_{max} = \mu N/M$, where μ is the static friction coefficient, N is the normal component of the contact force, and M is the mass that must be accelerated.

If the wheel is driven by a force in the forward direction from the axis, the horizontal contact force on the wheel is in the backward direction, as illustrated in Fig. 12–16(c). The rate of momentum transfer in the forward direction is then the difference between the force at the axis and the

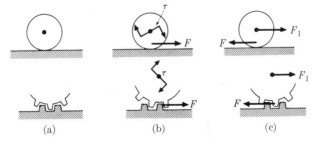

Fig. 12–16. Rolling. The direction of the horizontal component of the contact force depends upon the manner in which the wheel is driven.

contact force at the ground. In this case, the driving force at the axis has *no torque* about the center axis of rotation. The angular-momentum transfer to the wheel about the axis of rotation is provided by the horizontal component of the contact force.

When both the driving torque and force are absent, the horizontal component of the contact force becomes zero, and the body will roll at a constant speed. In reality, the rolling body will be slowed by what is called *rolling friction*. The corresponding energy loss is caused by the (small) deformations, of both the body and the surface, which are produced during rolling. There are always some energy losses involved in such deformations and the corresponding net deformation work is taken from the kinetic energy of the body. It should be noted that rolling friction does not correspond to either static or sliding friction.

The mechanism of walking is somewhat similar to that of rolling. When walking or running on horizontal ground, we accelerate forward and receive forward impulses from the ground at every step, just as do the cogs in a wheel (see Fig. 12–17).

F

FIG. 12–17. Walking is somewhat similar to rolling.

EXAMPLE 1. A wheel is pulled forward by a force F_1 on its center-of-mass axis. Let us denote the horizontal component of the contact force by F. The equations governing the motion of the center of mass and the rotation of the body about the center of mass are then

$$F_1 - F = M \frac{dV}{dt}$$

and

$$FR = I_0 \frac{d\omega}{dt} = k_0^2 M \frac{d\omega}{dt},$$

where $k_0 = \sqrt{I_0/M}$ is the radius of gyration and R is the wheel radius.

If the wheel rolls without slipping, the angular velocity ω of the wheel and the velocity V of the center of mass are related by

$$V = R\omega.$$

This relation follows directly, since for every complete revolution of the wheel the center of mass moves forward a distance $2\pi R$. If there are f rev/sec, the center of mass will move forward a distance $(2\pi f)R = \omega R$ per sec, which is the velocity of the center of mass.

Eliminating F from these relations, we obtain

$$\frac{dV}{dt} = \frac{F_1}{M(1 + k_0^2/R^2)}.$$

This equation shows that the translational motion of the rolling body will be the same as that of a sliding body that has a mass $M(1 + k_0^2/R^2)$. The *apparent* increase in the inertial mass results from the rotational motion, as well as the translational motion which must be given to the mass of the wheel.

The total kinetic energy of the wheel is the sum of the kinetic energies of translation and of rotation about the center of mass:

$$E = \tfrac{1}{2}MV^2 + \tfrac{1}{2}I_0\omega^2 = \tfrac{1}{2}M\left(1 + \frac{k_0^2}{R^2}\right)V^2.$$

The relation between the kinetic-energy increase and the forces on the body is of interest. For the increase in the translational energy, we have [see Eq. (12–7)]

$$\int_0^x (F_1 - F)\,dx = \tfrac{1}{2}MV^2,$$

and for the rotational energy about the center of mass [see Eq. (12–8)],

$$\int_0^\theta FR\,d\theta = \tfrac{1}{2}I_0\omega^2.$$

When these two work contributions are added, and with $R\,d\theta = dx$, we have

$$\tfrac{1}{2}MV^2 + \tfrac{1}{2}I_0\omega^2 = E_{\text{tot}} = \int_0^x F_1\,dx.$$

In other words, the change of the *total kinetic energy* of the body is equal to *the work done by the driving force* alone. The net work done by the (static) friction force F is zero, since the loss in translational energy due to F is compensated by the contribution by F of an equal amount of rotational energy.

We have previously pointed out that the horizontal component of the contact force is identical to the static friction force in the ideal case when there is no deformation of the bodies. But the static friction force cannot exceed μN, where μ is the coefficient of static friction and N is the normal component of the contact force. The condition for the prevention of slipping is $F \leq \mu N$, where $N = Mg$ is the normal component of the contact force. If this condition is introduced into the translatory motion expression, $F_1 - F = M(dV/dt)$, the corresponding condition which must be imposed on the driving force F_1 is

$$F_1 \leq \frac{1 + k_0^2/R^2}{k_0^2/R^2}\,\mu Mg.$$

The maximum acceleration which can be given to the cylinder before it starts to slip is

$$\left(\frac{dV}{dt}\right)_{\text{max}} = \mu \, \frac{R^2}{k_0^2} \, g.$$

For the case of a homogeneous cylinder, $(dV/dt)_{\text{max}}$ is $\mu g/2$.

EXAMPLE 2. A homogeneous cylinder is given a horizontal velocity V_1 and a counterclockwise angular velocity $\omega_1 = V_1/R$ on the frictionless part of a horizontal surface. Beyond point A, the surface changes so that the friction coefficient to the right of A is μ (see Fig. 12–18).

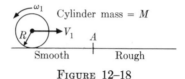

FIGURE 12–18

After the cylinder passes A, it first will slip on the rough plane, but will eventually roll with a constant velocity without slipping. At what point does the cylinder start to roll without slipping, and what is the corresponding velocity of the center of mass?

The only force on the body in the direction of motion is the contact force, and consequently its line of action is in the plane. Therefore, *the angular momentum of the cylinder remains constant, with respect to a reference point in the plane, throughout the entire motion.*

The angular momentum of the cylinder taken about any point in the plane, say A, is

$$L = MV_1R - I_0\omega_1 = MV_1R\left(1 - \frac{k_0^2}{R^2}\right),$$

which is the sum of the angular momentum of the center of mass and the angular momentum with respect to the center of mass. Here we have introduced $\omega_1 = V_1/R$, as specified by the initial conditions of the problem.

When the body rolls without slipping, the relation between the angular and translational velocity is $V_2 = \omega R$, and the angular momentum is

$$L' = MV_2R + I_0\omega = MV_2R\left(1 + \frac{k_0^2}{R^2}\right).$$

Then, equating L and L', we have

$$V_2 = \frac{1 - k_0^2/R^2}{1 + k_0^2/R^2} \, V_1 = \frac{1/2}{3/2} \, V_1 = \tfrac{1}{3}V_1.$$

The final velocity is one-third of the original velocity.

12–4 Rotation about a fixed axis. The pendulum. There are many important examples of motion in which the axis of rotation is fixed. Therefore we shall study this problem in some detail.

The parallel-axis theorem. First, we shall investigate how the angular momentum and the kinetic energy of a rigid body depend upon the location of the fixed axis of rotation. If the angular velocity of the body is ω, and the axis of rotation goes through the center of mass, we have seen that the angular momentum is $I_0\omega$ and the kinetic energy is $I_0\omega^2/2$, where I_0 is the moment of inertia with respect to the axis through the center of mass. In this case, the center of mass has no translational kinetic energy. However, if the body rotates about a parallel axis a perpendicular distance a from the center-of-mass axis, the center of mass will have a velocity $V = a\omega$ (Fig. 12–19). The body will still rotate with the angular velocity ω, and the total kinetic energy then becomes

$$E = \frac{MV^2}{2} + I_0\frac{\omega^2}{2} = (I_0 + Ma^2)\frac{\omega^2}{2}. \qquad (12\text{–}13)$$

Similarly, the total angular momentum of the body is the sum of the spin angular momentum $L^* = I_0\omega$ and the orbital angular momentum $MVa = Ma^2\omega$. Hence, we obtain

$$L = MVa + L^* = (I_0 + Ma^2)\omega. \qquad (12\text{–}14)$$

It is clear that the kinetic energy and the angular momentum can also be expressed as $I\omega$ and $I\omega^2/2$, where $I = \int r^2\,dm$ is the moment of inertia with respect to the new axis of rotation. Then, by comparison with the expression given in Eqs. (12–13) and (12–14), we see that the moment of inertia, with respect to a parallel axis located a perpendicular distance a from the center-of-mass axis, is related to I_0 in the following simple way:

$$I = I_0 + Ma^2. \qquad (12\text{–}15)$$

This relation is usually called the *parallel-axis theorem.*

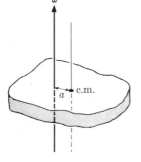

FIGURE 12–19

Of course, this same relation can be obtained by integration directly from the definition of the moment of inertia. In Fig. 12–20, the distance of a mass element dm from the center of mass is denoted by R, and the distance from the parallel axis P is denoted by r. Then, by definition, the moments of inertia with respect to O and P are $I_0 = \int R^2 \, dm$ and $I = \int r^2 \, dm$. From the law of cosines, $r^2 = R^2 + a^2 - 2aR \cos \theta$, and the integral $\int r^2 \, dm$ then contains three terms,

$$I = \int R^2 \, dm + a^2 \int dm - 2a \int R \cos \theta \, dm = I_0 + Ma^2 - 0.$$

The first term is I_0, the moment of inertia about the center of mass. The second term is Ma^2 because $\int dm$ is M, the mass of the rigid body. We observe that $R \cos \theta$ is the x-coordinate of dm with respect to the center of mass, and we have $\int x^* \, dm = 0$ (Chapter 11), so that $I = I_0 + Ma^2$, as before.

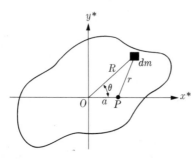

FIG. 12–20. The parallel-axis theorem: $I = I_0 + Ma^2$.

FIG. 12–21. The moment of inertia about an axis through a point on the periphery of a uniform disc of radius R is $I_a = \frac{3}{2}MR^2$.

EXAMPLE. Determine the moment of inertia of a circular disc of radius R with respect to an axis A that is perpendicular to, and through a point on, the periphery of the disc, as shown in Fig. 12–21.

The moment of inertia of the disc, with respect to the center of mass, is

$$I_0 = \frac{MR^2}{2}.$$

The distance between the center-of-mass axis and the parallel axis through A is now $a = R$, and we obtain

$$I_a = I_0 + Ma^2 = \frac{MR^2}{2} + MR^2 = \tfrac{3}{2}MR^2.$$

EXAMPLE. Determine the moment of inertia about one end of a thin uniform bar of length L and mass M.

The moment of inertia about the center of mass is $ML^2/12$. The axis under consideration is a distance $a = L/2$ from the center of mass. Therefore we have

$$I = \frac{ML^2}{12} + M\left(\frac{L}{2}\right)^2 = \frac{ML^2}{3}.$$

The pendulum. The motion of a pendulum is a familiar example of rigid-body motion and involves many of the basic features of motion that we have studied. The idealized case of a mathematical pendulum, in which the mass was concentrated in a single point, was treated in Chapter 8. We shall now discuss the physical pendulum, which has a continuous mass distribution. A typical example of such a physical pendulum is shown in Fig. 12–22. The fixed axis of rotation is horizontal and is denoted by A. The center of mass of the pendulum is located a distance a from A. The displacement of the pendulum from its equilibrium position is described by the angle θ. The pendulum is acted on by two external forces, the gravitational force and the contact force from the axis at A. When we consider the torque about A, only the gravitational force contributes and the torque is $-Mga \sin \theta$. If the moment of inertia of the pendulum is I_a, the rate of change of angular momentum about A is $I_a (d\omega/dt) = I_a (d^2\theta/dt^2)$, and we obtain

$$I_a \frac{d^2\theta}{dt^2} = -Mga \sin \theta. \tag{12–16}$$

As in the case of the simple pendulum, we shall restrict our considerations to situations in which the angle θ is always small. Then $\sin \theta$ may be replaced with θ, and we have

$$I_a \cdot \frac{d^2\theta}{dt^2} = -Mga\theta.$$

As before, this equation describes harmonic motion, and the solution has the form

$$\theta = \theta_m \sin \omega_0 t,$$

where the characteristic angular frequency of oscillation is

$$\omega_0 = \sqrt{\frac{Mga}{I_a}} = \sqrt{\frac{ga}{k_a^2}} \tag{12–17}$$

and the period is

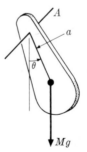

FIG. 12–22. A pendulum that rotates about a fixed horizontal axis.

$$T_0 = 2\pi\sqrt{\frac{I_a}{Mga}} = 2\pi\sqrt{\frac{k_a^2}{ga}}. \tag{12–18}$$

Here k_a is the radius of gyration of the rigid body, with respect to the point A. (Recall that the radius of gyration of a rigid body of mass M and moment of inertia I_a is located at a distance from the axis at which a point mass M must be placed in order to have a moment of inertia I_a. The radius of gyration is therefore defined by $Mk_a^2 = I_a$.) Note that for a mass point a distance a from a fixed axis, the moment of inertia is $I_a = Ma^2$ and the radius of gyration is just a.

EXAMPLE 1. What is the period of oscillation of a uniform bar that oscillates about an axis through the upper end of the bar? The length of the bar is $L = 1$ m. The moment of inertia of the bar with respect to A is $I_a = ML^2/3$. The distance to the center of mass is $a = L/2 = 0.5$ m. The period is then

$$T_0 = 2\pi\sqrt{\frac{L^2 \cdot 2}{3 \cdot g \cdot L}} = 2\pi\sqrt{\frac{2L}{3g}}.$$

Since $L = 1$ m, we get $T_0 \simeq 1.6$ sec.

EXAMPLE 2. Consider the pendulum of the previous example. Suppose the location of the axis of rotation can be varied. Where should it be located so that the period of the pendulum is a minimum?

Suppose the axis A of rotation is located a distance x from the center of the pendulum, as shown in Fig. 12–23. In this case, the moment of inertia with respect to A is

$$I_a = I_0 + Mx^2 = M(k_0^2 + x^2),$$

where k_0 is the radius of gyration with respect to the center of mass. The distance to the center of mass from A is x, and the period is therefore

$$T_0 = 2\pi\sqrt{\frac{k_0^2 + x^2}{gx}}.$$

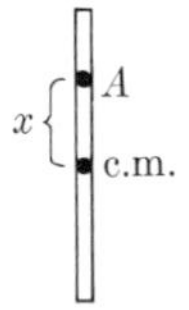

FIGURE 12–23

The period has a minimum when $(k_0^2 + x^2)/x = k_0^2/x + x$ is a minimum. The derivative of this function is $-k_0^2/x^2 + 1$, which is zero when $x = \pm k_0$. The axis of rotation for which the period is a minimum is located a distance k_0 from the center of mass.

EXAMPLE 3. *The equivalent length of a pendulum.* A simple pendulum, we know, has a period $T_0 = 2\pi\sqrt{L/g}$ where L is the distance from the point of suspension to the point mass. We shall define L_{eq}, the equivalent length of a physical pendulum, as the length of a simple pendulum which has the same period as the physical pendulum. The physical pendulum is characterized by its radius of gyration k_a and the distance a of the center of mass from the axis. In what way are L_{eq}, k_a, and a related?

The period of a physical pendulum is $T_0 = 2\pi\sqrt{k_a^2/ga}$, and the equivalent length is defined by $T_0 = 2\pi\sqrt{L_{eq}/g}$. The equivalent length L_{eq} is therefore

$$L_{eq} = \frac{k_a^2}{a}$$

or, alternatively, we may say that the radius of gyration is the geometric mean of the equivalent length and distance to the center of mass.

If we introduce the radius of gyration $k_0 = \sqrt{I_0/M}$, with respect to an axis through the center of mass, from the parallel-axis theorem we have $I_a = I_0 + Ma^2$. Hence $k_a^2 = k_0^2 + a^2$, and we have

$$L_{eq} = a + \frac{k_0^2}{a} = a + b,$$

where

$$b = \frac{k_0^2}{a} \quad \text{or} \quad ab = k_0^2,$$

as illustrated in Fig. 12–24. The length L_{eq} defines a point B which lies a distance $b = k_0^2/a$ from the center of mass. If the body is made to oscillate about an axis through B, the period of oscillation is the same as that obtained for the oscillation about an axis through A.

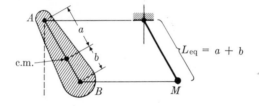

FIGURE 12–24

The points A and B have the interesting property that the geometric mean of their distances from the center of mass is equal to the radius of gyration *about the center of mass*. Point B is the *center of percussion* of the rigid body with respect to A. Correspondingly, of course, point A is the center of percussion with respect to B. Thus it has been shown that the equivalent length of the pendulum, when pivoted at either A or B, is the distance between A and B, $L_{eq} = a + b$.

The force at the axis of rotation. The force on the pendulum at the axis of rotation did not enter into the above analysis, since we used the torque about that axis. In order to obtain the contact force, we can always use the general equations of motion that govern the translation of the center of mass and the rotation about the center of mass. The contact force on the pendulum at the axis of rotation is conveniently split into two components, F_r and F_θ, as shown in Fig. 12–25. When we consider the forces in the radial and tangential directions, and the corresponding changes of

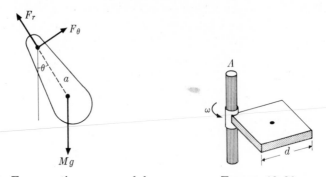

FIG. 12–25. Forces acting on a pendulum.   FIGURE 12–26

momentum in these directions, the equations of motion of the center of mass are

$$F_\theta - Mg \sin \theta = M \frac{dv_\theta}{dt} = Ma \frac{d\omega}{dt}$$

and   (12–19)

$$F_r - Mg \cos \theta = Ma\omega^2,$$

since $a\omega^2$ is the radial acceleration of the center of mass.

The rotation about the center of mass is described by the equation

$$I_0 \frac{d\omega}{dt} = -F_\theta a. \qquad (12\text{--}20)$$

Here, with $\omega = d\theta/dt$, we have three equations from which, at least in principle, we can determine the three unknown quantities θ, F_θ, and F_r as functions of time.

EXAMPLE 1. As a simple illustration of rotation about a fixed axis, consider the square plate rotating about a vertical axis A through one corner of the plate, as shown in Fig. 12–26. The angular velocity of the plate is ω, its mass is M, and its side length is d. What force does the axis exert on the plate?

The center of mass of the plate moves in a circle of radius $d/\sqrt{2}$. Consequently, the net force on the plate is directed toward the center of the circle, and the magnitude of the force is

$$F = M\omega^2 r = M\omega^2 \frac{d}{\sqrt{2}}.$$

The contact force from the axis is the only horizontal force on the plate in the radial direction, therefore this contact force must be F.

In this connection, it is interesting to study this problem from a coordinate system that rotates with the plane at an angular velocity ω. In this coordinate system, the plane is at rest under the influence of the contact interaction force at the axis and the inertial force. The inertial force on a mass element with the position vector **r** is $\omega^2 \mathbf{r}\,dm$ (see Chapter 11) and the total inertial force is then $\omega^2\!\int \mathbf{r}\,dm = \omega^2 M\mathbf{R}$, where **R** is the position vector of the center of mass. Thus if the contact force is **F**, we have the equilibrium condition

$$\mathbf{F} + M\omega^2\mathbf{R} = 0 \quad \text{or} \quad \mathbf{F} = -M\omega^2\mathbf{R}.$$

In Chapter 13, we shall consider asymmetrical-body rotation, in which not only an inertial *force*, but also an inertial *torque*, exists.

EXAMPLE 2. A thin bar of mass M and length L is free to rotate about a fixed horizontal axis, as shown in Fig. 12–27. The bar is released from a position corresponding to an angle θ_0 with the vertical.

(a) What is the angular velocity of the bar when it passes through its lowest point?

There are two external forces on the bar, the gravitational force and the contact force at the axis. Only the gravitational force does work, and the work done is $Mg(L/2)(1 - \cos \theta_0)$, since the vertical displacement of the center of mass is $(L/2)(1 - \cos \theta_0)$. If at the lowest point the angular velocity of the bar is ω, the kinetic energy is $I\omega^2/2$, where I is the moment of inertia of the bar, with respect to the axis of rotation. Thus, we have

$$\frac{I\omega^2}{2} = Mg\,\frac{L}{2}\,(1 - \cos \theta_0).$$

The moment of inertia of the bar, with respect to the axis of rotation, is $I = ML^2/3$. Introducing this value in the equation above, we find that

$$\omega = \sqrt{\frac{3g}{L}\,(1 - \cos \theta_0)}.$$

If the bar is released from the horizontal position ($\theta_0 = 90°$), we get $\omega = \sqrt{3g/L}$.

(b) What is the contact force from the axis on the bar when it passes the vertical position?

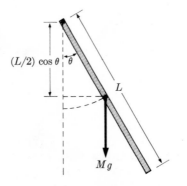

$(L/2) \cos \theta$

θ

L

Mg

FIGURE 12–27

The motion of the center of mass of the rigid body is just like an isolated mass point with a total mass M upon which all the external forces are acting—in this case, the contact and gravitational forces. The center of mass moves in a circle, and the acceleration of the center of mass at the lowest point is $\omega^2 L/2$, directed toward the axis. If the vertical contact force at the axis is denoted by N, we then have

$$N - Mg = M\omega^2 \frac{L}{2},$$

so that

$$N = Mg\left[1 + \tfrac{3}{2}(1 - \cos\theta_0)\right].$$

12-5 Equilibrium (statics) of a rigid body. If a rigid body is in equilibrium, the *net* force on the body must be zero. Otherwise, its center of mass would be accelerated. Similarly, the net *torque* must be zero on a rigid body in equilibrium, for otherwise the angular momentum of the body would change. Clearly, the torque must be zero with respect to any arbitrary point in space. In other words, the conditions for equilibrium are

$$\begin{aligned} \mathbf{F} &= 0 \quad \text{or} \quad F_x = 0, \quad F_y = 0, \quad F_z = 0, \\ \tau &= 0 \quad \text{or} \quad \tau_x = 0, \quad \tau_y = 0, \quad \tau_z = 0. \end{aligned} \tag{12-21}$$

When we have forces and torques in three dimensions, these equilibrium conditions represent six equations from which it is possible to determine six unknown quantities. When all the forces are in the same plane, the number of equations reduces to three,

$$F_x = 0, \qquad F_y = 0, \qquad \text{and} \qquad \tau_z = 0.$$

EXAMPLE. A uniform bar of length L and weight mg is held by two frictionless supports, as shown in Fig. 12–28. What are the forces F_1 and F_2 that the supports exert on the bar? There are no horizontal force components, since the supports are frictionless. For the vertical force components F_1 and F_2, the equilibrium condition that the net force must be zero gives

$$F_1 + F_2 - mg = 0.$$

The net torque about *any* axis must be zero. Let us take as an axis the point of contact of the first support. We have

$$-mg\frac{L}{2} + \frac{F_2 3L}{4} = 0.$$

When these two relations are combined and solved for F_1 and F_2, we have

$$F_1 = \frac{mg}{3}, \qquad F_2 = \frac{2mg}{3}.$$

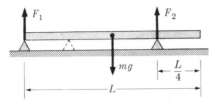

FIGURE 12–28

Suppose now the uniform bar of the previous example is supported in three places, the third support being $L/4$ from the first support. Then we have

$$F_1 + F_2 + F_3 - mg = 0$$

and

$$F_3 \frac{L}{4} - mg \frac{L}{2} + \frac{F_2 3L}{4} = 0.$$

Here we have just two equations and three unknown quantities, F_1, F_2, and F_3. The problem cannot be solved from these equations alone. This can be seen physically from the following argument. We know that the supports 1 and 2 will support the bar. If, now, support 3 is introduced with a point of contact cushioned by an imaginary small spring or piece of felt, it is clear that the amount of the load support 3 takes will depend upon how hard support 3 is pushed up against the bar. If this support is pushed hard enough, just to the point at which support 1 carries no load, supports 2 and 3 will each be carrying $mg/2$. The load on support 3 can therefore be of any value between 0 and $mg/2$. Problems of this kind are said to be *statically indeterminate*.

In practice, when there are more than two supports, the distribution of the load is determined by the elastic or bending properties of the bar. Then the rigid-body assumption is no longer sufficient for the solution of a problem and the equations of equilibrium must be supplemented by further conditions which involve the bar's elastic properties.

EXAMPLE 1. The wheels of a small wagon are separated by a distance d, and the center of mass is a distance h above the ground. The wagon is at rest on a hill of slope angle θ, and between the wheels and the surface of the hill the coefficient of static friction is μ. How steep a hill can the wagon rest on without tipping over or sliding?

The wagon is acted on by three forces, gravity and two contact forces at the wheels. Both the direction and the magnitudes of the contact forces are unknown. Consequently, we have four unknown force components, which are denoted by F_1, F_2, f_1, and f_2 in Fig. 12–29. Since we have only three equilibrium equations, this problem normally is statically indeterminate in the sense that f_1 and f_2 cannot be determined separately. However, we are now interested only in the condition when the wagon is on the verge of sliding or on the verge

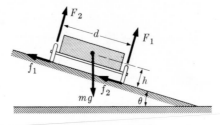

FIGURE 12–29

of tipping. In these cases, we have additional relations imposed between the variables. When the wagon is on the verge of sliding, the friction forces are fully developed at both wheels and, as we recall, are then simply related to the force components normal to the plane. If we let the symbols F_1, F_2, f_1, and f_2 denote the forces which obtain when the wagon is on the verge of sliding, we have

$$f_1 = \mu F_1 \quad \text{and} \quad f_2 = \mu F_2.$$

If we combine these relations with the general conditions for equilibrium,

$$F_x = -f_1 - f_2 + mg \sin \theta_1 = 0,$$
$$F_y = F_1 + F_2 - mg \cos \theta_1 = 0,$$

we obtain $\mu\, mg \cos \theta_1 = mg \sin \theta_1$ or

$$\tan \theta_1 = \mu.$$

In other words, in order to prevent sliding, we must have $\theta < \theta_1$.

When the wagon is on the verge of tipping, the forces F_1 and f_1 will be zero, since then the contact between the upper wheel and the plane will be broken. Then, if we consider the torque with respect to the contact point of the lower wheel, we see that for the total torque to be zero, the lever arm of the gravitational force with respect to this point must be zero. This will occur when the angle of inclination of the plane has the value given by

$$\tan \theta_2 = \frac{d}{2h},$$

and tipping will be prevented if $\theta < \theta_2$. If $\theta_1 = \theta_2$, it follows that tipping and sliding will occur simultaneously when $\mu = d/2h$. If μ is less than $d/2h$, sliding will occur before tipping as the angle θ is increased. The opposite, of course, occurs if μ is larger than $d/2h$.

EXAMPLE 2. As an illustration of a problem in which the forces are not all in the same plane, let us consider the equilibrium of a rigid bar under the influence of three forces, as shown in Fig. 12–30. The bar is supported at its upper end at A by a pivot suspension, about which it can rotate freely. The length of the bar is $L = 2$ ft. The external forces on the bar are $\mathbf{F}_1$, with components $F_{1x} = 0$,

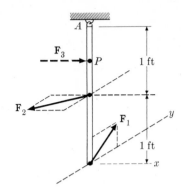

FIGURE 12–30

F_{1y} = 3 lb, and F_{1z} = 1 lb, applied at the lower end of the bar; $\mathbf{F}_2$, with components F_{2x} = —4 lb and F_{2y} = —2 lb; and $\mathbf{F}_3$ which is applied perpendicular to the bar at a point P located $\frac{1}{2}$ ft from the upper end. What should be the direction and magnitude of $\mathbf{F}_3$ to keep the bar in equilibrium?

For the bar to be in equilibrium, the torque with respect to A or any other fixed point must be zero. The torque produced by $\mathbf{F}_1$ and $\mathbf{F}_2$ has the components

$$\tau_x = 3 \cdot 2 - 2 \cdot 1 = 4 \text{ ft·lb}, \qquad \tau_y = 4 \cdot 1 = 4 \text{ ft·lb}.$$

Consequently, the torque components of $\mathbf{F}_3$ must be τ_{3x} = —4 ft·lb and τ_{3y} = —4 ft·lb. The magnitude of the torque is $\tau_3 = 4\sqrt{2}$ and the corresponding magnitude of the force is then $4\sqrt{2}/\frac{1}{2}$ = $8\sqrt{2}$ lb. The components of the force are F_{3x} = +8 lb and F_{3y} = —8 lb. The force on the bar at A then must have the components

$$F_{ax} = -(0 - 4 + 8) = -4 \text{ lb},$$
$$F_{ay} = -(3 - 2 - 8) = +7 \text{ lb},$$
$$F_{az} = -(1 + 0 + 0) = -1 \text{ lb}.$$

EXAMPLE 3. A spool, of inner radius r and outer radius R, lying on a rough floor, is pulled with a force $\mathbf{F}$ by a string wound around its inner cylinder (Fig. 12–31). The string is held at an angle θ with the horizontal. It is observed that there is a critical angle θ_0, such that for $\theta < \theta_0$ the spool rolls without slipping in the direction in which it is pulled, and for $\theta > \theta_0$ the spool rolls without slipping in the opposite direction. What is the value of the critical angle θ_0?

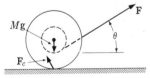

FIGURE 12–31

The spool is acted on by three forces, the tension $\mathbf{F}$ in the string, the weight W, and the contact force F_c that has horizontal and vertical components F_{cx} and F_{cy}.

The equations that express the translational motion of the center of mass and the rotation about the center of mass are

$$F_{cy} + F \sin \theta - Mg = 0,$$

$$F \cos \theta + F_{cx} = MR \frac{d\omega}{dt},$$

$$-F_{cx}R - Fr = I_o \frac{d\omega}{dt}.$$

Elimination of the force F_{cx} gives

$$\frac{d\omega}{dt} = F \frac{R \cos \theta - r}{I_o + MR^2},$$

and it follows that $d\omega/dt > 0$ (forward motion) when $\cos \theta > r/R$, and $d\omega/dt < 0$ (backward motion) when $\cos \theta < r/R$. The critical angle corresponding to $d\omega/dt = 0$ is

$$\cos \theta_0 = \frac{r}{R}.$$

Problems

12-1. Consider two mass points which are moving through space, and which are connected by an elastic spring. How many coordinates are required for a unique description of the locations of these mass points? If the spring is suddenly frozen stiff, how many coordinates are then required for the specification of their locations? How does the result compare with the general considerations about the number of degrees of freedom of a rigid body?

12-2. Consider a body rotating in a plane about a fixed axis with an angular velocity ω, so that all points of the body perform circular motions. Then consider an arbitrary point P, and imagine an axis drawn through this point parallel with the fixed axis. Describe the motion of the body *with respect to the axis through P*.

12-3. Consider the earth and the moon as an isolated system of bodies which interact only with each other. Their center of mass remains at rest. If we ignore the spin of the earth about its own axis, what kind of motion does the earth have about the center of mass of the earth-moon system? What is the speed of the center of the earth in this motion? What is the speed of the North Pole? For numerical values of the earth-moon distance, etc., see the Appendix.

12-4. A straight bar of mass M and length L, lying on a horizontal table with its center of mass at $x = 0$, $y = 0$, is inclined at an angle θ with the positive x-axis. The bar is translated a distance ΔX, in the positive x-direction, and then rotated through an angle $\Delta\theta$ about the center of mass. (a) At the end of this motion, what are the x- and y-coordinates of a

point P on the bar, which originally had the coordinates x_0, y_0? (b) Determine $x - x_0$ and $y - y_0$ in terms of ΔX and $\Delta\theta$. (c) If these displacements are made simultaneously during the time Δt, find the average velocity components $\Delta x/\Delta t$ and $\Delta y/\Delta t$ of P. Show that the instantaneous velocity of the point P in the limit $\Delta t = 0$ is given by

$$v_x = V_x - y_0\omega, \qquad v_y = x_0\omega,$$

where $V_x = dX/dt$ is the velocity of the center of mass.

12-5. A thin rod of length $d = 2$ m is initially aligned with the vertical y-axis. Let the upper end of the rod be denoted by A and the lower end by B. What are the center-of-mass velocity and angular velocity of the body about its center of mass, if (instantaneously) (a) $\mathbf{v}_a = \mathbf{v}_b = 3$ m/sec along the x-axis? (b) $\mathbf{v}_a = 3$ m/sec along the x-axis, $\mathbf{v}_b = 0$? (c) $\mathbf{v}_a = 3$ m/sec along the x-axis, $\mathbf{v}_b = 1$ m/sec along the x-axis? (d) $v_{ax} = 4$ m/sec, $v_{ay} = 3$ m/sec, $v_{bx} = 2$ m/sec, $v_{by} = 3$ m/sec?

12-6. The thin rod described in the previous problem has a mass of 2 kgm. (a) What are the momentum and angular momentum for the conditions of part (d)? (b) If the rod moves only under the influence of gravitational force, what will the subsequent motion be? (c) How many complete turns will the rod make by the time its center of mass returns to the initial height?

12-7. Explain why the choice of the point of application of an external force on a rigid body is irrelevant so far as the center-of-mass motion of the body is concerned.

12-8. A square plate of side d and mass m is on a horizontal frictionless surface. In each of the cases shown in Fig. 12–32, is it possible to reduce the force system to a single force? In each case, reduce the system to a resultant force through the center of mass and a couple which produce the same motion as the initial force system.

force, perpendicular to the bar, at one end of the bar. The bar starts from rest. The length of the bar is L and its mass is M. What point of the bar has zero initial acceleration?

12–14. A uniform cylindrical disc of radius R is pulled along a horizontal

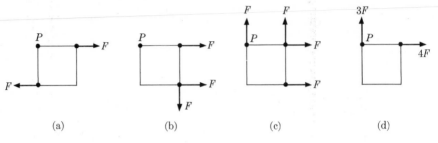

(a)   (b)   (c)   (d)

FIGURE 12–32

12–9. Refer to Problem 12–8. What, in each case, is the instantaneous acceleration of point P?

12–10. Two uniform thin bars of equal lengths $l = 0.5$ m, one weighing 8 lb and the other 24 lb, are welded together to form one bar of length 1 m. Consider now the moment of inertia of this composite bar with respect to an axis perpendicular to the bar. Determine the location of the axis with respect to which the moment of inertia has the smallest value. Determine this value.

12–11. Show that for any arbitrary plane uniform plate we have $I_0 = I_x + I_y$, where I_0 is the moment of inertia with respect to the axis perpendicular to the plate through the origin of the xy-system, and I_x and I_y are the moments of inertia with respect to the x- and y-axes, respectively.

12–12. Check the expressions for the moments of inertia of a sphere and a cube as given in Fig. 12–8 in the text.

12–13. A uniform bar on a horizontal table is acted on by a horizontal

(frictionless) surface by a string wound around the cylinder. The other end of the string carries a body with the same mass M as the cylinder. The string runs over a pulley, as shown in Fig. 12–33. (a) Determine the tension in the string as the system moves. (b) If the system starts from rest, what is the velocity of the disc when its center has traveled a distance of $5R$?

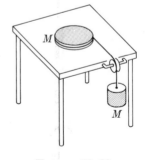

FIGURE 12–33

12–15. Two homogeneous cylinders of the same material rotate with the same angular velocity about their center-of-mass axes. What is the ratio between their kinetic energies if the radius of one cylinder is twice the radius of the other?

12-16. A thin circular plate rotates about a center-of-mass axis that is perpendicular to the plate. What must be the angular velocity such that the kinetic energy will be large enough to lift the weight of the plate to a height equal to the diameter $2R$ of the plate?

12-17. The collision experiments of Chapters 2 and 3 utilized cars of mass M which rolled on four wheels each of mass m, radius r, and radius of gyration k. (Assume always that the wheels roll.) (a) What velocity would such a car attain if, after it started from rest, a force F acted on it along the track for a time Δt? What would be the effective mass of the car? (b) What velocity would such a car attain if, after it started from rest, a force F acted on it for a distance Δx along the track? What now would be the effective mass of the car?

12-18. A straight uniform bar of mass m and length l is held at an inclination angle θ_0 with its lower end resting on a smooth plane (neglect friction). The bar is released from this position. (a) Show that the bar hits the plane flush, i.e., that the lower end will always be in contact with the plane. (b) Determine the angular velocity as a function of the inclination angle. (c) Determine the velocity of the center of mass just before the bar hits the floor. (Hint: Use conservation of total mechanical energy.)

12-19. In Fig. 12-34 are shown two homogeneous cylinders, each of radius R and mass M. The top cylinder, held by a horizontal axis through its center, is free to rotate. A rope is wrapped around both cylinders, and the bottom

cylinder is permitted to fall. There is enough friction between the rope and the cylinders so that both may rotate without slipping. (a) What is the acceleration of the center of mass of the bottom cylinder? (b) What is the tension in the rope? (c) What is the velocity of the lower cylinder when it has fallen a distance $10R$?

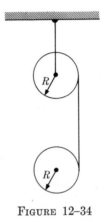

FIGURE 12-34

12-20. A uniform cube of mass m slides in a horizontal plane under the influence of a constant force on a horizontal string. The string is attached to the center of the top surface of the cube, as shown in Fig. 12-35. (a) The friction coefficient is zero. At what value of the force will the cube start to tip? (b) Suppose the coefficient of sliding friction is μ. Now, what is the value of the force at which the cube starts to tip?

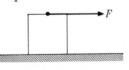

FIGURE 12-35

12-21. A bar $A–B$ of mass M and length l is suspended from a pin by a string OA, as shown in Fig. 12-36.

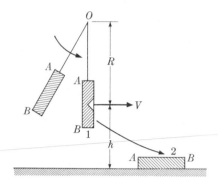

FIGURE 12–36

The distance from the pin to the center of the bar is R. The bar is released and swings down into a vertical position (position 1), where its center of mass has a velocity V. At this instant, the string breaks and the rod flies off. It turns through $\frac{1}{4}$ revolution such that as it hits the floor (position 2), it is horizontal. When the string breaks, what is the height h between the center of the rod and the floor?

12–22. (a) Suppose an impulse is applied to a rigid body. Indicate one or several points, with respect to which the total angular momentum of the body is not changed by the impulse. (b) If an impulse on a body is not instantaneous, but extends over a certain period of time, can the angular-momentum transfer be expressed generally in terms of the impulse? Discuss.

12–22. A body, free to move on a plane, is at rest when it is struck by an instantaneous impulse. It is possible that a point of the body has zero velocity immediately after the impulse? If so, discuss how this point changes as the application point of the impulse changes.

12–23. A straight homogeneous bar of length $L = 3$ m and mass $M = 4$ kgm is at rest on a horizontal surface. An instantaneous horizontal impulse is applied perpendicular to the bar. At what distance from the center of the bar should the impulse be applied to make the resulting translational and rotational kinetic energies of equal values?

12–24. When two rigid bodies collide, the total angular momentum of the bodies remains constant. Does this mean that the contact forces between the bodies pass through the center of mass of the bodies? Discuss.

12–25. In a collision between rigid bodies, is it possible that the spin angular momentum of one body can change without a change in the spin angular momentum of the other?

12–26. In a collision between two extended rigid bodies, is it possible that after the collision both bodies have only rotational kinetic energies about their individual centers of mass? If so, give an example.

12–27. A circular wooden hoop of mass m and radius r rests on a horizontal frictionless surface. A bullet, also of mass m, and with velocity v directed as shown in Fig. 12–37, strikes the hoop and becomes embedded in it. The thickness t is much smaller than the radius r. (a) What is the velocity of the center of mass of the system before and after the bullet strikes the hoop? (b) What is the angular momentum of the system about its center of mass before the bullet strikes the hoop? (c) What is the angular velocity with which the system rotates after the bullet strikes the hoop? (d) How much kinetic energy was lost in the collision?

FIGURE 12–37

12-28. A uniform circular puck A of radius R and mass M slides on one of its flat surfaces over a horizontal frictionless plane with a constant velocity V. Puck A collides with another identical puck B, which is originally at rest with its center located a distance R from the line of motion of A, as indicated in Fig. 12–38. After the collision, the two discs stick together and form one rigid body. What are (a) the translational velocity, and (b) the angular velocity of this body after the collision? (c) How would the answer in (b) be changed if A has an initial angular velocity $\omega_a = V/R$, corresponding to a positive (counterclockwise) spin? (d) How much kinetic energy is lost in the collision?

FIGURE 12–39

(c) Suppose the wheel bearing is *not* frictionless. What will be the final motion of the wheel and locomotive if both are at rest when the current is turned on? (d) If, instead of being held in position by a fixed axis, the wheel is lying on a frictionless horizontal surface, describe the motion of the system after the locomotive starts moving.

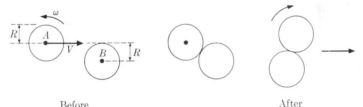

Before   After

FIGURE 12–38

12-29. A horizontal circular track of mass $M = 1.5$ kgm and radius $R = 0.5$ m is mounted on a wheel which can rotate (neglect friction) about its fixed vertical axis, as shown in Fig. 12–39. The mass of the wheel may be neglected. On the track, a toy locomotive of mass $m = 0.5$ kgm starts from rest and soon reaches a constant speed $v_0 = 2$ m/sec with respect to the laboratory system. (a) What then is the angular velocity of the wheel if it starts from rest? Indicate direction. (b) The locomotive slows and finally stops. What is the final angular velocity of the wheel?

12-30. A homogeneous cylinder starts from point A and rolls down an inclined plane (Fig. 12–40) to B without slipping. Continuing from B to C,

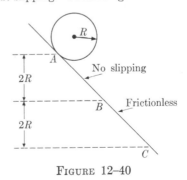

FIGURE 12–40

it moves on a frictionless surface. The vertical distances between A and B and between B and C are both equal to the diameter of the cylinder. (a) When the cylinder is at point B, what are the velocity of the center of mass and the angular velocity of the cylinder? (b) When the cylinder is at point C, what now are the velocity of the center of mass and the angular velocity?

12–31. A weightless piston in a frictionless guide pushes a uniform cylinder of mass M and radius R on a horizontal plane, as shown in Fig. 12–41. The horizontal force on the piston is F. The friction coefficient between the piston and the cylinder is μ. The cylinder rolls on the plane without slipping. (a) Write the equation, or equations, which govern the motion. (b) Determine the acceleration of the center of mass of the cylinder.

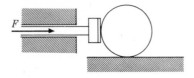

FIGURE 12–41

12–32. A wheel rolls up an incline of elevation angle θ under the influence of a torque, as shown in Fig. 12–42. What is the maximum acceleration of the wheel if its mass is M, its radius of gyration is k_0, and the coefficient of static friction is μ?

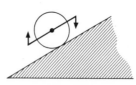

FIGURE 12–42

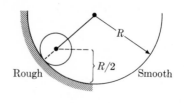

FIGURE 12–43

12–33. A homogeneous cylinder of radius $R/4$ moves on the inside of a circular pipe of radius R, as shown in Fig. 12–43. The left-hand half of the pipe is rough enough to assure rolling without slipping, whereas the other half has zero friction coefficient. In the rough half of the pipe, the cylinder starts to roll from a point where its center of mass is a distance $R/2$ above the lowest point of the pipe. (a) What is the angular velocity of the cylinder at the lowest point? (b) On the smooth half of the pipe, what maximum height does the cylinder reach?

12–34. What is the moment of inertia of (a) a long slender rod about an axis through one of its ends? (b) a thin circular hoop about an axis on its rim and perpendicular to its plane? (c) a thin circular hoop about an axis on its rim and in the plane of the hoop? (d) a thin circular plate about an axis on its rim and perpendicular to its plane?

12–35. A circular hoop of radius R oscillates about a horizontal axis through point A, as shown in Fig. 12–44. (a) What is the period of oscillation of the hoop if the axis

FIGURE 12–44

is perpendicular to the plane of the hoop? Show that this period is the same as that of a simple pendulum of length $2R$. (b) What is the period of oscillation of the hoop if the axis is in the plane of the hoop? (c) In (a) and (b), what are the angular velocities required at the lowest points such that the hoop will make a complete revolution?

12–36. A slender homogeneous rod of mass M and length L is hinged at one end and supported in a horizontal position by a vertical spring. The spring is attached at a distance d from the hinged end of the rod (Fig. 12–45). If the free end of the rod is given a small vertical displacement and then released, calculate the period of the ensuing oscillations if the force constant of the spring is K.

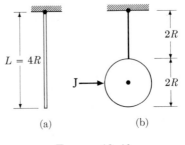

FIGURE 12–46

sions are as given in the figure. The sphere is given an instantaneous impulse J through its center, so that it swings out to a horizontal position. Where should J be applied to the bar so that it will swing out to the horizontal position?

12–39. A uniform bar of length L and mass M can rotate about a horizontal frictionless shaft through the upper end of the bar, as shown in Fig. 12–47. The shaft hangs from two horizontal wires upon which it can slide without friction. The bar is given a horizontal velocity V in such a way that it remains vertical during the motion. The motion is stopped as the shaft collides with the fixed wire support S and sticks to it. The bar then starts to swing about the shaft. (a) What is the angular momentum of the bar with respect to S before and immediately after the collision? (b) What is the angular velocity of the bar after the collision? (c) What fraction of the initial kinetic energy is lost in the collision?

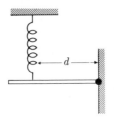

FIGURE 12–45

12–37. A pendulum consists of a uniform bar of length L, with a horizontal axis of rotation through one of its ends. The bar is released from the horizontal position. (a) What is the contact force on the bar from the axis immediately after release of the bar? (b) What is the contact force when the bar makes an angle of 30° with the vertical?

12–38. Consider the two pendulums shown in Fig. 12–46. Part (a) shows a straight uniform bar, and (b) is a uniform sphere hanging at the end of a very light bar. The masses of the pendulums are equal, and their dimen-

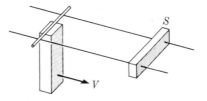

FIGURE 12–47

12–40. A straight-bar pendulum is arranged to oscillate in two ways, as shown in Fig. 12–48. In (a), it oscillates about a fixed horizontal axis through the upper end. In (b), the upper end is free to slide along a horizontal frictionless wire. (a) What is the ratio between the period of small oscillations of these two pendulums? (b) The pendulum oscillates back and forth on the wire with a certain amplitude. The upper end is suddenly clamped to the wire, but the pendulum is still able to oscillate freely about this point of clamping. Discuss the amplitude in the continued motion if the ring is clamped when the pendulum passes through the vertical position, and also when the deflection of the pendulum is a maximum.

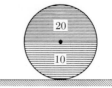

FIGURE 12–49

position shown. What will be the maximum kinetic energy in the subsequent oscillatory motion?

12–42. A homogeneous cube slides with constant velocity on a horizontal frictionless surface, as shown in Fig. 12–50. At what speed will the block overturn after colliding with the stop at S?

FIGURE 12–50

12–43. Consider the systems shown in Fig. 12–51(a), (b), and (c), all of which perform oscillatory motion. (a) The first system consists of a cylinder of mass m and radius r and a very light bar. Calculate the characteristic frequency f_a of this system. (b) A cylinder of mass m *slides* back and forth in a semicircular ditch. Neglecting friction, calculate the characteristic frequency f_b of this system. Is it equal to, larger than, or smaller than f_a? Explain. (c) The cylinder

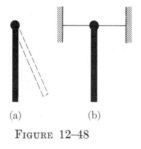

(a)   (b)

FIGURE 12–48

12–41. A cylinder of radius $R = 1$ ft is made from two uniform halves, one weighing 10 lb, and the other 20 lb, as shown in Fig. 12–49. The cylinder stands on a frictionless plane and is released from the unstable

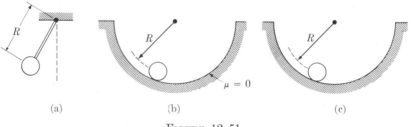

(a)   (b)   (c)

FIGURE 12–51

of part (b) is now *rolling* back and forth without slipping. Is the characteristic frequency f_c of this system equal to, larger than, or smaller than f_b? Explain.

12–44. A 40-ft ladder weighs 50 lb and leans against a smooth building. The angle between the ladder and the building is 30°. (a) Sketch a diagram of all the forces on the ladder. (b) What force does the building exert on the ladder? (c) What force does the ground exert on the ladder?

12–45. A boom is 30 ft long, weighs 300 lb, and is supported as shown in Fig. 12–52. It holds a 1000-lb weight at its free end. (a) Indicate on a diagram all the forces on the boom. (b) What are these forces?

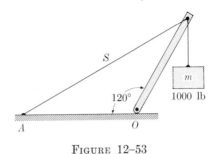

FIGURE 12–53

pivot at P is frictionless. Each of the boards are of mass m and length l, and each makes an angle of 60° with the floor. What must be the coefficient of static friction to maintain the balanced system?

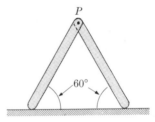

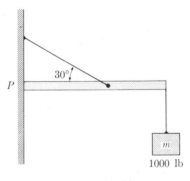

FIGURE 12–52

12–46. A clothesline 100 ft long supports a 20-lb weight at its center. Each half of the clothesline makes a 5° angle with the horizontal. What is the tension in the clothesline?

12–47. A boom 100 ft long and weighing 300 lb is supported as shown in Fig. 12–53. The distance A to O is 100 ft. What is the tension S in the cable?

12–48. Two smooth boards are pivoted together at one end and are balanced as shown in Fig. 12–54. The

FIGURE 12–54

12–49. As shown in Fig. 12–55, a homogeneous cylinder of mass M and radius R is kept at rest on an inclined plane (elevation angle θ) under the influence of a torque. Determine this torque.

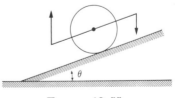

FIGURE 12–55

12–50. A uniform bar of length L and weight W is kept in equilibrium in a vertical plane, as indicated in

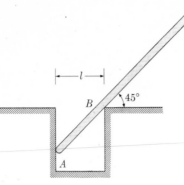

FIGURE 12–56

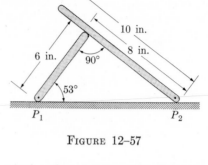

FIGURE 12–57

Fig. 12–56. The width of the ditch holding the bar is $l = L/3$. The friction force at the contact point A is a maximum, and may be neglected at B. At A, what is the friction coefficient and what direction has the friction force on the bar?

12–51. Two uniform bars, one of 6-in. length and 10-lb weight, the other of 10-in. length and 40-lb weight, are held by pins P_1 and P_2 such that they lean against each other, as shown in Fig. 12–57. (a) What can be said about the coefficient of static friction between the bars if there is no slipping? (b) What are the horizontal and vertical components of the force exerted by the pin P_1?

CHAPTER 13

EXAMPLES OF FORCES AND MOTION — V

Summary. In two-dimensional motion, as we have seen in Chapter 12, the angular momentum of a rigid body has only one component, and a torque on a body changes only the magnitude of the angular momentum. In three-dimensional motion the direction of the angular momentum also can change, and such a change requires an external torque, as discussed formally in Chapter 9. This vector relation between angular momentum and torque is illustrated first for a single particle and a spinning dumbbell. Then an analysis of the motion of spinning, symmetrical, rigid bodies is given. We include the precession of gyroscopes and tops, and a qualitative study of nutation. Inertial forces and torques produced in a rotation about a fixed axis are then determined and the concepts of principal axes and principal moments of inertia are introduced. We note that the angular momentum in a rotation about a nonprincipal axis (usually) is not directed along the axis of rotation. Having shown the vector nature of angular velocity, we derive the general expression for the angular momentum and the kinetic energy of a spinning rigid body in terms of the principal moments of inertia and the angular-velocity components along the principal axes.

The motion of a rigid body, as we have seen in Chapter 12, can be considered as a superposition of a translation and a rotation. The translation is described by the motion of the center of mass of the body, and this part of the motion is completely analogous to the motion of a particle. When compared with particle motion, then, the novel features of rigid-body motion are the rotation about the center of mass and the relationship that exists between the spin angular momentum and the external forces. In Chapter 9, we introduced the concept of angular momentum and studied its properties in the case of a system of particles. In Chapter 12 the general equations of motion for a rigid body were presented in the forms

$$\frac{d\mathbf{P}}{dt} = \mathbf{F}, \tag{13-1}$$

$$\frac{d\mathbf{L}^*}{dt} = \tau^*, \tag{13-2}$$

where $\mathbf{P}$ is the total momentum of the body, $\mathbf{L}^*$ is the spin angular momentum, $\mathbf{F}$ is the resultant external force, and τ^* is the resultant torque with

371

respect to the center of mass. However, so far we have applied these equations only to motion in a plane and in this case there is only one component of the angular momentum. In this chapter, our previous studies will be extended to include motion in three dimensions, which is encountered in bodies that spin (gyroscopes, etc.).

When we turn from motion in a plane to motion in space, no new concepts regarding the translational motion of a body are encountered. In other words, in terms of the motion of the center of mass, etc., the interpretation of Eq. (13-1) is the same in two- and in three-dimensional motion. However, with regard to rotational motion, we find that it is basically different in two and three dimensions. In two dimensions, the direction of the angular momentum is confined to the fixed line perpendicular to the plane of motion, and an external torque on the body always produces a change in the *magnitude* of the angular momentum. In space, however, the direction of the angular-momentum vector can change, and then it no longer is true that a torque produces a change in only the magnitude of the angular momentum. In fact, in many cases the sole effect of the torque is to produce a change of *direction* of the angular momentum, while the magnitude remains constant. Many of the interesting and seemingly puzzling features of the motion of gyroscopes and tops result from this effect, which is quite unfamiliar from the standpoint of the knowledge we have so far acquired.

It may be helpful in this connection to recall the analogous situation which obtained in our studies of the momentum of a body, first in one-dimensional motion and then in two-dimensional motion. We found that in one dimension the direction of the momentum vector was confined to the line of motion of the body, and an external force always changed the magnitude of the momentum. However, in two (and three) dimensions the direction of the momentum was no longer confined, and a force did not necessarily change only the magnitude of the momentum. In uniform circular motion, for example, the force changed only the direction, and not the magnitude, of the momentum. This fact seemed somewhat puzzling from the standpoint of the knowledge acquired solely from our one-dimensional studies. However, once we became familiar with circular and curvilinear motions, the meaning of the vector relation expressing the rate of change of momentum in terms of the force was no doubt clarified. Similarly, in order to become thoroughly familiar with the vector nature of the relation between angular momentum and torque, it is helpful to study in detail some simple examples; this will be done in the following discussions.

13–1 Change of angular momentum of a particle. To introduce the vector relation $d\mathbf{l}/dt = \boldsymbol{\tau} = \mathbf{r} \times \mathbf{F}$ and the corresponding impulse rela-

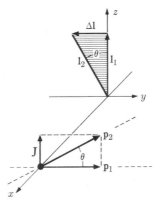

Fig. 13-1. Vector diagram showing the relations between the momenta and angular momenta before and after an instantaneous impulse.

tion $\Delta \mathbf{l} = \mathbf{r} \times \mathbf{J}$, we shall consider the motion of a single particle, the angular momentum of which is changed by means of an instantaneous impulse.

Figure 13-1 illustrates a particle moving with a constant momentum $p_y = p_1$ along a straight line $x = x_1$ in the xy-plane. The angular momentum of the particle with respect to the origin is then constant; that is, $l_z = l_1 = x_1 p_1$, which is represented by a vector along the z-axis. As the particle crosses the x-axis it receives an instantaneous impulse $\mathbf{J}$. If the impulse is in the xy-plane, the particle will remain in the xy-plane after the impulse and only the magnitude, and not the direction, of the angular momentum will change. If, on the other hand, the impulse has a component perpendicular to the xy-plane, the path of the particle will be deflected out of the xy-plane. If the impulse is directed in the positive z-direction the change of the angular momentum, according to the vector relation $\Delta \mathbf{l} = \mathbf{r} \times \mathbf{J}$ (see Chapter 9), is in the direction of the negative y-axis. Therefore, after the impulse the angular momentum has the components $l_z = x_1 p_1$ and $l_y = -x_1 J$. The magnitude of the angular momentum after the impulse is then $l_2 = \sqrt{(x_1 p_1)^2 + (x_1 J)^2}$ and the direction of l_2 makes an angle $\theta = \cos^{-1}(l_1/l_2)$ with the z-axis, as shown. This result now can be illustrated directly, without the use of the vector relations above. The effect of the impulse will be to change both the direction and the magnitude of the particle's momentum. After the impulse the particle will move in a *new plane*, and if the impulse is applied at the instant shown, this new plane and the original plane of motion intersect along the x-axis. The angle between the initial and final planes of motion is the same as the angle between the initial and final momenta p_1 and p_2 and so is given by $\cos \theta = p_1/p_2$. Then, quite apart from all angular-momentum considerations, the effects of the impulse are (a) to increase the magnitude of the momentum from p_1 to $p_2 = \sqrt{p_1^2 + J^2}$, (b) to make the particle travel in a new plane which intersects the original plane along the y-axis, and (c) to make the angle between these two planes such that $\cos\theta = p_1/p_2$.

The perpendicular distance from the new line of motion to the origin is still x_1, and the magnitude of the angular momentum of the particle after the impulse is then $l_2 = x_1 p_2 = \sqrt{(x_1 p_1)^2 + (x_1 J)^2}$. The direction of the angular momentum, as we have seen in our previous work, is perpendicular to the new plane of motion. Since the angle between two planes is the same as the angles between their normals, it follows that the new angular-momentum vector makes an angle θ with the z-axis given by $\cos\theta = p_1/p_2 = l_1/l_2$, as before. This simple example thus demonstrates that the vector representation of angular momentum and the vector relation $\boldsymbol{\tau} = d\mathbf{l}/dt$ (or $\Delta\mathbf{l} = \mathbf{r} \times \mathbf{J}$) are consistent and easily understandable. It is important to note that although the change in the momentum of a particle is always in the direction of the impulse or the force, the change in the angular momentum depends on the angular deflection of the plane of motion and is in the direction of the angular impulse, or torque, on the particle. A completely analogous discussion can be carried through for the motion of a particle under the influence of a central force, as in the case illustrated in Fig. 13–2. A small ball attached to one end of a string moves in a horizontal circular path in the xy-plane with constant angular velocity. (We neglect the effect of gravity.) The only force on the ball is then the tension in the string. We now give this ball impulses in various directions and examine the effects. In the first case, illustrated in Fig. 13–3, the impulse is applied in the direction of motion of the ball. The ball remains in the initial plane of motion and only the magnitude of the angular momentum changes, as indicated in the figure.

Next, let an instantaneous angular impulse be applied to the ball in a direction perpendicular to the ball's plane of motion, as illustrated in Fig. 13–4. The impulse now causes the ball to move in a new plane, and the change in angular momentum is seen to be described consistently by the vector relation $\Delta\mathbf{l} = \mathbf{r} \times \mathbf{J}$.

EXAMPLE. A mass point attached to a string of length r has an angular velocity ω. What angular impulse must be delivered in order that the magnitude of the angular momentum remains unchanged and yet the plane of rotation changes by 90°?

Initially, the angular momentum has a magnitude $mr^2\omega$ directed upward. Finally, the angular momentum is directed in the positive x-direction but still has the magnitude $mr^2\omega$. The *angular impulse* is therefore directed as shown, and has a magnitude $\Delta l = \sqrt{(mr^2\omega)^2 + (mr^2\omega)^2} = \sqrt{2}(mr^2\omega)$. The impulse $\mathbf{J}$ tends to produce a rotation which would cause a right-handed screw to advance along $\Delta\mathbf{l}$.

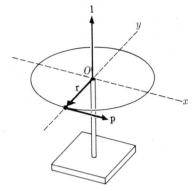

FIG. 13–2. Ball attached to a string rotating about a fixed point.

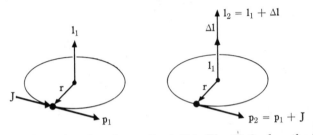

FIG. 13–3. Effect of an impulse on the ball in Fig. 13–2 when the impulse is in the plane of motion.

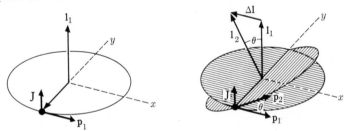

FIG. 13–4. The ball is given an impulse perpendicular to its momentum.

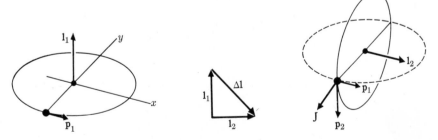

FIG. 13–5. An impulse which changes the plane of rotation by 90° but leaves the magnitude of the angular momentum unchanged.

13-2 Examples of motion of spinning symmetrical bodies. Having illustrated the relation between angular momentum and torque in the motion of a single particle, we now proceed to the study of the motion of spinning rigid bodies. As a simple introductory example let us consider a system consisting of two balls of equal mass mounted on opposite ends of a thin rod of length $2R$ and negligible mass (Fig. 13–6). The rod has a bearing at its center and is free to rotate on a shaft. Initially the balls and rod rotate in a horizontal plane. What angular impulse must be given to the system in order that the plane of rotation change in the manner indicated?

The required change in angular momentum is along the positive x-axis, and therefore the angular impulse must be in this direction. If we apply two equal but oppositely directed impulses (the impulses of a *force couple*), we need not concern ourselves with the system's center-of-mass motion.

One possibility is to apply simultaneous impulses to each of the balls. Since the balls are a distance R from point O, each impulse would have a magnitude $J_1 = \Delta l/2R$, directed as shown in the figure. Clearly, these impulses are in a direction such that they deflect the ball's motion into the new plane and this, of course, produces an angular impulse directed along Δl.

Another possibility is to apply the impulses to the shaft. Here their magnitudes depend upon the distance from O to the points of contact. Most important, though, are the *directions* of the impulses. The impulses must produce angular impulses directed along Δl (the x-axis), and so must be directed along the positive and negative y-axes respectively, as shown. As a result of these impulses the top end of the shaft will tilt in the direction of the positive x-axis. This behavior of the shaft may seem rather puzzling at first glance. A person may argue that, according to his experience, a point on a shaft at rest will start to move in the same direction as the impulse applied at that point. However, this intuitive notion

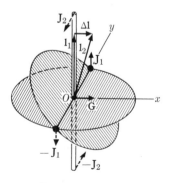

FIGURE 13–6

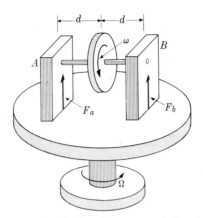

Fig. 13–7. A spinning disc on a rotating table.

clearly does not apply when we deal with bodies possessing angular momentum, since the body will turn in such a way that the change in the angular-momentum vector will be in the direction of the applied torque or angular impulse.

The examples we have studied so far have involved angular-momentum changes produced by instantaneous angular impulses, but the essential features of the results obtained are still applicable when we have continuously acting torques, as illustrated in the following example.

Consider a uniform disc that rotates about a horizontal axis mounted on a turntable, as in Fig. 13–7. The spin angular momentum of the disc has a magnitude $L = I_0\omega$, where $I_0 = MR^2/2$ is the moment of inertia of the disc. The direction of the angular-momentum vector is perpendicular to the plane of the disc. When the table does not rotate, $\Omega = 0$, the angular momentum of the disc remains constant, and the net torque is zero. We have $F_a d - F_b d = 0$. The contact forces on A and B are alike and equal to $Mg/2$, neglecting all weights other than that of the disc. However, as the table is set in rotation, the direction of the angular momentum of the disc, with respect to the ground, will indeed change.

As the disc turns, the direction of the angular-momentum vector will also turn at a constant angular velocity Ω, as illustrated in Fig. 13–8.

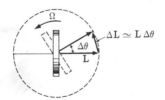

Fig. 13–8. As the angular-momentum vector turns with an angular velocity Ω, the magnitude of its rate of change is $dL/dt = \Omega L$.

From this figure, it follows that during the time Δt the angular momentum vector turns through an angle $\Delta\theta = \Omega\,\Delta t$ and the magnitude of the corresponding change in the angular-momentum vector is $\Delta L = L\Omega\,\Delta t$. The direction of $\Delta \mathbf{L}$ becomes perpendicular to $\mathbf{L}$ when $\Delta\theta$ approaches zero.

Since this change is continuous, the magnitude of the rate of change of $\mathbf{L}$ and the torque is

$$\tau = \frac{dL}{dt} = L\Omega.$$

The direction of $d\mathbf{L}/dt$ is perpendicular to $\mathbf{L}$. Consequently, the torque on the body is perpendicular to the axis of the disc and has a magnitude $L\Omega$. Therefore we have $(F_a - F_b)\,d = L\Omega$. In addition, the sum $F_a + F_b$ must equal the weight of the disc, $F_a + F_b = Mg$, and from this, it follows that

$$F_a = \frac{Mg}{2} + \frac{L\Omega}{2d} \quad\text{and}\quad F_b = \frac{Mg}{2} - \frac{L\Omega}{2d}.$$

The explanation of the unequal contact forces therefore is simply that the disc has a changing angular momentum, and for this changing angular momentum to be maintained, there must be a torque on the disc.

Note that when $L\Omega/d$ is equal to Mg, the support at B has no contact force at all and might just as well be removed, and we then obtain what is known as a *precessing gyroscope*, as we shall see in the following section. If $L\Omega$ is allowed to become greater than Mg, the force on the bearing B reverses direction and this end must be held down, while the other end presses down on the platform with a force greater than Mg.

The gyroscope. The example above has demonstrated that if a constant angular momentum changes direction at a constant rate, a torque is required to sustain this motion. This torque can be calculated directly from the known constant angular velocity Ω of the turning motion of the axis and the magnitude of the spin angular momentum. It is clear that so far as the disc is concerned, it is irrelevant whether this torque is produced by the contact forces from a table or from some other external force. Consequently, if we mount the disc as in a gyroscope (Fig. 13–9), and if the direction of the axis of the disc is turned at a *constant* angular velocity Ω in a horizontal plane, a torque $\tau = L\Omega$ will be required to sustain the motion. We can, for example, produce this torque by hanging a weight at one end of the axis, as shown in the figure. When the angular momentum vector of a rotating mass rotates at a uniform rate, Ω, the motion is called *precession*. In the precessional motion we may say that the angular momentum vector $\mathbf{L}$ "tries" to line up with the torque vector $\boldsymbol{\tau}$ as the tip of the angular-momentum vector turns in the direction of the torque vector. Of course, since the torque acts continuously at right angles to $\mathbf{L}$,

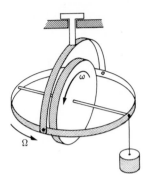

FIG. 13-9. Precessing gyroscope.

the angular-momentum vector will turn continuously but will never "catch up" with the torque.

Note carefully that in this discussion of the precessional motion of a gyroscope we assumed the existence of the motion and then derived the external torques and forces from the known motion. If we consider the complementary problem in which the forces are given and the motion is sought, we must find, of course, that the precessional motion indeed represents one possible motion, since it satisfies the equation of motion. However, there are other possible motions which can be produced by the given external torque, and just what happens depends upon the way the motion is started. If the gimbals and weight are first held stationary and then released, the gyroscope will start a complicated *nutating* motion. But if the gimbals are given initially the angular velocity Ω appropriate to the torque and angular momentum, the precessional motion will follow.

When the torque and the angular momentum are perpendicular to each other, as in Fig. 13-9, the precessional angular velocity is

$$\Omega = \frac{\tau}{L} = \frac{\tau}{I_0\omega}, \tag{13-3}$$

where we have introduced $L = I_0\omega$, where I_0 is the moment of inertia of the spinning mass in the gyroscope and ω is the spin angular velocity. Note that the larger the spin angular momentum **L**, the larger is the torque required to produce a given precessional angular velocity of the gyroscope.

If there is no external torque on the gyroscope the angular-momentum vector will always point in the same direction, and if the angular momentum is large a considerable angular impulse is required to change the orientation of the gyroscope. It is the angular momentum which gives a spinning body its peculiar stability, or "inertia" to changes in direction. By giving a projectile such as a bullet, a discus, or a rocket a spin angular momentum, it is possible to make it travel without tumbling and with the spin axis of rotation pointing in a fixed direction. Similarly, it is possible to stabilize ships by means of rotating bodies with a large angular momentum.

A gyroscope can be used as a navigational instrument. In the gyrocompass, for example, a gyroscope is mounted in such a way that the spin axis of the gyroscope is always kept in a horizontal plane but is free to turn in this plane. Then, as a result of the rotation of the earth, the spin axis always adjusts itself so as to line up in the true north-south direction (see Problem 13–21).

The spinning top. If we release a *non*spinning top from a vertical position we know very well that the top will fall. However, if the top is set in rapid rotation about its axis, the top can indeed keep itself upright when placed on its tip. We find that in general the axis of the top then will change its direction in a slow, circling motion, which is called the precession of the top. This precession is analogous to the precession of the gyroscope.

Let us first consider the simple case in which the top has a smooth precessional motion with an angular velocity of precession Ω, as indicated in Fig. 13–10. To find the precessional angular velocity, we must first determine the torque of the external forces on the top. Let us take the contact point, A, as the reference point. Then the angular momentum of the top is the sum of the spin and orbital angular momenta with respect to $A: L_a = L^* + R \times P$. The magnitude of the torque with respect to A is simply $MgR \sin \theta$, where R is the distance between the center of mass and A, and θ is the angle between the axis of the top and the vertical. If we consider first the special case in which the spin angular momentum L^* is much larger than the orbital contribution $R \times P$, we can set the total angular momentum with respect to A approximately equal to L^*. If friction is neglected, there is no torque component along the axis of the top. The spin angular momentum then will remain constant in magnitude; only its direction will change. The torque from the force Mg is always perpendicular to L^*. Therefore the tip of L^* will

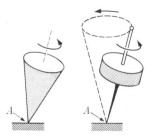

FIG. 13–10. Examples of spinning tops.

describe a horizontal circle of radius $L^* \sin \theta$, as shown in Fig. 13–11. The corresponding magnitude of the rate of change of the angular momentum then becomes $dL^*/dt = \Omega L^* \sin \theta$, in complete analogy with the discussion of the gyroscope. The relation between the torque and the angular velocity of precession is then

$$\tau = MgR \sin \theta = \Omega L^* \sin \theta$$

or

$$\Omega = \frac{MgR}{L^*} = \frac{MgR}{I_0\omega}, \qquad (13\text{–}4)$$

where I_0 is the moment of inertia of the top with respect to its axis of rotation. Note that Ω is independent of the angle θ and that our analysis applies only for sufficiently large values of $\mathbf{L}^*$.

Nutation. As mentioned before, gyroscopes and tops can be made to precess smoothly if their motion is started properly. But *nutations* or vertical oscillations can occur also. Although a detailed analysis of nutation is somewhat complicated, the qualitative features can be understood easily.

Consider for simplicity the case in which initially the axis of the top is horizontal, as in Fig. 13–12, where a spinning bicycle wheel is supported by a pivot at one end of its axis. When the wheel is released from "rest," it initially has only the spin angular momentum $\mathbf{L}^*$. However, as soon as the wheel starts to precess, it will acquire an angular velocity Ω about the

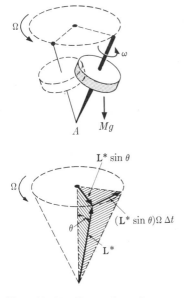

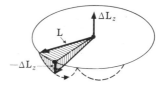

Fig. 13–11. Precession of a top.   Fig. 13–12. Nutation of a gyroscope or a top.

vertical or z-axis. Consequently, there will develop an angular momentum component in the *z-direction* (equal to $I_z\Omega$, where I_z is the moment of inertia of the wheel with respect to the z-axis). This angular-momentum component increases from zero to a certain value during the time it takes for the precession to get started. Therefore during this time there will be a rate of change (dL_z/dt) of the orbital angular-momentum component in the z-direction. However, since there is no external torque component in the z-direction, the rate of change of the *total* angular momentum can have no component in the z-direction. Therefore as the angular momentum develops a component in the z-direction the spin angular momentum must develop a compensating component in the negative z-direction. Therefore the spin axis of the system must turn downward at a rate sufficiently large to compensate for the angular momentum which develops in the positive z-direction because of the precession. If this downward motion of the spin axis were to continue, there would be an overcompensation for the positive angular-momentum component in the z-direction. Therefore the axis turns upward again. If there is no damping in the system, this downward-upward motion will continue in the form of an oscillation, which is the *nutation* of the gyroscope or the top. However, because of friction damping, the nutational oscillations are often damped out after a few oscillation periods, and thereafter the precession of the top proceeds in a "smooth" fashion, as described above.

We can also understand the necessity for this nutation from an energy argument. In the precessional motion of the bicycle wheel of Fig. 13–12 the kinetic energy is somewhat larger than it is for just the stationary, spinning wheel. Therefore, if the spinning wheel is held at rest with its axle horizontal, we can hardly expect it to start off in a pure precessional motion when released. Where would the additional energy come from? Rather, the center of mass of the wheel starts to drop, thereby losing some potential energy, and it is this "lost" potential energy that appears as the precessional kinetic energy. When the nutational oscillations eventually damp out, the precessional motion continues with the axle inclined some-what below the horizontal.

EXAMPLE. *The "gyro-pendulum."* A gyro-pendulum consists of a bar in the form of a T, supported by bearings at the points B and C, as shown in Fig. 13–13. At point A, a distance R from CB, the pendulum carries a thin, circular disc (mass m, radius r) which spins with an angular velocity ω about OA, as indicated. Using the dimensions shown in the figure, we wish to determine the forces on the bearings when the pendulum passes its lowest point after having been released from the angle $\theta = 90°$. We shall neglect the mass of the bar OA.

If we denote the angular velocity of the pendulum at its lowest point by Ω, we can obtain the forces at B and C as follows. The acceleration of the center of mass of the disc at the lowest point is $\Omega^2 R$, directed upward. At the lowest

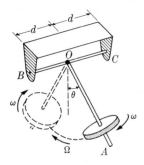

Fig. 13–13. Pendulum with spinning disc (gyro-pendulum).

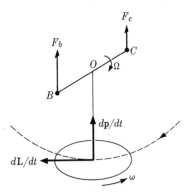

Fig. 13–14. Vector diagram illustrating forces and rates of change of momentum and angular momentum of the gyro-pendulum.

point the spin angular momentum $\mathbf{L}^*$ of the disc points downward, and the magnitude of its rate of change is ΩL^*. The direction of $d\mathbf{L}^*/dt$ is the same as the direction of motion of A, i.e., horizontally toward the left, as shown in Fig. 13–14.

The remaining contribution to the angular momentum of the pendulum with respect to the center of mass or with respect to the axis of rotation has no rate of change at the lowest point. Thus if the vertical components of the forces on the axis BC from the bearings are denoted by F_b and F_c, we get

$$F_b + F_c - mg = m\Omega^2 R,$$

$$(F_b - F_c)\, d = \Omega L^* = I_0\omega\Omega.$$

From these equations, we find

$$F_b = \frac{mg}{2} + \frac{m\Omega^2 R}{2} + \frac{I_0\omega\Omega}{2d}$$

and

$$F_c = \frac{mg}{2} + \frac{m\Omega^2 R}{2} - \frac{I_0\omega\Omega}{2d}.$$

Since there are no other components of $d\mathbf{p}/dt$ and $d\mathbf{L}^*/dt$, we realize that there are no horizontal force components at B and C.

The angular velocity Ω can be found directly from the work-energy principle. The moment of inertia with respect to the axis of rotation, BC, of the disc is obtained from the parallel-axis theorem. The moment of inertia with respect to the center-of-mass axis parallel to CB is $I_0 = mr^2/4$, and therefore we have $I = I_0 + mR^2 = mr^2/4 + mR^2$. The angular velocity is then obtained from $\frac{1}{2}I\Omega^2 = mgR$, and we have

$$\Omega = \sqrt{\frac{8gR}{r^2 + R^2}}.$$

Insertion of this value of Ω into the equations for F_b and F_c gives the final answer.

It is interesting to note that the force on the bearing at C can become zero when the angular velocity of the disc is $\omega = (mg + m\Omega^2 R)\,d/I_0\Omega$. Thus, under such conditions, when the pendulum passes its lowest point the bearing at C can actually be removed for an instant without disturbing the motion.

If instead of a fixed axis of rotation we have a pivot suspension, it is impossible to produce any torque on the pendulum from the suspension to keep the pendulum oscillating in a vertical plane. To make the torque zero at the suspension point, the pendulum has to move out of the vertical plane and describe a precessional motion, usually with strong superimposed nutations, as illustrated schematically in Fig. 13–15.

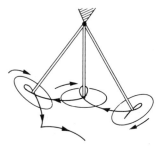

FIG. 13–15. Pivot-suspended gyropendulum with spinning disc.

13–3 Centrifugal torques and principal axes. When a rigid body is made to rotate about a fixed axis there are three basically different sources of bearing forces, i.e., forces which the bearings exert on the rigid body. First there are the forces attributable solely to the weight of the body; these forces are present whether or not the body is rotating. Next, if the center of mass of the body is not on the rotation axis there must be bearing forces that amount to $MA = M\omega^2 R$, since the center of mass has an acceleration $\omega^2 R$, where R is the distance from the axis to the center of mass. From the point of view of a coordinate system rotating with the rigid body, the body is in equilibrium under the influence of the inertial force $M\omega^2 \mathbf{R}$ and the net contact force $\mathbf{F}$ at the axis (neglecting the force due to gravity and other interaction forces) so that $\mathbf{F} = -M\omega^2 \mathbf{R}$, as already mentioned in Chapters 11 and 12. If the center of mass *is* on the axis of rotation, the net centrifugal force is zero but the net *centrifugal torque* need not be zero. In the examples shown in Fig. 13–16, for example, the net centrifugal force is zero in all cases. However, in case (c) a centrifugal torque exists, which of course produces forces at the bearings, whereas in cases (a) and (b) the centrifugal torque is zero. An axis of rotation for which the centrifugal torque is zero is called a *principal axis* of the body.

We can easily calculate the centrifugal torque produced in Fig. 13–16(c) if we assume that the rotating body consists of two mass points A and B at the ends of a massless bar. In a coordinate system rotating with the body let the coordinates of one of the mass points with respect to the

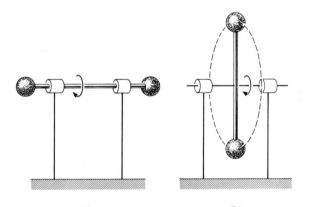

(a)   (b)

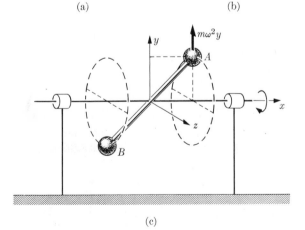

(c)

Fig. 13–16. In (a) and (b) the rigid body rotates about a principal axis and there are no bearing forces.

center of mass be x, y. The body rotates about the x-axis, and the centrifugal force is in the y-direction and has the magnitude $m\omega^2 y$. The z-component of the torque is then $m\omega^2 xy$. The same result is obtained for the other mass point of the body, and the total centrifugal torque with respect to the center of mass is found to be $\tau_z = 2m\omega^2 xy$. This result can easily be generalized to an arbitrary body, as follows.

Imagine a rigid body rotating about a fixed axis which passes through the center of mass (see Fig. 13–17). Let the angular velocity vector coincide with the x-axis. The coordinate system has its origin at the center of

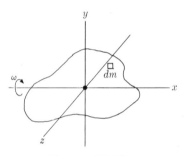

FIGURE 13–17

mass, and rotates *with* the rigid body. The inertial torque contribution from a mass element dm has the z-component $\omega^2 xy\,dm$ and the y-component $\omega^2 zx\,dm$, so that the total torque components are

$$\tau_z = \omega^2 \int xy\,dm \qquad \text{and} \qquad \tau_y = \omega^2 \int zx\,dm. \qquad (13\text{--}5)$$

Clearly, the inertial torque components are zero if

$$\int xy\,dm = 0 \qquad \text{and} \qquad \int zx\,dm = 0.$$

If the body is symmetric with respect to the coordinate axes there are as many positive as negative contributions to the products yx and zx and the centrifugal torque then is zero. Axes of symmetry of this kind are called *principal axes* of the body.

In Fig. 13–18 are shown the principal axes of some simple bodies. When a body rotates about any of these axes there will be no centrifugal torques with respect to the center of mass of the body, and since the principal axes all go through the center of mass the net centrifugal force is also zero. Bodies other than symmetrical bodies like those in Fig. 13–18 possess principal axes. It is always possible, for a body of any arbitrary shape, to find three mutually orthogonal axes through the center of mass with respect to which the products of inertia $\int yz\,dm$,

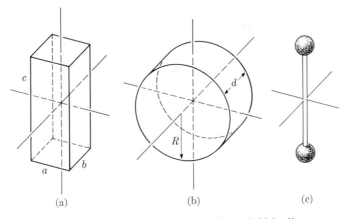

(a)   (b)   (c)

FIG. 13-18. Principal axes of three rigid bodies.

$\int zx\,dm$, and $\int xy\,dm$ are all zero. These axes then are the *principal axes* of the body. For simple homogeneous and symmetrical bodies the principal axes usually can be found directly by inspection. To each principal axis there corresponds a principal moment of inertia which, as we shall see, plays an important role in the description of the general rotational motion of a rigid body.

EXAMPLE. Determine the principal moments of inertia of a thin rectangular plate of mass M, with side lengths a and b.

Two of the principal axes go through the center of the plate and are parallel with the sides of the plate; the third axis is perpendicular to the plate. The moments of inertia with respect to the axes in the plane of the plate are the same as for a slender bar, and we have

$$I_x = M\frac{a^2}{12}, \qquad I_y = M\frac{b^2}{12}.$$

As indicated in Chapter 12 (see Problem 12-11), the third principal moment of inertia in this case is simply

$$I_z = I_x + I_y = M\frac{a^2 + b^2}{12}.$$

13-4 The relation between the angular velocity and the angular momentum of a rigid body. The angular momentum of a mass point, we recall, can be expressed as the vector $\mathbf{r} \times \mathbf{p}$ with respect to the reference point $\mathbf{r} = 0$. The total angular momentum of a rigid body with respect to the center of mass can be expressed as the vector sum of elementary contributions of this type. The resultant angular momentum can be decomposed into components along the axes of a coordinate system which has its origin at the center of mass. In the discussion of motion in a plane in Chapter 12 we were concerned with only one of the angular-momentum components, and in this chapter the real vector nature of angular momentum has been demonstrated in some special examples of motion. These examples were such that the angular-momentum vector and its motion in space were given and the problem was essentially to determine the rate of change of the angular momentum and hence the torque on the body.

In more general types of rigid body motion, however, the angular momentum vector does not always behave in an obvious manner. For example, if we consider a rigid body rotating about a fixed axis, we shall find that only when this axis coincides with one of the principal axes does the angular momentum vector point along the rotation axis. Otherwise it twirls around in space and the angular momentum and angular velocity are not related by just "$L = I\omega$." We shall find, however, that it is possible to express angular momentum in terms of angular velocity if we consider the components of these quantities along the directions of the principal axes of the rigid body. We shall begin the study of these matters by showing that angular velocity can be described as a vector quantity.

Angular velocity as a vector. Imagine a rigid body rotating about its center of mass. In a short interval of time Δt a given point on the rigid body moves along a circle and, since the body is rigid, other points must move (during Δt) along paths which are in parallel planes. The motion is equivalent to rotation about an axis. All points on the axis remain at rest in this motion; in fact, these points define the axis of rotation.

In Fig. 13–19 is shown a sphere of radius a mounted on gimbals. If we rotate the sphere through a small angle about the y-axis, the point P moves a distance Δs_1 to R. If, instead, we rotate the sphere through a small angle about the x-axis, the point P moves a distance Δs_2 to S. When the angles through which we rotate the sphere are small, the displacement Δs of P to Q is the vector sum of Δs_1 and Δs_2, and would be the same whether we rotate first about the x-axis, or first about the y-axis and then about the x-axis, or perform both rotations simultaneously. If we perform both rotations simultaneously, P moves directly to Q and the displacement can be regarded, if we wish, as a result of a rotation about an axis perpendicular to PQ, with angular velocity ω during the time Δt, so that $\Delta s = \omega a \, \Delta t$. Similarly, the displacements PR and PS can be considered to be the results of angular velocities ω_y and ω_x; that is, $\Delta s_1 = \omega_y a \, \Delta t$, $\Delta s_2 = \omega_x a \, \Delta t$. It follows, then, from $\Delta s = \Delta s_1 + \Delta s_2$, that not only the displacements, but also the angular velocities add like vectors.

Note carefully that although angular velocities and infinitesimal angular displacements can be regarded as vectors, finite angular displacements cannot. (Suppose, for example, the displacement PR had carried P around a full quarter-circle!)

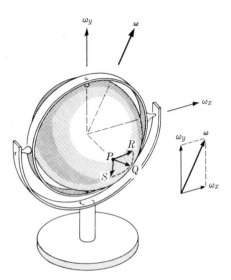

FIG. 13-19. Angular velocity is a vector quantity.

As a rigid body rotates, all points in the body (except those on the axis of rotation) will move, and then velocity can be expressed as

$$\mathbf{v} = \boldsymbol{\omega} \times \mathbf{r}, \tag{13-6}$$

where $\mathbf{r}$ is the position vector of the point with respect to a point on the axis of rotation.

Angular momentum of a rotating rigid body. As an introductory example, let us determine the angular momentum of the simple bodies shown in Fig. 13-16(c) and in Fig. 13-20. We shall consider such a body as two mass points A and B connected by a rigid massless bar. The bar rotates about a nonprincipal axis which makes an angle ϕ with the bar, and the sense of rotation is such that the angular velocity vector is directed toward the right, as shown in Fig. 13-20. The two mass points clearly describe circular paths of radius $r \sin \theta$ if the length of the bar is $2r$. When the mass points are in the position shown in Fig. 13-20, that is, in the plane of the paper, the velocity $\mathbf{v}_a = \boldsymbol{\omega} \times \mathbf{r}_a$ of A is directed out from the plane of the paper and $\mathbf{v}_b$ has the opposite direction. The angular momentum $\mathbf{l}_a = \mathbf{r}_a \times \mathbf{p}_a$ then is in the plane of the paper and is directed as shown. Similarly, the angular momentum of B is $\mathbf{l}_b = \mathbf{r}_b \times \mathbf{p}_b$. The velocity of A has the magnitude $v_a = (r \sin \phi)\omega$, and consequently the magnitude of the angular momentum is $l_a = mr^2\omega \sin \phi$. The magnitude of the total angular momentum then is $L = 2mr^2\omega \sin \phi$.

The magnitude of the angular momentum remains constant but the direction changes continuously as the angular momentum vector rotates

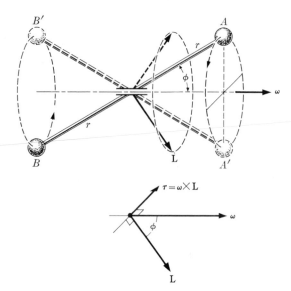

FIG. 13–20. Angular momentum of a body rotating about a nonprincipal axis.

with the body and traces out the surface of a cone, as shown in the figure. The components of the angular-momentum vector parallel and perpendicular to the axis of rotation have the constant magnitudes $L \sin \phi$ and $L \cos \phi$. Only the latter component will change its direction, as it rotates in a plane with an angular velocity ω. The rate of change of the angular momentum produced by this rotation is obtained in the same way as in the case of the precessing gyroscope or the top (see Fig. 13–8), and we obtain

$$\left| \frac{d\mathbf{L}}{dt} \right| = \omega L \cos \phi = 2mr^2\omega^2 \sin \phi \cos \phi.$$

The torque required to maintain this rate of change of angular momentum is $\tau = d\mathbf{L}/dt$, and it is produced by the forces in the bearings. The direction of the torque clearly points in toward the plane of the paper when the body is in the position shown in Fig. 13–20. It is interesting to note that we can express both the magnitude and the direction of the torque in terms of the vector product

$$\boldsymbol{\tau} = \boldsymbol{\omega} \times \mathbf{L}, \tag{13–7}$$

which is also illustrated in the figure.

In anticipation of the following more general discussion of the angular momentum we observe that the expression for the angular momentum, $L = 2mr^2\omega \sin \phi$, can be interpreted as the product of the principal moment of inertia $I_0 = 2mr^2$ and the angular velocity component $\omega \sin \phi$

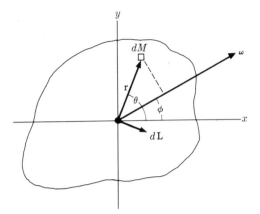

FIG. 13–21.   Each mass element dM has an angular momentum $dL = \omega r^2 \sin (\theta - \phi) \, dM$.

along the principal axis of the body. It will be clear that this interpretation has general validity, so that when the principal moments of inertia of a body are known the angular momentum can be obtained immediately in terms of the angular-velocity components along the principal axes.

To prove this result we study the rotation of a body of arbitrary shape about a fixed axis and derive an expression for the component of the angular momentum along one of the coordinate axis. Unessential complications are avoided if we discuss a two- rather than a three-dimensional body. Thus, in Fig. 13–21 the x- and y-axes are in the plane of the body and go through the center of mass. The angular velocity of the body is ω and makes an angle ϕ with the x-axis, as shown. A mass element dM with the position vector $\mathbf{r}$ has a velocity $\boldsymbol{\omega} \times \mathbf{r}$ of magnitude $\omega r \sin (\theta - \phi)$; an angular momentum, with respect to the center of mass, $d\mathbf{L} = (\mathbf{r} \times \mathbf{v}) \, dM$, of magnitude $dL = \omega r^2 \sin (\theta - \phi) \, dM$; and a direction perpendicular to $\mathbf{r}$, as shown. The x- and y-components of the angular momentum are then $dL_x = (dL) \sin \theta$ and $dL_y = -(dL) \cos \theta$. For the x-component of the total angular momentum we obtain

$$L_x = \int \omega r^2 \sin \theta (\sin \theta \cos \phi - \cos \theta \sin \phi) \, dM$$
$$= \omega \cos \phi \int y^2 \, dM - \omega \sin \phi \int xy \, dM.$$

If we choose the coordinate system so that x, y, and z coincide with the *principal axes*, the second term is zero and the x-component of the angular momentum is $L_x = \omega_x I_x$, where $\omega_x = \omega \cos \theta$ is the component of ω along the x-axis and $I_x = \int y^2 \, dM$ is the moment of inertia of the rigid body about the x-axis. [For a three-dimensional rigid body I_x would be $\int (y^2 + z^2) \, dM$.] Thus, the angular-momentum components *along the principal axes* of the body are related to the angular-velocity components along the same axes in the following simple way:

$$L_x = I_x\omega_x, \qquad L_y = I_y\omega_y, \qquad L_z = I_z\omega_z. \qquad (13\text{–}8)$$

Next we wish to find the torque that must be exerted to keep the rigid body rotating with the angular velocity $\boldsymbol{\omega}$. The angular-momentum vector $\mathbf{L}$ of the rigid body will rotate with the body's angular velocity $\boldsymbol{\omega}$, and we have $\boldsymbol{\tau} = d\mathbf{L}/dt = \boldsymbol{\omega} \times \mathbf{L}$, according to an observer at rest. The z-component of the torque is $\tau_z = \omega_x L_y - \omega_y L_x$. If the coordinate axes coincide with the principal axes we have $L_y = I_y\omega_y$ and $L_x = I_x\omega_x$, and we get

$$\tau_z = I_y\omega_x\omega_y - I_x\omega_y\omega_x = \omega_x\omega_y(I_y - I_x), \qquad (13\text{–}9)$$

and similarly for the x- and y-components. From (13–9) we see that τ_z is zero if either ω_x or ω_y is zero. If $\omega_y = 0$ the rotation is about the x-axis, which is a principal axis, and thus we see that the expression (13–9) properly gives zero torque for rotation about a principal axis. Further, τ_z is zero if $I_y - I_x$ is zero. This difference is zero, for example, for a square plate rotating about *any* center-of-mass axis in the plane of the plate, and is similarly zero for other bodies having a high degree of symmetry.

EXAMPLE. A rectangular plate rotates about an axis along its diagonal (see Fig. 13–22). What is the torque on the plate? The angular velocity has components $\omega_x = \omega \sin\theta$ and $\omega_y = \omega \cos\theta$, where $\tan\theta = b/a$. The moments of inertia of the plate are $I_x = Ma^2/12$ and $I_y = Mb^2/12$. The torque τ_z is therefore

$$\tau_z = \omega_x\omega_y(I_y - I_x) = \omega^2 \sin\theta \cos\theta \left(\frac{Mb^2}{12} - \frac{Ma^2}{12}\right).$$

This torque is produced by equal and opposite forces on the shaft from the two bearings shown in the figure.

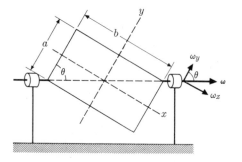

FIG. 13–22. Example.

In the foregoing discussion we have seen that when a rigid body rotates about a fixed nonprincipal axis, the angular-momentum vector will not be in the direction of the angular velocity. The angle between the vectors, in the case of a two-dimensional body, can be found from Eq. (13–8), from which we have $L_y/L_x = (I_y/I_x)(\omega_y/\omega_x)$. Consequently, if the angular-velocity vector makes an angle ϕ with the x-axis (which is a principal axis), the angle ϕ_1 between the angular-momentum vector and the x-axis is given by $\tan \phi_1 = (I_y/I_x) \tan \phi$, and the angle between the two vectors is $\phi_1 - \phi$. This angle will be zero if $\phi = 0$, that is, when the body rotates about a principal axis (the x-axis), and also in the special case when $I_x = I_y$. Then, if the angular-velocity vector is fixed, as in the case when the body rotates about a fixed axis, the angular-momentum vector will rotate (precess) about the angular-velocity vector, and although the magnitude may be constant the direction of the angular momentum changes continuously. The corresponding rate of change of the angular momentum requires that a torque $\tau = \omega \times L$ act continuously on the body.

On the other hand, if the body rotates freely in space about a nonprincipal axis, with no external torque acting, the direction (and magnitude) of the angular-momentum vector will stay fixed and the instantaneous axis of rotation of the body will whirl (precess) about the angular-momentum vector. This is the reason for the wobbling type of motion observed when an object, for example a tennis racket, is thrown. Only if the object is made to rotate about one of its principal axes will the rotation be "smooth."

Kinetic energy of a rotating rigid body. The kinetic energy of a rigid body rotating with angular velocity ω is, of course, $I\omega^2/2$, where I is the moment of inertia about the rotation axis. But, as with angular momentum, it is convenient to express the kinetic energy simply in terms of the angular-velocity components and moments of inertia about the principal axes.

The kinetic energy of the mass element dM of Fig. 13–21 is $dE = \omega^2 r^2 \sin^2 (\theta - \phi) \, dM/2$. When this is expanded, we obtain

$$E = \omega_x^2 \int y^2 \, dM + \omega_y^2 \int x^2 \, dM - 2\omega_x\omega_y \int xy \, dM. \qquad (13\text{–}10)$$

Because we have agreed to have our coordinate system coincide with the principal axes, the last term is zero, while the first two integrals are just I_x and I_y respectively. In general, then, we have

$$E = \tfrac{1}{2}I_x\omega_x^2 + \tfrac{1}{2}I_y\omega_y^2 + \tfrac{1}{2}I_z\omega_z^2, \qquad (13\text{–}11)$$

where I_x for a three-dimensional body would be $\int (y^2 + z^2) \, dM$, etc.

EXAMPLE. Find the kinetic energy of the rotating plate of Fig. 13–22.

We can certainly find the kinetic energy of this plate by integrating over the kinetic energy contribution of each mass element. It is easier, however, to find the components of the angular velocity $\boldsymbol{\omega}$ along the principal axes of the body. These components are $\omega_x = \omega \sin \phi$ and $\omega_y = \omega \cos \phi$. Then, since I_x is $Ma^2/12$ and I_y is $Mb^2/12$, the kinetic energy is

$$E = \frac{Ma^2b^2\omega^2}{12(a^2 + b^2)}.$$

"Stability" of rotation. No physical body is really rigid, and this fact has interesting consequences when bodies such as space vehicles are torque-free for long periods of time.

Consider, for example, a long uniform metal cylinder which rotates initially about its longitudinal axis (Fig. 13–23). The metal of the cylinder is subject to centrifugal forces directed radially outward. These inertial forces tend to distort or stress the body somewhat, but so long as the rotation is only about the longitudinal axis (a principal axis) the stresses are constant and no energy is lost. If, on the other hand, the cylinder's motion is not a pure rotation about a principal axis, these inertial or "body" forces are not constant. Then a given mass element may be pushed one way at one instant and another way the next. These *changing* body forces and deformations produce energy losses because of internal friction and the kinetic energy of rotation is reduced accordingly. (Recall that a piece of iron gets hot when bent back and forth many times.)

While these changing body forces can reduce the rotational kinetic energy, they *cannot* change the angular momentum of a torque-free body. The only way a torque-free body can have a decreasing kinetic energy and yet a constant angular momentum is for it to have a motion which tends more and more to be a pure rotation about the principal axis having the largest moment of inertia. That is, expressed in terms of the angular momentum, the kinetic energy (for rotation about a principal axis) is $E = L^2/2I$. If E decreases while L remains constant, I must increase.

These phenomena have been observed in the motions of some earth satellites. Rocket-shaped satellites are intentionally made to spin about a

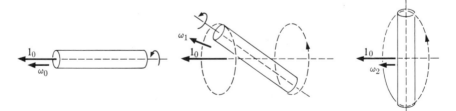

FIGURE 13–23

longitudinal axis at launching. Then the angular-momentum and angular-velocity vectors are parallel, for the longitudinal axis is a principal axis. If the moment of inertia about this principal axis is I_0, the angular momentum is $L_0 = I_0\omega_0$ and the kinetic energy is $E_0 = I_0\omega_0^2/2 = L_0^2/2I_0$.

For a variety of reasons this initial spin is never *exactly* along the principal axis, and the changing body forces cause the kinetic energy to decrease somewhat. Then the satellite starts to precess. The rotation is no longer even approximately about a principal axis and the body axis and angular velocity vector whirl about the *constant* angular-momentum vector. Finally (in several days) the motion reverts to a pure rotation about a principal axis. Then the angular-velocity and angular-momentum vectors are again parallel. The angular momentum is just as it was initially, for the motion is torque-free, but the angular velocity and kinetic energy are smaller. Because the motion is a pure rotation about a principal axis, the body forces (centrifugal inertial forces) are constant and the kinetic energy can decrease no more. It is for these reasons that rotation about the principal axis having the largest moment of inertia is said to be stable, for a torque-free body made of any real material will always finally attain this type of motion.

Problems

13–1. A mass m_1 on the end of a string of length d rotates about a fixed point in a horizontal plane with an angular velocity ω (Fig. 13–24). As the mass crosses the y-axis it collides with a second mass m_2 which moves parallel to the z-axis. After this collision, the velocity of the second mass, which was originally $v = \omega\,d/2$, becomes $\omega\,d/4$; it is deflected 45° but still travels in a plane parallel to the xz-plane. (a) What is the angular momentum of each of the two masses before collision? What is the total angular momentum? (b) What is the angular impulse imparted to the first mass? What is the angular impulse imparted to the second mass? (c) What is the total angular momentum after the collision? (d) What is the orienta-

angular velocity ω, what impulses must be applied to the shaft, at a distance d from the bearing, in order that the plane of rotation will change by an angle θ and still have the center of mass of the system remain at rest?

13–3. A uniform disc of radius R and mass m, mounted at its center on a universal bearing, rotates originally in a horizontal plane with an angular velocity ω (Fig. 13–25). A mass m with velocity $v = \omega R/2$ directed along the z-axis collides with the edge of the disc and rebounds with an equal but oppositely directed velocity. (a) What is the angular momentum of the disc and of the mass before collision? (b) What angular impulses are imparted to the disc and to the mass? (c) What is the angular momentum of the disc after the collision?

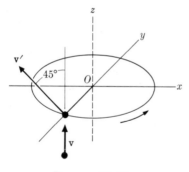

FIGURE 13–24

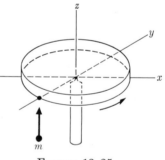

FIGURE 13–25

tion of the new plane of the motion of mass m_1? (e) Why must the angular momentum about O be conserved? Is there any other such point?

13–2. A dumbbell consists of two particles, each of mass m, on the ends of a rod of negligible mass and length d (see Fig. 13–6). The rod has a bearing mounted at its center and is free to turn in a plane perpendicular to a supporting shaft. If the rod has an

13–4. A man stands on a turntable that is free to rotate about a vertical axis and holds in his hands a spinning bicycle wheel, as indicated in Fig. 13–26. When the spin axis of the wheel is horizontal the man is at rest. Discuss what happens: (a) When the man changes the angle of inclination of the spin axis with the horizontal plane. (b) When the spin axis is turned in a horizontal plane. (c) If

FIGURE 13-26

the man stops the rotation of the wheel when it is vertical.

13-5. A gyroscope consists of a uniform circular disc of mass $M = 1$ kgm and radius $R = 0.2$ m. The disc spins with an angular velocity $\omega = 400$ sec^{-1}. The gyroscope precesses, with the axis making an angle of 30° with the horizontal, as shown in Fig. 13-27. The gyroscope is pivoted about a point a distance $d = 0.3$ m from the center of the disc. What is the precessional angular velocity?

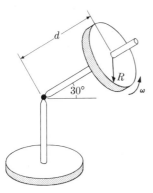

FIGURE 13-27

13-6. What is the precessional angular velocity of a solid sphere mounted on an axis along a diameter and free to pivot about a point on the axis at the sphere's surface? Let the rota-

tional angular velocity of the sphere be ω. Would your answer be the same if the sphere were just a shell rather than a solid object?

13-7. When mounted in a good set of bearings the speed of a small wheel of mass 100 gm and moment of inertia 400 gm·cm^2 will decrease from 6000 to 1000 rev/min in one hour. (a) What torque do the bearings exert on the rotating wheel? (Assume the torque to be constant.) (b) Suppose bearings of the same type are used to construct gimbals for the above wheel, and the gyroscope is then mounted on a rotating table and its spin axis lined up with north. In what direction will the gyroscope spin axis point after 1 hour? Assume that the wheel now rotates at a constant angular velocity of 6000 rev/min (it may be driven by a small motor) and that the gimbal torque is the same as that found in part (a).

13-8. Consider a pendulum consisting of a thin bar which can rotate about a horizontal axis through its upper end, as shown in Fig. 13-28. At its other end the bar supports a disc of radius R and mass m which spins with a constant angular velocity ω about a horizontal axis through its center. The mass of the bar may be neglected. (a) The pendulum is released from its horizontal position. What must be the magnitude and direction of the spin angular velocity of the disc to make the total angular

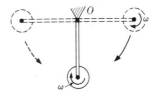

FIGURE 13-28

momentum of the pendulum, with respect to the point O, be zero at the lowest point of the pendulum? Assume that the pendulum swing is from right to left. (b) What is the total angular momentum of the pendulum about O when it swings from left to right through its lowest point?

13–9. Consider again the pendulum of Problem 13–8, but now let the disc spin about the axis of the bar (Fig. 13–29). If the angular velocity of the disc is ω, what now is the total angular momentum at the lowest point of the pendulum?

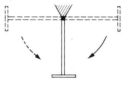

FIGURE 13–29

13–10. Let the pendulum in Problem 13–9 perform circular pendulum motion, as shown in Fig. 13–30. (a) What is the total angular momentum of the pendulum with respect to A when its angular velocity is Ω and the angle between the pendulum and the vertical is θ? (b) Discuss the effect of the directions of motion of the pendulum and the disc.

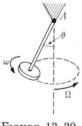

FIGURE 13–30

13–11. A small motor is to be mounted with its axis perpendicular to the spin axis of a satellite. The rotor of the motor has a mass m and radius of gyration k, and the bearings on which the rotor is mounted are a distance d apart. If the motor's angular velocity is ω_1, how large can ω_2, the satellite's spin angular velocity, be if the force on the motor bearings is not to exceed twice the value of the bearing forces when the motor is run in the laboratory?

13–12. A rigid body consists of three spheres, each of mass m and radius r, which are located at the corners of a massless equilateral triangle. The distance between the centers of the spheres is $6r$. Determine the principal moments of inertia of the body.

13–13. (a) Determine the principal moments of inertia of the bodies shown in Fig. 13–18(b) and (c). (b) What should be the dimensions of a solid uniform right circular cylinder in order that the moments of inertia about the three principal axes be equal?

13–14. An earth satellite weighs 24 lb and is spherical. (Assume uniform density.) The radius of the satellite is 12 in., and initially the sphere spins about a diameter at 8 rev/sec. It is desired to have a spin rate of only 0.1 rev/sec after the satellite is in orbit, and it is proposed that four $\frac{1}{2}$-lb weights be ejected on strings in order to increase the moment of inertia and so decrease the spin rate. (a) How far from the center would the weights have to be, if previously they were at the sphere's surface? (Assume the weights to be point masses.) (b) Do you think the proposal is a sensible one? Consider the kinetic energy, and propose a method for solving the problem it raises. (c) What would happen if three of the four weights failed to be released?

13–15. Three weights of 8, 16, and 24 lb respectively are mounted on rods and an axle of negligible mass (Fig. 13-31). (a) Where should the 24-lb weight be positioned in order that the system be statically balanced (center of mass on the axis)? (b) With the system statically balanced and with $x = 1$ ft, find the angular momentum with respect to the center of mass if the system is turning at $\omega = 10$ sec. (c) What is the bearing torque under these conditions? (d) Where should the 24-lb weight be positioned in order that the system be dynamically balanced (inertial force and torque equal to zero)?

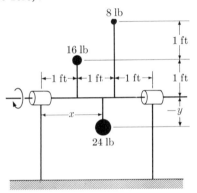

FIGURE 13-31

13-16. A uniform slender rod of mass M and length d is mounted at its center of mass on an axis inclined 45° to its length. What is the bearing torque if this rod rotates at angular velocity ω?

13-17. A slender rod of mass M and length d is suspended from the ceiling by a point suspension through one end. The rod is given an initial motion which makes its lower end describe a circular path with an angular velocity ω. (a) What is the direction of the angular-velocity vector? (b) If the angle between the vertical and the rod axis is θ, what are the components of

ω along the principal axes? (c) What is the angular momentum of the rod with respect to the point of suspension? (d) What is the rate of change of the angular momentum?

13-18. An earth satellite weighs 100 lb and has the shape of a cylinder 6 ft long and 1 ft in diameter. Assume the mass distribution within the cylinder to be uniform. Initially the satellite spins about its longitudinal axis with a speed of 10 rev/sec. (a) What are the principal axes and what are the corresponding moments of inertia? (b) What are the initial values of the rotational kinetic energy and angular momentum? (c) After a long time, the satellite rotates about its principal axis of largest moment of inertia. What then is the rotational speed and the rotational kinetic energy? (d) Would the dissipated kinetic energy raise the temperature of the satellite significantly?

13-19. In Chapter 11 it was shown that if the time rate of change of a vector $\mathbf{A}$ is $(d\mathbf{A}/dt)_{S'}$ with respect to a coordinate system S' rotating with a constant angular velocity ω, the rate of change of the same vector with respect to a fixed coordinate system S is $(d\mathbf{A}/dt)_S = (d\mathbf{A}/dt)_{S'} + (\omega \times \mathbf{A})$. Apply this result to the angular-momentum vector and determine the inertial torque on a spinning body in the coordinate system S'. Analyze the problem illustrated in Fig. 13-7 in the text from this point of view.

13-20. It is known that the spin angular momentum of the earth does not stay absolutely fixed in space but has a slight precession. Consequently there must be a torque on the earth with respect to its center of mass. (a) Describe how it is possible that the sun's gravitational field can produce this torque and (b) estimate the magnitude of the torque. (c) Then estimate the precessional angular velocity of the earth.

13–21. A huge meteor from outer space strikes the earth at the North Pole, making an angle θ with the earth's axis. The meteor has a mass 1/100 that of the earth, and has escape velocity. Will this impact disturb the earth's rotational motion? In what way? You may assume the earth to be a homogeneous sphere and ignore the influence of the meteor on the earth's moment of inertia.

CHAPTER 14

TEMPERATURE AND HEAT

Summary. The concepts of temperature and heat were developed originally from macroscopic effects, and the connection with molecular motion and energy was established later. Some of the subjects dealt with in this chapter are the operational definition of temperature, linear expansion-type thermometers, the constant-volume gas thermometer, and the absolute temperature scale. Thermal interaction experiments then lead to the ideas of thermal equilibrium, specific heat, and the mechanisms of heat transfer: conduction, convection, and radiation. The chapter is concluded with a short historical note.

In previous chapters we have been concerned, for the most part, with the gross motion of matter, i.e., the motion described by the translation of the center of mass and rotation about the center of mass. We have not been particularly concerned with the possible internal motion of the elementary particles of which matter is made or with properties of matter itself. In this and the following several chapters we shall study some of the macroscopic (gross) properties of matter and the microscopic (atomistic) explanation of these properties.

We are probably all aware that the molecules in matter are not at rest but are in continuous motion with respect to each other. In a gas the molecules fly about over the entire available volume, whereas in a solid the molecules oscillate, or vibrate, about equilibrium positions. We shall find in our later work that *temperature* is a measure of the *average translational* energy per molecule and that *heat* or heat content is a measure of the *total* molecular energy (including rotational and vibrational energy). The connections between the macroscopic concepts of temperature and heat and the microscopic concepts of molecular motion developed gradually. This development followed a very intricate path that is one of the most fascinating parts of the history of physics.* Some historical highlights are presented in a later section.

---

* See *Harvard Case Histories in Experimental Science,* Vol. I, edited by James B. Conant, Harvard University Press, Cambridge, Mass. (1957). In particular, Case 1, "Robert Boyle's Experiments in Pneumatics," Case 3, "The Early Development of the Concepts of Temperature and Heat," and Case 4, "The Atomic-Molecular Theory," are the most pertinent to the discussions in this chapter.

In this chapter we shall be concerned primarily with the macroscopic aspects of temperature and heat. (The reader may nonetheless find it helpful to keep the molecular motion, i.e., the microscopic interpretation, of these concepts in mind.) Temperature and heat must be carefully distinguished from each other. Temperature is an intensive property of a body, while heat is an extensive property. If a quart of water at 50°C is separated into two pints, each pint remains at the original 50°C temperature. (Temperature, we recall, is a measure of the *average* translational energy per molecule.) But the heat content of a pint of 50°C water is just half the heat content of a quart of 50°C water. (Heat is a measure of total molecular energy, and there are twice as many molecules in a pint of water as there are in a quart.)

14-1 Temperature. Temperature, like length, time, and mass, must be defined operationally, and we are led to say that temperature is what one measures with a thermometer. But what is a thermometer and how is it calibrated?

Consider first a thermometer based upon the linear expansion of mercury, water, alcohol, or even a metal. The temperature scale of such an instrument can be established with the help of two reference baths. Melting ice and boiling water are most convenient, and the expansion of the thermometric substance can be measured when the device is placed first in the cold bath and then in the hot. This expansion can then be divided into a number of equal parts called *degrees*. [We shall, for the most part, use the celsius* (centigrade) scale, for which the temperatures of the reference baths are taken as 0°C and 100°C respectively. For the fahrenheit† scale, the two reference baths are taken as 32°F and 212°F, respectively. One fahrenheit degree is therefore only 5/9 as large as one celsius degree.]

Thermometers using different thermometric substances must obviously agree when compared at the 0 and 100°C points, because of the very procedure used in establishing the scales. But they do not necessarily agree when compared at intermediate temperatures. The discrepancies at intermediate temperatures are caused by the different rates of expansion of various liquids or solids in different temperature regions. Our choice of a particular thermometric substance for the definition of the temperature scale would therefore be somewhat arbitrary. From this point of view, we shall find that a gas is much more satisfactory than other thermometric substances.

---

* A. C. Celsius, Swedish astronomer (1701–1744).
† G. D. Fahrenheit, German physicist (1686–1736).

14–2 The gas thermometer and the absolute temperature scale. While the rates of expansion with temperature of liquids and solids vary, the behavior of all gases tends to be the same under certain conditions. Before discussing the details of the gas thermometer, let us pause briefly to review the idea of gas pressure and its measurement.

The pressure in a gas. The pressure in a gas (or in a liquid) is the force per unit area on the wall of a container of the gas, or on any other surface in the gas. If a small test plate is inserted in the gas, we find that the gas will exert no net force on the plate, and the pressure on one side of the plate is balanced by the pressure on the other side, as illustrated schematically in Fig. 14–1(a). Then, in order to be able to measure the pressure with a force-measuring device such as a coil spring, it is necessary to eliminate the gas on one side of the plate. This can be done by enclosing and evacuating one side of the plate. In this way, a pressure-measuring device (manometer) is obtained, as shown in Fig. 14–1(b). In this device, an assumed weightless movable piston is held by a coil spring in a position such that it blocks one end of an evacuated cylinder. The spring is calibrated so that the displacement of the piston from its equilibrium position immediately determines the external force and consequently the pressure on the piston. The behavior of this pressure device is, of course, quite similar to the well-known demonstration of the buckling of a tin can, caused by the external atmospheric pressure as some of the air inside the can is pumped out.

A basic property of pressure can now be determined immediately. Turning the pressure probe in Fig. 14–1 in any direction shows that the pressure

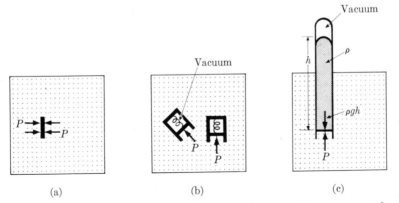

(a)   (b)   (c)

Fɪɢ. 14–1. (a) When a test plate is inserted into a gas, there is no net force exerted on it by the gas. (b) If on one side of the plate is an evacuated chamber, the pressure in the gas can be measured, in principle, by means of a spring. (c) The spring force can be replaced by the weight of a liquid column that produces a force $\rho g h$ per unit area. This also serves to measure the pressure in the gas.

in a gas or a liquid is independent of the direction of the surface upon which the pressure is detected. When the piston points downward, we find the same pressure as when it points upward. The piston clearly can be held in equilibrium by balancing the gas pressure by a force other than the spring force. For example, with the piston pointing downward, we can replace the spring force by the weight of a liquid column, for example a column of water or mercury, as illustrated schematically in Fig. 14–1(c). If the height of the liquid column required for equilibrium is h, a force $\rho g h$ is produced by the liquid per unit area of the piston, where ρ is the mass density of the liquid and g is the acceleration due to gravity. This force per unit area then equals the pressure which was to be measured. This method of measuring pressure is very often employed. In fact, pressure is frequently expressed in terms of centimeters of mercury. (Atmospheric pressure, for example, is approximately 76 cm of mercury.)

In the next chapter we shall see that from a molecular standpoint, gas pressure is a result of collisions between the gas molecules and the container walls, or any other surface in the gas. In Chapter 3, we discussed the force produced by a stream of particles, and gave the essentials of the relation between molecular motion and pressure. The magnitude of the force, and consequently the gas pressure, was shown to be proportional to the square of the translational speed of the molecules and the number of molecules per unit volume. Therefore, when the number of molecules is kept constant (constant volume of the gas), the pressure depends only on the average squared translational speed (or, better, the average translational kinetic energy) of the molecules.

The gas thermometer. The thermometer used to define temperature in terms of gas pressure is shown schematically in Fig. 14–2. This instrument is called a constant-volume gas thermometer. Although all gases tend to behave alike at sufficiently low pressures and high temperatures, hydrogen has been chosen as the standard gas in the thermometer, both because it liquefies at a very low temperature and because it is easily available in a pure form. The volume of gas in the bulb and in the adjoining tube is held constant and level with the mark A by adjusting the mercury level to A. The region above B is evacuated, and the pressure in the bulb is determined by h, the separation between the levels B and A.

The scale of the gas thermometer is now obtained in the following way. The gas bulb is dipped into a bath of melting ice, and the pressure P_0 is measured. Next, the bulb is dipped into a bath of boiling water, and the new pressure P_{100} is measured. The pressure scale between P_0 and P_{100} is divided into 100 equal parts. A pressure increase equal to $(P_{100} - P_0)/100$ is then chosen to represent one unit of temperature, i.e., one degree celsius.

This procedure can be illustrated graphically as in Fig. 14–3, where we

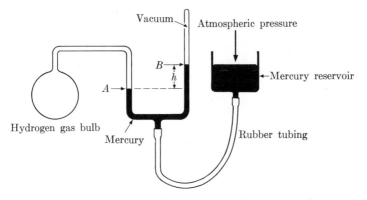

FIG. 14–2. Constant-volume gas thermometer. To measure the temperature of a particular environment, the gas bulb is located in this environment. The mercury reservoir is then moved until the mercury level in the left-hand capillary is at a fixed mark, A. This mark defines the constant volume. The distance h between A and B then determines the pressure of the gas, $P = \rho g h$. For a given apparatus, the pressure P defines the temperature.

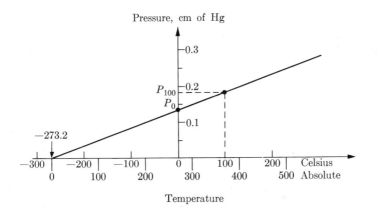

FIG. 14–3. Calibration of a constant-volume gas thermometer. The pressure of the gas, at temperatures at which ice melts and water boils, is measured. The pressure ratio is found to be $P_{100}/P_0 \simeq 1.366$. The temperatures of these two baths are taken, by definition, to be 100° apart. The straight line through these two points then defines the temperature scale. The absolute, or kelvin, temperature scale is zero at the point at which the straight line intercepts the temperature axis.

have designated the vertical scale as pressure and the horizontal scale as temperature. By definition, on the celsius scale the temperature of ice is 0°C and that of boiling water is 100°C, thus the pressures P_0 and P_{100} may be plotted. A straight line that passes through these two points then establishes and defines the temperature scale. When the bulb is placed in an environment of unknown temperature, the pressure can be measured, and the temperature is defined by the graph.

The slope of the straight line in Fig. 14–3 is determined by the *measured* pressures P_0 and P_{100}. For hydrogen, careful measurements of the ratio P_{100}/P_0 have given the value 1.366, and so the slope of the line for hydrogen is defined by $(P_{100} - P_0)/100 = 0.366P_0/100 = P_0/273.2$. In other words, the straight line of Fig. 14–3 intersects the temperature axis at $-273.2°C$ and, taken literally, this would imply that a gas at $-273.2°C$ would exert no pressure and would correspond to zero speed of the molecules. The relation between pressure and temperature, measured in degrees celsius, can then be expressed algebraically as

$$P = \frac{P_0}{273.2} t + P_0 = \frac{P_0}{273.2} (t + 273.2) \qquad (14\text{--}1)$$

or

$$t + 273.2 = \frac{P}{P_0} 273.2.$$

The absolute temperature scale. If we move the zero point on the temperature scale from the freezing-water point to $-273.2°C$, we obtain a new scale, called the *absolute temperature scale*. The relation between the corresponding absolute, or *kelvin*,* temperature T and the celsius temperature is then

$$T = t + 273.2,$$

as indicated in Fig. 14–3. From Eq. (14–1) and Fig. 14–3, it follows that the absolute temperature is directly proportional to the pressure, i.e.,

$$T = \frac{P}{P_0} 273.2. \qquad (14\text{--}2)$$

Note that the size of the unit of temperature is the same on both scales; that is, there are 100° between the points which correspond to freezing and boiling water. To signify that a temperature is expressed in terms of the absolute, or kelvin, scale, either $T°$ abs or $T°K$ may be written. (The letter T will not be reserved solely for the absolute temperature, but will be used to signify temperature in general.)

In comparison with liquid and solid thermometers, the gas thermometer is particularly useful because its temperature scale, for any gas of sufficiently small density, is found to be consistent throughout the entire range. In other words, the ratio between the pressures at the boiling and freezing points of water, $P_{100}/P_0 \simeq 1.366$, is the same for all gases. We recall that this measured ratio provides the basis for the establishment

_____

* William Thomson Kelvin, British mathematician and physicist (1824–1907).

of the temperature scale as a whole and of the absolute zero point at
−273.2°C. By our statement that the temperature scale based on different gases has been found to be consistent throughout the "entire range,"
we imply, of course, that the temperatures to which we refer are higher
than that of the condensation point of the gas. For the measurement of
temperatures below the condensation point of the thermometer gas (for
hydrogen, about 20°K), it is clear that the gas thermometer cannot be
used and that the temperature scale must be redefined, as will be discussed
in Chapter 19.

A thermometer that uses a liquid or solid substance can be calibrated
in terms of the gas thermometer by placing it, together with a gas thermometer, in a variable temperature bath. The points corresponding to

Table 14-1

Temperature, °K	Phenomena
0	Absolute zero
~0.005	Lowest attained in laboratory
1	Helium freezes under pressure
4	Helium boils
20	Hydrogen boils
45	Surface of the planet Pluto
90	Oxygen boils
234	Mercury melts
273.2	Water freezes
373	Water boils
900	Steam turbine
2000	Iron melts
3000	Tungsten-lamp filament
4500	Carbon boils
6000–10,000	Stellar surfaces
6170	Tungsten boils
15,000	Almost all substances fully ionized
25,000	Shock wave with a speed 20 times the speed of sound
300,000	Atomic-bomb fireball, 45 ft in diameter
10^6	Solar corona
10^7–10^8	Stellar interior
10^8	Hydrogen bomb

0°C and 100°C agree, of course, if they have been used as reference points in the construction of the scales of the thermometers, but at other temperatures some deviations may occur. As it happens, an uncorrected mercury-in-glass thermometer reads about 0.1°C too high at 50°C.

Range of temperatures. In modern scientific and engineering investigations the range of temperatures encountered is tremendous. However, there is a definite limit on how low temperatures may be, although there is no apparent limit on high temperatures. A representative scale of the range of temperatures for various phenomena is given in Table 14–1.

14–3 Thermal equilibrium. Specific heat. Heat measurements (calorimetry).

We shall now proceed to investigate the interaction of bodies that have different temperatures. Since here we are not interested in the gross motion of the bodies, we shall consider them to be at rest. Our interest lies in the interactions between the thermal or molecular motions within the bodies. Consider the situation in which a hot body, i.e., a collection of fast-moving molecules, is brought into contact with a cold body, in which the molecules move slowly. We expect that the slower molecules will gain speed and that faster molecules will lose speed until some kind of equilibrium is reached. In other words, thermal energy (heat) will "flow" from the hotter body to the colder one, until a state of equilibrium is reached. We wish to find the temperatures of the bodies before and after such an interaction.

Specific heat. Let us now discuss the experimental results obtained by experiments on thermal interaction. Two bodies that initially have different temperatures are brought into contact, and it is noted that they tend to assume a common intermediate temperature. The temperature changes do not occur instantaneously, but usually take place gradually. The speed with which this change occurs depends upon the nature of the contact, upon the shapes and sizes of the bodies, and upon the materials of which the bodies are comprised. During the time that the temperature of a body is changing, various parts of the body have different temperatures. When the temperature of a body does not change with time, the body is said to be in *thermal equilibrium.* For now, we shall concern ourselves with the temperatures of bodies only after they are in thermal equilibrium.

In the first set of experiments, we shall use bodies of the *same* material but with *different* initial temperatures. As the bodies contact each other, they approach a common final equilibrium temperature, say T_f, and the temperature changes are found to be inversely proportional to the respective masses of the bodies. Hence, we have $m_a \Delta T_a = -m_b \Delta T_b$, where $\Delta T_a = T_f - T_a$ is the temperature change of body A, and $\Delta T_b = T_f - T_b$ is the temperature change of body B.

When two bodies of *unlike* material are brought in thermal contact, factors other than mass are influential in determining the temperature changes. For example, when thermal experiments are conducted with equal-mass bodies of lead and copper, the temperature change of the lead is found to be about three times that of the copper; when thermal experiments are conducted using equal masses of water and copper, the temperature change of the copper is found to be about eleven times that of the water; and when similar experiments are conducted using lead and water, the temperature change of the lead is found to be thirty-three times that of the water. In a sense, 1 gm of lead "acts like" only 1/33 gm of water, and 1 gm of copper acts like only 1/11 gm of water. Further experiments reveal that 33 gm of lead act like 1 gm of water, etc. We are therefore led to the definition of a quantity which measures the "effectiveness" of a material in thermal experiments. This quantity is called the *specific heat, c*. The ratio between the specific heats of two bodies is defined by the ratio of the temperature changes experienced when two bodies of equal mass are brought into thermal contact. Thus, if the temperature changes of two bodies A and B with equal masses are found to be ΔT_a and ΔT_b, the ratio between the specific heats c_a and c_b is defined as

$$\frac{c_a}{c_b} = -\frac{\Delta T_b}{\Delta T_a} \qquad (m_a = m_b).$$

Consequently, if the specific heat of water is set equal to unity, the specific heats of lead and copper are 1/33 and 1/11, respectively, according to experimental results. We can now proceed to determine the specific heats of other liquid and solid substances, some of which are indicated in Table 14–2. Specific heats of some gases will be given in Chapter 16, Table 16–2.

Table 14–2. Specific heats of some familiar liquids and solids, determined relative to the specific heat of water at 15°C.

Liquids		Solids	
Acetone	0.53	Iron	0.55
Benzene	0.41	Aluminum	0.21
Methyl alcohol	0.60	Copper	0.092
Mineral oil	0.5	Lead	0.031
Water	1 at 15°C	Ice	0.48 at −20°C
		Glass	0.093
		Asbestos	0.20
		Silver	0.056

Further thermal interaction experiments with bodies of different specific heats and masses show that the corresponding temperature changes obtained are related by the equation

$$m_a c_a \, \Delta T_a = -m_b c_b \, \Delta T_b$$

or

$$m_a c_a (T_f - T_a) = -m_b c_b (T_f - T_b), \qquad (14\text{--}3)$$

as was to be expected from our previous discussion and experimental results.

EXAMPLE. A 500-gm piece of aluminum at 300°C is plunged into one liter of water at 20°C. With the assumption that no heat leaks from the system, what is the temperature of the water-aluminum system when thermal equilibrium has been reached?

With the equilibrium temperature denoted by T_f and with $c_{Al} = 0.21$, we have $500 \cdot 0.21(300 - T_f) + 1000(20 - T_f) = 0$, or $T_f \simeq 46$°C.

If the specific heat c_a of a body A is known, clearly one can obtain the specific heat c_b of body B from a mixing (contact) experiment in which ΔT_a and ΔT_b are measured. We have then $c_b = (m_a/m_b)(|\Delta T_a|/|\Delta T_b|)c_a$. It should be mentioned that the specific heats of, say, copper and lead, obtained from individual mixing experiments with water, are consistent with the value for the ratio c_{Cu}/c_{Pb} obtained from direct contact experiments with copper and lead.

Heat. Note the similarity of the result given by Eq. (14–3) to the various conservation laws we have discussed in earlier chapters. A quantitative change, $m_a c_a \, \Delta T_a$, in a property of body A is accompanied by an equal but opposite quantitative change, $m_b c_b \, \Delta T_b$, in a property of body B. It is as though the sum of the properties mcT of both of the bodies remained constant. The property to which we refer is called *heat*, and it is denoted by Q. We shall find in subsequent chapters that this quantity is indeed equivalent to energy, and that we can regard heat as the energy of the molecular motion in a body.

If the change in heat is denoted by

$$\Delta Q = cm \, \Delta T, \qquad (14\text{--}4)$$

the result in Eq. (14–3) can be rewritten as

$$\Delta Q_a + \Delta Q_b = 0 \qquad \text{or} \qquad \Delta Q_a = -\Delta Q_b. \qquad (14\text{--}5)$$

The change in the heat (content) of a body is then positive or negative, depending on whether the temperature of the body increases or decreases. When two bodies are in contact, heat can be thought of as flowing from the hotter to the colder body, in such a way that the amount of heat that leaves one body is received by the other.

The specific heats of all substances, including that of water, vary somewhat with temperature. The specific-heat variations over the range from 0°C to 100°C are not large for most substances; for example, the specific heat of water changes by only about 1%, but that of nickel changes by about 10%. When a body's temperature changes from T_1 to T_2, the change in heat is

$$\Delta Q = m \int_{T_1}^{T_2} c(T) \, dT, \qquad (14\text{–}6)$$

which reduces to Eq. (14–4) when c is constant.

The unit of heat is defined as the heat required to change the temperature of *one gram of water from* 14.5°C *to* 15.5°C. This unit is called 1 *gram-calorie* or simply 1 *calorie*; for convenience, a unit 1000 times larger, the *kilocalorie*, is often used. Another frequently used unit is the so-called *British thermal unit* (Btu), which is based on the amount of heat needed to increase the temperature of 1 lb of water by 1 F°.

Similarly, the specific heat of a body is measured in calories per gram per degree celsius in the cgs system and in kilocalories per kilogram per degree celsius in the mks system. Clearly, the numerical values of the specific heats in these two systems are the same.

Fusion and vaporization. When substances change from a solid to a liquid or from a liquid to a gas, experiments show that a relatively large amount of heat is absorbed, although the temperature remains constant. These heat changes are not directly related to the specific heat, since there is a change in heat that is not accompanied by a temperature change. These changes in heat, which are called the *latent heat of fusion* and the *latent heat of vaporization*, refer to the heat absorbed when one gram of a substance melts or evaporates, respectively. Materials also change directly from the solid to the gaseous state, and in this case the heat absorbed per gram is called the *latent heat of sublimation*. The latent heats of fusion and vaporization for some familiar substances are shown in Tables 14–3 and 14–4.

Table 14–3. Latent heats of fusion.

Substance	Melting temperature, °C*	Latent heat of fusion, cal/gm
Water	0	79.7
Paraffin	52.4	35.1
Lead	327	5.86
Copper	1083	42.0
Mercury	−39	2.82
Silver	961	21.1

* At 76 cm of mercury pressure.

Table 14–4. Latent heats of vaporization.

Substance	Boiling temperature, °C*	Latent heat of vaporization, cal/gm
Water	100	539.6
Mercury	357	65.0
Argon	−186	37.6
Helium	−268.6	6.0

* At 76 cm of mercury pressure.

14–4 Heat and energy. From the point of view of kinetic theory, heat is no more than molecular energy, and the identification of heat as a form of energy is an inherent part of the theory. Historically, however, this identification was made through the work of James Joule (1818–1889), Julius Mayer (1814–1878), and others, who showed that *whenever a given amount of mechanical energy is dissipated, the same amount of heat is produced.* We shall discuss this matter in more detail in Chapter 17. The units of heat and mechanical energy, incidentally, are related by 4.1815 *joules = 1 calorie.*

The reader should recall that the development of mechanics and heat had progressed along quite separate paths. On the one hand was the study of motion and the *mechanical interaction* of bodies. On the other hand was the study of temperature and the *thermal interaction* of bodies. These two almost entirely independent disciplines were joined by the work of Joule and, as has always been the case when links are found between disciplines, new insights developed quickly. The linking of heat and energy, and the somewhat earlier development of the atomic theory of chemistry, resulted in the development and acceptance of the kinetic theory.

14–5 Heat conduction. In previous sections we considered the states of thermally interacting bodies before and after the interactions, i.e., the initial and final states of thermal equilibrium of the bodies. During the interaction, the system is not in thermal equilibrium; the temperatures of the interacting bodies are different and change with time. Heat flows from the hotter to the colder body, and the amount of heat transferred per second depends on the temperature difference between the bodies and the material of the medium between them. There are three types of heat transfer: conduction, convection, and radiation. In conduction, heat is transferred solely as a result of molecular motion and the collisions between fast- and slow-moving molecules, without any gross motion of matter. Convection, on the other hand, is a result of gross motion of matter, and is important only in liquids and gases. Finally, heat radiation is an electromagnetic interaction between bodies and does not require a material medium between the bodies. At present, we shall consider only heat conduction. Convection and radiation will be discussed briefly in a later section.

To investigate heat conduction experimentally, we can, at least in principle, use an arrangement such as that illustrated schematically in Fig. 14–4. The two ends, a and b, of a uniform straight bar are held at constant temperatures T_a and T_b respectively. For example, end b might be submerged in an ice bath, in which case $T_b = 0°C$, and a might be held in contact with a heat source such that it maintains a constant temperature T_a. The sides of the bar are thermally insulated so that the heat that flows into the bar at a must flow into the ice bath at b. The heat delivered to this bath per second can then be measured in terms of the amount of ice that melts per second. The temperature at a, as well as the temperature distribution along the bar, can also be measured. Imagine now that we use such an experimental arrangement and study the heat flow, i.e., the amount of heat per second that flows through the bar, as a function of various parameters, such as the temperature difference $T_a - T_b$, the length L of the bar, the cross-sectional area A of the bar, and the material in the bar. In addition, we can study the effect of isolating the side walls of the bar, both on the heat flow and on the temperature distribution along the bar.

The results of a series of measurements of this type show that the heat flow is (a) proportional to the temperature difference $T_a - T_b$, (b) inversely proportional to the length L of the bar, (c) proportional to the cross-sectional area of the bar, and (d) dependent on the material in the rod. Furthermore, we find that the temperature along the bar decreases linearly from T_a to T_b so long as the bar is thermally insulated along the sides to prevent heat leakage. If this thermal insulation is

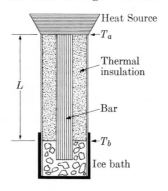

FIG. 14–4. Heat conduction through a bar.

removed, the temperature distribution deviates from linearity, as shown schematically in Fig. 14–5. In this latter case, the heat flow through the bar is not the same at all points along the bar.

From the results of experiments with a thermally insulated bar, it follows that the heat flow is proportional to the *slope* or *gradient* $(T_a - T_b)/L$ of the temperature distribution along the bar. Actually, we find that even if the temperature distribution is not linear, the heat flow through the bar at a certain point is proportional to the gradient dT/dx, at that point. Since, in addition, the heat flow is proportional to the area of the bar, we can set the magnitude of the heat flow proportional to $(dT/dx)A$.

The heat flows in the direction of decreasing temperature. In other words, if the temperature increases with x so that dT/dx is positive, the heat flow is in the negative x-direction, and if the temperature decreases with x so that dT/dx is negative, the heat flow is in the positive x-direction. Consequently, if we introduce the notation q for the heat flow, counted positive in the positive x-direction, dT/dx and q have opposite signs, and we obtain

$$q = -KA \frac{dT}{dx}. \tag{14–7}$$

The constant of proportionality K, which depends on the material of the bar, is called the *heat-conduction coefficient*. In the cgs system, the heat-conduction coefficient is measured in units of cal/(sec·cm·deg), and in the mks system, in units of kcal/(sec·m·deg). The values of the heat-conduction coefficients of some common materials are given in Table 14–5. Heat-conduction coefficients usually depend somewhat on temperature.

In the discussion of the experiment on heat conduction, it has been assumed that the bar has been in contact with the heat source a and the ice bath b long enough so that it has settled into what is called a *steady-state* condition. The temperature along the bar then no longer changes

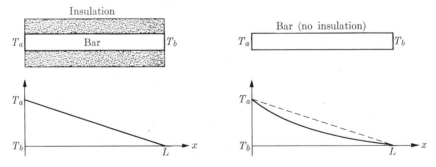

FIG. 14–5. Temperature distribution along a thermally insulated and a non-insulated bar.

Table 14–5. Heat conduction coefficients.

Substance	K, cal/sec·cm·deg
Aluminum	0.49 at 100°C 0.56 at 300°C
Copper	0.92
Lead	0.08
Steel (1% carbon)	0.125 at 100°C 0.089 at 600°C
Silver	0.97
Wood	$2 \cdot 10^{-4}$
Glass wool (400 kgm/m^3)	$1.7 \cdot 10^{-4}$
Concrete	$2 \cdot 10^{-3}$
Air (dried)	$5.6 \cdot 10^{-5}$
Helium	$3.4 \cdot 10^{-4}$
Oxygen	$5.6 \cdot 10^{-5}$
Water	$1.32 \cdot 10^{-3}(1 + 0.003t)$; ($t = 0$ to $t = 80$°C)
Machine oil	$(0.28$ to $0.40) \cdot 10^{-3}$

with time, and *the heat flow into the bar at a is the same as the measured heat flow out of the bar at b.* If this were not the case, there would be a net flow of heat into the bar, and the temperature of the bar would increase continuously. Clearly, during the first few moments after the heat source has been turned on, the temperature distribution in the bar will change, and more heat will flow into the bar at a than leaves at b. The time required to reach the steady-state condition is proportional to the total heat capacity of the bar, and inversely proportional to the heat-conduction coefficient of the bar. In the next section, we shall study briefly a case in which the temperature and the flow through the bar *do* change with time.

EXAMPLE 1. Two bars, one of copper and the other of steel, are joined as shown in Fig. 14–6. The length of the copper bar, $L_2 = 20$ cm, is twice the length L_1 of the steel bar. One end of the copper bar is held at a temperature of $T_2 = 0$°C, and the free end of the steel bar is held at the temperature $T_1 = 100$°C. Determine the temperature at the junction of the two bars and the total heat flow through the bars. The cross-sectional area A of the two bars is equal, $A = 10$ cm^2. The bars are thermally insulated along the sides.

Let us denote by T_j the unknown temperature at the junction between the two bars. If the heat-conduction coefficient of the steel bar is K_1, the total heat flow through the steel bar is $q_1 = K_1 A(T_1 - T_j)/L_1$. Similarly, we obtain

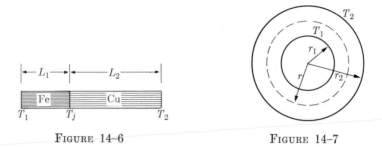

FIGURE 14-6   FIGURE 14-7

$q_2 = K_2 A(T_j - T_2)/L_2$ for the magnitude of the heat flow through the copper bar. Under steady-state conditions we have $q_1 = q_2$, which gives an equation for the calculation of the junction temperature T_j:

$$T_j = \frac{(T_1 + T_2)(K_2 L_1/K_1 L_2)}{1 + (K_2 L_1/K_1 L_2)}.$$

If we introduce the numerical values $K_1 = 0.125$, $K_2 = 0.92$ (see Table 14-5), and if $L_2 = 2L_1$, we obtain

$$T_j = \frac{100}{(1 + 0.92)/(0.125 \cdot 2)} \simeq 21°C.$$

The corresponding heat flow through the bars is then

$$q = \frac{(0.92 \cdot 10)(21 - 0)}{20} \simeq 9.6 \text{ cal/sec.}$$

EXAMPLE 2. A long cylindrical tube has an inner radius r_1 and an outer radius r_2, as shown in Fig. 14-7. The inner and outer surfaces of the tube are held at the temperatures T_1 and T_2, respectively. What is the heat flow through the cylinder, per unit length of the cylinder, and what is the radial distribution of temperature if the heat-conduction coefficient of the material of the cylinder is K?

Consider the heat flow through a circular cylinder of radius r in the tube, as shown in Fig. 14-7. If we denote the temperature gradient at r by dT/dr, the heat flow through the cylindrical surface at r is

$$q_r = -K(2\pi r) \frac{dT}{dr},$$

since the area of the cylinder surface, per unit length of the tube, is $2\pi r$. Under steady-state conditions, this heat flow is the same as the total heat flow q per unit length through the cylinder (independent of r). Therefore, we have

$$\frac{dT}{dr} = \frac{-q}{2\pi K r}.$$

This equation can be integrated directly, and we obtain

$$T = - \left(\frac{q}{2\pi K}\right) \ln r + \text{const.}$$

If we set $T = T_1$ at $r = r_1$, and $T = T_2$ at $r = r_2$, we obtain the following expression for q:

$$q = 2\pi K \frac{T_2 - T_1}{\ln (r_1/r_2)}.$$

The corresponding temperature distribution then is

$$T = T_1 + (T_2 - T_1) \frac{\ln (r/r_1)}{\ln (r_2/r_1)}.$$

14–6 Time-dependent heat flow. In the experiment on heat conduction through a bar described in the previous section, only the steady-state conditions were considered. Under such conditions, the heat source is similar to an infinite heat reservoir, in the sense that it is able to keep the temperature constant at one end of the bar, despite the fact that heat is continuously drawn from the source. If the heat source is a finite heat reservoir, on the other hand, it is clear that the temperature of the reservoir, and the heat flow from it, will *decrease* continuously with time. Correspondingly, if the receiver of this heat is a finite heat reservoir, its temperature will *increase* continuously with time, except in cases in which the heat is used to produce a phase transition, such as the melting of ice. In any event, the difference in temperature of the two interacting heat reservoirs then decreases continuously until it becomes zero, at which time thermal equilibrium has been attained.

In order to understand the variation of temperature with time during the thermal interaction of two bodies, we shall consider again the special case of a heat-conducting bar (Fig. 14–4). Let us again assume that one end of the bar is in an ice bath, so that the temperature at this end of the bar is held constant during the interaction, and that the other end of the bar is in contact with a finite heat reservoir. The heat capacity of the conducting bar will be assumed small in comparison with the heat capacity of the source reservoir, so that the temperature along the rod can be considered to adjust itself instantaneously to the linear steady-state temperature distribution described previously. Furthermore, we shall assume that the heat conduction of the source reservoir is very large, and that the temperature of the source is uniform and equal to the temperature at the end of the bar that is in contact with the source. Then, if the temperature of the source is T at a certain time t, the temperature difference between the ends of the bar at that same time is $T - 0 = T$, and the temperature gradient along the bar is T/L, where L is the length of the bar. Consequently, the heat flow from the source is then

$$q = \frac{KA}{L} T, \qquad (14\text{--}8)$$

where A is the cross-sectional area of the bar and K is the heat-conduction coefficient of the bar.

As a result of this heat flow, the source will lose an amount of heat $q\,dt$ during the time interval dt, and the corresponding temperature change dT of the source is given by $cm\,dT = -q\,dt$, where m is the mass and c is the specific heat of the source reservoir. By inserting the corresponding expression $q = -cm(dT/dt)$ into Eq. (14–8), we obtain the following equation for the variation of the source temperature with time:

$$\frac{dT}{dt} = -\frac{KA}{Lcm} T = -\frac{T}{\tau}, \qquad (14\text{--}9)$$

where

$$\tau = \frac{Lcm}{KA}.$$

This equation can be integrated directly to $\ln T = -(t/\tau) + \text{const}$, or can be expressed in a different manner as

$$T = T_0 e^{-t/\tau}, \qquad (14\text{--}10)$$

where T_0 is the initial temperature of the source at $t = 0$. Thus, the temperature of the source and at the beginning (or any other point) of the bar decreases exponentially with time, at a rate which is determined by the heat conduction of the bar and the heat capacity of the source reservoir. After the characteristic time τ, the *relaxation time* of the system, the temperature of the source has decreased by a factor of $1/e \simeq 1/3$.

In this example, the temperature at the receiver end of the bar was held constant and equal to 0°C by the ice bath, and the temperature difference between the source and the receiver is then simply the source temperature. We leave it as an exercise to work out the corresponding problem which involves a receiver reservoir that can change temperature. Even in this case, the temperature difference between the source and the receiver decreases exponentially, as in Eq. (14–10), with cm replaced by the total heat capacity of the source and the receiver (see Problem 14–17).

If the number of interacting bodies or reservoirs is increased, or if we have a continuous distribution of matter, the problem of determining the variation of temperature with time can be worked out basically as in the preceding simple example. However, the mathematical problem becomes somewhat more complicated. For example, to determine the temperature variation of one of the bodies or elements of the system, we must consider the interaction of all the other members of the system. We then obtain an equation similar to Eq. (14–9) for each member, and each such equation contains all the unknown temperatures of the bodies in the system. In the limiting case of a continuous, rather than a discrete, distribution of reservoirs, the temperature variation with time is best described in terms of a differential equation which relates the time rate of change of the temperature at a point to the space rate of change of the heat flow, or to the space rate of change of the gradient of the temperature. We shall now perform a derivation of such an equation, which is of considerable importance in many branches of physics concerned with *diffusion phenomena*, of which heat conduction is one example.

Let us consider a long straight bar which is thermally insulated along its sides so that the heat flow is in only one direction. If, under such conditions, the temperature gradient dT/dx is independent of the position along the bar, it follows that the heat flow through the bar at the position x_1 is the same as the heat flow at any other arbitrary position x_2. The section of the bar between x_1 and x_2 then receives as much heat at x_1 as it delivers at x_2, and there will be no net influx of heat to this (or any other) section of the bar. The temperature distribution of the bar will not vary with time, and since $dT/dx = $ const, the temperature varies linearly with x.

Then, to obtain the temperature variation of an element of the bar, it is necessary that there be a net influx (or outflux) of heat to (from) this element; i.e., the slope or gradient dT/dx can no longer be a constant but must vary from one position to another. Consider an element of the bar between x and $x + \Delta x$. The influx of heat into the element at x is then $-KA \, (dT/dx)_x$, and the outflux at the other end is $-KA \, (dT/dx)_{x+\Delta x}$, where A is the cross-sectional area of the bar (Fig. 14–8). The net influx of heat per second to this element is then

$$-KA \left(\frac{dT}{dx}\right)_x - \left[-KA \left(\frac{dT}{dx}\right)_{x+\Delta x}\right] = KA \left(\frac{d^2T}{dx^2}\right) \Delta x.$$

As a result of this net influx of heat, the temperature of the element will increase. This increase, of course, depends upon the mass and the specific heat of the element. If the temperature increase is dT, the corresponding

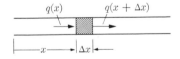

FIG. 14–8. The temperature will vary with time, when the heat flow varies with x.

heat influx is $(\rho A \, \Delta x)c \, dT$, where $\rho A \, \Delta x$ is the mass of the element and c is the specific heat. Since we have obtained an expression for the *rate* of heat influx, $KA \, (d^2T/dx^2) \, \Delta x$, we can obtain now the basic equation

$$\rho c A \frac{dT}{dt} = KA \frac{d^2T}{dx^2}$$

or

$$\frac{dT}{dt} = \frac{K}{\rho c} \frac{d^2T}{dx^2}. \tag{14–11}$$

The time rate of change of the temperature at a point along the bar is proportional to the rate of change of the slope of the temperature curve; i.e., it is proportional to the second derivative of the temperature curve. Furthermore, the time rate of change of the temperature is proportional to the heat-conduction coefficient of the material, and inversely proportional to the density and the specific heat. The quantity $\rho c/K$, then, is a measure of the thermal "inertia" of the material: the larger this quantity, the longer it takes, e.g., for the temperature to equalize in a body which has an initially nonuniform temperature distribution. Equation (14–11) is known as a *diffusion equation* and, as mentioned, equations of this type play a very important role in physics. Not only heat flow, but also many other diffusion phenomena are described by equations of this type.

14–7 Other mechanisms of heat transfer. In heat conduction, heat is transferred from one point to another by *molecular motion* alone; fast-moving molecules deliver energy to slow-moving molecules without any gross motion of the matter or substance involved. In solids, this type of heat transfer is usually the most important one. In gases and liquids, on the other hand, the heat transfer produced by *gross motion* or *convection* is often larger than that caused by conduction. For example, the winds in the atmosphere and the currents in the ocean carry enormous amounts of heat from one region to another, and blowing on hot soup is an effective way of increasing heat transfer by convection. There are numerous other familiar examples of the significance of the convection of heat. Conversely, our clothing is a means of decreasing the convective heat transfer from our bodies.

Heat conduction and heat convection both require a material medium. It is well known, however, that heat can be transferred through a vacuum. This form of heat transfer is called *heat radiation* and, like gamma- and x-rays, light and radio waves, it is known to be electromagnetic radiation. It can easily be demonstrated that heat radiation can be reflected, etc., in the same way as other electromagnetic waves. For example, a heat lamp placed at the focus of a parabolic reflector will produce a radiation

which can easily be picked up about 50 ft away by means of another parabolic reflector; a match placed at the focus of this reflector can be lighted
by the received heat radiation.

All bodies in nature radiate heat, and often, as they radiate, their temperatures decrease; thermal energy is evidently converted into electromagnetic radiation. However, in general, a body not only *radiates*, but
also *absorbs* radiation from surrounding bodies. If the bodies in an isolated
system interact with one another *only* through radiation, the temperatures
of the bodies may at first vary with time, as in any other case of heat transfer, but eventually an equilibrium is reached in which the temperatures of
the bodies are independent of time. The heat radiation from a body, then,
is the same as the heat absorption by it. If this were not the case, there
would be a net influx of heat to the body, and consequently a variation in
its temperature. If a body A in the system does not absorb as much energy
as another body B, it also follows that the radiation from A must be less
than the radiation from B if equilibrium is to be upheld; a good absorber
of heat is also a good radiator.

A body that absorbs all the radiation which falls on it is called a *blackbody*. A blackbody is not only the most efficient absorber but also the most
efficient radiator. A blackbody is an idealization; most bodies in nature
do not absorb all the energy falling on them, but reflect some of it, a familiar
fact at least so far as light is concerned. A sign of no reflection of light is
the absence of color, i.e., the body looks black.

The ideal absorption and radiation of a blackbody can be approximated
quite closely in the laboratory by means of a hole in the wall of a cavity
that is painted black on the inside. Almost all of the radiation that enters
the hole will not return, and the hole behaves almost like a perfect absorber, i.e., like a blackbody.

The radiation from a blackbody depends on the temperature of the body,
and extensive experimental investigations have been devoted to the determination of the relation between the radiated energy and the temperature
of the body. The interpretation of heat radiation and of the experimental
results in terms of molecular motion has been one of the very important
problems in physics. Max Planck (German scientist, 1858–1947), in his
studies of blackbody radiation, made the discovery, which later proved to
be revolutionary, that in order to make his theoretical interpretation of
heat radiation consistent with the experimental results, it was necessary
to postulate that the energy of a molecular oscillator is a multiple of a
certain energy quantum which is proportional to the frequency of oscillation. Shortly after its inception, this postulate, which may be regarded as
the springboard to quantum theory, was used by Bohr in his studies of
atomic spectra and by Einstein in his studies of electron emission produced
by radiation.

It is beyond the scope of this book to enter into a detailed discussion of the nature of heat radiation. We shall merely point out that experiments with and the theory of heat radiation show that the total amount of energy radiated per unit area from a blackbody kept at a constant temperature $T°$ abs is given by

$$q = \sigma T^4, \tag{14-12}$$

where σ is a constant: $\sigma = 5.66 \cdot 10^{-5}$ erg·cm^{-2}·deg^{-4}·sec^{-1}. Radiation from other than blackbodies is less than the value given in Eq. (14–12), by a certain factor which depends strongly on the nature of the surface of the body.

14–8 Historical notes. The experimental facts we have presented concerning thermometry and heat had been established by the beginning of the second half of the 18th century. The historical account is intricate; a great many persons contributed to the development of the subject. In about 1592, Galileo is believed to have devised an instrument which responded to temperature. His device was essentially an air-containing bulb connected to one end of a glass tube. The other end of the tube was under water, and the height of the air-water interface in the tube depended upon the temperature of the gas in the bulb and also upon atmospheric pressure. During the 17th century, because there was no general agreement as to what should be the fixed points on the temperature scale, several forms of liquid thermometers and many different temperature scales were developed. Sometimes the scales were completely arbitrary: perhaps a centimeter scale was simply held next to the glass stem. Sometimes the fixed points were purely a matter of convenience: melting butter, the hottest day in summer, the coldest day in winter, the human body, and, of course, melting ice and boiling water. Eventually the latter two, called the ice and steam points, respectively, were generally adopted, and as further refinements both in concept and in temperature-measuring techniques evolved, the ice and steam points at a pressure of one standard atmosphere (76 cm of mercury) were specified. Both the celsius (ice point at 0°, steam point at 100°) and the fahrenheit (ice point at 32°, steam point at 212°) thermometers were in use by 1750. Mercury was, by then, a commonly accepted liquid for thermometers.

For a long while there was no clear separation of the concepts of temperature and heat. This is understandable, since quantitative heat measurements, even in a modern laboratory with small and reliable thermometers, are not particularly easy to make, because of many rather subtle complicating effects. Then, too, our sensitivity to heat and cold tends to lead us astray: a piece of metal feels colder to our touch than does a piece of wood, even if both the metal and the wood are at the same temperature.

Significantly, the availability of good thermometers was followed shortly by the very beautiful and illuminating work of Joseph Black (1728–1799), a Scottish physician. It was Black who put forth the notion that bodies in temperature or thermal equilibrium do not contain equal amounts of heat, but that the amount of heat in a body depends upon some property (the specific heat) other than mass or volume. Fahrenheit had previously performed mixing experiments wherein water at one temperature was mixed with water or some other substance such as mercury at another temperature. These experiments, as well as others, led Black to introduce the important notion of specific heat. Measurements of the specific and latent heats of many substances were made shortly thereafter.

PROBLEMS

14-1. The linear expansion coefficient α is defined from the relation $l = l_0(1 + \alpha T)$, where l_0 is the length of a bar at $T = 0°C$, and l is the length at the temperature T. The coefficient α usually depends somewhat on temperature. Figure 14-9 shows this dependence for both copper and aluminum. Suppose, now, that you have available a linear-expansion type thermometer that uses copper and aluminum as the thermometric substances, and freezing and boiling water as the reference or calibration points. (a) Would such thermometers read too low or too high in comparison with a gas thermometer in the range from 0°C to 100°C? in the range from 100°C to 500°C? (b) At what points will the two thermometers agree? (c) In what temperature region will the aluminum thermometer show a higher temperature than the copper thermometer or vice versa? (*Hint.* Plot the true length as a function of temperature.)

14-2. Suppose that, in an experiment with a constant-volume gas thermometer, the ratio between the pressures P_{100} and P_0 is measured and found to be 1.34. (P_{100} corresponds to boiling water and P_0 to freezing water.) What would be the corresponding value of the absolute-zero point in celsius degrees?

14-3. In order to obtain controlled fusion of deuterons, a temperature of the order of 100 million degrees is required. Explain qualitatively the reason why a high temperature is required in such a process.

14-4. Ten grams each of aluminum, copper, and lead at 0°C, 20°C, and 40°C, respectively, are immersed in 50 gm of water at 60°C. What is the final temperature?

14-5. A piece of copper is plunged into 100 gm of 50°C water. When the system comes to equilibrium, only 90 gm of 100°C water remain. What can be said about the mass and temperature of the piece of copper?

14-6. Equal masses (100 gm) of lead and water, initially at 10°C, are placed over identical Bunsen flames which supply 25 cal/sec. Plot graphs showing in each case how the temperatures increase with time.

14-7. An electrical resistor which dissipates 20 calories of heat per second

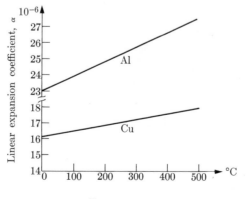

FIGURE 14-9

is frozen into 100 gm of ice, originally at −20°C, contained in a thermally insulated container. Plot a graph of the temperature of the water *vs.* time, starting from the time the current through the resistor is turned on and continuing to the time when all the water has been evaporated.

14–8. If the entire kinetic energy of a 10-kgm earth satellite (assume an orbit 200 mi high) were converted into heat, what mass of water could be vaporized? Assume the water to be at 0°C initially.

14–9. If the entire power output of an automobile (use 100 hp) were used to stir 50 gal of water contained in a barrel, how long a time would be required to increase the temperature of the water 20C°? (1 hp = 746 watts = 746 joules/sec.)

14–10. How many square feet of a ¼-in. glass window would conduct as much heat as a 100-sq ft wall of 4-in. concrete? The temperature differences between the inside and the outside surfaces of the window and the wall are the same. Estimate the amount of heat conducted out through the concrete wall in one hour, if the inside temperature is 20°C and the outside temperature is −10°C. ($K_{gl} \simeq K_{co}$.)

14–11. A straight bar of area $A = 2 \text{ cm}^2$ connects a reservoir at temperature 100°C to a reservoir of ice at 0°C. The bar consists of two parts, one of copper of length $L_1 = 30$ cm, and the other of steel of length $L_2 = 20$ cm. The bar is thermally insulated along the sides and the steel contacts the ice. (a) What is the temperature at the junction? (b) How much ice melts per minute?

14–12. A sphere of radius R_1 has a surface temperature of T_1. A spherical shell of inner radius R_1 and outer radius R_2 is added to the sphere. If

the outer-surface temperature of the shell is T_2, and the heat-conduction coefficient of the shell material is K, what then is the heat flow out from the sphere? How does the temperature vary with location in the shell?

14–13. A steam pipe with a diameter of 4 cm carries steam that has a temperature of 120°C. The pipe is wrapped with a heat-insulating material, 5 cm thick, that has a heat-conduction coefficient of 10^{-4} cal/sec·cm·deg. The outer temperature of the insulating material is measured to be 40°C. (a) How large is the thermal gradient in the insulating material close to the pipe? (b) What is the radial flow of heat per centimeter length of the pipe?

14–14. A bar that is thermally insulated along its sides has a cross-sectional area which increases linearly from one end to the other. The area at the beginning of the bar is A_1, and at the end it is $A_2 = 3A_1$. The temperatures at the beginning and at the end of the bar are T_1 and T_2, respectively. Make a qualitative sketch of the temperature distribution along the bar.

14–15. In Fig. 14–10 is shown a uniform straight bar, the ends of which are held at constant temperatures T_1

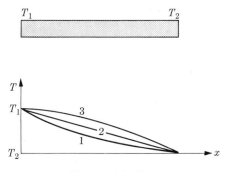

FIGURE 14–10

and T_2. Three temperature-distribution curves are shown. (a) Determine which of these curves indicates a bar with thermal insulation along its sides, and which a bar with no insulation along its sides, so that heat is lost along its sides. (b) Describe a physical situation which corresponds to a temperature distribution similar to the remaining curve. Explain.

14–16. A 25-gm piece of copper is heated electrically and receives 0.4 watt of energy, which is converted into heat. At the same time, the piece of copper loses heat, through heat conduction, to its surroundings, which are at a constant temperature of 0°C. The equilibrium temperature of the copper becomes 5°C. How long after the current has been turned off will the temperature of the copper piece be 1.84°C? (The specific heat of copper is 0.091 cal/gm·deg.)

14–17. Refer to Sec. 14–7. Two bodies, each of mass m and specific heat c, have different temperatures T_1 and T_2 ($T_1 > T_2$). These bodies are connected by a heat-conducting bar (neglect the heat capacity of the bar), so that heat is conducted from one body to the other. If the bodies are connected at $t = 0$, determine the subsequent variation with time of the temperature difference between the bodies. The heat-conduction coefficient of the bar is K, its area is A, and its length is L. Consider heat conduction to be the only mechanism of heat transfer between the bodies.

Assume that the temperature distribution over each body is uniform.

14–18. At a time t, the temperature distribution in a long uniform straight bar (thermally isolated) is

$$T = A \frac{1}{x_0} e^{-(x/x_0)^2},$$

where A is a constant and $x_0 = \sqrt{at}$ ($a = $ const). (a) Sketch qualitatively the temperature distribution along the bar at various times $t > 0$. (b) At a fixed time $t = t_1$, determine the region of the bar where the rate of change of the temperature is positive (negative). (c) Next, consider a fixed position $x = x_1$ on the bar. Show that the temperature at that point reaches a maximum value at the time $t_m = x_1^2/a$.

14–19. Consider the earth as a blackbody radiator, and estimate the amount of power radiated from the earth per square meter if the surface temperature of the earth is 10°C.

14–20. Imagine a spherical body in outer space. Suppose that the body receives no radiation. How long would it take for the temperature of the sphere to decrease by a factor of two, if only radiation from the sphere is considered? The density of the sphere is ρ, the radius is R, and the specific heat is c. Assume that the sphere is a blackbody radiator and that the heat-conduction coefficient is infinite, so that the temperature throughout the sphere is uniform.

CHAPTER 15

ATOMS AND MOLECULES

Summary. This chapter provides some of the basic ideas and facts about atoms and molecules which will be needed in subsequent chapters. We start with a discussion of the early experimental evidence for the atomic structure of matter, expressed by the laws of definite- and multiple-weight proportions in chemical reactions (Lavoisier and Proust), and the foundations of Dalton's atomic theory of matter. Then follows the problem of incorporating Gay-Lussac's law of multiple-volume proportions in gas reactions into the Dalton theory, and Avogadro's solution of the problem. Avogadro's number and the molecular weight are introduced and applied in calculations of masses and sizes of atoms and molecules.

In the previous chapter, we started to direct our attention to the interior motion in matter, and we described briefly in qualitative terms the relation between the concepts of temperature, heat, and molecular motion. In Chapter 16, we shall pursue these introductory studies further by discussing the kinetic (molecular) theory of gases, and still later we shall discuss briefly the molecular properties of liquids and solids. Since atoms and molecules are frequently referred to in our future discussions, it is appropriate to present now a discussion of some of the elementary notions about them. We shall begin with a review of some of the experimental observations upon which the atomic theory of matter was originally based.

15–1 The law of multiple proportions and Dalton's atomic theory of matter. The idea of the atomic structure of matter is very old indeed; it dates back to Democritus (about 400 B.C.), who proposed that matter consists of indivisible, inconceivably small building blocks (atoms), each surrounded by empty space. However, like any other scientific idea, this particular one did not bear fruit until it could be expressed in quantitative terms and could be supported by some experimental observations. The idea remained more or less dormant for about 2000 years, until it was revived by a series of discoveries, mostly in chemistry. John Dalton (English chemist, 1766–1844), Joseph Gay-Lussac (French physicist and chemist, 1778–1850) and Amadeo Avogadro (Italian scientist, 1776–1856) were instrumental in re-establishing the atomic theory of matter and putting it into quantitative terms.

Experiments on the quantitative analysis of chemical reactions were started systematically in the late 1700's by Antoine Laurent Lavoisier (French chemist, 1743–1794) and Joseph Louis Proust (French chemist,

1754–1826). The results of these experiments can be described in terms of a few simple laws: (1) The law of *conservation of mass,* which states that the total mass or weight of a chemical compound is always the sum of the masses of the individual constituents. (2) In addition to this relation for the masses, it was found that elements always combine in certain definite proportions by weight. For example, one part of oxygen was found to combine always with 1.52 parts by weight of magnesium and with 3.7 parts by weight of tin. Observations of this kind formed the basis for the *law of definite (weight) proportions* in chemical reactions. (3) It was found that when oxygen (or some other substance) combines in more than one way with another element, e.g., copper, the amounts of oxygen in these compounds are related by *multiple* proportions.

Concurrently, and independently of the work of Lavoisier and Proust, John Dalton, a teacher in Manchester, England, was exploring similar matters. The importance of Dalton's contribution to the subject is attributed not so much to his own experimental findings as to the conceptual model he developed. In essence, Dalton assumed that (a) matter consists of indivisible discrete particles, atoms, which remain unchanged when they combine with other atoms, (b) all atoms of the same element are identical, but the atoms of different elements differ from each other in mass, and (c) in the chemical combination of two elements, the atoms combine in simple numerical proportions.

In other words, Dalton's atomic interpretation of the combination of two substances A and B was that one or more atoms of A combine with one or more atoms of B. Suppose that it is known that n_a atoms of A combine with n_b atoms of B to form the substance $A + B$. If the masses of the atoms of A and B are m_a and m_b, the total masses of A and B, after combination, are $M_a = n_a m_a$ and $M_b = n_b m_b$. These combining masses, M, can readily be measured with a high degree of accuracy. Then, if the ratio n_a/n_b between the number of atoms of the two substances is known, it follows that the ratio between the masses of the atoms can be determined directly from the measured ratio of the total masses. That is,

$$\frac{m_a}{m_b} = \frac{n_b}{n_a} \frac{M_a}{M_b}. \tag{15-1}$$

In applying this interpretation, Dalton had to make assumptions regarding the ratio n_a/n_b; he assumed, for example, that water was formed from an equal number of hydrogen and of oxygen atoms. Then, since 1 part of hydrogen combines with 8 parts of oxygen to form water, he concluded (erroneously) that the oxygen atom was 8 times heavier than the hydrogen atom. Such rather arbitrary assumptions about n_a/n_b soon led to inconsistencies. Dalton was forced to continuously readjust his assumed ratios in an effort to reach a consistent description, in terms of multiple proportions by atoms, for his law of multiple proportions by weight in chemical reactions.

After Dalton's formulation and atomic interpretation of the law of multiple proportions by weight (in 1803), during the years from 1805 to 1808 Gay-Lussac investigated the manner in which gases combine by volume to form compounds. He found relationships very similar to those of Dalton's: gases of the same pressures and temperatures combine in simple multiple proportions by *volume*. For example, it was found that 2 volumes of hydrogen and 1 volume of oxygen combine to form 2 volumes of water vapor; 1 volume of hydrogen and 1 volume of chlorine combine to form 2 volumes of hydrogen chloride; and 1 volume of oxygen and 1 volume of nitrogen combine to form 2 volumes of nitric oxide.

Dalton pointed out that if gases combine in simple multiple proportions by volume, and also in simple multiple proportions by atoms, it follows that there must be a simple relationship between the number of atoms per unit volume of the reacting gases. Dalton assumed that equal volumes of different gases at the same temperature and pressure contain equal numbers of *atoms*. This assumption, which seemed reasonable at first, led to inconsistencies: for example, 1 volume of nitrogen (n atoms) combines with 1 volume of oxygen (n atoms) to form 2 volumes of nitric oxide. According to Dalton's assumption of equal numbers of atoms in equal volumes, there should be $2n$ compound atoms in the 2 volumes of nitric oxide. On the other hand, the atomic picture of the combination of atoms requires that n atoms of oxygen and n atoms of nitrogen form n, *not* $2n$, compound atoms of nitric oxide.

This kind of inconsistency was resolved in 1811 by Avogadro, who modified Dalton's assumption by postulating that equal volumes of different gases at the same temperature and pressure contain the same number of *compound* atoms, not elementary atoms. Avogadro called the compound atoms *molecules*. This hypothesis resolved the apparent inconsistencies between Dalton's and Gay-Lussac's observations, and made possible the interpretation of Gay-Lussac's law of simple multiple proportions by volume, in terms of multiple proportions by atoms. As an example, consider the combination of nitrogen and oxygen mentioned previously. If it is assumed that both the nitrogen and oxygen molecules consist of 2 atoms, then, as they combine, 1 nitrogen and 1 oxygen molecule form 2 molecules of nitric oxide, and consequently 2 volumes of nitric-oxide gas.

With Avogadro's hypothesis, it was possible to obtain a consistent explanation of gaseous reactions in terms of simple multiple proportions by atoms. It was then established that the molecules of, for example, hydrogen, oxygen, chlorine, nitrogen, etc., consist of two atoms. These molecules are called *diatomic*. On the other hand, the gases helium, neon, argon, krypton, and xenon have only one atom per molecule; they are *monatomic*.

Table 15–1. Periodic table of the elements.

(Numbers in parentheses indicate mass number of most stable known isotope.)

Outer electrons are in the	I	II	III	IV	V	VI	VII	VIII			O	Electrons per shell
First or K-shell	1 H 1.0080										2 He 4.003	2
Second or L-shell	3 Li 6.940	4 Be 9.013	5 B 10.82	6 C 12.011	7 N 14.008	8 O 16.000	9 F 19.00				10 Ne 20.183	2, 8
Third or M-shell	11 Na 22.991	12 Mg 24.32	13 Al 26.98	14 Si 28.09	15 P 30.975	16 S 32.066	17 Cl 35.457				18 Ar 39.944	2, 8, 8
Fourth or N-shell	19 K 39.100	20 Ca 40.08	21 Sc 44.96	22 Ti 47.90	23 V 50.95	24 Cr 52.01	25 Mn 54.94	26 Fe 55.85	27 Co 58.94	28 Ni 58.71		
	29 Cu 63.54	30 Zn 65.38	31 Ga 69.72	32 Ge 72.60	33 As 74.91	34 Se 78.96	35 Br 79.916				36 Kr 83.80	2, 8, 18, 8
Fifth or O-shell	37 Rb 85.48	38 Sr 87.63	39 Y 88.92	40 Zr 91.22	41 Nb 92.91	42 Mo 95.95	43 Tc (99)	44 Ru 101.10	45 Rh 102.91	46 Pd 106.4		
	47 Ag 107.880	48 Cd 112.41	49 In 114.82	50 Sn 118.70	51 Sb 121.76	52 Te 127.61	53 I 126.91				54 Xe 131.30	2, 8, 18, 18, 8
Sixth or P-shell	55 Cs 132.91	56 Ba 137.36	57–71 La series*	72 Hf 178.50	73 Ta 180.95	74 W 183.86	75 Re 186.22	76 Os 190.2	77 Ir 192.2	78 Pt 195.09		
	79 Au 197.0	80 Hg 200.61	81 Tl 204.39	82 Pb 207.21	83 Bi 209.00	84 Po (210)	85 At (210)				86 Rn (222)	2, 8, 18, 32, 18, 8
Seventh or Q-shell	87 Fr (223)	88 Ra 226.05	89 — Ac series**									

*Lanthanide series:	57 La 138.92	58 Ce 140.13	59 Pr 140.92	60 Nd 144.27	61 Pm (145)	62 Sm 150.35	63 Eu 152.0	64 Gd 157.26	65 Tb 158.93	66 Dy 162.51	67 Ho 164.94	68 Er 167.27	69 Tm 168.94	70 Yb 173.04	71 Lu 174.99 — 2, 8, 18, 32, 9, 2
**Actinide series:	89 Ac (227)	90 Th 232.05	91 Pa (231)	92 U 238.07	93 Np (237)	94 Pu (244)	95 Am (243)	96 Cm (247)	97 Bk (247)	98 Cf (251)	99 Es (254)	100 Fm (253)	101 Md (256)	102 No (253)	103 — 2, 8, 18, 32, 32, 9, 2

15-2 Atomic and molecular weights. Since, on the basis of Avogadro's hypothesis, equal volumes of different gases at the same temperatures and pressures contain equal numbers of compound atoms, it follows that *the ratio between the mass densities of two gases is the same as the ratio between the molecular masses.* Then, from gas-density measurements, it is possible to make up a *relative* mass scale of molecules, and if the number of atoms in the molecules is known, a corresponding scale of *relative* atomic masses can be determined. Only the ratio of the molecular masses can be obtained in this way, of course. For a numerical scale oxygen was chosen as a reference, and the numerical value of its atomic mass was set equal to 16 (molecular mass, 32). The particular choice of oxygen was motivated by the fact that oxygen reacts with a large number of substances. The choice of the numerical value 16 was justified on the basis that the numerical values of other elements then would have convenient values, starting with 1 (or, rather, 1.008) for the lightest element, hydrogen.

The number assigned to an element, i.e., 16 for oxygen, 1.008 for hydrogen, 12 for carbon, etc., is called the *atomic weight* (or the atomic mass) of the element in question. Once the composition of a molecule is known, the corresponding molecular weight is obtained by summing the atomic weights of the constituents. For example, the molecular weight of oxygen, O_2, is 32, and the molecular weight of water, H_2O, is 18.

15-3 Avogadro's number. Masses and sizes of molecules. An amount of a substance containing a number of grams equal to the molecular weight is called one *gram-molecular mass,* or one *molar mass* (M), or one *mole* of the substance. Similarly, the volume occupied by a molar mass, $V = M/\rho$ $(\rho =$ density of substance), is called the *molar volume.* Since the ratio between the molar masses of different substances is the same as the ratio between the masses of the corresponding molecules, it is clear that the number of molecules comprising a molar mass is the *same* for all substances. If this number N_0 were known, the mass m of an individual molecule would be obtained from the relation $Nm = M$, or

$$m = \frac{M}{N_0}. \tag{15-2}$$

This same relation applies to the mass of an atom if M stands for the mass of a gram-atom, i.e., the number of grams equal to the atomic weight of the substance.

The number N_0, called *Avogadro's number,* can be measured in a number of more-or-less direct ways. One of the first estimates of Avogadro's number (and of molecular size) resulted from a study of oil films on water (Lord Rayleigh, 1890). If a minute amount of oleic acid, for example, is deposited on the surface of clean water, it will spread over a surprisingly large area;

one milligram will cover almost 10,000 cm^2. Since the density of oleic acid is about 0.9 gm/cm^2, the thickness of such a film must be about 10^{-7} cm, and so one of the dimensions of the oleic-acid molecule (molecular weight $M = 282.5$) must be at least this small. If we assume all three dimensions of the molecule to be about 10^{-7} cm, the volume per molecule is 10^{-21} cm^3. Since the volume per mole is about 300 cm^3 ($M/\rho = 282.5/0.9$), the number of molecules per mole, under these assumptions, is $300/10^{-21}$ or $3 \cdot 10^{23}$.

This is one rather simple method by which to obtain an estimate of Avogadro's number. Accurate values of N_0 have been obtained by means of x-ray studies of crystals. Here, the structure of the crystal and the spacing of the atoms can be determined accurately, and so the number of atoms in a given volume or the mass of a substance of known molecular weight can be found. Another method for the accurate determination of N involves the measurement of the electronic charge and the amount of charge carried from one electrode to another when a given mass of material is electroplated. Hereafter, we shall use the currently accepted value of Avogadro's number:

$$N_0 = 6.025 \cdot 10^{23} \text{ molecules/mole.}$$

Given Avogadro's number, atomic and molecular masses may be expressed on an absolute scale. The mass of an atom of oxygen, for example, is $m = 16/N_0 \simeq 2.65 \cdot 10^{-23}$ gm, and the mass of an atom of hydrogen is 1/16 of this value.

Sizes of molecules. The meaning of the size of an object depends upon the method or operation used for measurement. When we place a ruler beside an object and determine the length of the object by reading on the ruler the points of coincidence with the ends of the object, the length of the object is defined by the positions of the surfaces from which light is reflected. If we perform the measurement in a dark room, we may use our fingers or some other means of contact to establish the positions of the ends of the object and the corresponding points on the ruler. In this case, the size of the object is defined by the positions in space where the repulsive force between our fingers and the object becomes sufficiently large to distort somewhat the nerve tissues in our fingers.

Similarly, atomic and molecular sizes can be determined by means of two basic types of experiments. In the first type we can use the reflection of light or other electromagnetic radiation as means of measurement, and in the second we determine where the repulsive forces among atoms become large. Molecular and atomic sizes estimated from molar volumes are clearly of this latter type. (Recall that liquids and solids, as compared with gases, are practically incompressible.) Hydrogen, for example, has a density of 0.07 gm/cm^3 when in its liquid form. The volume per mole (of atomic hydrogen) is $1.008/0.07 \simeq 14.4$ cm^3, and the volume occupied by one *atom* is therefore $v \simeq 14.4/(6.02 \cdot 10^{23})$ cm^3. The approximate linear dimension of a hydrogen atom must therefore be $d \simeq (v)^{1/3}$ or $2.9 \cdot 10^{-8}$ cm. In Table 15–2 are shown a number of representative atomic sizes computed in this way. Note the surprisingly small variation with atomic weight. No atom has a radius very much larger or smaller than 10^{-8} cm.

Table 15–2. Representative atomic sizes.

Element	Atomic weight, M	Density ρ, gm/cm^3	Volume per mole M/ρ, cm^3	Approximate atomic size, $d \simeq (M/\rho N_0)^{1/3}$
Hydrogen	1.008	0.07*	14.4	2.9×10^{-8} cm
Carbon	12.01	2.25†	5.35	2.1
Oxygen	16.00	1.14‡	14.1	2.9
Aluminum	26.97	2.70	10.0	2.5
Potassium	39.1	0.85	46.00	4.2
Iron	55.85	7.8	7.15	2.3
Copper	63.54	8.9	7.13	2.3
Silver	107.88	10.5	10.25	2.6
Lead	207.21	11.34	18.4	3.1
Uranium	238.07	18.7	12.7	2.8

* Liquid, at −252°C.   † Graphite.   ‡ Liquid, at −184°C.

PROBLEMS

15–1. When magnesium reacts with oxygen, 1.52 parts of magnesium (by weight) combine with 1 part of oxygen. According to Dalton's hypothesis, what can be concluded about the ratio between the atomic weights of magnesium and oxygen?

15–2. On the basis of the work by Lavoisier, Dalton, Gay-Lussac, and Avogadro, explain the statement that the ratio between the molecular weights of two gases is the same as the ratio between their densities (assume equal temperatures and pressures).

15–3. Estimate the average distance between the molecules in oxygen at atmospheric pressure and at a temperature of 273°K when the density of oxygen is 1.43 gm/liter. What is the corresponding distance in helium, in hydrogen, and in argon? Explain.

15–4. In an oil-film experiment with oleic acid ($M = 282.5$, $\rho = 0.9$ gm/cm^3), it is found that one milligram of the acid will cover an area of 0.9 m^2 of the water surface. What is the thickness of the film? If the film is assumed to be one atom thick, estimate Avogadro's number from the experiment.

15–5. How many molecules are needed to make 64 gm of oxygen? 12 gm of hydrogen? 1 gm of uranium?

15–6. What is the mass of one atom of silver? Estimate the number of silver atoms in one cubic centimeter.

15–7. The density of iron is 7.8 gm/cm^3. What is the molar volume?

15–8. Estimate the attractive gravitational force between two atoms in copper. The density of copper is $\rho = 8.9$ gm/cm^3.

CHAPTER 16

KINETIC THEORY OF GASES

Summary. After a brief discussion of experimental evidence for the internal motion in matter and the assumptions underlying the kinetic theory of gases, the gas pressure and temperature are expressed in terms of the average translational kinetic energy of the molecules. The molecular velocity is determined, and the results are compared with effusion and molecular-beam experiments. The latter experiment is used as an introduction to the discussion of the molecular velocity distribution. The Maxwell-Boltzmann distribution is presented next, the internal energy of a monatomic gas is treated, and as an introduction to the equipartition of energy, the mixture of two gases is studied and compared with the results from effusion experiments. The principle of equipartition of energy is extended and applied to the calculation of specific heats. Phenomena in gases which are directly related to collisions between molecules are discussed, the collision frequency and the mean free path are calculated, and a scattering experiment, from which molecular size is determined, is analyzed. Finally, the crude theory of transport phenomena in gases is illustrated by calculations of the heat-conduction and viscosity coefficients.

The success of the atomic or molecular theory of matter in the interpretation of chemical reactions, as outlined in the previous chapter, soon led to attempts to understand other properties of matter also in terms of a molecular theory. One such attempt was directed toward a kinetic or molecular theory of gases. Although suggestions along the lines of a particle theory of gases had been made in 1738 by D. Bernoulli, the detailed theory was first developed during the latter half of the 19th century by Rudolph Clausius (German physicist, 1822–1888), James Clerk Maxwell (English physicist, 1831–1879), Ludwig Boltzmann (Austrian physicist, 1844–1906), and others. The kinetic theory of gases as developed by these investigators stands today very much as it was left by them, although it has been and is still being refined to include the growing knowledge of intermolecular forces and modern theoretical and experimental techniques. It is our purpose in this chapter to discuss the kinetic theory of gases in its elementary form and to study some of its consequences.

16–1 First assumptions. The starting point in the kinetic theory of gases is a molecular or particle model of the gas in which the molecules are in (random) motion. Reasonably direct evidence for this random motion is provided by observations of Brownian motion. Smoke particles, for example, when observed under a microscope are seen to move about in a random or jerky fashion. The explanation of this phenomenon, we know now, is that randomly moving air molecules hit a smoke particle first on one side, then on another. (See Fig. 16–1.) The distance between the molecules must be assumed large compared with the dimensions of the molecules, in view of the observed fact that the volume of a given mass of a gas decreases by such a large factor when the gas condenses into its liquid form, in which the molecules are presumably comparatively closely packed. With this swarm of moving molecules or interacting particles as the model of the gas, it may seem a hopeless task to attempt to determine the motion of the particles since, as we recall, the problem of motion of more than two interacting particles defies general theoretical solution. From the very outset, then, it is clear that we must make some simplifying assumptions about the motion so that we may proceed with an analysis.

We thus shall assume that the molecules fly about in a container, at random, with no interactions or collisions with each other. We can then focus our attention on the motion of one molecule, which is representative of the rest. Next, having studied this motion, we can obtain the properties or effects of the motion of the whole group of molecules by proper averaging. However, in order to take these averages, we must clarify the meaning of "random motion." We shall assume that the motion of the molecules is governed by chance, i.e., that the laws of probability can be applied to molecules in the same way that they can be used in games of flipping coins and throwing dice. All locations in the container of the gas are assumed to be equally probable or available for all the molecules, and consequently the average number of particles per unit volume is assumed to be the same throughout the container. Thus, if the total number of molecules in the volume V is N, the number of molecules per unit volume, n, is

$$n = \frac{N}{V}. \tag{16–1}$$

When we refer to an *average* in our discussions of kinetic theory, we mean an *ensemble average*. In other words, in the interpretation of Eq. (16–1) we have to imagine a large number, an ensemble, of identical containers of volume V, each with N particles. Then, if we were able to take a flash picture and make a count of the molecules in all the con-

Fig. 16–1. Brownian motion.

tainers, we should find that the average number of particles found in one cubic centimeter, for example, in the center of the containers, would be the same as the average number of particles in a cubic centimeter located at another position (if our assumption of uniformity is correct).

We shall assume that not only all positions in the container but also all directions of motion are equally probable. In the ensemble of containers there will, on the average, be as many molecules moving in one direction as in the opposite direction. The average transfer of mass, momentum, and energy in any one direction then will be zero. The average kinetic energy of the molecules in the container, of course, will not be zero. We shall picture the molecules as spherical, perfectly elastic, identical balls.

If we follow the procedure outlined above, as we shall in the first part of the development of kinetic theory, we shall not be directly concerned with the collisions between molecules. However, later when we discuss the effects and properties of a gas which are directly dependent on the collisions, we shall consider the influence of the size of the molecules and the collisions between them.

16-2 Gas pressure and the molecular interpretation of pressure and temperature. As a first step in our study of the kinetic theory of gases, we shall attempt to evaluate the pressure in a gas in terms of molecular motion. At constant temperature, as we have seen in Chapter 13, the pressure is inversely proportional to the volume. From the kinetic theory viewpoint, as the molecules move about they collide with the walls of the container. At each collision there will be a momentum transfer to the wall, and if the number of collisions per second is large, the effect of the collisions will be similar to a continuous push or pressure on the wall. To study the problem quantitatively, we shall consider N molecules in a rectangular container of volume V. The number of molecules per unit volume is then $n = N/V$. Clearly, the situation is quite analogous to the question treated in Chapter 3 that dealt with the force produced when a stream of particles impinged on a wall. A stream of n particles per unit volume which moves with a speed v and strikes a wall at normal incidence produces nv particle impacts per second and per unit area of the wall. In a time Δt, all the molecules in a column of length $v \, \Delta t$ will strike the wall. There are $nv \, \Delta t$ molecules in this column, therefore the collision rate is nv (Fig. 16-2). If each collision is perfectly elastic, each particle bounces back with a speed v, and the momentum transfer to the wall is $2mv$, where m is the mass of the particle. The momentum transfer per unit time to a unit area of the wall is then $2mv \cdot nv = 2nmv^2$, and this is the pressure produced by the particle stream on the wall.

When we carry through a similar argument in the calculation of the

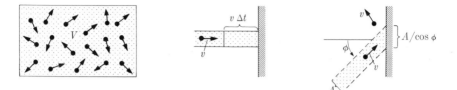

FIG. 16–2. When a beam of n particles per unit volume strikes a wall at normal incidence with a speed v, the number of collisions per second is nv per unit area of the wall. The corresponding pressure is $2nmv^2$ if the collisions are perfectly elastic. When molecules fly in all directions with equal probability, the pressure on the wall is $P = \frac{1}{3}nmv^2$.

pressure in a gas, we shall again assume that all collisions between molecules and container walls are perfectly elastic. However, it no longer is reasonable to assume that all the molecules move in the same direction, as was the case in the simple example of the stream. Rather, we assume that all directions of motion are equally probable. As a result, the pressure on the container walls will be less than the value $2nmv^2$; in fact, it follows from the following analysis that the pressure P is only one-sixth of the value $2nmv^2$. That is,

$$P = \frac{n}{3}\ \overline{mv^2} = \frac{2}{3}n\ \frac{\overline{mv^2}}{2}, \qquad (16\text{–}2)$$

where $\overline{v^2}$ is the average of the squared velocity of all the molecules in the container.

To prove this result, refer to Fig. 16–3, where there are $nA\,\Delta x$ molecules in the volume $A\,\Delta x$ just outside one of the walls. Suppose n_1 of these molecules have an x-component of velocity v_{1x}. Since motion in the positive and the negative x-directions is equally probable, on the average only half of the molecules in $A\,\Delta x$ move toward the wall. Consequently, in a time $\Delta t = \Delta x/v_{1x}$, $n_1 A\,\Delta x/2$ molecules will have struck the wall. (Some molecules will leave through the edges of the elementary box, but since the number of molecules crossing an area per second is proportional to the area, the number of molecules which leave through the edges is zero in the limit $\Delta x = 0$.) Some molecules, such as those halfway between the parallel A faces, would leave in a time less than Δt, but all $n_1 A\,\Delta x/2$ molecules will have left the box in time Δt. The number of molecules striking the wall per second is then $n_1 A\,\Delta x/\Delta t = n_1 A v_{1x}/2$. The momentum transfer to the wall by one of the molecules is $2mv_{1x}$, if we assume the collisions to be perfectly elastic.

The average force on the area A is the product of the momentum transferred per collision and the number of such collisions per second:

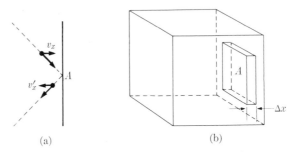

(a)   (b)

FIG. 16-3. (a) A molecule with an x-component of velocity v_x collides with the wall and rebounds with a velocity component $v'_x = -v_x$, so that a momentum $2mv_x$ is transferred to the wall. (b) If there are n molecules per unit volume in the large box, there are $nA\,\Delta x$ in the small volume shown, and $nAv_x/2$ will strike the wall per second.

Average force on A
= (momentum transfer per collision) · (number of collisions per second),

$$F_1 = 2mv_{1x}\,\frac{nAv_{1x}}{2} = n_1 mv_{1x}^2 A. \tag{16-3}$$

The average pressure contribution by the n_1 molecules, i.e., the force per unit area, is then $P_1 = F_1/A = mn_1v_{1x}^2$.

Similarly, if we have n_2 particles with an x-component of velocity v_{2x}, their contribution to the pressure is $mn_2v_{2x}^2$. Thus, if the number of particles is n_1, n_2, n_3, . . . , with the velocity components v_{1x}, v_{2x}, v_{3x}, . . . , the total pressure becomes

$$P = m(n_1v_{1x}^2 + n_2v_{2x}^2 + n_3v_{3x}^2 + \cdots) = mn(\overline{v_x^2}).$$

We have introduced here the average $\overline{v_x^2}$ of the squared value of the velocity components of all the molecules: $\overline{v_x^2} = (n_1v_{1x}^2 + n_2v_{2x}^2 + \cdots)/(n_1 + n_2 + \cdots) = (n_1v_{1x}^2 + n_2v_{2x}^2 + \cdots)/n$, where $n = n_1 + n_2 + \cdots$ is the total number of molecules per unit volume.

Instead of expressing the pressure in terms of the average squared velocity component $\overline{v_x^2}$, we shall use the squared total velocity $\overline{v^2} = \overline{v_x^2} + \overline{v_y^2} + \overline{v_z^2}$. Because the motion is assumed random, we have $\overline{v_x^2} = \overline{v_y^2} = \overline{v_z^2}$, and $\overline{v_x^2} = \overline{v^2}/3$. Consequently, the total pressure can be written as

$$P = n\,\frac{m\overline{v^2}}{3} = \frac{2}{3}n\,\frac{m\overline{v^2}}{2},$$

which is the same as Eq. (16-2). In future discussions, we shall usually refer to the average of the squared velocity as v^2 instead of $\overline{v^2}$. The square root of $\overline{v^2}$ is called the *root-mean-square value* of the velocity:

$$v = \sqrt{\overline{v^2}} \, .$$

The pressure, then, is proportional to the *translational kinetic energy* per unit volume of the gas. From the definition of temperature in Chapter 14, the absolute temperature T is proportional to the pressure, $T = 273P/P_0$. Since P now has been shown to be proportional to the average translational kinetic energy of the molecules, it follows also that the absolute temperature, according to the kinetic theory of gases, is proportional to the *average translational kinetic energy* of the molecules. It is customary to express this proportionality as

$$\frac{2}{3} \frac{\overline{mv^2}}{2} = kT \qquad \text{or} \qquad \frac{\overline{mv^2}}{2} = \frac{3}{2} kT. \tag{16-4}$$

It is important to note that only the translational energy, and not any possible rotational or vibrational energy, of the molecules is involved. The reason is, of course, that the result obtained stems from the momentum transfer to the walls, to which only the translational motion contributes. Furthermore, the result applies to any type of gas, monatomic or diatomic, regardless of the molecular mass. The constant k, which is independent of m, is called the *Boltzmann constant*, and in terms of this constant the relation between the pressure and the kinetic energy in Eq. (16–2) can be expressed as

$$P = nkT. \tag{16-5}$$

16–3 The ideal gas law. If we introduce in Eq. (16–5) the total number of particles $N = nV$, we obtain $P = (N/V)kT$, or

$$PV = NkT = RT, \tag{16-6}$$

where the new constant R equals Nk. The relation (16–6) was known for a long time prior to the formulation of the kinetic gas theory. From simple experiments, Robert Boyle found that at a constant temperature the product of the pressure and volume of a given amount of gas remains constant (Boyle's law). Jacques Charles (French physicist, 1746–1823) and Joseph Gay-Lussac extended Boyle's law to include the dependence on temperature and formulated the ideal gas law, which is given by Eq. (16–6). Actually, when temperature is defined in terms of the gas thermometer, the ideal gas law follows directly from Boyle's law and the definition of temperature. Some of the early experiments which led to Boyle's law and the ideal gas law are discussed briefly in the historical notes at the end of this section.

It should be pointed out that the definition of temperature, in terms of a gas thermometer, is applicable only when the density of the thermometric gas is sufficiently low, and also that the validity of the ideal gas law is limited to gases of sufficiently low densities and high temperatures. From the point of view of kinetic theory, this latter limitation stems from the assumptions that the distance between the molecules is very large compared with the molecular dimensions and that the interaction between the molecules can be neglected. A discussion of the limits of applicability of the ideal gas law will not be given here, but will be taken up in the next chapter.

The universal gas constant. The kinetic theory of gases, then, has led to a result that is consistent with well-established experimental results. In addition, it has provided a kinetic (molecular) interpretation of temperature: the product of the pressure and volume is proportional to the temperature and the total number of molecules. Since one mole of any gas contains the same number of molecules, Avogadro's number, it follows that the product of pressure and volume per mole is the same for all gases at the same temperature. In other words, if Eq. (16–6) refers to *one mole* of the gas, the number of molecules is N_0, Avogadro's number, and the constant

$$R = N_0 k \tag{16–7}$$

is the same for all gases. This constant is called the *universal gas constant.* Experimentally, this constant can be determined by measuring the ratio $R = PV/T$ for one mole of a gas.

At a temperature of $T = 273.2°K$ and at atmospheric pressure $P = 1 \text{ atm} = 10^6$ dynes/cm^2, the volume of one mole of a gas is found to be 22.4 liters, and therefore the universal gas constant becomes

$$R = 1 \cdot 22.4/273.2 = 0.0821 \text{ liter·atm/deg·mole.}$$

The dimension of the constant R is the dimension of energy/mole·deg and, of course, it can be expressed in units other than liter·atm/deg·mole. We have, for example,

$$R \simeq 0.0821 \text{ liter·atm/deg·mole}$$
$$\simeq 8.31 \cdot 10^7 \text{ ergs/deg·mole}$$
$$\simeq 8.31 \text{ joules/deg·mole.} \tag{16–8}$$

With $R = 8.31 \cdot 10^7$ and $N_0 = 6.02 \cdot 10^{23}$, it follows that the Boltzmann constant $k = R/N_0$ [see Eq. (16–7)], which can be regarded as the gas constant per molecule, has the value

$$k = \frac{8.31 \cdot 10^7}{6.02 \cdot 10^{23}} = 1.38 \cdot 10^{-16} \text{ erg/deg.} \tag{16–9}$$

The gas law of Eq. (16–6), with R given by Eq. (16–8), refers to one mole, i.e., to $6.02 \cdot 10^{23}$ particles. For any other amount of gas, we have

$$PV = \mu RT,$$

where μ is the number of moles of gas.

EXAMPLE. Ten grams of helium are contained in a volume of 2 liters at a temperature of 300°C. What is the pressure?

The molar mass of helium is 4, and the number of moles involved in this case is $10/4 = 2.5$. It follows from the gas law that $PV = 2.5 \cdot 0.082 \cdot 573$, from which we obtain $P = 59$ atm.

The pressure, volume, and temperature of a gas are called *state variables*, and when values of these are given, the *state* of the gas is specified. Note that the state variables are not independent of one another; their relationship is expressed by Eq. (16–6), which is often called the *equation of state*. When two variables are given, the third can be found directly from this equation. Instead of the volume V, it is sometimes convenient to use the density ρ as a state variable. If we consider 1 gm of a gas, i.e., $1/M$ moles, we have $\rho V = 1$, and the ideal gas law can be written as

$$P = r\rho T, \qquad\qquad (16–10)$$

where $r = R/M$ is the gas constant per gram of the gas.

Historical notes. The first really enlightening experiments on gases were devised by Evangelista Torricelli (1608–1647), an Italian mathematician and one-time student of Galileo. The apparatus used by Torricelli was essentially the same as our modern barometer. A long glass tube with one closed end is filled with mercury. The filled tube is then inverted, its open end being submerged in an open dish of mercury. The height of the mercury in the glass tube, measured perpendicular to the surface of the mercury in the open dish, is about 76 cm. If the glass tube is less than 76 cm long, the mercury continues to fill the tube.

At the time of this experiment (1643), the concept of pressure as force per unit area and the general principles of the equilibrium of a liquid were well known. Torricelli then put forth the idea of a "sea of air" surrounding the earth or, in other words, a general atmospheric pressure. Hence, in the equilibrium experiments shown in Fig. 16–4 the (downward) force on the imaginary area A across the end of the tube is given by the product of the pressure $P = \rho g h'$ and the area A, where ρ is the density of mercury and g is the acceleration due to gravity. The upward force at this same point is $P'A = [\rho g(h' - h) + P_0]A$, where P_0 is the pressure of the "sea of air" on the surface of the exposed mercury. Since the mercury is in equilibrium, we have $P'A = PA$ (the upward force must equal the downward force) and $P_0 = \rho g h$. That is, atmospheric pressure P_0 is $\rho g h$, where h (experimentally about 76 cm) is the height of the column of mercury measured from the surface of the mercury in the open dish. Note that we have taken the pressure at the top of the mercury columns to be zero, the implication being that there is no air in this region. This indeed was one of the early and quite satisfactory methods of producing a vacuum.

Torricelli's interpretation of his experiment was by no means widely accepted immediately. Important experimental tests of his interpretation were carried out shortly thereafter by Pascal and by Boyle. Pascal arranged to have a Torricelli experiment performed at two different elevations, to prove the contention that since the pressure of a fluid varies with depth, so also should atmospheric pressure vary with depth in the atmosphere. In 1648, a Torricelli apparatus was carried up a mountain and an experiment was performed which fully supported Torricelli's interpretation.

Boyle, on the other hand, set about to test the notion that if the air were removed from the region above the mercury in the open dish (Fig. 16–4), the height of the mercury column should fall, for it was the air pressing down on the mercury surface, according to Torricelli, that supported the mercury columns. For this experiment Boyle wanted an air pump, and although it was not absolutely necessary, he designed and built one that could (partially) evacuate a region such as A shown in

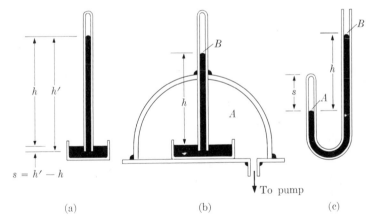

(a)   (b)   (c)

FIG. 16–4. (a) The Torricelli experiment. The tube was initially filled with mercury. It was then inverted and the open end submerged beneath the surface of the mercury in the open dish. (b) One of Boyle's experiments. When A is open to the atmosphere, the height of the mercury column is about 76 cm, but when some of the air is pumped from A, the level drops. (c) Boyle's experimental apparatus for the study of the "spring of air." The volume of the gas under study is proportional to s, and is under a pressure equal to that of the atmosphere plus $\rho g h$, where ρ is the density of mercury.

Fig. 16–4(b). The mercury level did decrease as the air was pumped from A. This experiment, and others in which pressure in A was increased and that in B varied, offered further evidence that the atmosphere could indeed consistently be regarded as a sea of air.

The above experiments led Boyle to investigate the compressive properties of air, which he called the "spring of the air." The apparatus which Boyle used in these studies was ingeniously simple [see Fig. 16–4(c)]. When the difference in the heights of the mercury levels A and B is zero, the pressure of the gas above A must be atmospheric. As mercury is added at C, the gas above A is compressed to a smaller valume, and is under a pressure $P = P_0 + \rho g h$. Similar experiments were performed by Boyle to investigate air at pressures less than atmospheric. Interestingly, Boyle himself did not hypothesize the relationship $PV = \text{const}$; acquaintances who had been shown his experimental findings formulated the relation.

Vacua. Customarily, when referring to pressure in a partially evacuated region, we speak in terms of the height of a column of mercury that is supported by the residual pressure, rather than of the actual pressure in dynes/cm^2 or lb/in^2. Atmospheric pressure, which is about 10^6 dynes/cm^2 or 14.7 lb/in^2, is often expressed simply as "76 cm of mercury." Boyle's pumps were probably capable of reducing the pressure to about 1 cm of mercury in an enclosure such as A in Fig. 16–4(b). The best modern mechanical pumps can achieve pressures 10,000 times less than this, or 10^{-3} mm of mercury. The pressure of the residual gas in a radio tube is about 10^{-6} mm of mercury, and with considerable care and patience, pressures of 10^{-8} to 10^{-10} mm of mercury can be attained. The pressure of the gas in our galaxy (the Milky Way) is about 10^{-16} mm of mercury, and the pressure of the gas between galaxies is probably of the order of 10^{-20} mm of mercury.

Measurements of pressures that are less than a millimeter or so of mercury cannot be made directly with a mercury column, even though the resulting measurements are usually expressed in terms of millimeters of mercury. Pressures larger than atmospheric are commonly measured in atmospheres, or directly in units of pounds per square inch, for example. Hence, a pressure of 10 atm is a pressure of 147 lb/in^2.

16–4 Molecular velocities. Effusion and molecular-beam experiments. Perhaps the most important result obtained from kinetic theory is the relation (16–4) between the average kinetic energy of a molecule and the temperature of the gas. According to this relation, the root-mean-square (rms) value of the molecular speed is given by

$$v = \sqrt{\frac{3kT}{m}} = \sqrt{\frac{3RT}{M}}. \tag{16–11}$$

The speed increases as the square root of the absolute temperature. To get some idea about the speeds involved, let us consider hydrogen (H_2), for which $M = 2$. Then, with $R = 8.31 \cdot 10^7$ ergs/deg·mole, we obtain a speed of $v \simeq 1900$ m/sec, at room temperature $T = 300°K$. For oxygen (O_2, $M = 32$) at the same temperature, we obtain $v \simeq 475$ m/sec.

Some early objections to the kinetic theory of gases were based upon the largeness of these predicted molecular velocities. If molecular velocities are typically hundreds of meters per second, why does a gas released at one place in a room take so long to distribute itself throughout the room? The answer, we know now, is that the molecules of a gas do not travel from one point to another along a straight line. Rather, the molecules collide with each other after traveling only very small distances, and to reach a distant point they must travel very large distances in zig-zag paths, along which an incredibly large number of collisions take place.

The relation between the molecular speed and temperature lends itself to a direct experimental check of the kinetic theory of gases. Later in this section we shall briefly describe the molecular-beam experiments by means of which molecular speed can be measured. However, before we present the results of these experiments, a much simpler experiment can be performed to determine the ratio between the molecular speeds of two different gases.

Effusion. We shall now study the effusion (efflux) of a gas from a container through a small hole in the container wall, as illustrated schematically in Fig. 16–5. The region outside the hole is evacuated. The molecules of gas which otherwise would have hit the wall can now escape through the hole. In connection with the discussion of gas pressure in the previous section, we determined the rate at which molecules collide with a unit area of a wall. This rate, $nv_x/2$, can also be expressed as

$$\text{Number of collisions per unit area and unit time} = \frac{n\bar{v}}{4}, \quad (16\text{–}12)$$

where $\bar{v}$ is the average speed (see Sec. 16–5). When the area of the hole is A, the number of molecules that escape through the hole per second is

$$Q = \frac{An\bar{v}}{4}.$$

The effusion rate is proportional to the number density and average speed. If, in a mixture of two gases, we assume that the molecules fly about independently of one another with speeds as given by Eq. (16–11),

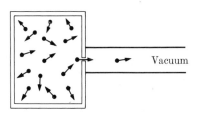

FIG. 16–5. Effusion.

we should be led to predict that the speeds of different molecules are re-lated inversely as the square root of their masses (Sec. 16–7).

If there are two different gases in the container, the ratio between the effusion rates of the molecules of the two gases is then

$$\frac{Q_1}{Q_2} = \frac{n_1 \bar{v}_1}{n_2 \bar{v}_2} = \frac{n_1}{n_2} \sqrt{\frac{M_2}{M_1}}.$$

In other words, the composition of the gas stream through the hole is not the same as that in the container. According to kinetic theory, it is modified by a factor equal to the square root of the molecular weights; thus the stream contains more lighter (faster) than heavier (slower) mole-cules. Such an effect indeed has been observed, and by analysis of the composition of the gas stream, the ratio between the molecular weights of the gas can be determined. However, a more convenient and more accurate procedure is based on a study of the decrease of the pressure in the container from which the gas effuses. To analyze this problem quanti-tatively, we start from the rate at which molecules leave through the hole in the container wall. According to the previous discussion, this is $Q = An\bar{v}/4 = AN\bar{v}/4V$, where N, as before, is the total number of molecules in the volume V. The rate of change of this number is then

$$\frac{dN}{dt} = -\frac{A\bar{v}}{4V} n = -\alpha N, \qquad \alpha = \frac{A\bar{v}}{4V}.$$

With $dN/N = -\alpha \, dt$, we have $\ln N = -\alpha t + \text{const}$, so that if N' is the number of molecules at $t = 0$, the number of molecules at a later time is

$$N = N' e^{-\alpha t} = N' e^{-t/\tau},$$

where $1/\tau = \alpha = A\bar{v}/4V$.

After the time τ, called the *relaxation time*, the number of molecules present in the container will have decreased by a factor e. Since $\bar{v}$ is known in terms of the temperature and the molecular weight, a measure-ment of relaxation times for gases effusing through holes of known area affords one method for the determination of molecular weight. However, usually the hole area is not known to a very high accuracy, and the study must be limited to a determination of the ratios of relaxation times and, hence, the ratios of the molecular weights of various gases. This treat-ment of effusion phenomena is valid only when the hole is very small, so that there is little chance that a molecule will collide with other mole-cules while traveling a distance equal to the hole diameter. If the hole diameter is large, the gas in the vicinity of the hole is grossly disturbed, and our description of molecular velocities is then quite inaccurate.

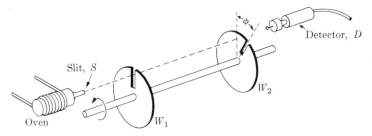

FIG. 16–6. Molecular-beam experiment by which molecular velocities can be determined.

Molecular-beam experiments. A more direct experimental test of kinetic theory can be obtained from molecular-beam experiments. In these experiments a substance is vaporized in an oven, and the gas in the oven is allowed to emerge through a hole in the oven wall into an evacuated region. Here, the molecular stream is collimated by slits so that a well-defined beam is formed. This beam is passed through a velocity-measuring device or velocity selector and is finally deposited on a detector.

An example of such an apparatus is shown in Fig. 16–6. The stream of atoms which is emitted from the oven passes through a slit and then through a second slit in a rotating wheel, W_1. A wheel, W_2, is connected to the same shaft as W_1, but the slits in this wheel are displaced with respect to those in W_1 by an angle ϕ. The beam will also pass through the second wheel if the time of flight of the molecules between the wheels is the same as the time required for the shaft and wheels to rotate through an angle ϕ. If the distance between the wheels is L, the angular velocity is ω, and the angular separation between the slits is ϕ, the speed of the molecules which pass through both wheels is then $v = \omega L/\phi$. Since the slits have a finite width, there will be a range of speeds represented among the molecules which pass through both wheels and reach the detector D. (In order to pass through the two wheels, a molecule which enters at the leading edge of a slit need not have as high a speed as a molecule which enters at the trailing edge.) By varying ω, we can select molecules of different speeds with this apparatus.

The method of measurement is, of course, entirely analogous to the well-known simple method of measuring the speed of a bullet, as illustrated schematically in Fig. 16–7. A bullet is shot through two cardboard discs which are mounted on the same rotating shaft and separated by a certain distance. The holes made by the bullet as it goes through the discs are displaced by a certain angle ϕ, from which the speed of the bullet can be determined when the distance between the discs and the angular velocity are known. In the molecular-beam experiments, the slits correspond to the "bullet holes," which in this case are made in advance.

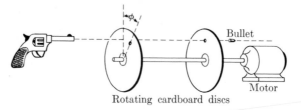

FIG. 16–7. Measurement of the speed of a bullet by means of rotating discs.

There are several other types of molecular-beam experiments by means of which the velocity of molecules can be measured. In Fig. 16–8 an arrangement is shown in which a molecular beam enters a slit in a rotating drum. If the drum is at rest, the beam, of course, strikes the wall diametrically opposite the slit, but when the drum rotates, the beam will be displaced laterally, and the molecular speed can be determined from this displacement.

Whatever method is used, the experiments all show the very important result that in a gas at a certain temperature, all molecules do not have the same speeds. Although there is a definite predominant speed, we find that all speeds, from very low to very high values, are represented. In the rotating-disc experiment in Fig. 16–6, for example, there will be molecules passing the velocity selector not only for one specific angular velocity but for a whole range. Similarly, in the rotating-drum experiment, the molecular beam is not deposited at one single spot on the wall of the drum, but is spread out in a band, as shown in Fig. 16–8. By measuring the density distribution of the molecular deposit at various positions along this band, the relative distribution of speeds among the molecules in the beam can be determined. The same information can be obtained from the rotating-disc experiment by measurement of the molecular deposit for different angular velocities of the discs. The velocity distribution in the beam is not the same as in the oven, but the distribution in the oven can easily be derived from the measured distribution (see Problem 16–13).

Because a distribution of velocities, rather than a single velocity, is obtained in the experiments, a direct comparison of experimental results with the calculated value in Eq. (16–11) cannot be made. As we recall, this value is the rms value of the molecular speed, and in order to compare it with the experimental results, we must determine the average of the square of the measured molecular speeds. We have already mentioned that for each setting of the velocity selector there is a corresponding speed range Δv which depends on the slit width. Thus, if the number of molecules in the velocity band between v_1 and $v_1 + \Delta v_1$ is denoted by Δn_1,

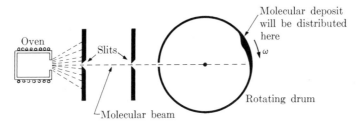

FIG. 16–8. Rotating-drum method for measurement of molecular velocity.

and the number of molecules in the band between v_2 and $v_2 + \Delta v_2$ by Δn_2, etc., the average of the square of the molecular speeds is given by the relation

$$\overline{v^2} = \frac{\Delta n_1 v_1^2 + \Delta n_2 v_2^2 + \Delta n_3 v_3^2 + \cdots}{N},$$

$$N = \Delta n_1 + \Delta n_2 + \Delta n_3 + \cdots.$$

The rms value of the speed is then obtained by taking the square root of this result. Experimental results obtained in this way have been found to be in excellent agreement with the speed predicted from kinetic theory. However, the theoretical analysis can be carried further, and it is indeed possible to determine not only the rms value of the speed, but also the distribution of the speeds among the molecules. Maxwell and others derived this distribution long before the above experiments had been performed.

16–5 The Maxwell-Boltzmann distribution. It is clear that in the above experiments, the number of molecules detected at a certain setting of the velocity selector depends on the slit width and the corresponding velocity range Δv. Then, in order to present the result properly, it is important that all velocity data be reduced to the same range. For small values of the range Δv, the number of molecules in Δv is directly proportional to Δv. It is customary, particularly in theoretical discussions, to reduce the data to a speed range of 1 m/sec. In other words, if, in the experiments, the speed range is Δv_1 and the number of molecules with speeds between v_1 and $v_1 + \Delta v_1$ is Δn_1, the average number of molecules per unit speed range is simply $\Delta n_1/\Delta v_1$. If the total number of molecules is N, the fraction of the molecules which fall in unit speed range at the speed v_1 is then $(\Delta n_1/N)/\Delta v_1$. Denoting this fraction of molecules per unit velocity range as $f(v_1)$, we can clearly see that the fraction of molecules which fall in the range Δv_1 can be written as $(\Delta n_1/N) = f(v_1)\,\Delta v_1$.

Similarly, the fraction of molecules at another velocity v_2 is $f(v_2)\,\Delta v_2$, and so on. The total fraction of molecules is, of course, unity, so that $f(v_1)\,\Delta v_1 + f(v_2)\,\Delta v_2 + f(v_3)\,\Delta v_3 + \cdots = 1$ or, expressed in the form of an integral,

$$\int_0^\infty f(v)\,dv = 1. \tag{16-13}$$

The function $f(v)$, the fraction of molecules per unit speed range, is called the *speed-distribution function*.

It may be helpful at this point to give a more familiar illustration of a distribution function. Imagine that it is your task to measure the distribution of heights of the people in a town. First, you would measure the height of each individual. Then, in order to show how these heights were distributed, you could sort your data and find the *number* of individuals with heights between 50 in. and 51 in., between 51 in. and 52 in., between 52 in. and 53 in., etc. This data could then be presented in the form of a graph or histogram, on which you would plot Δn versus Δh (Δn = the number of people with heights between h and $h + \Delta h$, that is, between 51 in. and 51 in. + 1 in. = 52 in.). Of course, if you had subdivided the population into groups with heights between 50 in. and $50\frac{1}{2}$ in., $50\frac{1}{2}$ in. and 51 in., etc., each ordinate in the graph would be about half as large as before. On the other hand, if you were to plot $\Delta n/\Delta h$, rather than Δn versus h, the ordinate would not depend upon Δh. If 10,000 people are of a height between 50 in. and 51 in. ($\Delta n/\Delta h = 10{,}000/1 = 10{,}000$ people/in.), only about 5000 would have heights between 50 in. and $50\frac{1}{2}$ in. ($\Delta n/\Delta h \simeq 5000/0.5 \simeq 10{,}000$ people/in.), and as you choose finer and finer intervals Δh, the value of $\Delta n/\Delta h$ would approach a limiting value, which in this case will not be far different from 10,000. If the total number of persons measured is $N = 100{,}000$, the fraction of the people who have a height between h and $h + \Delta h$ is then $(1/N)\,\Delta n/\Delta h$, which in our example gives about 1/10 when $h = 50$ in. The limiting value of the quantity $(\Delta n/N)/\Delta h = f(h)$, when Δh approaches zero, is the height-distribution function. The fraction of the populus of heights between h and $h + \Delta h$ is then $f(h)\,\Delta h = \Delta n/N$. There will be no persons with zero or infinite height, therefore the distribution function reaches a maximum.

The speed-distribution function obtained by Maxwell and Boltzmann is

$$f(v) = Av^2 e^{-v^2/v_0^2}, \tag{16-14}$$

where

$$v_0^2 = \frac{2kT}{m} \quad \text{and} \quad B = \frac{4}{\sqrt{\pi}}\frac{1}{v_0^3}.$$

The constant B must be such that it fulfills the condition (16–13). We shall see (Problem 16–14) that the appropriate value of the constant is indeed

$$B = \frac{4}{\sqrt{\pi}} \frac{1}{v_0^3}. \tag{16–15}$$

By differentiating the velocity-distribution function $f(v)$, we can readily find that it has a maximum value of $4/(\sqrt{\pi} \cdot v_0)$ at the velocity

$$v_0 = \sqrt{\frac{2kT}{m}} = \sqrt{\frac{2RT}{M}}. \tag{16–16}$$

(See Problem 16–15.) We can also determine other characteristic properties of the distribution function. We have already indicated in Eq. (16–12) a method by which we can obtain the average of the square of the molecular velocities. If we introduce $\Delta n/N = f(v)\,dv$ into this expression, it follows that the average of the squared velocity can be expressed by the integral

$$\overline{v^2} = \int_0^\infty v^2 f(v)\,dv \tag{16–17}$$

and, similarly, the average speed is determined by

$$\bar{v} = \int_0^\infty v f(v)\,dv. \tag{16–18}$$

To determine these averages, integrals of the form $\int_0^\infty v^s \exp\,(-v^2/v_0^2)\,dv$ must be known for $s = 3$ and 4. In some of the problems at the end of this chapter, this integral for other values of s, as given in Table 16–1, will be needed. From the given values and the value of A, we find that the *average speed* is

$$v_1 = \bar{v} = \frac{2}{\sqrt{\pi}} \sqrt{\frac{2kT}{m}} = \frac{2}{\sqrt{\pi}} v_0 \simeq 1.12 v_0, \tag{16–19}$$

Table 16–1

$$I_s = \int_0^\infty v^s e^{-v^2/v_0^2}\,dv.$$

s	0	1	2	3	4
I_s	$\dfrac{\sqrt{\pi}}{2} v_0$	$\dfrac{v_0^2}{2}$	$\dfrac{\sqrt{\pi}}{4} v_0^3$	$\dfrac{v_0^4}{2}$	$\dfrac{3}{8}\sqrt{\pi}\, v_0^5$

and the *root-mean-square value* of the speed is

$$v_2 = \sqrt{\overline{v^2}} = \sqrt{\frac{3kT}{m}} = \sqrt{\frac{3}{2}}\, v_0 \simeq 1.22 v_0, \qquad (16\text{--}20)$$

where $v_0 = \sqrt{2kT/m}$. The various velocities are indicated on the distribution curve in Fig. 16–9, which shows the velocity-distribution function of nitrogen at a temperature of 273°C.

EXAMPLE. What is the most probable speed, v_0, of nitrogen molecules at a temperature of 20°C, and what is the fraction of molecules in the velocity range between $0.9v_0$ and $1.1v_0$?

The most probable velocity is $v_0 = \sqrt{2RT/M}$. The molecular weight of nitrogen is $14 \cdot 2 = 28$, since nitrogen is diatomic. The most probable velocity is therefore

$$v_0 = \sqrt{\frac{2 \cdot 8.31 \cdot 10^7 \cdot 293}{28}} = 4.2 \cdot 10^4 \text{ cm/sec.}$$

The fraction of molecules in the interval from $0.9v_0$ to $1.1v_0$ is

$$\frac{\Delta n}{N} = \int_{0.9v_0}^{1.1v_0} f(v)\, dv,$$

which we can approximate as

$$\frac{\Delta n}{N} = \int_{0.9v_0}^{1.1v_0} f(v)\, dv \simeq f(v_0)0.2v_0.$$

With

$$f(v) = \frac{4}{\sqrt{\pi}} \frac{v^2}{v_0^3} e^{-v^2/v_0^2},$$

we obtain $f(v_0) = 4/(\sqrt{\pi} \cdot v_0 \cdot e)$, and multiplication by $0.2v_0$ yields $\Delta n/N = 0.2 \cdot 4/(\sqrt{\pi} \cdot e) \simeq 0.17$. In other words, about 17% of the molecules have speeds in the range from $0.9v_0$ to $1.1v_0$.

The Maxwell-Boltzmann distribution indicates that the velocity distribution depends on temperature. The maximum value $4/(\sqrt{\pi} \cdot v_0)$ of the distribution function decreases with increasing temperature as the location of the maximum moves toward higher speeds, as shown in Fig. 16–10. Although the maxima and the shapes of the curves change with temperature, all curves are such that the areas under them remain the same. That is, $\int_0^\infty f(v)\, dv = 1$.

According to the distribution function, there will be molecules with velocities of all values between zero and infinity. One consequence of this distribution is that some of the molecules in the atmosphere of a planet will have speeds which exceed the escape velocity of the planet. Consequently, a planet is subject to a continuous loss of its atmosphere,

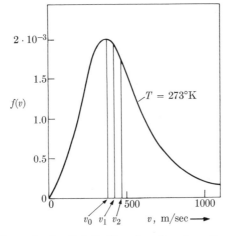

Fig. 16–9. The velocity-distribution function for nitrogen at $T = 273°\text{K}$. The most probable speed, v_0, the average speed, $v_1 = \bar{v} = \int v f(v)\, dv$, and the rms value, $v_2 = \sqrt{\int v^2 f(v) dv}$, are shown.

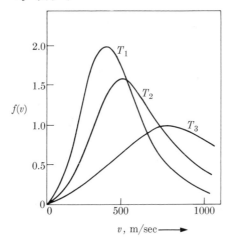

Fig. 16–10. The distribution function varies with temperature. $T_3 > T_2 > T_1$.

and this loss is particularly important at high temperatures and for light gases.

16–6 Specific heat. In Chapter 14 heat was introduced as a quantity that is conserved when bodies interact thermally. Recall that if the temperature change of a body of mass m is found to be ΔT in a thermal interaction, the heat content of the body is changed by an amount $\Delta Q = cM\, \Delta T$, where c is the specific heat of the body. Kinetic theory has now given us an interpretation of temperature in terms of the kinetic energy of the molecules. If two gases of different temperatures interact with each other, we know that the temperatures of the two gases will change, but the total kinetic energy of the molecules will remain the same. It is natural, then, to assume that heat corresponds to the total mechanical energy of the molecular motion. This assumption has proven to be completely consistent with experimental results and the general law of conservation of energy, and can be regarded as a well-established fact (see Chapter 17).

According to kinetic theory, a gas of mass M has a total kinetic energy of $Nmv^2/2 = Mv^2/2 = 3NkT/2$, where N is the number of molecules involved. As the temperature is increased by an amount ΔT, the total kinetic energy increases by the amount $3Nk\,\Delta T/2$. On the other hand, according to the definition of specific heat, the heat increase $Mc\,\Delta T$ corresponds to the temperature increase ΔT. Thus, if we identify the increase in heat with the increase in kinetic energy, we obtain $3Nk\,\Delta T/2 = Mc\,\Delta T$. For one mole of the gas, we have $N_0k = R$, and M is the molar weight. The specific heat of one mole of the gas is then $Mc = C$, or the molar specific heat is $C = 3R/2$. We have seen that R, the universal gas constant, has the value $8.31 \cdot 10^7$ ergs/mole·°C or 8.31 joules/mole·°C. If now we take 4.185 joules of mechanical energy to be equivalent to 1 cal of heat, as found from experiments in which mechanical energy is dissipated, we can express R as 1.99 cal/mole·°C. Hence, the specific heat of a gas is predicted to be $C = 3R/2 = 2.98$ cal/mole·°C or approximately 3 cal/mole·°C.

The comparison between this prediction and experimental results on real gases is, of course, important. But we must first decide how we are going to measure the specific heat of a gas, for when a gas is heated it tends to expand, and we must then choose either a constant pressure or a constant volume. Conceivably, both the pressure and the volume could be allowed to vary, but certainly both cannot be held constant if the temperature is to change.

In the development of the kinetic theory and the ideal gas law from which we obtained the result $C = 3R/2$, it was assumed that the walls of the container were held in fixed positions, so that in the elastic collisions between the molecules and the wall the energy of the molecules did not change. If, on the other hand, the walls had moved, there would have been a change of the molecular energy in the collision with the moving wall, as we shall discuss in more detail in the next chapter. Consequently, the theory refers to a gas of constant volume. In order to indicate that the specific heat refers to the conditions of constant volume, we shall denote the corresponding molar specific heat by C_v:

$$C_v = \tfrac{3}{2}R. \qquad (16\text{--}21)$$

We shall later investigate the specific heat at constant pressure and find that it is related in a simple way to C_v.

The specific heats of some representative gases in the region from 0°C to 30°C are given in Table 16–2. When expressed in cal/gm·°C, there seems to be very little regularity or order in the specific heats. They vary from a high of 2.4 to a low of 0.015 cal/gm·°C. It takes 16 times as much heat to increase by one degree the temperature of one gram of hydrogen gas as it does to increase by one degree the temperature of one gram of mercury gas (vapor). When the specific heats are expressed, instead, in cal/mole·°C, the values for the various gases (except ether) are much nearer one another. We find the encouraging result that the specific heat of some gases is indeed 3 cal/mole·°C, as predicted by this first version of kinetic theory. Clearly, however, there are other results which deviate considerably from the predicted value. The gases that *do* have specific heats in accordance with our prediction are the monatomic gases: helium, neon, argon, krypton, xenon, and mercury. The specific heats of the polyatomic gases are larger, but we shall see that these results

Table 16–2. Specific heats of gases.

| Gas | C_v | | C_p | $\gamma = C_p/C_v$ |
	cal/gm·°C	cal/mole·°C	cal/mole·°C	
H_2	2.4	4.8	6.8	1.41
He	0.755	3.02	5.00	1.66
N_2	0.176	4.93	6.93	1.40
O_2	0.155	4.99	6.99	1.40
Ne	0.153	3.1	5.1	1.64
Cl_2	0.0848	6.01	8.15	1.36
A	0.075	3.0	5.0	1.67
Kr	0.0359	2.9	4.9	1.68
Xe	0.0228	3.0	5.0	1.67
Hg*	0.0150	3.0	5.0	1.67
NO	0.166	4.97	6.97	1.40
CO	0.179	5.017	7.014	1.40
CO_2	0.153	6.86	8.89	1.30
HCl	0.137	5.02	7.08	1.41
SO_2	0.117	7.5	9.7	1.29
Ether	0.416	30.8	33.3	1.08

* At 300°C.

can also be interpreted in terms of kinetic theory. (The molecules of polyatomic gases can have kinetic energy of rotation and vibration, as well as that which arises from the translation of their centers of mass.) Also in Table 16–2, we have indicated the measured values of the specific heat at constant pressure, C_p, and the ratio C_p/C_v, which we shall further discuss in the next chapter.

Equipartition of energy. If the temperature of a gas is increased locally, the corresponding local increase in molecular kinetic energy eventually will be distributed throughout the entire gas volume until the kinetic energy per unit volume is everywhere the same. The average translational kinetic energy per molecule in this state of thermal equilibrium is then $3kT/2$. Note that this energy does not depend on the masses of the molecules. All gases, regardless of their molecular weight, will have a molecular translational kinetic energy of this amount at the temperature T. Similarly, if two different gases are mixed in the same container, thermal equilibrium is reached when the temperatures of the two gases are the same. The average kinetic energy of the molecules of the two gases is then the same, despite the difference in the molecular weights. The successive collisions between molecules in the container thus tend to uniformly distribute the *kinetic energy* (and not the speed, for example) throughout the volume. This uniform distribution of kinetic energy among the molecules of different masses is the simplest example of the *principle of equipartition of energy.* This result applies not only to molecules but also to larger particles, such as smoke, which are in thermal equilibrium in the gas. We have already discussed an experiment, the effusion of gases (Sec. 16–2), which is a direct experimental test of the equipartition of energy in mixtures.

EXAMPLE. A smoke particle of mass $m = 5 \cdot 10^{-14}$ gm moves about in air whose temperature is 30°C. What is the rms value of the velocity of the smoke particle? If the smoke particle can be regarded as a sphere with a radius $r = 2 \cdot 10^{-5}$ cm, estimate the number of collisions per second that it makes with the molecules of the gas.

According to the principle of equipartition of energy, we assume that not only the molecules in the gas but also any other particle free to move in the gas acquires a translational energy of $3kT/2$ as a result of the interaction with the gas. The rms value of the speed of the particle is then

$$\sqrt{\frac{3kT}{m}} = \sqrt{3 \cdot 1.38 \cdot 10^{-16} \cdot 293/(5 \cdot 10^{-14})} \simeq 1.6 \text{ cm/sec.}$$

The surface area of the smoke particle is $4\pi r^2$. The number of molecular collisions per unit area is $n\bar{v}/4$ per second, and the number of collisions with the smoke particle is then $4\pi r^2 n\bar{v}/4$ per second. At atmospheric pressure, the volume of one mole of air is $(293/273)22.4 \simeq 26.2$ liters, the number of particles per unit volume is $n = (6.02 \cdot 10^{23})/26.2 \cdot 10^3 \simeq 2.3 \cdot 10^{19}$ cm^{-3}, and the average speed (with $M = 28$) is 420 m/sec. The collision rate with the smoke particle is then $4\pi \cdot (2 \cdot 10^{-5})^2 \cdot (2.3 \cdot 10^{19}) \cdot (420 \cdot 10^2)/4 \simeq 1.2 \cdot 10^{15}$ per second.

Diatomic and polyatomic molecules. In the study of experimental results on specific heat, we have seen that the values predicted from Eq. (16–19) apply only to monatomic molecules (at ordinary temperatures), as shown in Table 16–2. For diatomic and polyatomic molecules, the molar specific heat is always found to be larger than the monatomic value of 3 cal/mole·°C. In terms of a molecular interpretation, this result indicates that a diatomic or polyatomic gas possesses more kinetic energy than a monatomic gas at the same temperature. How can we account for this difference between monatomic and diatomic gases in terms of the kinetic theory?

First, we observe that kinetic theory requires that the translational kinetic energy must always be $3kT/2$ per molecule, *regardless of the mass or nature* of the molecule. Consequently, the diatomic or polyatomic gas, in addition to translational energy, must also possess other forms of energy. It is reasonable to assume that in addition to undergoing translation, these molecules also rotate and perhaps vibrate. When molecules bounce around in a gas, one of the atoms of a diatomic molecule will be hit from all directions, and not only momentum but also spin angular momentum will be transferred to the molecule. The corresponding rotational energy of the molecule will account for part of the specific heat of the gas. But how can we ever determine how the total energy of the molecule is divided between translational and rotational (or vibrational) energy? We have already mentioned that at constant volume, most of the diatomic gases listed in Table 16–2 have specific heats of about 5 cal/mole·°C, while for monatomic gases it is near $3R/2$ or 3 cal/mole·°C. Diatomic gases, then, in addition to the $3 \cdot (R/2)$ per mole that expresses their translational kinetic energy alone, have another term equal to $2 \cdot (R/2)$. This additive part, in terms of the average energy per molecule, is $2 \cdot (kT/2)$.

We can interpret this result in the following way. The translational energy is $mv^2/2 = mv_x^2/2 + mv_y^2/2 + mv_z^2/2 = 3kT/2$, and we see that with each of the three velocity components, or degrees of freedom, there is associated a kinetic energy $kT/2$. If we now assume that in thermal equilibrium each rotational degree of freedom also acquires an energy $kT/2$, and if we further assume that two of the three rotational degrees of freedom of the diatomic molecule are excited, we can account for the rotational energy $2kT/2$ of the diatomic molecule. Although this interpretation will, no doubt, give us the energy $(3 + 2)kT/2 = 5kT/2$, as required by the experimental results, a question comes to mind as to why we should consider the rotation of only two out of the three possible degrees of freedom. This can be clarified as follows.

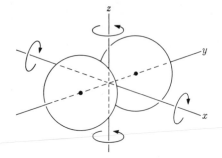

FIG. 16–11. A diatomic molecule acquires rotational kinetic energy about the two axes indicated.

Let us imagine that the diatomic molecule is shaped like a dumbbell, or perhaps like two spheres or atoms in contact with each other, as in Fig. 16–11. As a result of collisions, it is clear that we must assume that the molecule will be set in rotation about the x- and z-axes shown in the figure. However, if the molecules are assumed to be smooth spheres, as before, there will be no possibility of transferring angular momentum about the y-axis. Then, if the molecule starts without rotation about this axis, it will always remain in this state of motion. Furthermore, in the calculation of the specific heat for a monatomic gas, we did not consider rotation of the atoms, and if the theory is to be consistent, we should not consider the corresponding rotation of the diatomic molecule either. (Complete justification can be given only by the quantum theory.) Therefore, accepting the interpretation of the equipartition of energy given above, the angular velocity of rotation of the diatomic molecule is expressed as

$$\frac{I_x \omega_x^2}{2} = \frac{kT}{2}, \tag{16–22}$$

where I_x is the moment of inertia of the molecule.

EXAMPLE. While we can calculate the rotational velocities of diatomic molecules in much the same way that we calculated molecular translational velocities, there is no analogous direct method for measuring rotational velocities. Nevertheless, it is interesting to see what the rotational velocity of oxygen, say, is at room temperature.

An oxygen atom has a mass of $m = M/N_0 = 16/(6.02 \cdot 10^{23}) = 2.65 \cdot 10^{-23}$ gm. If the molecule consists of two spherical atoms of radius r in contact, and if all the mass of an atom is concentrated at its center, the moment of inertia of the molecule is

$$I = 2mr^2.$$

Then, by the equipartition principle, we have

$$\tfrac{1}{2}I\omega^2 = \tfrac{1}{2}kT = \tfrac{1}{2} \cdot 1.38 \cdot 10^{-16} \cdot 300 \simeq 2.1 \cdot 10^{-14} \text{ erg.}$$

If we take r, the atomic radius, to be 1.4 angstroms $= 1.4 \cdot 10^{-8}$ cm, we have for the moment of inertia

$$I = 2 \cdot 2.65 \cdot 10^{-23} \cdot (1.4 \cdot 10^{-8})^2 \simeq 1.04 \cdot 10^{-38} \text{ gm·cm}^2.$$

The angular velocity is therefore $\omega = \sqrt{kT/I} = 1.4 \cdot 10^{12}$ rad/sec or about 10^{11} rotations per second.

Generalizing the results of these observations regarding the distribution of energy, we can say that for each degree of freedom of motion of the molecule there corresponds an energy of $kT/2$. In other words, if we write the total energy of a molecule and count the number of terms, f, that involve the square of a velocity or angular velocity (or a displacement), the average energy of the molecule will be $fkT/2$. This procedure illustrates the *principle of equipartition of energy.*

On this basis, we might expect that the specific heat of polyatomic molecules would be $6R/2$, since rotation about all three axes would be possible. However, the situation clearly is not so simple, since in Table 16–2 the three polyatomic molecules listed have specific heats of 6.86, 7.5, and 30.8 cal/mole·°C. Actually, we need not go to a polyatomic gas to experience this type of discrepancy. Measurements of the specific heat of a diatomic gas, hydrogen, taken at different temperatures are indicated in Fig. 16–12. Although there is a region of temperature in which the specific heat is $5R/2$, as predicted by the theory above, C_v can vary all the way from $3R/2$ at a very low temperature to $7R/2$ at a very high temperature. The value $7R/2$ can be understood in terms of the equipartition theory if we assume that, in addition to the rotational motion,

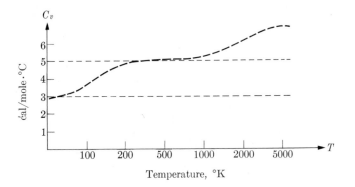

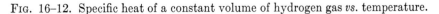

FIG. 16–12. Specific heat of a constant volume of hydrogen gas *vs.* temperature.

the molecule also vibrates. We discussed molecular vibrations in Chapter 8, where we saw that the intermolecular force between two molecules is analogous to a spring-type force in the neighborhood of the equilibrium point. The energy of vibration in the molecular harmonic motion is $H = mv^2/2 + Kx^2/2$; that is, the sum of the kinetic and the potential energies. If we assign a value of $kT/2$ to each of these terms, we obtain for the specific heat a total of $7R/2$ ($3R/2$ translational, $2R/2$ rotational, and $2R/2$ vibrational). However, the behavior of the specific heat at other temperatures, the transitions between $5R/2$ and $7R/2$, and in particular the behavior of the specific heat in the temperature region between $0°K$ and $100°K$, cannot be explained in terms of the kinetic theory. As a matter of fact, this problem of specific heat was one of the first which represented a serious conflict between experiments and the classical theory of motion and which led to the development of quantum theory. The classical theory agrees with the quantum theory only in the region of high temperatures.

In the case of a polyatomic gas there are several different possible modes of vibration in addition to the three translational and three rotational degrees of freedom, and the specific heat can soar to very high values, as indicated in Table 16–2.

Quantum-mechanical explanation of specific heat variation with temperature. According to classical (newtonian) mechanics, a rigid body can rotate with any value of angular momentum. Certainly there is no obvious limit, for example, on how slowly a bicycle wheel can turn. The quantum theory, however, requires that the angular momentum of a body have only certain fixed values, $l = nh/2\pi$, where $h = 6.625 \cdot 10^{-27}$ erg·sec is Planck's constant, and n is any integer, 0, 1, 2, 3, etc. Planck's constant represents a very small amount of angular momentum; e.g., a bicycle wheel rotating at 3 rev/sec or so has an angular momentum of about 10^7 erg·sec. This means that for such a rotating bicycle wheel, n in $nh/2\pi$ is about 10^{34}. For all practical purposes therefore, a bicycle wheel can rotate with all values of angular momentum, because n is such a large number and the integers n are so closely spaced, relatively speaking, when an object as large as a bicycle wheel rotates at any reasonable speed.

With an object as small as a molecule, however, the situation is very different. The kinetic energy of rotation is $E_{rot} = I\omega^2/2$, or $l^2/2I$ when expressed in terms of the angular momentum. With the quantum-mechanical restriction we then have $E_{rot} = n^2h^2/8\pi^2I$, and the smallest possible rotational kinetic energy that a molecule can have (other than zero) is $h^2/8\pi^2I$, the value for $n = 1$. We have seen that according to the principle of equipartition of energy, each degree of freedom that a molecule has should have associated with it an average energy $kT/2$, but for objects as small as hydrogen molecules (at say $10°K$), $kT/2$ is smaller than the minimum possible rotational kinetic energy.   In other words, the quantum-mechanical restriction prevents molecules from acquiring rotational kinetic energy at low temperatures.   It is only when kT becomes much larger than the minimum rotational kinetic energy that the molecules can acquire the amount of rotational kinetic energy specified by the principle of equipartition of energy.

Similarly, there is a quantum-mechanical restriction on the values of the energy of vibration that a molecule can have.   The possible values are $E_{\text{vib}} = nhf_0$, where n is an integer and f_0 is the natural vibration frequency, $\sqrt{K/m}$.   The minimum energy of vibration for hydrogen is even larger than the minimum energy of rotation, and it is only at the higher temperatures that hydrogen molecules can vibrate as well as rotate.   *In the limit of high temperature the specified heat of hydrogen is as predicted by the classical principle of equipartition of energy.*   At low temperatures there are quantum-mechanical deviations.

We can also offer, from these considerations, a reasonable explanation (though not an entirely correct one, according to quantum mechanics) of why single atoms (monatomic molecules) do not acquire rotational kinetic energy and why diatomic molecules can apparently rotate about only two of the three possible axes of rotation.   While a typical atom is about 10^{-8} cm in radius, the nucleus, which contains practically all of the mass of an atom, is only 10^{-12} or 10^{-13} cm in radius.   This means that the moment of inertia of a diatomic molecule, while the same and relatively large about two axes, is much smaller about the third axis, which is the axis defined by a line that connects the nuclei.   Similarly, the moment of inertia of an atom is very small about all of its three axes.   Since the minimum possible kinetic energy of rotation is inversely proportional to the moment of inertia, it is clear that rotations about these axes of very small moments of inertia would require enormous amounts of energy.

16–7 Collisions between molecules. Mean free path. Scattering experiment.   Until now, there has been no direct need for a quantitative study of the effect of the collisions between molecules.   We have been concerned with these collisions only in a qualitative way; in other words, as the physical phenomenon responsible for establishing thermal equilibrium and producing equipartition of energy.   Once this equipartition is assumed, however, we have not needed to consider the collisions in our derivation of, for example, the gas law and the specific heat of a gas.   However, many effects and properties of gases and molecules, such as heat conduction and viscosity, cannot be understood on a molecular basis without a quantitative study of molecular collisions.   Furthermore, since such collisions are intimately related to the sizes of molecules, they must be considered in experiments that are conducted to determine molec-

ular sizes.   Before studying these questions, we shall present a simple
theoretical analysis of collisions between molecules, from which we can
determine, in terms of molecular dimensions and the density of the gas,
the collision rate and the so-called *mean free path*.

Collision rate and the mean free path. Let us imagine a gas as a collection
of spherical molecules, each of radius r, as illustrated in Fig. 16–13. There
are n such molecules per unit volume. Let us focus our attention on one
of the molecules, labeled A in the figure. As A moves forward, it will
bounce into every molecule that comes within a distance $2r$ of A, if the
distance is measured between the centers of the molecules. The problem
now is to determine the number of collisions in which a molecule is involved
in terms of the molecular speed, the radius, and the number of molecules
per unit volume. This problem is somewhat complex if we take into account the fact that all of the molecules are moving. However, without
sacrificing the essence of the problem, we can simplify it considerably
by assuming that all of the molecules except A are at rest. The number
of molecules colliding with A per second can then easily be estimated in
the following manner. For simplicity, assume that the mass of A is much
larger than the mass of the other molecules, so that in a collision the
change in the velocity of A can be neglected. Thus A will move forward
like a plow, throwing to either side all of the molecules that are in its
path. As indicated in Fig. 16–13, all the molecules that lie within a cylinder of radius $2r$, i.e., twice the molecular radius, will be hit by A.
In a time Δt, molecule A will sweep through a cylinder of length $v\,\Delta t$
and of volume $\pi(2r)^2 v\,\Delta t$. The number of molecules in this cylinder is
$n \cdot \pi(2r)^2\,\Delta t$, and A collides with them all. The number of collisions
per second by A is then

$$\nu = 4\pi r^2 \cdot nv. \tag{16–23}$$

The corresponding average time between collisions is then $\tau = 1/\nu$, and

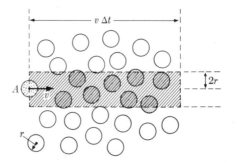

Fig. 16–13. All of the molecules that come within a distance $2r$ (center-to-
center distance) of A will collide with A.

the average distance traveled between collisions is $l = v\tau$. This distance
is called the *molecular mean free path*. If we introduce the value $\tau = 1/\nu$
given by Eq. (16-7), we obtain

$$l = \frac{1}{4\pi r^2 \cdot n}.$$
(16–24)

In this simplified analysis, the results obtained differ only slightly from
those of a more rigorous analysis in which we account for the motions of
the molecules, the changes of direction in collisions, and the distribution
of velocities among the molecules. Instead of the factor $1/4\pi$ in Eqs.
(16–23) and (16–24), we then find $1/(\sqrt{2} \cdot 4\pi)$. The velocity v in
Eq. (16–23) should be interpreted as the average speed $\bar{v}$.

Since the pressure in a gas is proportional to the number of particles per
unit volume, it follows from Eq. (16–24) that the mean free path is inversely proportional to the gas pressure. In fact, if we insert $n = N_0/V =
N_0P/RT$, where N_0 is Avogadro's number, we obtain $l = RT/2\pi r^2 N_0 P$.
With a molecular radius of about 10^{-8} cm, we find that the mean free
path is of the order of 10^{-5} cm in a gas at atmospheric pressure and at
a temperature of about 300°K; that is, it is 1000 times larger than the
assumed molecular dimensions. To obtain a mean free path of 1 meter,
the pressure must be only $1.5 \cdot 10^{-5}$ mm Hg. This pressure is found, for
example, at a height of about 100 miles in our atmosphere. (In the region
between the stars in the Milky Way there is only about one atom per
cubic centimeter, and the corresponding molecular mean free path is
several billion miles.) Since atoms have speeds which are typically about
500 m/sec at ordinary temperatures, the collision frequency at atmospheric pressure is of the order of $v/l = 50{,}000/10^{-5} = 5 \cdot 10^9$ per second.

Scattering experiment. Scattering experiments from which mean free
paths can be determined provide some of the most important measures
of the sizes of atoms and molecules. We shall study a molecular beam
as it travels through a region filled with a gas, instead of in a vacuum
as in the velocity measurements discussed in a previous section. The
density of the gas in this region can be varied at will by means of pumps.
It is clear that as a molecule of the beam hits a gas molecule, which we
shall refer to as a *target molecule,* it will usually be deflected and thrown
out of the beam. Consequently, as the beam goes through the gas, the
beam intensity, i.e., the number of beam molecules per unit area and per
second, will decrease with distance. By measuring this decrease, we should
be able to learn something about the rate of collisions and the mean free
path, and consequently about the dimensions of the molecules. Following
the previous study of molecular collisions, we can easily analyze a molecular-beam scattering experiment.

Consider a beam of atoms headed toward a detector D, as illustrated in Fig. 16–14. If, as before, we assume both the beam and the target atoms to be hard spheres of radius r, then a beam atom will collide with a target atom if the center of the beam atom passes inside a circle of radius $2r$ about the center of the target atom. In other words, so far as collisions are concerned, the effective cross section of a target atom, as presented to the center of a beam atom, is $4\pi r^2$. Consequently, if we neglect the overlapping of the cross sections of different target atoms, it follows that the $nA\,dx$ atoms contained in the elementary volume $A\,dx$ of the beam of area A will offer a total obstructing area $(nA\,dx) \cdot 4\pi r^2$. The fraction of the beam molecules which will collide with the target molecules in the distance dx is the same as the fraction of obstructed area, that is, $(nA\,dx \cdot 4\pi r^2)/A$. In other words, if the intensity of atoms at the location x is denoted by $I(x)$, the amount by which the intensity will decrease in the distance dx is $In4\pi r^2\,dx$. The variation of beam intensity with x is then described by the equation

$$\frac{dI}{I} = -4\pi r^2 n\,dx.$$

This equation can be integrated directly, and we find

$$I = I_0 e^{-4\pi r^2 n x} = I_0 e^{-x/l}, \tag{16–25}$$

where $l = 1/4\pi r^2 n$ is the mean free path, which was found in Eq. (16–24). The molecular-beam intensity at $x = 0$ has been denoted by I_0.

Let us now discuss briefly how a mean-free-path measurement might be made. A simple and adequate apparatus is indicated schematically in Fig. 16–15. A vacuum pump capable of reducing the pressure within the system to less than 10^{-5} mm of mercury and the means by which the scattering gas, for example argon, is introduced are not shown in the figure. In the capsule to the left is a small amount of metallic potassium. The potassium, which is heated electrically, melts, resulting in a gas of potassium atoms within the capsule or oven. Some of the potassium atoms pass through the slit S and, because of the shape and orientation of the slit, they pass down the evacuated chamber toward the detector D. If the slit is carefully made and accurately aligned, all the atoms in the beam will strike the detector, except, of course, those which are scattered. The gas pressure in the vacuum chamber is measured with the ion gauge. An ion gauge is not an absolute measuring device, in the sense that it must be calibrated against other pressure-measuring devices that are absolute. The details of operation of both the ion gauge and the beam detector are of no particular concern here.

The measurement could be carried out in two ways. The pressure could

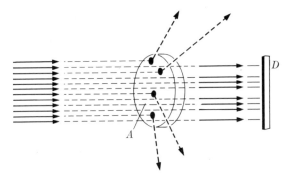

FIG. 16–14. The target molecules in an elementary volume $A\,dx$ offer an obstructing area $4\pi r^2 nA\,dx$ and scatter a fraction $4\pi r^2 nA\,dx/A = 4\pi r^2 n\,dx$ of the incoming beam.

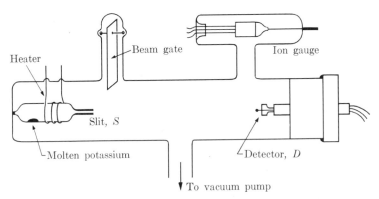

FIG. 16–15. Schematic diagram of apparatus for the measurement of a mean free path. The beam gate can, with the aid of a magnet, be dropped into a position that prevents any direct beam from reaching the detector.

be held constant and the distance x could be varied between the source S and the detector D. We would then expect that the intensity I of the detected beam would vary in accordance with

$$I = I_0 e^{-x/l},$$

where l is the mean free path. Alternatively, the distance x could be held constant and the pressure P varied. Since the mean free path is inversely proportional to the pressure, $l = C/P$, we have

$$I = I_0 e^{-CxP} = I_0 e^{-P/P_0}, \tag{16–25a}$$

where P_0 is a new constant, given by

$$P_0 = \frac{RT}{4\pi r^2 N_0 x}. \tag{16–26}$$

An experimental determination of either l or P_0 provides a measure of the quantity $N_0 r^2$, and if we assume N_0 to be known, we can evaluate the atomic radius r.

EXAMPLE. Some experimental data taken with an apparatus similar to that shown in Fig. 16–15 are plotted on the graphs in Fig. 16–16. The distance x between the source and the detector was 11.5 cm, and the scattering gas was argon at room temperature. In the right-hand graph, log I has been plotted vs. pressure P, in mm Hg. This is a useful way to plot the data, because if I depends on P, as indicated by expression (16–25a), the experimental points should lie on a straight line. That is, we have

$$\log \left(\frac{I}{I_0} \right) = -\frac{P}{P_0} \log e,$$

and the slope of the straight line is $-(\log e)/P_0$. The experimentally determined slope is $-0.29 \cdot 10^4$ (mm Hg)$^{-1}$. Then for P_0 we obtain

$$P_0 = \frac{-\log e}{\text{slope}} = \frac{-0.434}{-0.29 \cdot 10^4} = 1.5 \cdot 10^{-4} \text{ mm Hg} = 0.20 \text{ dyne/cm}^2.$$

We can then find a value of $N_0 r^2$ from Eq. (16–26):

$$N_0 r^2 = \frac{RT}{4\pi P_0 x} = \frac{8.31 \cdot 10^7 \cdot 300}{4\pi \cdot 0.20 \cdot 11.5} \simeq 9 \cdot 10^8.$$

The modern value for Avogadro's number is $6.02 \cdot 10^{23}$, and with $N_0 r^2 = 9 \cdot 10^8$, we have $r \simeq 4 \cdot 10^{-8}$ cm.

This is a typical atomic radius, and it is seen to be consistent with the estimates of atomic dimensions that we have made in other ways.

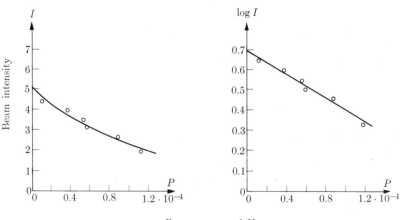

Pressure, mm of Hg

FIG. 16–16. Dependence of detected beam intensity on gas pressure.

Scattering experiments like the one we have just described afford an important method for the determination of atomic radii. The exact value obtained for the radius depends to some extent upon the geometry of the apparatus. The size of the detector, in effect, determines how small the scattering angle can be, such that the beam atom can still be detected. Ideally, the scattering gas should be restricted to a small length of the beam, so that this minimum scattering is well defined.

16–8 Transport phenomena. So far, our discussion of the kinetic theory has been limited to a uniform gas, i.e., a gas in thermal equilibrium and in which all the properties, such as density, temperature, and pressure, are the same throughout the entire volume. Under these conditions, we have seen that there is no net transfer of mass, momentum, or energy from one region of the gas to another. On the other hand, in a non-uniform gas, for example one in which the temperature varies from one point to another, there will be an energy transfer (heat flow) in the direction of decreasing temperature (Chapter 14). Similarly, in a gas with a density gradient, a transfer (diffusion) of mass will take place, and when the gas is in motion and the speed or momentum per unit volume of the gas varies from point to point, the molecular (thermal) motion will cause a momentum transfer from regions of high speed to regions of low speed. These *transport phenomena*, as they are called, can be described quantitatively in terms of relatively simple empirical relations, but the detailed kinetic theory is quite involved. Therefore, the treatment of transport phenomena in the present section will be limited to qualitative and simplified quantitative relations. Of the three transport phenomena mentioned, transport of mass, momentum, and energy, we have previously encountered only one, namely, transport of energy (heat conduction). We shall discuss this subject first.

Heat conduction. In Chapter 14, we studied the empirical aspects of heat flow, and it was seen that the heat q conducted per unit area per second in a substance is proportional to the temperature gradient. When the temperature varied in the x-direction only, we obtained [Eq. (14–7)]

$$q = -K \frac{dT}{dx}, \qquad (16\text{–}27)$$

where K is the heat-conduction coefficient and the minus sign means that the heat flows in the direction of decreasing temperature. We shall now try to interpret this result from the standpoint of kinetic theory.

In terms of kinetic theory, heat is the kinetic energy of molecular motion, and we have seen in Sec. 16–6 that we can express the kinetic energy per unit mass as $c_v T$, where c_v is the specific heat per unit mass and T is the temperature. In addition to translational molecular energy, rotational and vibrational energy may also be present. Suppose now that the temperature of the gas (and consequently the kinetic energy per unit volume) varies (increases) in the x-direction. Imagine a plane P in a gas, perpendicular to the x-axis, as illustrated in Fig. 16–17. In the region to the right of the plane, the kinetic energy per unit volume and the kinetic energy per molecule are larger than to the left of the plane. Consequently, when a molecule crosses over the plane P from right to left, it carries more energy across P than does a molecule that crosses in the opposite direction. Then, if the same number of molecules hit P on both sides, it is clear that there will be a net flow of energy (heat) across P. This qualitatively explains the flow of heat in the negative x-direction when T increases in the x-direction.

To estimate the heat flow quantitatively, we shall refer to the molecular collision rate per unit area of a plane which, according to Eq. (16–12), is $n\bar{v}/4$, where n is the number of molecules per unit volume and $\bar{v}$ is the average molecular speed.* If the average kinetic energy per molecule crossing the plane from left to right is E_1, the corresponding energy crossing P per unit area and time is $E_1 n\bar{v}/4$. Similarly, the energy crossing P in the negative x-direction is $E_2 n\bar{v}/4$, where E_2 is the average kinetic energy of the molecules coming from the region to the right of P. The net energy flux across P in the positive x-direction is then $q \simeq (n\bar{v}/4)(E_1 - E_2)$. But how can we express $E_1 - E_2$ in terms of the known variation of temperature with x? The molecules which cross P from left to right had

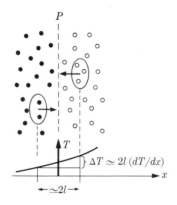

Fig. 16–17. Particles of low energy that cross plane P from the left are replaced by particles of higher energy that cross P from the right. A net energy flow in the direction of decreasing temperature results.

---

* The collision rates are somewhat different on the two sides of the plane because of the variation in temperature, but for the purposes of the present discussion we shall neglect this difference.

their last collision at a position P_1, which on the average is located about one mean free path l to the left of the plane. We shall assume that the energy of the molecules corresponds to the energy per unit volume at this particular point P_1. Similarly, the energy E_2 is assumed to correspond to a position P_2, which is about one mean free path to the right of P. The temperature difference between positions P_2 and P_1 can be expressed as $T_2 - T_1 = \Delta T \simeq 2l(dT/dx)$.

We note that one unit mass occupies a volume $1/\rho$, where ρ is the density of the gas. The corresponding number of molecules is n/ρ. Then, if the specific heat per unit mass is c_v, the energy per molecule is $\rho c_v T/n$, and the difference $E_2 - E_1$ can be written as $E_2 - E_1 \simeq (\rho c_v/n)(T_2 - T_1) \simeq (2l\rho c_v/n)(dT/dx)$. The heat flow per unit area in the positive x-direction is then obtained by multiplying this result by $n\bar{v}/4$, and we get

$$q = \frac{n\bar{v}}{4}(E_1 - E_2) \simeq -\frac{n\bar{v}}{4}\frac{2l\rho c_v}{n}\frac{dT}{dx}.$$

In view of the relation in Eq. (16–27), we can now express the experimentally determined heat-conduction coefficient of a gas in terms of the basic properties of the gas:

$$K \simeq \frac{l\bar{v}}{2}\rho c_v = \frac{l\bar{v}}{2}nmc_v, \tag{16–28}$$

where m is the mass of a molecule ($\rho = nm$). Equation (16–24) gave the mean free path as $l = 1/4\pi nr^2$, and by inserting this value into Eq. (16–27), we find the interesting result that the heat-conduction coefficient is *independent of n*. This means that at constant temperature the heat-conduction coefficient is *independent* of the pressure of the gas. (This result does not apply at very low pressures, when the mean free path is of the order of or greater than the dimensions of the apparatus. After all, the evacuated chamber in a thermos jug *does* help to prevent heat conduction.) Furthermore, Eq. (16–27) predicts that the heat-conduction coefficient depends on the square root of the temperature (since $\bar{v} \sim \sqrt{T}$).

Experiments indicate that the heat-conduction coefficient indeed is independent of pressure over a large range, but the temperature dependence is found to be stronger than $\sqrt{T}$. This discrepancy in temperature dependence can be accounted for if the hard-sphere model of the molecule is replaced by a model with an intermolecular force which varies continuously with distance between the molecules.

Viscosity and diffusion. Just as an energy-density gradient (temperature gradient) in a gas will produce a transfer (diffusion) of energy, a gradient of some other quantity or property of the gas can also result in a transfer of that quantity or property. For example, if a gas is in motion, and the velocity and consequently the momentum per unit volume vary from point to point in the gas, the thermal (molecular) motion in the gas will produce a transport of momentum in the direction of decreasing momentum density. This momentum transfer between regions of different gas speeds is equivalent to an interaction force between these regions. This interaction is known as the *viscosity* of the gas. The corresponding viscous force between two adjacent regions of the gas can be calculated by determining the momentum exchange produced by the thermal motion between the two regions, and we find that the procedure is completely analogous to that of the calculation of energy exchange in the analysis of heat conduction. In the special case in which the gas moves in the y-direction with a velocity U which varies with x, as illustrated in Fig. 16–18, the force per unit area along a plane parallel with the flow is found to be proportional to the velocity gradient across the plane:

$$F_y = -\eta \frac{dU}{dx}, \qquad (16\text{–}29)$$

where η is the coefficient of viscosity. The force in this equation is that exerted by the region to the left of the plane P on the region to the right of the plane, as shown in the figure. For example, if the left-hand region has a lower speed than the right-hand region, which corresponds to a positive value of dU/dx, the force $F_y = -\eta \, (dU/dx)$ is negative. The left-hand region then tends to decrease the speed of the faster right-hand region. Since the interaction force is mutual, the right-hand region at the same time tends to increase the speed of the left-hand region with a force $|\eta \, (dU/dx)|$ in the positive y-direction.

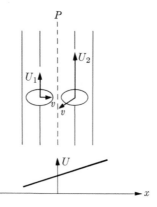

FIG. 16–18. Gas flow in the y-direction with a speed which varies with x. When gas molecules cross the plane P at an equal rate from both sides, there will be a net transfer of momentum, in the y-direction, across P.

Since the phenomena of heat conduction and viscosity are both caused by thermal motion in much the same way, it is not surprising to find that the coefficients of heat conduction and viscosity are related. From the simple theory illustrated above in the case of heat conduction, the following relation may be found:

$$\eta = \frac{K}{c_v}. \tag{16–30}$$

It is interesting to note that according to the kinetic theory both heat conduction and viscosity are independent of pressure (this does not apply at very low pressures) and are proportional to the square root of the temperature. The heat-conduction and viscosity coefficients of some common gases are given in Table 16–3.

Table 16–3. Heat-conduction and viscosity coefficients.

Gas	°C	Heat conduction, $K \cdot 10^5$ cgs units	Viscosity, $\eta \cdot 10^6$ cgs units
Air	0	5.22	170.8
Air	750		426.3
Argon	0	3.85	209.6
Carbon dioxide	0	3.25	142.0
Helium	0	32.7	186.0
Hydrogen	0	36.3	83.5
Oxygen	0	5.35	189.0
Water vapor	100		125.5

PROBLEMS

16–1. Consider a hypothetical gas in which one-third of the N molecules present in a cubical enclosure of side l move parallel to each of the three coordinate axes. Let all the molecules have the same speed v, and at any instant let the molecules be uniformly distributed in the box, such that, for example, just as many move toward $+x$ as move toward $-x$. The molecule-wall collisions are perfectly elastic. (a) What momentum is transferred to the wall per collision? (b) How many collisions are there per second? (c) What momentum is transferred to the wall per second? What is the force on the wall? What is the pressure? (d) How does the pressure vary with the volume V? (e) If this gas model is consistent with the gas law, what is the relationship between the molecular kinetic energy and the temperature?

16–2. Derive relation (16–2) from the following considerations. Consider one mole of a gas in a spherical container of radius R, as shown in Fig. 16–19, where the motion of one molecule of the gas is indicated. Study the motion when this molecule hits the container wall. The speed of the molecule is v, and it hits the wall at an angle ϕ, as shown. Neglect collisions with other molecules. (a) What is the momentum delivered to the wall per collision? (b) How many collisions per

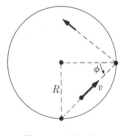

FIGURE 16–19

second is this molecule involved in as it flies about in the container, and what is the average momentum delivered by this molecule per unit area of the wall? (c) Assuming that all molecules have the same speed, determine the total momentum delivered by them per unit area of the wall. The result is then Eq. (16–2).

16–3. Refer to Fig. 16–2 in the text. Consider a beam of molecules (each of mass m) with n molecules per unit volume. The beam moves with a speed v toward a wall. The angle of incidence is ϕ. (a) What is the momentum delivered by the beam per unit time and per unit area of the wall, if the collisions are perfectly elastic? (b) If all directions of motion are equally probable, what is the relative number of molecules that strike the wall at an angle ϕ? (c) Prove that the frequency of collisions per unit area of wall is $nv/4$. considering the average of all angles of incidence.

16–4. Convince yourself that kT has the dimension of energy. What is the average translational kinetic energy, in ergs, of a molecule at a temperature of 27°C? Does this average energy depend upon the mass of the molecule?

16–5. (a) What is the ratio between the translational kinetic energies of hydrogen and oxygen molecules at a temperature of 300°K? (b) What is the ratio between their translational speeds?

16–6. Determine the gas constant per gram of oxygen. Is this constant the same for all gases? Explain.

16–7. Determine the root-mean-square value of the molecular speed of oxygen at 20°C, 1000°C, and −100°C.

16–8. Oxygen and helium are mixed

in a 45-liter container which has a small hole in its wall. There is 10^{-3} mole of each. The gas effuses into the surrounding evacuated chamber. (a) Determine the composition of the molecular beam as it effuses from the container, i.e., the ratio between the number of oxygen and of helium atoms escaping from the chamber per second. (b) How large a hole is required to make the relaxation time of helium 20 min? The temperature, 27°C, is constant (Sec. 16–4).

16–9. To show that the gravitational attraction between molecules in a gas can be neglected, compute the kinetic energy gained by two molecules if they start from rest at a large separation and approach each other under the influence of gravitation. Compare this energy with kT.

16–10. Consider a toothed-wheel apparatus for measuring molecular velocity. This apparatus has wheels that are 10 cm in diameter and that have 1-cm square slots cut into their circumferences. If the wheels are 500 cm apart, (a) how fast must they rotate, and at what angle should the slots be displaced to measure the rms velocity of hydrogen molecules at 400°K? (b) What spread of velocities is transmitted if the slots in the two wheels are 180° apart?

16–11. In a molecular-beam experiment, 0.1 gm of potassium is in the oven. If the beam intensity is 10^{12} atoms/sec, how long will the potassium in the oven last?

16–12. A beam of n potassium atoms/sec ($T = 500°K$) collides with and sticks to a piece of aluminum foil 1 cm² in area and 0.001 cm thick. The foil is held suspended by a 10-cm fiber of negligible mass. How large must n be in order for the fiber to be deflected 10 degrees?

16–13. In a scattering experiment, the gas atoms are of radius r_1 and the beam atoms are of radius r_2. What is the relationship between the mean free path l, the atomic radii, and the number of atoms per cubic centimeter in the gas?

16–14. What intensity of potassium atoms must there be at the slit of an oven in order to have an intensity of 1 atom/sec 3 ft away, in air at atmospheric pressure? Consider the effect of scattering only.

16–15. Show that the constant B in Eq. (16–14) (the Maxwell-Boltzmann distribution function), has the value given by Eq. (16–15). (Use Table 16–1.)

16–16. Prove that the most probable speed has the value given by Eq. (16–16). Similarly, obtain from the distribution function the values for the mean speed and for the rms value of the speed as given by Eqs. (16–19) and (16–20).

16–17. Of the molecules in a container at a temperature of 300°C, what fraction have velocities between $2v_0$ and $2.1v_0$, where v_0 is the most probable speed? How does this fraction vary with temperature?

16–18. Show that the Maxwell-Boltzmann distribution can be written as $f(v)\, dv = (4/\sqrt{\pi})x^2 e^{-x^2}\, dx$ in terms of the dimensionless variable $x = v/v_0$. Determine the fraction of molecules which have velocities larger than the rms value of the velocity, and express the result as an integral.

16–19. Prove Dalton's law of partial pressures in a gas mixture, by means of the kinetic theory (Sec. 16–6).

16–20. If the distance between the centers of the oxygen atoms in the O_2 molecule is 1.4 A, (a) what is the average number of revolutions per second the molecule makes at the temperature $T = 300°K$? (Use $\frac{1}{2}I\omega^2 = \frac{1}{2}kT$.) (b) What minimum force must hold the atoms together if their distance is not altered by thermal rotation?

16–21. If a chlorine molecule were to rotate at the angular frequency predicted by the equipartition principle, what would be the centripetal force? Assume the chlorine nuclei to be separated by a distance $d = 2 \cdot 10^{-8}$ cm.

16–22. Determine the number of rotations that an oxygen molecule makes between two successive collisions with other molecules. Prove that this number is independent of the temperature. Assume a pressure of 1 atm, and consider the oxygen molecule as two point masses separated by a distance of 1.4 A.

16–23. A uniform disc 1 cm in radius and of mass 1 gm rotates about an axis perpendicular to its plane and through its center of mass. (a) What are the minimum angular momentum and minimum angular velocity, according to the quantum theory? (b) If the disc rotates at 1 rev/sec, what is n in $l = nh/2\pi$? (c) If 1 rev/sec is an allowed value of rotational speed, what is the next highest allowed value?

16–24. Assume that the two nuclei of a hydrogen molecule are 10^{-8} cm apart. (a) What is the moment of inertia of the hydrogen molecule about an axis through its center of mass and perpendicular to the line which joins the two nuclei? (b) What is the minimum allowed rotational energy? (c) To what temperature does this minimum energy correspond? (d) If the minimum allowed vibrational energy of the hydrogen molecule is $2 \cdot 10^{-14}$ erg, what is f_0, the natural vibrational energy of the

hydrogen molecule? (e) What is the effective value of K, the force constant of the hydrogen molecular bond?

16–25. Carry through a calculation of the coefficient of viscosity, in complete analogy with the calculation of the heat-conduction coefficient, and prove the relation (16–30).

16–26. Does the viscosity of a gas depend on temperature? If so, explain the reason qualitatively.

16–27. Explain qualitatively why the heat-conduction coefficient is independent of pressure.

16–28. (a) At what temperature does the rms velocity of molecular hydrogen correspond to the escape velocity from the earth's gravitational field? (b) Find the escape velocity from the moon, and then find the temperatures at which hydrogen, argon, and radon have this velocity. The sunlit portion of the moon has been estimated to have a temperature of 100°C.

16–29. Consider a spherical container of nitrogen gas at 300°K. What should the radius r of the sphere be in order that the number of wall collisions in 1 sec be equal to the total number of molecules in the container?

16–30. People who work with vacuum systems are frequently annoyed by a small amount of water on the walls of the system. At 10^{-7} mm of Hg, what volume will 1 gm of water (when vaporized) occupy?

16–31. A "sealed" vacuum chamber has a volume of 10^3 cm^3 and has been evacuated to a pressure of 10^{-7} mm of Hg. It is observed that the pressure increases to 10^{-5} mm of Hg in one hour. (a) How large a hole would account for this leak? (b) If the chamber were really tight, how much water would have to evaporate to account for the increase in pressure?

16–32. Our galaxy is, roughly speaking, a flat disc 100,000 light-years in diameter and 1000 light-years thick. Spread uniformly throughout this disc are $2 \cdot 10^{11}$ stars, and hydrogen gas which has a number density of one atom/cm^3. (a) What is the mean free path of a 500 m/sec hydrogen atom in the galaxy? (b) While traversing a galactic diameter, a cosmic ray has a probability of only 10^{-3} of colliding with a hydrogen atom. What is the mean free path of a cosmic ray? (c) What is the mean free path for a collision between a cosmic ray and a star? Assume that all of the $2 \cdot 10^{11}$ stars have the diameter of our sun.

CHAPTER 17

THE FIRST LAW OF THERMODYNAMICS

Summary. The study in previous chapters of the gross motion of bodies and the internal motion in matter has led us to a consideration of the possible conversion of the energy in the gross motion to internal energy, or vice versa, and the possible equivalence between them. First we shall re-examine the energy exchange involved in the collisions treated in Chapters 2, 3, and 4, and we shall find that the energy equivalence is made plausible by certain types of experiments on inelastic collisions. A historical review of the experimental evidence for the equivalence between heat and mechanical energy follows. In the special case of an ideal gas, such an equivalence can be established directly from kinetic theory, and it is shown that the work done by a thermally insulated expanding gas is equal to the loss of molecular kinetic (internal) energy. These studies are extended to include thermal interaction also, and we find that the change in the internal energy of the gas is accounted for in terms of the work and the heat absorbed by the gas. For real gases and other substances, we appeal to the nonexistence of perpetual motion machines to establish this energy conversion and conservation. The result is the first law of thermodynamics. In the light of the first law of thermodynamics, some specific changes of state of an ideal gas are studied.

17–1 Introduction. Our studies so far can be divided roughly into two major parts. The first, Chapters 1 through 13, deals mainly with the gross motion of bodies, as described by the translation of their centers of mass and rotation about their centers of mass. The second part, Chapters 14 through 16, concerns the internal motion in matter, where heat has been described as molecular kinetic energy. We shall now consider the questions of possible equivalence between the energy in the gross motion and the energy in the internal motion, and the conversion of energy from one form to the other.

With this objective in mind, we shall review some of the results obtained in the study of the interactions between two (or more) bodies in the collision experiments in Chapters 2, 3, and 4. We found there that in certain types of collisions, such as in the spring-type interaction, the total kinetic energy was the same before and after the collision. These collisions were called *perfectly elastic*. In the spring type of interaction, the bodies slowed down as the spring between them was compressed. The corresponding loss in kinetic energy could be associated with a latent or potential energy in the compressed spring which was regained when the spring expanded. Similarly, the kinetic energy lost by a body sliding uphill on a frictionless inclined plane was regained when the body slid down again. Then, by extending the energy concept to include potential as well as kinetic energy, we were able to formulate the law of conservation of energy (still limited to perfectly elastic collisions). Consequently, the sum of the kinetic and the potential energies, the so-called total mechanical energy, $H = E + V$, was the same throughout the entire interaction. The conservation of total mechanical energy was found to apply to all cases in which the net force on a body depends only on the position, but not on the direction of motion or on the speed of the body. Gravitational force is a typical example of such a force.

In other types of interactions, those which we have called *inelastic*, kinetic energy of the gross motion is lost in a collision. For example, two bodies with a piece of putty between them seem to lose at least part of their original kinetic energy when they collide, and there are no obvious methods to regain what is lost. However, when we deal with collisions of this type, we can certainly conceive of situations in which the loss of kinetic energy is only apparent; close examination reveals that the lost energy is indeed present in the form of kinetic or potential energy or both. This fact is hidden when only a superficial examination is made.

As an example, consider the collision illustrated in Fig. 17–1(a). Body A is a car of mass m which has an initial velocity $\mathbf{V}$. Body B consists of two cars C and D, each of mass m, but these two cars are covered by a massless opaque cover attached to the center of mass of C and D. Consequently, superficial inspection gives only the center-of-mass motion of C and D, but the energy with respect to the center of mass is hidden. The energy associated with this latter motion then appears to have been lost, and the interaction is classified as inelastic, although no energy is lost if all the individual interactions are perfectly elastic. We leave it as a problem to show that the apparent loss of energy in the collision illustrated in Fig. 17–1(a) is $mV^2/4$ (Problem 17–1).

We would note a similar apparent loss of energy if cars A and B were to lock after the collision, as illustrated in Fig. 17–1(b). In this case the "lost" energy is stored as potential energy.

Still another example is illustrated in Fig. 17–1(c). Body B now consists of a large number of small, perfectly elastic balls. The motion of the balls with respect to the center of mass of B is now an irregular motion resulting from the elastic collisions between the balls and the walls, and the energy with respect to the center of mass appears to have been lost. Upon closer examination, the internal motion and the corresponding energy are revealed, and we find that no energy is lost in the collision after all.

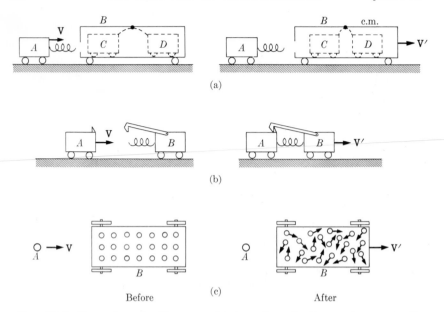

FIG. 17–1. Examples of collisions and interactions that are only apparently inelastic. In each case, close examination reveals that the total mechanical energy is conserved.

The question now arises as to whether all inelastic collisions might not produce hidden energy, thus accounting for the observed energy loss in the above collisions. Is it possible that the kinetic energy that is apparently lost in a putty-type collision, for example, only undergoes a transformation into internal molecular motion? The answer to this question can hardly come from direct inspection of the molecular motion by "opening up" the body. In the 18th century, investigators devoted much speculation to this type of question.

In the early study of heat the connection between energy and heat was unsuspected. Heat was imagined to be a fluid, given the name "caloric." Caloric could flow between bodies in thermal contact, and in these mixing or thermal-interaction experiments the total amount of caloric was imagined to remain constant. The particles of caloric were supposed to be able to flow between the particles of ordinary matter, and while the particles of caloric were mutually repulsive, ordinary matter attracted caloric. All this was worked into a reasonably satisfactory model which explained qualitatively the expansion of heated bodies, the large volume occupied by a gas, thermal equilibrium, etc.

This, then, was the status of the study of heat in the mid-1700's. Mechanics by this time was on very solid ground. Galileo, Brahe, Kepler, and Newton studied large-scale phenomena and their findings formed the basis of the modern mechanics that we study today. Heat, on the other hand, was destined to undergo drastic conceptual revision, but general acceptance of this revision did not occur for almost 100 years. The revision to which we refer, of course, is the kinetic theory of heat. As we have already mentioned in Chapter 16, Daniel Bernoulli, in 1738, had put forth the essential ideas of the kinetic theory of gases. He regarded heat as the kinetic energy of particles, and identified gas pressure with the collisions of the gas particles against the walls of the container. But the scientific community as a whole moved more slowly. In effect, this new concept was accepted only when there was compelling experimental evidence in its favor.

The possible connection between heat and energy was emphasized particularly by Benjamin Thompson (1753–1814; later to become Count Rumford). Since heat can be produced in apparently unlimited amounts by friction, Rumford argued that it was difficult to imagine heat to be a material substance such as caloric, and much more reasonable to imagine it to be motion. Rumford further attempted to weigh caloric, and made a series of most careful measurements of the weights of bodies at different temperatures. He was unable to find any weight differences attributable to heat, and this indeed was a blow to the caloric theory of heat.

The quantitative and most convincing evidence that connected heat and energy was put forth by Mayer and Joule in the period from 1840 to 1850. Julius Mayer (1814–1878), a German physician, presented arguments that rested to a great extent on the specific heat of air, a subject we shall pursue later in this chapter. With varied experimental conditions, James Joule (1818–1889), an Englishman, made a long series of remarkably accurate measurements of the amount of heat produced when a given amount of mechanical energy (apparently) disappears.

The concept that evolved from Joule's work is a most important one. Since very early times people have been aware that bodies become hot when mechanical work is done on them. There would have been nothing particularly profound about Joule's work, regardless of the care with which he took his measurements, if he had measured the heat produced by a given amount of mechanical work or the heat accompanying a kinetic-energy loss in just one experiment. That one measurement, or that one series of measurements, would not have identified heat as a form of energy. The significance of Joule's work centers about the fact that he measured the heat produced by a given amount of mechanical energy under *many* circumstances, and in this way he found that the ratio (heat produced)/(mechanical energy expended) was the same or essentially the same always. It was only under these conditions that heat could sensibly be assumed to be a form of energy. Among the many experiments that Joule performed on the "mechanical equivalent of heat" were measurements of the heat produced (1) when water is stirred by a mechanically driven paddlewheel, (2) when water is heated by a mechanically driven electric generator, (3) when water is heated as a result of flowing through pipes of small diameter, (4) when water is heated by falling over a waterfall, and (5) when various materials are heated by the friction between two iron plates in relative motion. From the data he collected, Joule proposed a value of $4.15 \cdot 10^7$ ergs per calorie for the mechanical equivalent of heat. In the mks system, this value would be 4.15 joules per calorie, and the modern value,

$$1 \text{ calorie} = 4.1855 \text{ joules (newton·meters)}, \qquad (17\text{–}1)$$

is not so very far from Joule's.

In retrospect, Joule's experiments seem to have offered almost compelling evidence that heat is a form of energy. However, the extended concept of the *conservation of energy* did not gain wide acceptance immediately. Hermann von Helmholtz (1821–1894), a brilliant German physiologist and physicist, was probably, more than anyone else, responsible for the eventual clear formulation and recognition of conservation of energy as a basic experimental law. He extended the concept of energy to include chemical and life processes, and interrelated so many phenomena that even the most skeptical were convinced. There are no known violations of the law of conservation of energy, and that the law has withstood the test of time is, of course, the real basis for its stature.

We should note carefully that up to this point we have discussed only cases wherein the mechanical-energy loss has appeared in the form of heat. (The reverse situation, in which heat energy is converted into mechanical energy, will be discussed in the next section.)

EXAMPLE. A copper bullet of mass 10 gm has a velocity of 300 m/sec. If the entire kinetic energy of the bullet were converted into heat, what would be the temperature rise of the bullet?

The kinetic energy of the bullet is $mv^2/2 = 450$ joules. This amount of kinetic energy is equivalent to $\Delta Q = 450/4.185 = 108$ calories of heat. The temperature rise of the bullet is therefore given by $\Delta Q = mc\,\Delta T$, where $c = 0.092$ (cal/gm)/°C is the specific heat of copper. The temperature rise is about 116°C.

17–2 Internal energy and the first law of thermodynamics. In the previous section we have discussed the historical experimental evidence for the equivalence between heat and energy, and we have interpreted heat as the energy associated with molecular motion. Now we wish to explore the question of whether equivalence between energy (work) and heat, and the interpretation of heat as the molecular energy of motion, are consistent with the kinetic theory of gases. The analysis of this question will lead us to the concept of internal energy and to the formulation of the first law of thermodynamics. In the study of the relation between the molecular energy and the work done by a gas, we shall investigate what happens when gas molecules collide with a moving piston in a container. Can we show that the molecules suffer an energy loss which is equivalent to the work done by the piston?

Ideal gas. Let us consider N molecules in a container that has a movable piston at one end, as illustrated in Fig. 17–2. The gas in the container, initially at a temperature T, exerts a pressure $P = nkT$ on the walls of the container and the piston, where $n = N/V$ is the number of particles per unit volume. The gas container is thermally isolated, so that there can be no heat transfer to the gas.

To keep the movable piston of area A in equilibrium, an external force $F = PA$ must be exerted on the piston. By decreasing the external force by an infinitesimally small amount, we can start the piston moving outward so that the volume of the container increases at a rate uA, where u is the velocity of the piston. Clearly, the gas does work against the external force on the piston (for example, a weight can be lifted). As the piston is displaced a distance dx, the gas does an amount of work $dW = PA\,dx$. The *rate* at which work is done, i.e., the power delivered, is $dW/dt = PAu$.

What now is the energy loss of the gas molecules? Under our assumption of perfectly elastic collisions between the gas molecules and the container walls, a molecule which collides with the *stationary* piston will bounce back with an unchanged speed. However, when the piston is moving in the positive x-direction with a velocity u, a molecule which initially had a velocity component v_x, after its collision will have a velocity component of only $v_x' = -(v_x - 2u)$.

This result follows directly from the fact that in a perfectly elastic collision the relative velocity before and after the collision is the same except for sign. Before the collision, the relative velocity is $v_x - u$, and after the collision, it is given by $v_x' - u = -(v_x - u)$, which proves that $v_x' = -(v_x - 2u)$ is the velocity of the molecule after it collides with the piston.

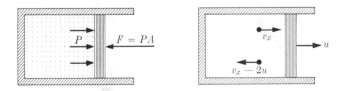

Fig. 17–2. As the molecules collide with the outward-moving piston, they lose kinetic energy.

In the collision, then, the molecule loses kinetic energy in the amount $mv_x^2/2 - m(v_x - 2u)^2/2 = 2mv_xu - 2mu^2$. If we multiply this value by the number of collisions per second, we obtain the total rate of energy decrease. However, we have determined the collision frequency only for the case in which the wall is at rest, and if we are going to use this value for the collision frequency, we must assume that the velocity u of the piston is very much smaller than the molecular speed v_x. Consequently, the term $2mu^2$ vanishes in comparison with $2mv_xu$ when u goes to zero, and we need only consider the term $2mv_xu$. The number of molecular collisions per second with the piston is $Anv_x/2$, and the total energy loss per second is then $\frac{1}{2}(Anv_x)(2mv_xu) = nmv_x^2Au$.

Now we have PAu for the power or rate at which energy is delivered *by* the gas and we wish to inquire as to whether this is equal to the rate of energy loss of the gas molecules, nmv_x^2Au, as found from kinetic theory. The gas pressure, according to kinetic theory, is $P = nmv_x^2$ [see Eq. (16–3)], and so nmv_x^2Au is just PAu. The mechanical work done by a gas *is* equal to the (kinetic) energy loss of the gas molecules. (Note that we have assumed here that the gas is in a thermally insulated cylinder.)

This analysis can be applied also to the case where the gas is compressed so that work is done *on* the gas; all we need do is replace u by $-u$. We find that the work done on the gas equals the increase in the kinetic molecular energy.

The foregoing discussion has shown in detail how the conservation-of-energy principle extends to the conversion of random molecular energy (the internal energy, or total kinetic energy, of the gas molecules) into ordered mechanical work or vice versa. If we call the internal energy of the gas U, we can say that the decrease $(-dU)$ in the internal energy is equal to the work, $dW = F\,dx = PA\,dx = P\,dV$, done by the gas:

$$(dU)_a = -P\,dV \text{ (no heat flow)}.$$

(If the work done by the gas is a positive quantity, the internal energy decreases. If the gas is compressed, dV and also dW are negative quantities and the internal energy of the gas increases.)

We have seen in Chapter 16 that heat also serves to change the internal or random molecular energy of the gas, and in fact from a detailed consideration of the specific heats of gases we were able to account for all the heat transferred to or from a gas in terms of its internal energy. These considerations were for a gas kept at a constant volume:

$$(dU)_b = dQ \text{ (constant volume, no work done)}.$$

(If heat flows into a gas, dQ is positive and the internal energy increases.)

The internal energy of a gas can change then, either (a) because the gas does work (the molecules bounce against a moving piston), or (b) because heat flows into the gas. If both (a) and (b) occur, we have

$$dU = (dU)_a + (dU)_b = -P\,dV + dQ,$$

or

$$dQ = dU + P\,dV. \qquad (17\text{–}2)$$

Equation (17–2), the mathematical form of the *first law of thermodynamics*, says that the heat absorbed by a gas serves on the one hand to increase its internal energy and on the other to supply the energy for the mechanical work which the gas does as the volume changes. It expresses the fact that heat and work are equivalent and that energy is conserved.

In this discussion we have been concerned with an ideal gas, and the internal energy has been identified with molecular kinetic energy. Then, according to the kinetic theory, the internal energy depends *only* on temperature. (Recall that temperature is a measure of average translational kinetic energy per molecule.) We know that if we keep the volume of a sample of gas constant, we must add an amount of heat $dQ = C_v\,dT$ to increase the temperature by dT. All of this heat must have served to increase the internal energy, and so we have

$$dU = C_v\,dT \qquad (17\text{–}3)$$

for *all* processes, because the internal energy (molecular kinetic energy) depends *only* on temperature. For example, although different amounts of heat are required to increase the temperature of a gas by one degree at constant pressure and by one degree at constant volume, the internal energy change is the same in either case.

When the pressure, volume and temperature of a given amount of an ideal gas are known, we say that the *state of the gas* is specified. Since the state variables pressure, volume, and temperature are related by the ideal gas law, it follows that only two variables are required for the specification of the state of a gas. In other words, we can for example, specify the state by a point in a pressure *vs.* volume diagram (*P–V* diagram), and a change of state by a line or a curve in this diagram, as in Fig. 17–3.

Suppose now that through a succession of compressions and expansions the state of an ideal gas is changed in such a way that the gas is brought back to its initial state. Such a process is called a *cycle*, and is represented by a closed path or loop in the *P–V* diagram. Since the initial and final temperatures of the gas are the same and since the internal energy of the ideal gas depends only on temperature, it follows that the net change of the internal energy in the cyclic process is zero. This means, according to

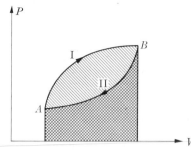

FIG. 17–3. When the gas passes from state A to state B along path I, the work done *by* the gas is represented by the area between curve I and the horizontal axis. When the gas passes back to state A from state B, work is done *on* the gas (it is compressed) and this work is represented by the area between curve II and the horizontal axis. The net work done by the gas on the round trip is thus represented by the area enclosed by the loop.

Eq. (17–2), that in a *cyclic process* the net heat absorbed by an ideal gas must equal the net work done by the gas. This is an alternate way of expressing the first law of thermodynamics.

Real substances. Does the first law of thermodynamics apply to substances other than an ideal gas, or is it possible that some particular real gas, liquid, or solid has properties that would permit us to construct a perpetual motion machine which in a cyclic process delivers more energy in the form of work than we put into it in the form of heat? The answer to this query can come only from experiments, and so far as anyone knows the first law of thermodynamics applies to all substances and processes; *no one has ever made a successful perpetual motion machine.* From this rather unusual type of experimental evidence we conclude, then, that when the state of an arbitrary real substance is changed in a cyclic manner the net heat absorbed is equal to the net work produced. With reference to Eq. (17–2) we can also express this result by saying that in all substances there is an internal energy which is a function of the state of the substance.

It may be helpful to elaborate upon this question somewhat further. For this purpose let the curves in Fig. 17–3 represent the change of state of a substance, for example a real gas, initially in state A. As indicated in the caption of Fig. 17–3, the work done by the gas as its state is changed along path I and back to state A again along path II is represented by the area enclosed by the paths. This work cannot be greater than the net heat absorbed in the cycle, for otherwise a portion of the net work could be converted into heat required for the next cycle and the remainder could be extracted and put to use elsewhere. The machine then would run by itself and constantly produce work, i.e., we would have a perpetual motion machine. Similarly, the net work cannot be less than the heat absorbed, for then we could arrange to have the gas traverse the closed path in the opposite direction and so get more energy in the form of heat out of the gas than we put in in the form of mechanical work W. A portion of this heat then could be used for the operation of a second machine from which work W is obtained and the remainder could be put to use elsewhere. We conclude, therefore, that the nonexistence of a perpetual motion machine requires that for all cyclic processes the net work output must equal the net heat absorbed, and that the first law of thermodynamics applies to all substances.

It follows, then, that the internal energy change in a cycle is zero. With reference to Fig. 17–3, if the internal energy change were ΔU_{ab} as the gas changes from state A to state B along the path I, there must be an equal but opposite change $\Delta U_{ba} = -\Delta U_{ab}$ as the gas is changed from state B to state A along path II. Since I and II are arbitrary paths, the change in internal energy as we go from A to B cannot depend on the path but only on the initial and the final states. In other words, the internal energy must be determined completely by the state of a substance and not, for example, by its past history.

In summary, then, the first law of thermodynamics is a statement of the law of conservation of energy and is valid for all substances. It serves to define the internal energy as a function of the state of a substance. The work W and the heat Q are not functions of state, and their values *do* depend on the path taken between two states, a fact that is obvious if we remember that the work done in a change of state can be represented by the area under the P vs. V curve. Then, if we keep the endpoints fixed in the P–V diagram and choose different paths between the endpoints, the area under the P vs. V curve, and consequently the work and the heat input, can be varied at will, as illustrated in Fig. 17–4. The internal-energy change, on the other hand, remains the same for all paths.

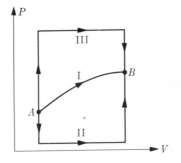

Fig. 17–4. The internal-energy change is determined completely by the initial and final states, but the work done, and hence the heat absorbed, depends upon the path. The work done can be made arbitrarily small with paths similar to II, or arbitrarily large with paths similar to III.

Whether we deal with an ideal gas or a real gas or any other substance, from the definition of specific heat as dQ/dT (see Chapters 14 and 16), it follows that the change in the internal energy always can be expressed as

$$dU = C_v \, dT,$$

where C_v is the (molar) specific heat at constant volume. The relation $dQ = dU + dW$ between the heat input dQ and the work dW done by a substance then can be written as

$$dQ = C_v \, dT + P \, dV.$$

The specific heat can itself be a function of the state variables, as will be shown in Chapter 18.

17–3 Changes of state of an ideal gas. The state of a gas is specified by its temperature, volume, and pressure. Only two of these variables are independent, since they are related by the gas law such that for one mole of gas,

$$PV = RT.$$

The state of the gas then can be uniquely described by a point in a P–V (or V–T or P–T) diagram. Specification of the state of the gas implies that the gas is in thermal equilibrium. The conditions are then the same throughout the gas. In this section, we shall investigate in detail the behavior of an ideal gas when it is heated, compressed, or otherwise induced to change from one state of equilibrium to another. Since the specification of the state applies only to equilibrium conditions, we are able to discuss, in principle, only the initial and final states, since *during* a change of state the gas is not in equilibrium. However, when the changes are sufficiently slow, there is time enough for the gas to settle into equilibrium at every point during the process. This process then can be considered as a succession of equilibrium states, and can be represented by a succession of points, or a line, between the initial and final states in a P–V diagram. A change of state of this type is sometimes called *quasi-static*. As a typical example of a nonequilibrium process, consider what happens if a piston in a gas container is moved outward much faster than the average molecular speed. There will be few molecular collisions with the piston, and little work done by the gas. A vacuum is created behind the piston, and the gas rushes out to fill the vacuum in a so-called *free expansion*. During this free expansion the gas is not in thermal equilibrium, and the conditions are not the same throughout the gas.

Constant-pressure (isobaric) process. Specific heat at constant pressure. To illustrate the change of state of an ideal gas, consider an example in

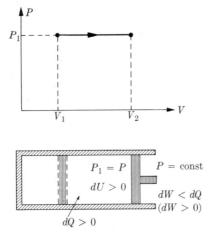

FIG. 17-5. Expansion at constant pressure (isobaric expansion).

which the gas is heated at constant pressure, as shown in Fig. 17-5. A movable piston closes one end of the gas container. If we neglect friction, the pressure on both sides of the piston must be the same when the piston is in equilibrium. In the present case, the outside pressure is constant, and with slow (quasi-static) changes of state, the pressure inside the container will also be constant throughout the entire process. When the gas in the container is heated, it must expand if the inside pressure is to remain constant. This constant-pressure (isobaric) process is represented by a horizontal line in the P–V diagram of Fig. 17-5.

If the pressure in the gas is P_1 and the area of the piston is A, as the piston is displaced a distance dx, the work of the gas is $dW = P_1 A \, dx = P_1 \, dV$. Since the volume increases at constant pressure, both the temperature and the internal energy must also increase. If the temperature change is dT, the internal-energy change is $C_v \, dT$ for one mole of the gas. Also, the work done by the gas can be expressed in terms of the temperature change, because from $PV = RT$ it follows that $P \, dV + V \, dP = R \, dT$, which reduces to $P \, dV = R \, dT$ when $dP = 0$. The heat input to the gas then can be written as

$$dQ = (R + C_v) \, dT = C_p \, dT,$$

where

$$C_p = C_v + R.$$

The new quantity C_p introduced here is the specific heat of the gas at constant pressure. The specific heat per mole, we recall, is defined as dQ/dT, where dQ is the heat required to increase the temperature of one mole by dT. A temperature change can come about in various ways, i.e., at constant pressure, at constant volume, adiabatically, etc., and the amount of heat required to produce a temperature change, and therefore the specific heat, depends on the particular process chosen.

The specific heat C_v, which we derived from kinetic theory, referred to a container with fixed walls, i.e., to a constant volume. We found then that no work was done by the gas as it was heated, and we had $dQ = C_v \, dT$. When the gas is heated at constant pressure, on the other hand, an additional amount of heat is required to produce the temperature change dT, since now the volume changes and work is done by the gas. For a monatomic gas, we have seen that the specific heat at constant volume is $C_v = 3R/2$; for the specific heat at constant pressure, we obtain

$$C_p = \tfrac{5}{2}R \qquad \text{(monatomic gas)}. \qquad (17\text{--}4a)$$

For a diatomic gas at ordinary temperatures, we have $C_v = 5R/2$ and therefore

$$C_p = \tfrac{7}{2}R \qquad \text{(diatomic gas)}. \qquad (17\text{--}4b)$$

The ratio between the specific heats at constant pressure and at constant volume, predicted on the basis of kinetic energy and thermodynamics, is then

$$\gamma = \frac{C_p}{C_v} = \frac{5}{3} = 1.67 \qquad \text{(monatomic gas)}$$

and

$$\gamma = \frac{C_p}{C_v} = \frac{7}{5} = 1.40 \qquad \text{(diatomic gas)}.$$

It can be seen from Table 16–2 that these results are in close agreement with the experimental results obtained at ordinary temperatures.

EXAMPLE. Eight grams of helium in a container are initially at a temperature of 27°C. A movable piston forms the upper wall of the container, as shown in Fig. 17–6. The mass of the piston may be neglected. The gas is heated until the volume has increased to twice its initial value. What are the work done by the gas, the change of the internal energy of the gas, and the total heat influx to the gas?

The pressure on the piston from the outside is 1 atm and, since the weight of the piston is negligible, the pressure P_1 in the container is also 1 atm. If the initial volume of the gas is V_1 and the final volume V_2, we have $V_2 = 2V_1$, and the work done by the gas is

$$W = P_1(V_2 - V_1) = P_1V_1. \qquad (17\text{--}5)$$

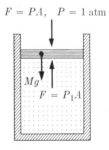

FIGURE 17–6

We have, from the equation of state, $P_1V_1 = \mu RT_1$, where $\mu = 2$, since we have two moles of helium ($M = 4$). The work then can be expressed also as $P_1V_1 = 2RT_1 = 0.164 \cdot 300 = 49.2$ liters·atm and can be interpreted as the area under the pressure *vs.* volume curve. The initial volume of the gas is evidently $V_1 = 49.2$ liters. Since this volume is increased by a factor of two at constant pressure, the temperature also increases by a factor of two. That is, $T_2 = 2T_1 = 600°$K. The internal-energy change is then $\Delta U = 2C_v(T_2 - T_1) = 2(3R/2)T_1 = 3RT_1$, and the total heat influx is

$$\Delta Q = 3RT_1 + 2RT_1 = 5RT_1 = 5 \cdot 0.082 \cdot 300 \simeq 123 \text{ liters·atm.}$$

It should be pointed out in this connection that if the mass of the piston is not negligible, the pressures inside and outside differ because of the weight of the piston. The piston is in equilibrium under the influence of the external pressure, the force of gravity, and the pressure in the container. Then, when the piston is of mass m and area A, and the pressure outside the piston is P, the pressure inside the container is

$$P_1 = P + \frac{mg}{A}.$$

Constant-temperature (isothermal) changes of state. We shall now follow up our discussion on the changes of state of a gas at constant volume and constant pressure, and consider the case in which the temperature is held constant but the pressure and the volume both vary. To ensure a constant temperature, we shall assume that the gas container is in thermal contact with a constant-temperature reservoir, for example a large body of water. The compressions and expansions of the gas are slow enough to keep the gas in continual thermal equilibrium with the reservoir. Since the reservoir is assumed to have an infinitely large heat capacity, the heat that flows from the reservoir to the gas will not change the temperature of the reservoir.

When the temperature is constant, we have $PV = $ const, and the change of state is represented in the P–V diagram by a hyperbola, as shown in Fig. 17–7. From an energy standpoint, the important characteristic feature of the constant-temperature (isothermal) change is that the *internal energy of the gas remains constant*, and all the heat that is transferred to the gas is then converted into work, since $dU = 0$ and thus $dQ = dW$. As the gas expands from a volume V_1 to a volume V_2, the work done by the gas is

$$W = \int_{V_1}^{V_2} P\,dV, \qquad (17\text{–}6)$$

a result which, of course, is not limited to isothermal changes, but is generally valid. [In the particular case of a constant-pressure change, as discussed earlier, we obtain $W = P(V_2 - V_1)$.] Note that the work can be interpreted as the area under the P vs. V curve. If we insert $P = RT/V$, for one mole of the gas, the work can be expressed as

$$W = \int_{V_1}^{V_2} P\,dV = RT \int_{V_1}^{V_2} \frac{dV}{V} = RT \ln \frac{V_2}{V_1}. \qquad (17\text{--}7)$$

EXAMPLE. One mole of a gas is carried through a cycle, as shown in Fig. 17–8. The gas expands at constant temperature from a volume V_1 to $V_2 = 2V_1$. It is then compressed to the initial volume at constant pressure, and finally is brought back to its initial state by heating at constant volume. What is the total work done by the gas in one such cycle, in terms of the initial temperature T_1?

In the isothermal expansion, the work is positive and equal to

$$W_1 = RT_1 \ln 2,$$

according to Eq. (17–7). In the compression from V_2 to V_1, work is done *on* the gas, and the work done *by* the gas is negative. This, of course, follows directly from the general expression (17–6). We have

$$W_2 = \int_{V_2}^{V_1} P\,dV = P_2(V_1 - V_2) = -P_2 V_1 = -\frac{P_1 V_1}{2},$$

since $P_2 = P_1/2$. In the final heating at constant volume no work is done, and the total work done by the gas in the cycle is then

$$W = W_1 + W_2 = RT_1 \ln 2 - \frac{P_1 V_1}{2} = RT_1\,(\ln 2 - 0.5) \simeq 0.19\,RT_1.$$

Adiabatic change of state. In the changes of state discussed so far, the gas has interacted thermally with its surroundings, so that heat has been transferred to and from the gas. For example, in the constant-pressure change starting from point A (Fig. 17–9), an expansion of the gas requires a heat transfer to the gas and ΔQ is positive. The same holds true in an isothermal expansion, as we have seen. On the other hand, if the pressure is decreased from the value at A under constant volume, the gas must be cooled and ΔQ is negative. We shall now investigate a case in which the gas is thermally insulated from its surroundings such that $\Delta Q = 0$ during the entire process. In this case, we have an *adiabatic process*, and it follows from Fig. 17–9 that the curve that represents this process should be steeper than the isothermal curve.

Since there is no heat flow to or from the gas, it follows that any work done by the gas must be accounted for by an identical decrease of the internal energy. That is, we have

$$dQ = dU + P\,dV = 0,$$

or

$$dU = -P\,dV. \qquad (17\text{--}8)$$

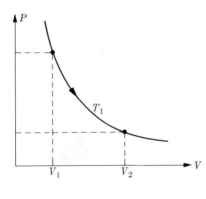

FIG. 17-7. Isothermal expansion.

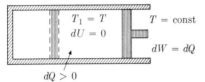

$T_1 = T$
$dU = 0$
$T = \text{const}$
$dW = dQ$
$dQ > 0$

FIGURE 17-8

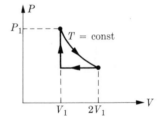

P_1
$T = \text{const}$
V_1 $2V_1$ V

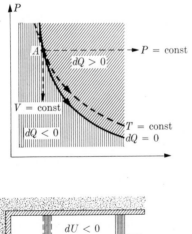

A
$P = \text{const}$
$dQ > 0$
$V = \text{const}$
$dQ < 0$
$T = \text{const}$
$dQ = 0$

FIG. 17-9. Adiabatic change of state.

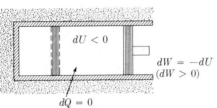

$dU < 0$
$dW = -dU$
$(dW > 0)$
$dQ = 0$

By inserting $dU = C_v\, dT$ and $P = RT/V$ into Eq. (17–8), we can find the manner in which pressure, volume, and temperature are interrelated in an adiabatic process. Equation (17–8) then reduces to

$$C_v \frac{dT}{T} = -R \frac{dV}{V},$$

which can be integrated directly to $\ln T = -(R/C_v)\ln V + \text{const}$ or, with $R/C_v = (C_p - C_v)/C_v = \gamma - 1$, we have $\ln(TV^{\gamma-1}) = \text{const}$. That is,

$$TV^{\gamma-1} = \text{const} = T_1 V_1^{\gamma-1}. \tag{17–9a}$$

We have introduced here the ratio between the specific heats, $\gamma = C_p/C_v$ ($\frac{5}{3}$ for a monatomic gas and $\frac{7}{5}$ for a diatomic gas). We can eliminate the temperature in Eq. (17–8) by inserting $P_1 V_1/T_1 = PV/T$, which then gives the relation between pressure and volume,

$$P_1 V_1^\gamma = PV^\gamma = \text{const}. \tag{17–9b}$$

Whereas in an isothermal process PV is constant, we see that in an adiabatic process PV^γ is constant and P varies as $V^{-\gamma}$. An adiabatic line in a P–V diagram, then, is steeper than an isotherm, as mentioned earlier.

The work done by the gas, of course, is obtained from the integral $\int P\, dV$, which, since $P\, dV = -dU = -C_v\, dT$, is most simply determined from the change in the internal energy. In other words, to find the work done by the gas, $W = C_v(T_1 - T_2)$, we need know only the difference between the initial and the final temperatures.

Although, in principle, a change of state must be made very slowly, i.e., quasi-statically, so that the gas is in a state of equilibrium at all times, we find that in practice, the relations obtained on the basis of this assumption apply adequately to processes in which the changes of state are quite rapid. For example, when the air in a bicycle pump is compressed rapidly, or when the pressure fluctuations in a sound wave are considered, we might question the validity of the equilibrium or quasi-static assumption. However, we find that both of these processes can be described to a high degree of accuracy as adiabatic processes. In other words, thermodynamic equilibrium in a gas is reached in a time that is short in comparison with the typical times involved in many processes in practice. The time required to establish equilibrium in a gas, the relaxation time, is related to the time between collisions of molecules. If changes are produced in a gas at a frequency which is of the order of the molecular-collision frequency, the assumption of thermodynamic equilibrium breaks down. Another example of a nonequilibrium process was given at the beginning of this section, where we considered a piston that moved outward at faster than typical molecular speeds.

When a gas expands, for example, at constant temperature we note that it absorbs a certain amount of heat from its surroundings, and work is done by the gas. If the process is reversed, so that the gas is compressed along the same isothermal path, we find that the same amount of heat is transferred from the gas to its surroundings, and the same amount of work has to be done *on* the gas to restore the gas to its initial state. In other words, by reversing the path we restore the gas and its surroundings to precisely their initial states. Not only isothermal changes, but all quasi-static or equilibrium types of changes of state, are *reversible* in this sense. Although these processes are idealizations (for example, friction is neglected), they play a very important role in the study of matter. Later, in Chapter 19, we shall further explore the question of reversibility.

EXAMPLE. As a review example, let us compute the work done and the heat absorbed by μ moles of an ideal monatomic gas which expands from a volume V_1 to a volume $2V_1$. The initial temperature of the gas is T_1. We shall consider expansions that take place (a) at constant pressure, (b) at constant temperature, and (c) adiabatically. The three paths are illustrated in Fig. 17-10.

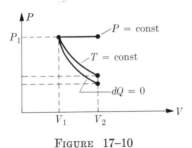

FIGURE 17-10

(a) The initial pressure is given by $P_1V_1 = \mu R T_1$. The work done by the gas in the expansion is $P_1(V_2 - V_1) = P_1V_1$. Consequently, the work is

$$W_a = \mu R T_1.$$

The temperature changes by a factor of two in the expansion, so that the internal-energy change is $\Delta U_a = \mu C_v(T_2 - T_1) = \mu C_v T_1$. Since $C_v = 3R/2$, we obtain

$$\Delta U_a = \tfrac{3}{2}\mu R T_1 = 1.5\mu R T_1.$$

The heat transfer to the gas is then

$$\Delta Q_a = W_a + \Delta U_a = \tfrac{5}{2}\mu R T_1 = 2.5\mu R T_1.$$

This last result we could have obtained directly as $\Delta Q = \mu C_p \Delta T$, where $C_p = C_v + R = 5R/2$.

(b) In the isothermal expansion, the internal energy of the gas remains constant. The work done by the gas is

$$W_b = \mu R T_1 \int_{V_1}^{V_2} \frac{dV}{V} = (\ln 2)\mu R T_1 \simeq 0.69\mu R T_1,$$

and the heat input to the gas has the same value,

$$\Delta Q_b = W_b = (\ln 2)\mu R T_1 \simeq 0.69\mu R T_1.$$

(c) In the adiabatic change of state, we have $dQ = 0$. In order to obtain the change of the internal energy, we determine the new temperature T_2. According to Eq. (17–9a), we have $T_1 V_1^{\gamma-1} = T_2 V_2^{\gamma-1}$ and therefore $T_2 = (1/2)^{\gamma-1}T_1 = (1/2)^{2/3}T_1$. The change in the internal energy is then, with $C_v = 3R/2$,

$$\Delta U_c = \mu C_v(T_2 - T_1) = -(1 - 2^{-2/3})\mu R T_1 \simeq -0.37\mu R T_1.$$

[handwritten: LN ~ 0.56]

The amount by which the internal energy decreases must be equal to the work done by the gas,

$$W_c = -\Delta U_c = 0.37\mu R T_1.$$

[handwritten: 0.56]

To obtain some numerical values, let us consider one liter of helium at an initial temperature of 300°K. The number of moles is

$$\mu = \frac{P_1 V_1}{R T_1} = 2 \cdot \frac{1}{0.082 \cdot 300} \simeq 0.081 \text{ mole.}$$

[handwritten correction: 0.082·300]

We then have (with $R \simeq 2$ cal/mole·deg)

$$\mu R T_1 = 0.081 \cdot 2 \cdot 300 \simeq 48.5 \text{ cal,}$$

and this value must be inserted in the expressions above for the work, internal energy, and heat.

17–4 The compressibility of a gas. The gas in a container is similar to a spring in one respect. If, as shown in Fig. 17–11, we disturb the piston from its equilibrium position, for example by pushing it farther into the container, the piston will rebound when it is released and then will oscillate about the equilibrium position. The air in the container has "stiffness," just as does a spring, and it provides a restoring force on the piston. It is of interest to determine the "spring constant" of the air in the container or, what amounts to the same thing, the compressibility of the gas. Figure 17–11 shows the volume change dV which results when the external pressure (and also the internal pressure in the container) is increased by an amount dP. The relative change of the volume is dV/V (in the case shown, dV is negative). The compressibility κ is defined as the relative

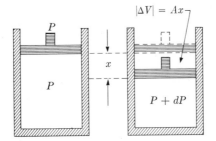

Fig. 17–11. The compressibility of a gas is $\kappa = -(1/V)(dV/dP)$.

change in volume per unit pressure increment, and is formally expressed as

$$\kappa = -\frac{1}{V}\frac{dV}{dP}. \tag{17–10}$$

The compressibility depends upon the relation between the pressure and the volume during the compression. In an isothermal compression we have $PV = $ const and $V\,dP + P\,dV = 0$, which means that $dV/V = -dP/P$, or

$$\kappa_i = \frac{1}{P} \quad \text{(isothermal)}. \tag{17–11}$$

If the compression is adiabatic, the relation between the pressure and the volume is given by $PV^\gamma = $ const, so that $V^\gamma\,dP + \gamma V^{\gamma-1}P\,dV = 0$, and thus the compressibility is

$$\kappa_a = \frac{1}{\gamma P} \quad \text{(adiabatic)}. \tag{17–12}$$

In isothermal compression heat will flow out from the gas container, and the restoring pressure provided by the gas will be smaller than in the adiabatic case, where the temperature of the gas is allowed to increase. In the adiabatic case, the stiffness of the gas is larger and the compressibility is smaller than in the isothermal case. To obtain adiabatic conditions, the gas container, in principle, should be thermally insulated. However, adiabatic conditions can be approximately obtained without thermal insulation if the compression takes place sufficiently fast so that there is no time for heat flow. (The changes must, of course, be slow enough so that thermal equilibrium within the container is maintained.)

Example. Let us consider the above-mentioned oscillations. In practice, this experiment can be performed easily with a steel ball that fits into the neck of a flask, as shown in Fig. 17–12. If the ball is displaced upward a distance x,

the volume changes by an amount
$\Delta V = Ax$, where A is the area of the
neck. The pressure change in the flask
becomes

$$dP = -\frac{dV}{V\kappa} = -\frac{Ax}{V\kappa}.$$

The restoring force on the ball is then
directed downward and has a magnitude of $(1/V\kappa)A^2x$, which corresponds
to a spring constant $K = A^2/V\kappa$. The
period of oscillation of the ball is
then

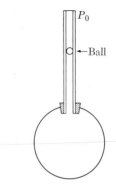

FIG. 17–12. Simple experiment for
the determination of $\gamma = C_p/C_v$.

$$T_0 = 2\pi\sqrt{\frac{m}{K}} = \frac{2\pi}{A}\sqrt{mV\kappa},$$

where m is the mass of the ball. Consequently, by measuring the period of
oscillation, we can determine the compressibility κ, and if the conditions are
adiabatic ($\kappa = 1/\gamma P$), we can determine the ratio γ between the specific heats
at constant pressure and at constant volume.

PROBLEMS

17-1. Refer to Fig. 17-1(a). Show that the apparent energy loss in this collision is $mV^2/4$.

17-2. Perform a similar analysis to that presented in Section 17-2 for determining the relation between internal energy and work done in the expansion of an ideal gas, but now consider a compression of the gas. Show that the work done on the gas appears as an increase in internal energy.

17-3. Imagine an experiment in which the state of a real gas is changed by a cyclic process from its initial state and back again. In this cycle, the gas interacts thermally with its surroundings and also produces a certain amount of work. From this experiment, how would you verify that the internal energy of the gas is a function of its state?

17-4. The internal energy is uniquely specified by the state of a gas. Is the reverse statement true, i.e., that a state is uniquely specified by the internal energy? Explain.

17-5. Explain in qualitative terms why the specific heat of a gas at constant pressure is larger than its specific heat at constant volume.

17-6. One mole of an ideal monatomic gas expands under constant pressure P_1 from a volume V_1 to a volume $2V_1$. To what volume should an identical gas expand isothermally from the same initial state (a) to produce the same amount of work, and (b) to absorb the same amount of heat as in the isobaric process?

17-7. Niagara Falls is about 50 m high. What approximate temperature increase would you expect for the water at the bottom of the Falls?

17-8. Prove that in an adiabatic process the relation between tem-

perature and volume is given by $TV^{\gamma-1} = $ const.

17-9. A cylinder contains one mole of a diatomic gas. One end of the container is closed by a movable piston of area A and mass m. When the cylinder lies on its side, the piston assumes an equilibrium position such that the volume of the enclosed gas is V. The cylinder is thermally insulated from its surroundings. (a) What will be the new equilibrium position of the piston if the cylinder is turned so that the piston is up, thus compressing the gas? (b) What will be the equilibrium position of the piston if the cylinder is turned so that the piston is down? (c) What is the work done by gravity in (a) and (b), and what are the new temperatures of the gas? Let the initial temperature of the gas be T.

17-10. Derive a relation which gives the pressure, in terms of temperature, of an ideal gas during an adiabatic process.

17-11. One mole of helium at 0°C and 1-atm pressure is compressed adiabatically to 5 atm, and then cooled to 0°C at constant volume. What is the final pressure?

17-12. A gas that consists of 10 gm of argon is initially at 3 atm pressure and 300°K. It changes state and finally is at a pressure of 1 atm and at 600°K. Find the work done, the heat absorbed, and the internal-energy change for the following processes, all of which can carry the gas from the initial to the final state: (a) Constant pressure, constant volume. (b) Constant volume, constant pressure. (c) Constant temperature, constant pressure. (d) Constant volume, constant temperature.

17-13. How many calories are required to heat one liter of helium from 50°C to 60°C at a constant pressure of 1 atm? Perform the same calculation for one liter of oxygen.

17–14. A container of volume V is divided into halves by a tight piston, as shown in Fig. 17–13. The two parts contain 1 mole of helium and 1 mole of oxygen, respectively. (a) What force is required to keep the piston in equilibrium if the temperatures of the two gases are the same and equal to T? (b) The piston is now displaced until the oxygen is compressed to half its initial volume. What now is the force required to keep the piston in equilibrium, if we assume adiabatic changes of state for the two gases? The area of the piston is A. What is the ratio between the final temperatures of the two gases? (c) In (b), what is the net work done by the external force on the piston? (d) Because of heat flow through the piston (the container is assumed to be thermally insulated), the temperatures of the two gases will eventually be the same. What is this temperature, and what is the new force required to keep the piston in equilibrium?

17–15. Refer to Fig. 17–13 and Problem 17–14. The piston, of mass m, is displaced a small amount and then released. What will be the frequency of oscillation if in both gases (a) the conditions are adiabatic? (b) the conditions are isothermal?

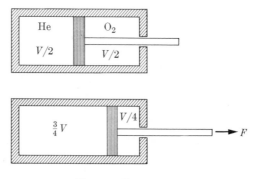

FIGURE 17–13

CHAPTER 18

SOME PROPERTIES OF MATTER

Summary. Now that we are somewhat familiar with atoms and molecules and their motion, in this chapter we shall investigate certain specific properties of matter which, as we shall see, can be related to the interaction forces between the molecules and atoms in matter. We start with a discussion of gases and liquids and the transition from one to the other (condensation), and compare the experimental results with van der Waals' equation of state. A brief discussion of vaporization, the reverse of condensation, follows. Then a description is given of some elastic properties of solids and the corresponding intermolecular forces. This leads to an estimation of the characteristic frequencies of molecular vibrations. The specific heat of solids is then interpreted in terms of the energy of molecular vibrations. Finally, the relation between thermal expansion and molecular vibration is mentioned.

In Chapter 1 it was pointed out that physics involves two basic types of problem, the problem that has to do with basic interactions (two-body interactions) and the problem that deals with the description of the bulk properties of matter in terms of its elementary constituents (many-particle interactions). The description of the properties of matter has been limited mainly to an ideal gas, which we have described in terms of kinetic theory. If we were to go into much more detail, we would have to introduce, for example, the dependence of intermolecular forces on the distance between molecules, etc., and so would be carried considerably beyond our intended scope. However, there are certain familiar phenomena and properties of matter which vividly demonstrate the effects of intermolecular forces at work, and although a quantitative discussion of these effects will not be given here, we can at least present a qualitative molecular description.

18–1 Free expansion of a gas. The Joule-Thomson effect. In the derivation of the equation of state for an ideal gas, two important assumptions were made: the molecules were assumed to be of negligible size, and their energy was assumed to be purely kinetic. Potential energy resulting from intermolecular forces was not included. Then, according to kinetic theory, the internal energy of the gas is determined entirely by the number

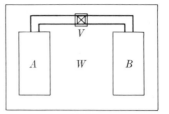

FIG. 18–1. Free-expansion experiment.

of molecules N in the gas and by the mean kinetic energy of the molecules. The internal energy depends only on the temperature of the gas, not on the volume.

An experimental test of the volume independence of the internal energy of a gas is provided by a free expansion of the gas. This experiment, which was first performed by Gay-Lussac and somewhat later by Joule, is illustrated in Fig. 18–1. A gas is contained in a flask A that is connected by means of a valve V to an evacuated flask B. The entire system is submerged in a thermally insulated calorimeter filled with water. As the valve is opened, the gas rushes into the evacuated container (free expansion) so that, when equilibrium is reached, the pressures in the two flasks are the same. If any energy were released or absorbed by the gas in this free expansion, there would be a temperature change in the water bath. However, Gay-Lussac and Joule found no temperature change, and consequently they concluded that there was no heat transfer to or from the gas. Since no work is done by the gas in free expansion, the experiments by Gay-Lussac and Joule indicated that the internal energy of the gas is independent of the volume, in accordance with the kinetic theory for the case of an ideal gas.

However, later and more sensitive experiments have shown that there is indeed a transfer of heat, although it is too small to be detected in experiments of the type performed by Gay-Lussac and Joule (the water baths used in their experiments had too large heat capacities). In other words, the internal energy of a gas *does* depend somewhat on the volume. If the temperature of a gas is kept constant, the internal energy is found to increase with volume, for most gases. Similarly, in free expansion the temperature of a thermally insulated gas does not remain constant, but decreases.

Another well-known, similar experiment is the Joule-Thomson throttling experiment. This experiment, illustrated in Fig. 18–2, is a modification of the free-expansion experiment. The gas now does not expand into a vacuum chamber, as in the free-expansion experiment, but into a chamber with a constant pressure P_2. This chamber is separated from a high-pressure chamber by a porous plug

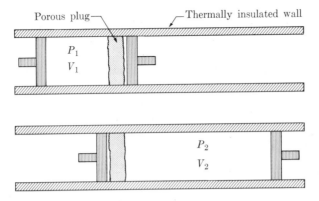

FIG. 18–2. As the gas to the left of the porous plug is pushed through the plug, it is brought to a pressure P_2 and the larger volume V_2. This expansion produces a temperature decrease.

through which the gas passes. In principle, the pressures on the two sides of the plug can be kept constant by means of pistons, as shown in the figure. An expansion of this kind is usually called a *throttling process;* the gas is throttled through the plug from a high to a low pressure.

The analysis of this experiment, which we shall not present here, shows that if the gas were ideal there would be no temperature change in the throttling process. However, experiments have indeed shown a noticeable temperature change (a decrease for almost all gases). For example, when air at a pressure of 50 atm and a temperature of 20°C is throttled down to a pressure of 1 atm, the temperature is found to decrease by 11.7°C. The observed temperature change can be related to the pressure and volume dependence of the internal energy.

The throttling process is of great practical importance in the liquefaction of gases. The gas to be liquefied is contained in a closed system. After having been cooled by throttling, the gas is returned to cool the high-pressure gas to be throttled, and by means of this regenerative process, the gas finally reaches temperatures so low that it can be liquefied. This process is ascribed to Linde and Hampson (1895), and has been used extensively for the liquefaction of air.

How can we now understand, in terms of kinetic theory, the decrease of temperature in a free expansion of a gas? If we regard the internal energy of the molecules as kinetic energy only, clearly it is not possible to account for such cooling. However, if we assume that between the molecules there is an attractive force that decreases continuously with distance, the molecules will possess potential energy in addition to their kinetic energy. As the separation between the molecules is increased when the gas expands, the molecules have to overcome their mutual attractive force, and they lose kinetic energy in the process (but, of course, they gain a corresponding amount of potential energy). As the kinetic energy decreases, so does the temperature. From this point of view, the cooling in a free expansion of a gas is then a direct result of intermolecular attractive forces.

In addition to the free-expansion experiment, there are numerous other properties of matter that demonstrate the attraction between molecules even more directly. The very fact that molecules in a solid are held in fixed average positions relative to one another, and that it takes a considerable force to pull them apart, is the most obvious demonstration of intermolecular forces at work.

The influence of intermolecular attractive forces depends on the relative magnitudes of the average kinetic and potential energies of the molecules; the higher the temperature and the lower the pressure (or density), the less should be the importance of the intermolecular forces and the better should an ideal gas describe the behavior of a real gas. If, on the other hand, the gas is cooled below a certain temperature, so that the kinetic energy is insignificant, the intermolecular attraction will pull the molecules together. This is in accord with the behavior of a real gas, since we know it will condense into a liquid at sufficiently low temperatures and high pressures. In succeeding sections, we shall discuss some experimental studies of the relations between the pressure, volume, and temperature of a gas, and we shall see how it is possible to account for the effects of intermolecular forces as well as the finite sizes of the molecules by a modification of the equation of state for an ideal gas.

18–2 Experimental studies of a real gas. The experimental studies we shall discuss concern the relation between the pressure and the volume of a gas at constant temperature. These experiments are extensions of the original experiment by Boyle (Sec. 16–3) to a wider range of pressures and temperatures. A simple way of obtaining high pressures is illustrated schematically in Fig. 18–3. In this experiment the gas under study is enclosed in a glass tube A, which is sealed at the top and open at the bottom. The open part is submerged in a water chamber in which very high pressures can be built up by means of a screw, as shown. The gas is separated from the water by means of a mercury seal. Clearly, the volume-pressure relationship of this gas can be compared with that of a reference gas, for example air, by the addition of a second test tube with the reference gas in communication with the high-pressure chamber. The gases are now compressed at constant temperature, and the corresponding values of the volume and the pressure are determined.

A typical result of this type of experiment is shown in Fig. 18–4, which shows the isotherms for carbon dioxide and for air. At high temperatures the isotherms for air follow closely the curves predicted from the ideal gas theory, whereas considerable deviations occur for carbon dioxide,

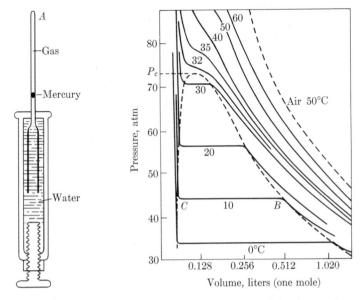

FIG. 18-3. Experiment on isothermal compression of a gas.

FIG. 18-4. Measured isotherms for carbon dioxide.

particularly at low temperatures. For example, at a temperature of 10°C and a pressure of about 45 atm (point B in Fig. 18-4), the carbon dioxide starts to liquefy, and part of the volume in the tube becomes filled with liquid. No increase in pressure is required to further decrease the volume, and the isotherm becomes a horizontal line in the P-V diagram. In the interval between B and C an interface between the gaseous and liquid carbon dioxide can be seen in the tube, but as C is approached, more and more of the volume becomes occupied by liquid, and at C the entire available volume is filled with liquid. To further decrease the volume the liquid carbon dioxide must be compressed; very high pressures are required for such compression, and the isotherm changes from a horizontal to an almost vertical line.

Isotherms at high temperatures are found to show the same general behavior and to contain a horizontal region where both gas and liquid are present. However, this region decreases with increasing temperature, until at a temperature of 31°C it has degenerated to a point at which the volumes of the gaseous and the liquid carbon dioxide are the same. Isotherms at temperatures above 31°C contain no horizontal part. The carbon dioxide remains in its gaseous form regardless of the pressure; it can no longer be liquefied by an isothermal compression. At sufficiently high temperatures, say above 80°C, the isotherms are much the same as for an ideal gas.

Table 18–1. Critical temperatures, pressures, and specific volumes
of some common gases.

Gas	Critical temperature T_c, °C	Critical pressure P_c, atm	Specific volume v_c, cm³/gm
Helium	−267.9	2.25	15.4
Hydrogen	−239.9	12.8	32.2
Argon	−122.4	48	1.88
Oxygen	−118.8	49.7	2.32
Nitrogen	−147.1	33.5	3.21
Carbon dioxide	31	72.8	2.17
Ammonia	132.2	112.3	4.24
Water	374.2	218	
Mercury	1460	1040	

The isotherms for carbon dioxide then are divided into two groups by the 31°-isotherm. This is called the critical isotherm, and the corresponding temperature is called the *critical temperature*. The pressure corresponding to point P in Fig. 18–4, where the gas volume is the same as the liquid volume, is called the *critical point*, and the corresponding pressure is called the *critical pressure*.

The results presented here refer to a particular gas, namely, carbon dioxide. However, similar isotherms are obtained for all gases, the essential difference being that each gas has its own particular critical temperature and critical pressure. In Table 18–1 are shown the critical temperatures, the critical pressures, and the corresponding critical specific volumes (volume per gram) of some common gases.

Beyond the critical temperature, the speed of a molecule evidently is so great that it is much too evasive a target to be caught permanently in the force field of a neighbor, even if the pressure in the gas is very large and the average distance between the molecules is comparatively small.

After this review of the experimental facts about the equation of state for gases, we shall proceed to discuss an equation of state which attempts to account for the intermolecular forces and also for the finite sizes of the molecules.

18–3 Van der Waals equation of state. In 1873, Johannes van der Waals, a Dutch physicist (1837–1923), proposed in his doctoral thesis an equation of state for gases which accounts not only for the intermolecular forces but also for the sizes of the molecules. We can understand the essence of this equation of state in terms of the following crude arguments.

In the equation of state for an ideal gas, $PV = RT$, as obtained on the basis of kinetic theory, we have neglected the volume of the molecules themselves, and V in this equation, then, is the volume in which the molecules are free to move. In this simple model, V conceivably could be zero. If we now are to account for the volume occupied by the molecules themselves, we note that the volume offered to the molecules for free motion is no longer V, but a smaller volume $V - b$, where b is a measure of the volume occupied by the molecules themselves. We expect, then, that to account for the sizes of the molecules themselves, we should replace V by $V - b$ in the equation of state.

In addition to this volume correction, there must also be a pressure correction. This correction is a result of the intermolecular forces. In the interior of the gas, the force on a molecule by the surrounding molecules is, on the average, zero and does not influence the average motion of the molecule. However, a molecule which is in the neighborhood of the boundary of the gas is pulled toward the interior of the gas, since there are no gas molecules on the other side to exert a pull.

This pull toward the interior exerted on molecules at the boundary is perpendicular to the boundary (the pull *along* the boundary in one direction is always canceled by an equal pull in the opposite direction) and is completely *equivalent to a pressure* provided by an (imaginary) wall. In other words, molecules which come from the interior of the gas and fly out toward the boundary receive a momentum transfer toward the interior of the gas.

Therefore, so far as the motion of the molecules is concerned, the effect of the intermolecular forces can be described in terms of an equivalent pressure which we shall denote by δ. In addition to this momentum transfer, there is also momentum transfer provided by the real wall at the boundary of the gas. This momentum transfer is what we measure as the pressure P of the gas. The motion of the molecules in the interior of a real gas whose pressure is P is then expected to be the same as the motion in an ideal gas with pressure $P + \delta$. In summary, then, we expect the real gas of volume V and pressure P to behave like an ideal gas with a volume $V - b$ and a pressure $P + \delta$, and the relation between P and V should therefore be given by

$$(P + \delta)(V - b) = RT. \qquad (18-1)$$

The additional pressure δ can be related to the volume of the gas in the following way. The effective intermolecular force acting inwardly on *one molecule* very near the boundary is proportional to the number of molecules per unit volume of gas; that is, $f = \text{const} \cdot n$. The effective additional *pressure* is proportional to the effective force on one molecule times the number of such molecules per unit area. Here "number of molecules per unit area" means the number per unit area within a very small distance from the boundary, and this too is proportional to n, the number of molecules per unit volume. In other words, the additional pressure produced by the intermolecular attractive force is proportional to n^2, $\delta \simeq \text{const} \cdot n^2$. If we introduce $n = N/V$, we obtain

$$\delta = \frac{a}{V^2},$$

where a is a constant. If we now introduce this expression for δ into Eq. (18–1), we obtain van der Waals equation of state,

$$\left(P + \frac{a}{V^2}\right)(V - b) = RT, \tag{18–2}$$

which we can write as

$$P = \frac{RT}{V - b} - \frac{a}{V^2}. \tag{18–3}$$

If the temperature and the volume are sufficiently large, we see that Eq. (18–3) reduces, in the limit, to the ideal gas law.

The isotherms obtained from van der Waals equation have the following general character (Fig. 18–5). At high temperatures, the isotherms are seen to be much the same as for an ideal gas. At low temperatures, van der Waals isotherms deviate from the ideal ones in just about the same manner as the experimental curves shown in Fig. 18–4. As the temperature is further decreased, we find that in a certain region the slope is reversed and each isotherm has both a maximum and a minimum; consequently, there will be three possible values of the volume for a given value of the pressure (van der Waals equation is of third order in the variable V). Of course, this result is unrealistic, but it nevertheless can be given an interesting interpretation, as we shall show later. The region containing the maxima and minima corresponds to the region of horizontal isotherms in Fig. 18–4. The maximum and minimum points of the isotherms move closer and closer as the temperature is increased, until finally they merge at one point. This point corresponds to the critical point discussed in the previous section and shown in Fig. 18–4.

At this critical point the isotherm is horizontal and, furthermore, is an inflection point of the curve. The constants a and b in van der Waals equation can then easily be expressed, in terms of the volume V_c, the pressure P_c, and the temperature T_c at this critical point, by setting both dP/dV and d^2P/dV^2 equal to zero (Problem 18–2). We then obtain

$$a = 3P_c V_c^2 = \frac{27}{64} R^2 \frac{T_c^2}{P_c}, \qquad b = \frac{V_c}{3} = \frac{R}{8} \frac{T_c}{P_c}. \tag{18–4}$$

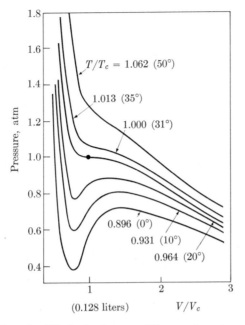

FIG. 18–5. Van der Waals isotherms. The numbers in parentheses refer to carbon dioxide. (Compare with Fig. 18–4.)

If we insert these values for a and b into Eq. (18–2), we find that the relation between pressure, volume, and temperature *at the critical point* is

$$P_c V_c = \tfrac{3}{8} R T_c,   (18\text{–}4a)$$

which represents a considerable deviation from the ideal gas law. At the critical point, the ideal gas law would predict a pressure $P = RT_c/V_c$, which is $\tfrac{8}{3} = 2.7$ times the van der Waals pressure.

It is now possible to estimate the values of the constants a and b for various gases, with the data given in Table 18–1. For carbon dioxide, for example, we have $P_c = 72.8$ atm and $T_c = 31.0°C$ (304°K); the corresponding values of a and b, according to Eq. (18–4), become $a \simeq 3.5$ atm·liter² and $b \simeq 0.042$ liter. Both values refer to one mole of the gas. If we use these numerical values of a and b in van der Waals equation, we obtain the isotherms for carbon dioxide, as shown in Fig. 18–5. These should be compared with the experimental curves in Fig. 18–4. As can be seen, the agreement is, at least qualitatively, quite satisfactory for temperatures above the critical temperature. Below this temperature, however, we have a region in which the pressure increases as the volume increases.

Let us investigate this region somewhat more closely. If we start at very large volumes and compress the gas, the pressure increases continuously until we reach the point P_1 in Fig. 18–6. Experiment has shown that at this point the gas starts to condense and the experimental isotherm becomes horizontal. On the other hand, a van der Waals isotherm indicates a continued increase of the pressure as the gas is compressed further, up to the point P_2. Although van der Waals equation fails to describe the behavior of the gas in this region, it does not completely lack physical significance. It is well known that a gas or vapor can be "supersaturated" in an unstable state, in which indeed the pressure of the gas increases as the volume decreases. The portion P_1P_2 of the van der Waals curve can be interpreted as representing a supersaturated or supercooled gas (the values of P and V in the region P_1P_2 correspond to a higher-temperature isotherm). A supercooled vapor or gas is unstable and may condense as a result of mechanical impacts for example. Similarly, the region P_3P_4 can be interpreted as representing a superheated (unstable) liquid, since the states along P_3P_4 actually belong to isotherms at lower temperatures. The intermediate region, P_2P_3, in van der Waals equation clearly represents a highly unstable condition, since the pressure decreases when the volume decreases. Such a situation would lead to a collapse of the gas.

Although van der Waals equation certainly is not a complete description of the equation of state of a gas, it contains many of the essentials inherent in the behavior of a real gas, particularly if the region below the critical temperature is interpreted in the manner described. Suppose we wish to draw the horizontal portion of the isotherm in Fig. 18–6, starting from van der Waals equation. Then it is necessary, of course, to know when the gas becomes unstable, i.e., the position of the point P_1. The van der Waals equation does not explicitly give this location, but from a further analysis of equilibrium conditions in a thermodynamic system it can be shown that the horizontal portion of the isotherm should be located in such a way that the two areas enclosed by this horizontal line and the van der Waals isotherm should be equal, as indicated in the figure.

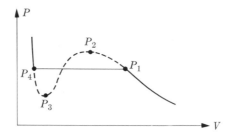

Fig. 18–6. Comparison between the experimental and the van der Waals isotherm for carbon dioxide.

Much of what we have said about van der Waals equation refers to one particular gas. However, the discussion applies equally well to any gas. In fact, if the pressure is measured in terms of the critical pressure, and if the volume and the temperature are measured in terms of the critical values, van der Waals isotherms become the same for all gases. We can see this result immediately by introducing the values of a and b in Eq. (18-4) into van der Waals equation. We then obtain

$$\left(P_r + \frac{3}{V_r^2}\right)(V_r - \tfrac{1}{3}) = \tfrac{8}{3}T_r, \tag{18-5}$$

where $P_r = P/P_c$, $V_r = V/V_c$, and $T_r = T/T_c$ are the so-called reduced values of the pressure, the volume, and the temperature. If two different gases have the same reduced temperatures and the same reduced volumes, they must also have the same reduced pressures, according to Eq. (18-5). This correspondence is called the *law of corresponding states*. The isotherms that correspond to the normalized van der Waals equation, Eq. (18-5), have been shown in Fig. 18-5.

EXAMPLE. According to van der Waals equation, what is the pressure of one mole of oxygen at a temperature double the critical temperature and a volume equal to the critical volume?

With $T = 2T_c$ (that is, $T_r = 2$) and $V = V_c$ (that is, $V_r = 1$), we obtain, from Eq. (18-5), $P_r = 5$ (that is, $P = 5P_c$). From Table 18-1 we find that the critical pressure of oxygen is $P_c = 49.7$ atm, and the pressure P is then $P = 5P_c = 248.5$ atm.

If we attempt to calculate the pressure on the basis of the ideal gas law, we use from Table 18-1 the critical volume 2.32 cm³ per gram (consequently $2.32 \cdot 32$ cm³ $\simeq 0.074$ liter for one mole) and the critical temperature $-118.8°C$ (154.4°K). Therefore, with $T = 2T_c = 308.8°K$, we obtain

$$P = 0.082 \cdot \frac{308.8}{0.074} \simeq 340 \text{ atm.}$$

As we see, even at ordinary temperatures, there is considerable difference between the ideal gas law and van der Waals law, when the pressures are of the order of hundreds of atmospheres.

18-4 Vaporization. In the previous section, it was noted that as a gas is compressed at a constant temperature that is lower than the critical temperature, eventually a point is reached at which the gas starts to liquefy (condense). We shall now extend this observation on condensation to the reverse phenomenon of vaporization.

In the process of isothermal condensation, we started with a certain number of gas molecules in a container and decreased the volume. As a consequence, the distance between the molecules was lessened until a certain characteristic value was reached, such that the intermolecular forces were able to pull the molecules together into the liquid state. As some of the molecules condensed, the average distance between the remaining molecules increased (if the volume was held constant). The condensation then stopped, unless the volume was decreased further so that the critical distance between the molecules was re-established. It was not possible to exceed this critical compression of the gas, because so long as there was a tendency for the gas pressure to increase a certain number of molecules went into the liquid form. Then, as the volume decreased, the number of gas molecules in the container decreased (and the number of liquid molecules increased by the same number), but the *number of gas molecules per unit volume*, and consequently the pressure, remained the same during the entire isothermal condensation process.

The process of condensation is reversible. If, instead of decreasing the volume to force more molecules into the liquid state, we increase the volume, the average distance between the molecules in the gas above the liquid increases beyond the critical condensation distance. The condensation then stops and, in addition, the process reverses itself; molecules will leave the liquid state until the pressure in the gas is re-established. This reverse process is called *vaporization*. Vaporization of a liquid will continue until the vapor pressure has reached the equilibrium value discussed above (corresponding to the horizontal isotherms in Fig. 18–4). This equilibrium pressure is called the *vapor pressure* of the liquid. When the vapor pressure has been established, equilibrium exists between the liquid and the gaseous states. From a molecular standpoint, this state of equilibrium can be thought of as a situation in which the rate of condensation is the same as the rate of vaporization: as many molecules cross the liquid interface in one direction as in the other.

When a molecule escapes from the surface of a liquid, its kinetic energy is decreased because the intermolecular forces of the liquid do (negative) work on the escaping molecule. Of course, if the kinetic energy is too small to start with, the molecule is unable to escape. As the temperature is increased, there will be an increase in the number of fast-moving molecules in the liquid, and hence a larger number which are able to overcome the potential barrier produced by the intermolecular forces. The equilibrium vapor pressure then will increase with temperature. The temperature dependence of the vapor pressure varies from one gas (liquid) to another. This temperature dependence can be determined directly from the horizontal portions of the isotherms, as already shown for carbon dioxide in Fig. 18–4.

We can measure the vapor pressure directly and simply, as indicated schematically in Fig. 18–7. The arrangement is the same as the original Torricelli experiment (Chapter 16). The open end of a test tube filled with

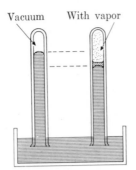

FIG. 18–7. Vapor-pressure measurement with Torricelli tube.

mercury is submerged in a mercury bath, as shown, and as the mercury column sinks to adjust to the height that corresponds to the external pressure, a vacuum is formed in the upper part of the tube. If a liquid is introduced into the tube from below, it will rise to the top of the mercury. The liquid will then vaporize until the equilibrium vapor pressure has been established. As a result, the height of the mercury column will decrease, and by measuring this decrease we can determine the vapor pressure.

Of particular interest is the vapor pressure of water; it is given at various temperatures in Table 18–2.

Table 18–2. Vapor pressure of water.

Temperature, °C	Vapor pressure, mm Hg
0	4.6
20	17.5
40	55.3
60	149.4
80	355.1
100	760
200	11,665

The equilibrium vapor pressure of a liquid has the important characteristic that it is independent of the presence of other gases over the liquid (we assume that no chemical reactions take place). For example, the vapor pressure of water is the same whether or not air is present above the water surface. The total pressure of the gas over a liquid is then the sum of the vapor pressure of the liquid and the partial pressures of the individual gases present.

EXAMPLE. A container has a volume of 2 liters and contains 1 liter of water. The pressure is 2 atm. The rest of the volume is occupied by nitrogen and water vapor. The temperature is 80°C. What is the ratio between the number of nitrogen molecules and water-vapor molecules in the container?

The vapor pressure of water at 80°C is $P_1 = 355.1$ mm Hg (Table 18–2). The partial pressure of nitrogen is then $P_2 = P_t - P_1$, where $P_t = 2$ atm. At the same volume and temperature, the ratio of the number of molecules of the two gases is simply the ratio between the partial pressures:

$$\frac{N_2}{N_1} = \frac{P_2}{P_1} = \frac{2 \cdot 760 - 355.1}{355.1} \simeq 3.3,$$

where we have taken 1 atm to be 760 mm Hg.

Heat of vaporization. As already mentioned, to escape from the liquid into the vapor outside the liquid, a molecule must have sufficient kinetic energy to overcome the work done by the intermolecular forces. From an energy standpoint, the intermolecular forces are, in effect, a potential barrier which holds back the molecules.

As the liquid vaporizes, it loses its most energetic molecules, and the temperature of the liquid decreases. If the vapor above the liquid is removed at a continuous rate, or if the volume outside the liquid is so large that the equilibrium vapor pressure is never reached, the liquid will vaporize continuously. To maintain the temperature of the liquid constant during vaporization, heat must be added to the liquid. The heat required for the vaporization of one gram of the liquid is called the *heat of vaporization*. The molar heat of vaporization, then, can be interpreted as the work required to separate N molecules (M grams) from one another, against the influence of the intermolecular binding forces. Recall that the heat of vaporization for water is 539 cal/gm at 100°C. The heat of vaporization of most liquids is of the order of 100 cal/gm and is temperature-dependent.

The process that involves the cooling of a vaporizing liquid is well known from many everyday observations. A wet body will cool as water vaporizes, and the difference in discomfort between a humid day at one temperature and a dry day at the same temperature is partially caused by the difference in the rates of vaporization and the resulting cooling effect. Similarly, the removal of the vapor above a hot cup of coffee increases the rate of vaporization and hastens the cooling.

Boiling. Suppose that a gas bubble is formed in a liquid. The pressure in the bubble is equal to the equilibrium vapor pressure. In general, the vapor pressure is much smaller than the outside gas pressure on the liquid, and the bubble will collapse under the outside pressure. However, when the temperature is sufficiently high, the vapor pressure is the same as the pressure in the liquid, so that it is possible for bubbles to form. Thus, vaporization of a liquid takes place not only from the surface of the liquid but throughout its entire volume; the liquid *boils*. In other words, boiling occurs when the vapor pressure is the same as the pressure in the liquid. For liquid layers that are not too deep, the inside pressure is the same as the outside pressure. The temperature required to make the vapor pressure of water one atmosphere is, as we know, 100°C, which is the boiling temperature of water at 1 atm (Table 18–2). At the bottom of a liquid, the pressure is somewhat higher than atmospheric pressure and the temperature is somewhat higher than 100°C. Therefore, a bubble that forms at the bottom of a liquid has a vapor pressure which is higher than atmospheric pressure, and it expands as it rises to the top. If the outside pressure is reduced, the boiling temperature of a liquid will be reduced. For example, at a pressure of $\frac{1}{2}$ atm, the boiling temperature of water is about 82°C, while at a pressure of 2 atm it is about 112°C.

18–5 Elastic properties of solids. *The crystal lattice.* In a liquid state, molecules are relatively closely packed but nevertheless are free to move about with respect to one another. This behavior is not unlike that of the molecules in a gas. In a solid, on the other hand, the molecules are held in fixed positions with respect to one another. In a crystalline solid, the atoms are arranged in an orderly repetitive pattern throughout the solid in such a way that they form a *lattice* of atoms. Sodium chloride is a simple example; its structure, called a *simple cubic lattice*, is shown in Fig. 18–8. If the distance between atoms in such a lattice is d, the volume per atom is d^3, and the average density of the material is

$$\rho = \frac{m}{d^3} = \frac{M}{N_0 d^3}, \qquad (18\text{–}6)$$

where m is the mass of one atom, M is the molar mass, and N_0 is Avogadro's number.

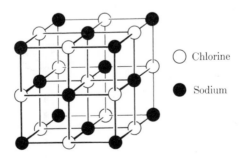

○ Chlorine

● Sodium

Fig. 18–8. The NaCl crystal.

EXAMPLE. Copper, which has a simple cubic lattice, has a density of 8.90 gm/cm^3 and an atomic weight of 63.5. Estimate the lattice constant, d.

From Avogadro's number, $N_0 = 6.02 \cdot 10^{23}$, and $d^3 = M/\rho N_0$, we obtain

$$d = \left(\frac{63.5}{6.02 \cdot 10^{23} \cdot 8.9} \right)^{1/3} \simeq 2.3 \cdot 10^{-8} \text{ cm.}$$

Young's modulus and interatomic forces. A solid is not completely rigid, but will be deformed somewhat by external forces. As the solid deforms, the separation between atoms changes. In the discussion of gases and liquids, we noted that atoms and molecules attract each other at long range, but clearly this attractive force cannot exist at arbitrarily small distances, since then matter would collapse. Instead, at small distances the force must be repulsive, as illustrated in Fig. 18–9 (see also Chapter 8). In the figure, the location r_0 corresponds to the equilibrium position of the atom. For sufficiently small displacements x from r_0, the restoring force will be proportional to the displacement x, and we have the familiar force law

$$F = -Kx.$$

Let us now try to express the molecular "spring" constant K in terms of measurements of the spring constant of the solid in bulk. If we perform experiments with the solid, we find that the force required to stretch a uniform bar an amount ΔL is proportional to the cross-sectional area A of the bar and inversely proportional to its length L:

$$F = YA \frac{\Delta L}{L}. \tag{18–7}$$

The constant of proportionality Y is called *Young's modulus*. The force per unit area, $\sigma = F/A$, is called the *stress* in the bar, and the relative change of the length of the bar, $\epsilon = \Delta L/L$, is called the *strain*. In terms of σ and ϵ, Eq. (18–7) can be written as

$$\sigma = Y\epsilon, \tag{18–8}$$

i.e., the stress is proportional to the strain. This relation applies both for positive and negative values of σ, i.e., both for tensile and compressive forces.

Table 18–3 gives Young's modulus for some common solids. Note that for most metals this constant is of the order of 10^{12} dynes/cm^2.

EXAMPLE. A uniform steel bar of cross-sectional area A and length $L = 1$ m is suspended so that it hangs vertically (Fig. 18–10). What is the stress at the midpoint of the bar?

Let us first isolate the lower half of the bar. We find that it is acted on by two forces, gravity and the stress at its upper plane. If the stress in this plane is σ,

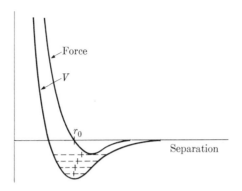

FIG. 18–9. Force and potential energy *vs.* separation of two atoms in a crystal.

Table 18–3. Young's modulus for some common solids.

Substance	Young's modulus, dynes/cm^2	Density ρ, gm/cm^3	Atomic weight
Aluminum (cast)	$6.0 \cdot 10^{11}$	2.702	26.98
Brass (cold-rolled)	9.0	8.80	
Copper	12	8.92	63.54
Gold	7.8	19.32	197.2
Iron (cast)	8 to 9	7.86	55.85
Iron (wrought)	18 to 20		
Lead (rolled)	1.5	11.34	207.2
Nickel	20 to 21	8.90	58.69
Steel (1% C)	20	7.83	
Tin	4	7.31	118.70
Tungsten	35	19.3	183.92

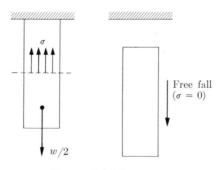

FIGURE 18–10

the force on the plane is $A\sigma$. The weight of the lower half of the bar is $w = AL\rho g/2$, and the equilibrium condition is then

$$A\sigma = \frac{AL\rho g}{2} \quad \text{or} \quad \sigma = \frac{L\rho g}{2}.$$

Expressed numerically, this value is

$$\sigma = \frac{100 \cdot 7.8 \cdot 981}{2} \simeq 3.8 \cdot 10^5 \text{ dynes/cm}^2,$$

where we have used $\rho = 7.8 \text{ gm/cm}^3$ for the density of the bar. The strain at the midpoint of the bar is then

$$\epsilon = \frac{\sigma}{Y} \simeq \frac{3.8 \cdot 10^5}{2 \cdot 10^{12}} \simeq 1.9 \cdot 10^{-7}.$$

Suppose now that the bar is released from its support so that it falls freely. What then is the stress at the midpoint of the bar?

If we study the bar in a coordinate system that accelerates with the bar, it can be seen that all portions of the bar are in equilibrium under the influence of gravity and the inertial force. The stress in each portion of the bar is then zero.

We can now relate Young's modulus to the intermolecular force constant K in the following way. The bar under consideration, of length L and cross-sectional area A, can be regarded as a collection of atomic "strings" or "chains," each of which contains L/d atoms, as indicated in Fig. 18–11. These chains are parallel and separated by a distance d, and the area occupied by each chain is then d^2. Therefore, there are A/d^2 parallel chains in the bar. If a force F is applied uniformly over the area A, there is a force Fd^2/A on each chain which tends to separate any two adjacent atoms in a chain. If, as a result, the distance between two adjacent atoms is increased by x, the total elongation of the bar is $(L/d)x = \Delta L$. From the definitions of the force constant and Young's modulus, it follows that

$$\frac{F}{A} = Y\frac{\Delta L}{L},$$

and the relative elongation of the bar can, of course, be expressed as $\Delta L/L = x/d$. From the definition of the atomic force constant K we then have $Fd^2/A = Kx$, and from the definition of Young's modulus we have $F/A = Y(\Delta L/L) = Y(x/d)$. From these two relations we obtain the relation between K and Y:

$$K = Yd.$$

If we use $10^{12} \text{ dynes/cm}^2$ and 10^{-8} cm as typical values for Y and d, we see that the atomic force constant K is of the order of 10^4 dynes/cm.

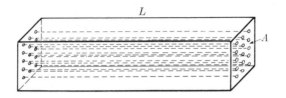

FIG. 18-11. A solid bar can be considered as a bundle of atomic chains.

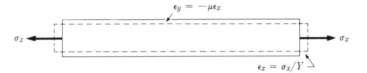

FIG. 18-12. A stress σ_x in the x-direction produces a strain $-\mu\sigma_x/Y$ in the transverse direction.

If the atom is displaced from its equilibrium value, we would expect it to perform simple harmonic oscillations with a frequency given by

$$2\pi f_0 = \sqrt{\frac{K}{m}},$$

where m is the mass of the atom. If we insert $K \simeq 10^4$ dynes/cm and $m \simeq 10^{-23}$ gm, we obtain a characteristic frequency of oscillation of the order of 10^{13} cycles/sec.

Other elastic properties. In the foregoing discussion of the stresses and strains obtained by means of a simple elongation or compression of a solid, it was tacitly assumed that we were dealing with a strictly one-dimensional deformation of the solid. However, it is a familiar observation that when we stretch a piece of rubber, for example, the thickness of the rubber decreases in the direction perpendicular to the stretching force, as indicated in Fig. 18-12. Conversely, when the piece of rubber is compressed, the thickness increases. Such a transverse contraction or expansion occurs to some extent in all solids, although it is particularly noticeable in substances like rubber.

To describe this effect quantitatively, we again consider a rectangular bar with its length along the x-axis, as shown in Fig. 18-12. A stress σ_x is applied in the x-direction, and a strain $\epsilon_x = \sigma_x/Y$ is obtained, as before. In addition to this strain, we also find strains (i.e., relative changes of the linear dimensions of the bar) in the y- and z-directions which are proportional to the strain in the x-direction. That is,

$$\epsilon_y = \epsilon_z = -\mu\epsilon_x = -\mu\,\frac{\sigma_x}{Y}, \qquad (18\text{-}9)$$

where the minus sign indicates that an elongation in the x-direction produces a contraction in the transverse directions. The constant of proportionality μ, often called the *Poisson constant* or the *Poisson ratio*, is of the
order of 0.2 to 0.3 for most solids.

It should be mentioned that the elastic modulus Y is the ratio between
the stress and the strain only in a case in which there is no stress in the
direction normal to the x-direction, i.e., when the bar is free to contract
or bulge. If the side walls of the bar are clamped and thus prevented from
moving, a stress will develop in the transverse directions (y- and z-axes)
when the bar is stretched or compressed in the x-direction. Conversely,
if, in addition to σ_x, transverse stresses are applied, the bar will change its
length not only as a result of σ_x but also as a result of the contraction
effects produced by the stresses in the transverse directions. If the stresses
in the y- and z-directions are σ_y and σ_z, the corresponding (contraction)
strains in the x-direction will be $-\mu\sigma_y/Y$ and $-\mu\sigma_z/Y$, according to
Eq. (18-9). Therefore, by linear superposition, the total strain resulting
from the stresses σ_x, σ_y, and σ_z becomes $\epsilon_x = \sigma_x/Y - \mu\sigma_y/Y - \mu\sigma_z/Y$.
Similar expressions apply for the strains in the y- and z-directions, and the
complete stress-strain relationship can be expressed as follows:

$$\epsilon_x = \frac{1}{Y}\left[\sigma_x - \mu(\sigma_y + \sigma_z)\right],$$

$$\epsilon_y = \frac{1}{Y}\left[\sigma_y - \mu(\sigma_z + \sigma_x)\right], \qquad (18\text{-}10)$$

$$\epsilon_z = \frac{1}{Y}\left[\sigma_z - \mu(\sigma_x + \sigma_y)\right].$$

EXAMPLE. A bar, clamped along its sides so that it is prevented from con-
tracting or expanding in the y- and z-directions, is stretched in the x-direction
by an applied stress in the x-direction. What is the stress required to produce
a strain ϵ_x in the x-direction?

Since the sides of the bar are clamped, we have $\epsilon_y = \epsilon_z = 0$. Equations
(18-10) reduce to

$$\epsilon_x = \frac{1}{Y}\left[\sigma_x - \mu(\sigma_y + \sigma_z)\right],$$

$$\epsilon_y = 0 = \frac{1}{Y}\left[\sigma_y - \mu(\sigma_z + \sigma_x)\right],$$

$$\epsilon_z = 0 = \frac{1}{Y}\left[\sigma_z - \mu(\sigma_x + \sigma_y)\right].$$

Solving for σ_x then gives

$$\sigma_x = Y\epsilon_x \frac{1-\mu}{1-\mu-2\mu^2} = Y\epsilon_x \frac{1-\mu}{(1+\mu)(1-2\mu)}. \qquad (18\text{-}11)$$

This relation indicates that the stiffness, or equivalent elastic modulus, in this type of stretching is larger than Y by a factor of $(1 - \mu)/(1 + \mu)(1 - 2\mu)$. Furthermore, it is interesting to note that there is an upper limit of $\mu = 0.5$ for the Poisson ratio. A substance with $\mu = 0.5$ should, according to Eq. (18–11), have infinite stiffness in the x-direction.

In the deformations described so far, the distances between the molecules were changed. There is another type of deformation, known as a shear deformation, in which the relative distances between adjacent molecules remain approximately constant. In this type of deformation, one atomic plane is displaced in a direction that is parallel to the plane, as indicated in Fig. 18–13. The relative displacement, or strain in this case, is defined as the ratio between the displacement of the plane with respect to the neighboring plane and the distance between the planes, that is, $\epsilon_y = \Delta y/d$, where Δy and d are as shown in the figure. For small values of the strain we have $\epsilon_s = \theta$, where θ is the angular displacement of the two planes. Just as the normal stress σ_x is proportional to the normal strain ϵ_x, experiments show that the shear stress required to produce a shear strain ϵ_s is

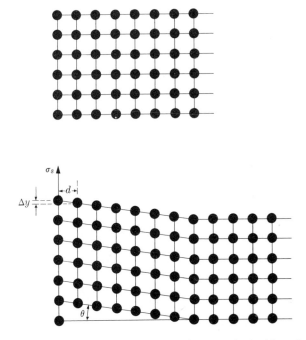

FIG. 18–13. A shear stress σ_s produces a shear strain $\Delta y/d \simeq \theta$ which is proportional to σ_s.

directly proportional to ϵ_s for small values of ϵ_s. We have

$$\sigma_s = S\epsilon_s \simeq S\theta.$$

The constant of proportionality S is often called the shear modulus of the solid. It can be shown (Problem 18–17) that S is related to Young's modulus Y and Poisson's ratio μ by the equation

$$S = \frac{Y}{2(1 + \mu)}. \qquad (18\text{–}12)$$

18–6 Specific heat of solids. About 100 years ago, Dulong and Petit, having measured the specific heat of a number of solids, noticed that the product of the specific heat and the atomic weight was approximately the same for a great number of elements, at least at ordinary temperatures. This product, the molar specific heat referred to in Chapter 14, was found to be approximately 6 cal/mole·°C (Dulong and Petit's law). Table 18–4 shows the molar specific heats of a few solids measured at a temperature of about 300°K. All measurements are consistent with the Dulong and Petit law.

The result obtained by Dulong and Petit can be simply explained in terms of the kinetic theory. Each atom in the solid is assumed to be in (thermal) motion and, as we have seen, this motion is an oscillation about an equilibrium position, with a frequency of the order of 10^{13} cycles/sec. Each atom is free to oscillate in any arbitrary direction; it has three independent degrees of freedom. If we assume that the law of equipartition of energy (Chapter 16) is valid also in this case, the kinetic energy per degree of freedom is $kT/2$, and the total average kinetic energy of an atom should be $3kT/2$. In addition to the kinetic energy in the harmonic oscillator, there is also a potential energy which, on the average, is the same as the kinetic energy. Consequently, the total energy per atom should be $3kT/2 + 3kT/2 = 6kT/2$. If we multiply this by Avogadro's

Table 18–4. Molar specific heats of a few solids.

Element	Atomic weight	Specific heat, cal/gm·°C	Molar specific heat, cal/mole·°C
Aluminum	27	0.208	5.6
Iron	56	0.104	5.8
Silver	108	0.056	6.1
Mercury	200	0.033	6.6
Lead	207	0.030	6.2

number N_0, we obtain the energy per mole, $6N_0kT/2 = 3RT$. The corresponding molar specific heat is then

$$C = 3R \simeq 6 \text{ cal/mole·°C}.$$

As already mentioned, this value of the molar specific heat is in good agreement with measurements taken on a great many substances, in support of the ideas developed in the kinetic theory of gases. However, more extensive measurements, particularly at lower temperatures, have revealed considerable deviations from the Dulong and Petit law. (See Fig. 18–14.) At very low temperatures, the specific heat varies as the third power of the temperature, and so approaches zero as the temperature approaches absolute zero.

The low-temperature deviation of the specific heat of solids from the value of 6 cal/mole·°C, the general problem of blackbody radiation, the emission and absorption spectra of the elements, and the photoelectric effect are among the phenomena that have no satisfactory explanation in terms of classical or newtonian physics. In fact, it was largely the study, by Planck, Bohr, and Einstein, of these phenomena that laid the foundation for development of the quantum theory in the early part of this century. Debye's application of quantum theory for the calculation of the specific heats of solids gave a result in good agreement with experimental results at all temperatures.

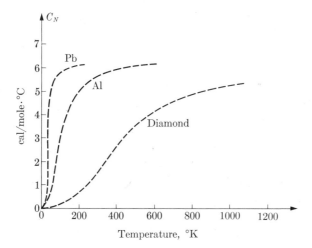

FIG. 18–14. Temperature dependence of the specific heat of solids.

18-7 Thermal expansion. We have already seen that, in general, matter expands as temperature is increased. A qualitative explanation of the thermal expansion of a solid, in terms of molecular vibrations and the asymmetry of the interatomic potential-energy curve, is given in Fig. 18-9, where the equilibrium separation of atoms is shown as a function of vibration amplitude. Some facts will now be given about the magnitude of this expansion for some common substances. The relative change of the linear dimension L of a solid is called the linear-expansion coefficient α:

$$\alpha = \frac{1}{L} \frac{dL}{dT}.$$ (18-14)

This coefficient is often substantially constant over a considerable temperature range, and if the length L_0 at 0°C is chosen as the reference length, the length at a temperature T is then

$$L = L_0(1 + \alpha T).$$

Values of α for some common substances are given in Table 18-5.

Table 18-5. Linear-expansion coefficients for some common substances.

Substance	$\alpha \cdot 10^6$, °C^{-1}	Range of temperatures
Aluminum	24.0	20–100°C
Brass	19.0	0–100°C
Carbon, diamond	1.18	40°C
Calcite, parallel to axis	25.1	0–85°C
perpendicular to axis	−5.58	0–85°C
Copper	16.8	25–100°C
Glass, soft	8.5	0–100°C
Iron	11.5	0–100°C
Iron, steel	29	above 900°C
Mercury	42	~0°C
Oak wood, parallel to fiber	4.92	2–34°C
perpendicular to fiber	54	2–34°C

PROBLEMS

18-1. Explain qualitatively why the ideal gas law predicts a higher pressure than that measured in a real gas at a given temperature and volume.

18-2. Derive the results presented in Eqs. (18-4) and (18-4a).

18-3. What is meant by the law of "corresponding states" for real gases?

18-4. What is the critical volume of 1 gm of carbon dioxide? What then is the average distance between the molecules in this gas?

18-5. The critical pressure of CO_2 is 73 atm, and the critical temperature is 31°C. (a) At what temperature is the pressure of this gas double the critical pressure, when the volume is the critical volume? (b) What is the corresponding temperature for oxygen when the pressure of oxygen is double its critical pressure? (Use Table 18-1.)

18-6. Give a qualitative explanation, in terms of molecular motion, of why vapor pressure increases with temperature.

18-7. The relative humidity of air is the ratio between the actual number of water-vapor molecules in air and the number of molecules which would exist if the air were saturated at the temperature in question. Suppose the relative humidity is 80% on a day when the temperature is 20°C, and 50% on a day when the temperature is 40°C. On which day is the number of vapor molecules per unit volume of air larger?

18-8. The heat of vaporization of water is 539 cal/gm. Make a rough estimate of the order of magnitude of the binding energy between two water molecules in water. (Binding energy is the energy required to separate the molecules.)

18-9. Explain why an increase of pressure increases the boiling temperature. Make a graph showing the boiling temperature of water as a function of pressure (in mm Hg). (*Hint.* See Table 18-2.)

18-10. Would a wet piece of cloth dry faster in a continuously pumped vacuum chamber or in a location such as a desert, where the relative humidity is essentially zero? Discuss.

18-11. A uniform steel bar (length L, cross section A, density ρ, Young's modulus, Y) is pulled along a horizontal frictionless plane so that its acceleration a_0 is constant (Fig. 18-15). (a) What is the stress at the center of the bar? (b) What is the total elongation of the bar as a result of the acceleration? (c) Give numerical answers to (a) and (b), using the values $a_0 = 100$ m/sec^2, $A = 2$ cm^2, $\rho = 7.8$ gm/cm^3, $L = 1$ m, and $Y = 10^{12}$ dynes/cm^2.

FIGURE 18-15

18-12. A uniform steel bar has a cross-sectional area of 1 cm^2. (a) Estimate the number of atomic "strings" that terminate in this area. (b) Estimate the "tension" in one of these atomic strings when the stress in the bar is 10^9 dynes/cm^2. (See Fig. 18-11.)

18-13. A uniform circular disc of radius R is spinning about its axis with an angular velocity ω. The thickness of the disc is t and the density is ρ. The radius of the shaft is r_0. Determine the stress in the disc as a function of the radial coordinate r.

18-14. In order to obtain a uniform stress (i.e., a stress independent of r)

in the spinning disc of Problem 18–13, the thickness t must vary with r. Discuss this variation qualitatively.

18–15. (a) Estimate the distance between the atoms in iron. (b) From the value of Young's modulus (Table 18–3), estimate the interatomic spring constant and determine the characteristic frequency of oscillation of the atoms. (c) Estimate the amplitude of oscillation at a temperature of 27°C. (d) At what temperature would the amplitude of oscillation be one-tenth of the interatomic distance, as determined from the linear oscillator theory? Compare this temperature with the melting point of iron.

18–16. Derive the relation (18–10) in the text.

18–17. The compressibility of a solid is defined as the relative change in volume per unit pressure:

$$\kappa = -(1/V)(dV/dP).$$

By setting $\sigma_x = \sigma_y = \sigma_z = -P$ in Eq. (18–10), obtain an expression for the compressibility of a solid in terms of Y and μ.

18–18. Derive the relationship between Young's modulus Y, the shear modulus S, and the Poisson ratio μ; that is, $S = Y/2(1 + \mu)$. Consider, for this purpose, a cubical block of a solid whose length is equal to unity, and with a stress in the y-direction equal to σ. As a result of this stress, the cube is deformed into a parallelepiped, as shown in Fig. 18–16. (a) What now is the length in the y-direction? (b) What now is the length in the x-direction? (c) Next, consider the inscribed cube shown in the figure. Show that as a result of the stretching in the y-direction the slope of the sides of this cube changes by an angle $\theta \simeq (\sigma/Y)(1 + \mu)/2$, for small values of σ/Y. (d) Show that the tangential component of the stress on the side surface of the inscribed cube is $\sigma/4$. (e) From the definition of shear modulus, express θ in terms of S and show that $S = Y/2(1 + \mu)$.

18–19. Below a certain temperature, known as the *Debye temperature*, the specific heat of a solid increases as the third power of temperature, i.e.,

$$C_v = K \left(\frac{T}{\theta_d}\right)^3 \qquad (K = \text{const}),$$

where θ_d is the Debye temperature (of the order of 200°C for many metals). Determine the heat required to increase the temperature of one mole of a solid from $0.1\theta_d$ to $0.2\theta_d$.

18–20. Interpret the Dulong and Petit law in terms of kinetic theory.

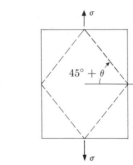

FIGURE 18–16

18–21. Show that, due to thermal expansion, the relative increase in the area of a plate is given by $\beta = (1/A)(dA/dT) \simeq 2\alpha$, where α is the linear-expansion coefficient. Similarly show that the volume-expansion coefficient is given by

$$\delta = (1/V)(dV/dT) \simeq 3\alpha.$$

18–22. A uniform bar with an elastic modulus Y and thermal expansion coefficient α is held between two rigid planes, one at each end of the bar. In this way, the bar is prevented from expanding in these directions when it is heated. What is the stress developed in the bar when the temperature is increased by $\Delta T°C$?

18–23. A bar of copper and a bar of iron of equal lengths L and cross-sectional areas A are butted together, such that the ends are held fixed. The temperature of the bars is increased by $\Delta T°C = 100°C$. How far does the junction between the bars move as a result of the heating, and what is the stress developed? In particular, use $L = 50$ cm and $A = 1$ cm^2.

CHAPTER 19

THE SECOND LAW OF THERMODYNAMICS

Summary. If the first law of thermodynamics is considered to deal with the *quantity* of energy (conservation) in a natural process, we can say that the second law is concerned with the *quality* of the various forms of energy involved. In the second law of thermodynamics, a quantitative measure for this quality is introduced, in terms of which the relative probability of occurrence of different processes is described. To explain these ideas, we start with a qualitative discussion of the *directionality* of natural processes, and the distinction between reversible and irreversible processes. Then follows a quantitative study of the conversion of heat into work, first in a unidirectional process and then in a cyclic, or periodic, process. The Carnot cycle is discussed and its efficiency calculated in terms of the properties of an ideal gas. The thermodynamic temperature scale is introduced. Then follows a comparison between an arbitrary cyclic reversible process and the Carnot cycle, and it is found that $\int dQ/T = 0$ for all such cycles. Entropy is introduced, and the second law of thermodynamics is interpreted from a molecular standpoint in terms of the relation between the entropy differences between states and their relative probability according to Boltzmann. The qualitative discussion of directionality of processes in the beginning of the chapter is reinterpreted quantitatively by means of the Boltzmann relation.

19–1 The directionality of events in nature. The physical world, as well as the biological world, is characterized by changes. Particles interact with one another and momentum and energy are exchanged, both on the microscopic and the macroscopic scale. However, all energy transactions made in nature are such that the total energy remains the same, as expressed by the law of conservation of energy. Although this law is one of the most powerful laws in physics, it is important to note that it does not predict the likelihood of a transaction, or the direction of energy flow between the bodies involved. So far as the conservation of energy is concerned, nature could equally well be static, without any changes at all. In fact, if we use the conservation law as a guide, and list the events which involve energy transformations that satisfy the conservation law, we find that we can include in this list many events that never seem to occur. To obtain such events, we need only make a motion picture film of an explosion, a ski jump, the growth of a flower, a waterfall, the decaying motion of a pendulum, etc., and then project these events backward (in time).

As an example, consider a pendulum which starts with a certain amplitude of oscillation. As time passes, the oscillations slowly decay because of collisions with the molecules of the air and because of other friction mechanisms. In this way, the pendulum is eventually brought to rest. The initial "organized" energy of the pendulum has then been transformed into thermal energy. The reversal of this transformation of energy would correspond to a situation in which all the molecules of the air would organize and push the pendulum back and forth until the initial energy is regained. As we well know, the likelihood of such an event is slight indeed.

Similarly, when two bodies of different temperatures are brought into contact with each other, heat will flow from the hot to the cold body, but not in the opposite direction.

Another, somewhat different example concerns the free expansion of a gas. So far as energy conservation is concerned, the gas could just as well stay in only half the container as be uniformly distributed throughout the entire volume. Similarly, the mixing of two gases does not reverse itself and produce separation of the gases again, although according to the law of conservation of energy there is nothing to prevent such an occurrence.

From examples of this kind, we realize that the law of conservation of energy does not require events to happen even if they *do* satisfy the conservation law. In fact, the conservation law has no influence whatsoever on the over-all plan according to which nature operates and according to which energy transactions are selected or rejected.

It is rather natural, then, to ask if it might not be possible to formulate another law expressing at least some feature of the plan of nature in regard to its choice of energy transactions. There is indeed such a law, and it is called the *second law of thermodynamics*. We shall not here record the interesting historical development which has led to the formulation of this law. The ingenious work of Carnot, Clausius, Kelvin, and Boltzmann finally led to a principle which concisely contains the various observations on the directionality of the energy flow and other events in nature.

The first law of thermodynamics, in essence, states that the total energy in nature remains constant, while the second law deals with the observation that in transformations in nature, energy is "degraded" from an organized form into a random form, called heat, and that heat, in turn, flows from regions of high to regions of low temperatures. Just as we were able to express the first law in terms of the nonexistence of a perpetual-motion machine, the second law can be formulated in a similar way. A machine which produces useful work by simply lowering the temperature of a heat reservoir (the ocean, for example) without heat transfer to a reservoir of lower temperature would not violate the first law of thermodynamics. But the second law of thermodynamics states that such a machine, a *perpetual-motion machine of the second kind*, cannot be made.

The second law goes beyond qualitative statements of this kind. It provides a procedure for calculating the relative probability of occurrence of different states. This latter interpretation of the second law of thermodynamics, in terms of the tendency of nature to go from less probable to more probable states, is attributed to Ludwig Boltzmann. Much of our discussion about the second law of thermodynamics will be based upon this idea of Boltzmann's. Before we enter into a quantitative discussion of these questions, we must comment on some matters that relate to the idealizations of reversibility and thermal equilibrium, which we simply assumed in our previous studies of changes of state. We shall then be prepared to consider in detail the conversion of heat into work and, finally, the general ideas of the second law of thermodynamics.

19–2 Reversible and irreversible processes. In the thermodynamics of an ideal gas, we have discussed the relations between the pressure, the volume, and the temperature of a gas *which is in equilibrium*. Equilibrium means that the pressure, the density, etc., do not vary with time. Whenever a system is in the process of changing, it is not in equilibrium, and so the relations we have thus far presented, for example the gas law, will not be applicable. Many systems which concern us *do* change with time and to circumvent this dead-end situation, the idea of a *quasi-static change of state* has been invented. As noted in Chapter 16, a quasi-static change of state is one which is so slow that the equilibrium relations between pressure, volume, etc., are appropriate at all times during the change of state. Strictly speaking, a quasi-static change of state should require an infinitely long time for a change of state to take place. Further, the concept of *reversibility* is associated with quasi-static changes of state.

The value of these idealizations hinges upon the extent to which they can be used as *approximate* descriptions of the relations between the state variables (such as pressure, temperature, etc.) in systems which *vary with time*. Many events can be described with a high degree of accuracy on the basis of the quasi-static picture, but other events cannot. For example, if we consider the rather rapid fluctuations of the pressure in a sound wave as quasi-static, the predicted speed of sound based on this assumption agrees with the experimental value to within about one part in 10^4. However, when the frequency of a sound wave approaches the molecular-collision frequency in the gas, the quasi-static assumption fails.

In a process such as the free expansion of a gas into a vacuum, the quasi-static description is meaningless, since during the process we cannot even define the pressure in the gas. Only after completion of the expansion is it possible to define the new equilibrium state of the gas. This process is typical of irreversibility; only the *end states* can be defined thermodynamically and the isolated system cannot be restored to its initial state.

If we are to say anything about an irreversible process in terms of equilibrium thermodynamics, it must be in terms of the end states.

Since a quasi-static change of state can be thought of as a succession of equilibrium states, a change of state can be represented in a diagram by a curve that connects the initial and final states of the system (for example, a P–V diagram for a gas). In an irreversible process, on the other hand, only the end states can be specified in the diagram.

19–3 Conversion of heat into work. *Efficiency of conversion in a nonperiodic process.* In Sec. 19–1 we discussed the conversion of the organized energy of a pendulum into the random internal heat energy of the gas in which the pendulum was swinging. This is just one of any number of examples we can recall in which heat is produced with an efficiency of 100% from mechanical energy or from some other form of "available" energy. By "available," we mean that the energy is in a form such that it can be used at any time for purposes of our choice. Once energy has been converted into the random motion of heat, it has become less available, or less useful, in this sense. The question arises as to the extent of the degradation of the energy into this less available form. Heat energy is certainly at least partially available, since it can be used for running various heat engines, such as a steam engine or steam turbine. But can the internal heat energy be converted into work with an efficiency of 100%?

To investigate this problem, let us consider a gas of initial temperature T_1. The internal energy of the gas is proportional to the temperature, so that if we have one mole of the gas, the internal energy is $U_1 = C_v T_1$, where C_v is the specific heat of the gas. Let us now arrange to decrease the internal energy of the gas. This decrease can be accomplished in many ways. The gas can be cooled at constant volume, in which case none of the internal energy is converted into work. However, if the temperature and hence the internal energy are decreased by a reversible adiabatic expansion, there is *no* heat flow through the walls of the gas container, and the decrease of internal energy equals the work done by the gas. At the end of the expansion, the internal energy of the gas has changed to $C_v T_2$. The work done by the gas during the expansion is then

$$W = C_v(T_1 - T_2),$$

which represents a fraction

$$\frac{W}{U_1} = \frac{T_1 - T_2}{T_1}$$

of the initial internal energy. The lower the value of T_2, the larger is the fraction of the heat energy that can be converted into work; in fact, if T_2

were at the absolute zero point, all the initial heat content of the gas could be converted.

In a nonadiabatic process, heat flows into the gas as it expands and cools, and some of the heat inflow is converted into work. In fact, if the gas expands at constant temperature, the heat influx to the gas just compensates for its tendency to cool during the expansion. Since the temperature remains constant, the internal energy also remains constant, and *all* the heat influx to the gas is converted into work. In other words, if we wish to convert heat into work in a unidirectional, nonperiodic process, we get the highest efficiency (100%) of conversion by using an *isothermal expansion of the working substance*, which in this case is a gas. The internal energy of the gas remains constant. The gas acts merely as an energy transformer.

It should be emphasized that this 100% efficiency of conversion *does not depend on the temperature*. However, in a practical situation the energy converter, i.e., the gas in the container, has a certain limited range of volume variation. Under such conditions, the *amount* of heat, Q_1, which can be converted in an isothermal expansion from volume V_1 to volume V_2 does indeed depend on temperature. In fact, the work done per mole in an isothermal expansion is

$$Q_1 = W_1 = \int_{V_1}^{V_2} p \, dV = RT_1 \int_{V_1}^{V_2} \frac{dV}{V} = RT_1 \log \frac{V_2}{V_1}. \quad (19\text{--}1)$$

In other words, the *amount* of heat converted in an isothermal expansion between two fixed volumes is *proportional* to the temperature.

The entire discussion above has been based on a quasi-static reversible change of state. Thus, all the processes we were concerned with can be reversed. For example, after the isothermal expansion, we could bring the gas back to its initial state (V_1, T_1) by an isothermal compression, in which the work obtained in the expansion is converted back to heat which leaks from the gas into the reservoir. The net conversion of heat into work in such a complete cycle, $V_1 \rightarrow V_2 \rightarrow V_1$, is then zero.

In this connection, it should be emphasized that when a gas is to be compressed isothermally from one fixed volume V_2 to another fixed volume V_1, the work required is proportional to the temperature. The lower the temperature, the easier the compression. It is important to bear this simple fact in mind in the subsequent analysis of a periodically operating machine.

The Carnot cycle. In our discussion of efficiency of conversion above, we dealt with a one-way process. From a practical standpoint, such a conversion is relatively useless, since in practice we wish to repeat the process over and over with the same machine. In the example given above, the machine was simply a gas in a container which had a movable piston in one end. In order to use this machine continuously, we must bring the piston back to its original position. If we bring the piston back by means of an isothermal compression at the same temperature as in the expansion, there will be no net conversion of heat into work. However, the discussion above strongly suggests the possibility of compressing the gas at a lower temperature so that less work will be required to accomplish this compression.

The goal for a periodically operating machine in which heat is converted into work should then be to convert a large amount of heat into work by means of an expansion at a relatively high temperature and to use some of the work obtained to compress the gas at a lower temperature. The problem of changing the temperature of the gas can be solved in many ways. We have already mentioned one possibility, an adiabatic expansion and compression. If we use these adiabatic changes, the cycle representing the periodically operating machine can be shown graphically as in Fig. 19–1. This is called a *Carnot cycle*, after the French scientist Sadi Carnot (1796–1832). As we pointed out in the previous section, it is clear that the net conversion of heat into work in the adiabatic expansion and subsequent compression add to zero. In the expansion, the internal-energy change is $C_v(T_1 - T_2)$, and this amount of energy is converted into work; in the

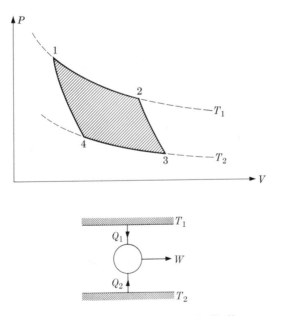

FIG. 19–1. The Carnot cycle represented in a P–V diagram, and the corresponding machine indicated symbolically.

compression, the process is reversed, and the net exchange is zero. Consequently, if the heat drawn from the high-temperature reservoir in the isothermal expansion of the gas is denoted by Q_1 and the heat drawn from the low-temperature reservoir in the isothermal compression is Q_2, the work produced in the cycle is

$$W = Q_1 + Q_2.$$

The efficiency of conversion can be defined as the ratio between the work output in one cycle and the heat Q_1 *drawn from the high-temperature bath*, and is then expressed as

$$\eta = \frac{W}{Q_1} = \frac{Q_1 + Q_2}{Q_1}. \tag{19-2}$$

Since in this process heat actually is flowing into the low-temperature bath during the compression, Q_2 in these relations will be negative, as we shall see.

It is a simple matter to express this efficiency in terms of the temperatures T_1 and T_2. If we denote the volumes in the corners of the cycle by V_1, V_2, V_3, and V_4, as shown in Fig. 19-1, we can express Q_1 and Q_2 as

$$Q_1 = RT_1 \log \frac{V_2}{V_1} \quad \text{and} \quad Q_2 = RT_2 \log \frac{V_4}{V_3},$$

according to Eq. (19-1). Furthermore, the volume ratios V_2/V_1 and V_3/V_4 are easily seen to be the same (see the example below), so that we have

$$\frac{Q_1}{Q_2} = -\frac{T_1}{T_2} \quad \text{or} \quad \frac{Q_1}{T_1} + \frac{Q_2}{T_2} = 0. \tag{19-3a}$$

The efficiency of the Carnot cycle then becomes

$$\eta = \frac{T_1 - T_2}{T_1} = 1 - \frac{T_2}{T_1}. \tag{19-3b}$$

In other words, the efficiency of this periodically operating machine can never be unity (100%) unless the low-temperature reservoir is at absolute zero.

EXAMPLE. What are the relations between the initial and final volumes in the adiabatic expansions and compressions in a Carnot cycle?

When we use the notation of Fig. 19-1, the volumes before and after the adiabatic expansion are V_2 and V_3, respectively. In an adiabatic change of state, we have $PV^\gamma = $ const, or $RTV^{\gamma-1} = $ const; that is, $T_1 V_2^{\gamma-1} = T_2 V_3^{\gamma-1}$. Similarly, for the adiabatic compression we get $T_1 V_1^{\gamma-1} = T_2 V_4^{\gamma-1}$. From these two relations, it follows that $V_4/V_1 = V_3/V_2$ or $V_2/V_1 = V_3/V_4$.

The Carnot process, or any other reversible process, can be operated in the reverse direction. In this case work is done on the machine as it transfers heat from the low-temperature to the high-temperature reservoir. If the heat capacity of the low-temperature reservoir is finite, it follows that its temperature can be decreased continuously, with absolute zero as the limit (at least in principle). This process represents a refrigeration machine. The relation between the work and the heat transfers is still given by the general equation (19-2). When it refers to a heat engine, this equation then contains positive W and Q_1 and negative Q_2. In the refrigeration cycle, on the other hand, W and Q_1 are negative and Q_2 is positive; heat is transferred *to* the high-temperature bath *from* the machine and transferred *from* the low-temperature bath *to* the machine. If the efficiency of the machine is η, we have

$$\eta = \frac{W}{Q_1},$$

as before. In connection with refrigeration, the heat absorbed from the low-temperature reservoir divided by the work, Q_2/W, is called the *coefficient of performance*. This quantity, unlike the efficiency of a heat engine, can be larger than unity.

All reversible heat engines operating between reservoirs at the same temperatures have the same efficiency. In the foregoing discussion of the Carnot cycle, we used an ideal gas as the working substance in the machine. On the basis of the equation of state of an ideal gas, we obtained the expression (19-3b) for the efficiency of the engine. Suppose now that we construct a reversible heat engine in which we may have a working substance other than a gas, for example a solid. Is it possible that such an engine can have a higher efficiency than the gas Carnot engine? If we do not know the equation of state for the substance, we cannot answer this question directly in terms of, say, the two temperatures T_1 and T_2, as we did in the previous case.

To explore this question, we shall assume that there exists a "super" heat engine with an efficiency higher than that of the gas Carnot engine. Then we shall investigate the consequences of this assumption and show that it leads to a violation of the second law of thermodynamics (Sec. 19-1).

Consider the thought-experiment shown in Fig. 19-2. Let us denote the super heat engine by A and the ordinary gas Carnot engine by B. We operate A as a heat engine and B as a refrigerator, between the same heat reservoirs of temperatures T_1 and T_2. If W_b is the work required to drive B and the efficiency of B is η_b, the heat delivered to reservoir T_1 by B is W_b/η_b. Let us use this heat for A, which then converts a certain fraction of it into work. If the efficiency of A is η_a, the work produced by A is $W_a = \eta_a(W_b/\eta_b)$. Then, if η_a is larger than η_b, the work produced

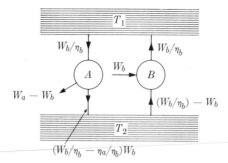

FIG. 19–2. A thought-experiment which shows that a super heat engine leads to a violation of the second law of thermodynamics.

by A is more than that needed to run B. Consequently, we can use part of W_a to run B and still have some left for the operation of some other machine. Note carefully that we have *not* changed the condition of the high-temperature bath at all, since the heat delivered to it by B was used for the operation of A. However, the low-temperature bath has been changed. The refrigerator B has removed the amount $W_b(1 - \eta_b)/\eta_b$ of heat from the low-temperature bath and A has delivered the smaller amount $W_b(1 - \eta_a)/\eta_b$ to it. The heat removed from the low-temperature bath is the same as the excess work obtained in the combined (hypothetical) operation of A and B, as described.

In other words, the net effect of operating the super heat engine A and the ordinary gas Carnot engine B together in this manner would convert heat into work in a cyclic operation and there would be *no other change in nature than the cooling of a heat reservoir* (the low-temperature reservoir). Consequently, this· machine should be able to convert the tremendous amount of heat in the ocean, in the atmosphere, or in the earth into work for the operation of machines of various kinds. A machine of this type, a perpetual-motion machine of the second kind, has never been constructed, and the second law of thermodynamics postulates that such a machine cannot be made. On the basis of this law, it follows that there are no super heat engines and that all reversible heat engines operating between the same temperature reservoirs have the same efficiency, regardless of the working substance used. (An argument entirely similar to that given above shows that no *reversible* heat engine can have an efficiency less than that of the ideal Carnot gas engine.)

19–4 The thermodynamic temperature scale. In the discussion of temperature in Chapter 14 we indicated briefly the problems involved in the definition of a temperature scale. The temperature scales that were based on expansion of solids and liquids not only gave slightly different scales but were limited considerably in range. The gas thermometer proved to be more satisfactory; the range was considerably larger, and all gases of sufficiently low densities gave very nearly the same scales. All the thermodynamic relations which we have obtained have been based upon the scales as defined by a gas thermometer.

We are now able to redefine temperature in terms of energy measurements, a definition that is *independent of the working substance* used in the "thermometer," which is now a Carnot engine that operates between two heat reservoirs. The transfers of heat from the two reservoirs are Q_1 and Q_2, respectively. The ratio between the temperatures of the two reservoirs is then defined as the ratio between the magnitudes of the heats Q_1 and Q_2:

$$\frac{T_1}{T_2} = \left|\frac{Q_1}{Q_2}\right|. \tag{19–4}$$

The zero point on the temperature scale is established by the temperature of the low-temperature reservoir when the efficiency of the Carnot engine is unity, i.e., when Q_2 is zero.

Since we have obtained the zero point, we need only one more point to establish the temperature scale. To determine this additional point, we can proceed as before and divide the scale between the freezing and boiling points of water into 100 equal parts (degrees). The temperature of freezing water on the thermodynamic scale is then obtained by running a Carnot engine between the boiling water and the freezing water and then measuring Q_1 and Q_2. The unknown temperature T_1 of the freezing water follows from the relation

$$\left|\frac{Q_1}{Q_2}\right| = \frac{T_1 + 100}{T_1}.$$

Measuring Q_1/Q_2 and solving for T_1, we obtain $T_1 = 273.2$ deg.

Since all Carnot engines have the same efficiency and hence the same ratio Q_1/Q_2, the temperature scale obtained is independent of the working substance. This definition of temperature, proposed by Lord Kelvin in 1848, is the real kelvin or *absolute* temperature scale. Thus we find that this scale is identical with that based on the ideal-gas thermometer, since our discussion of the Carnot engine in terms of the gas-thermometer temperatures led us to precisely the same relation as that of Eq. (19–4). However, the ideal gas-thermometer scale is based upon *no* real substance and therefore is conceptually unsatisfactory. When real gases are used, we know that the scales do differ. The virtue of the present thermodynamic definition is that it establishes a temperature scale on the basis of measurements involving *real* substances, and therefore the scale obtained is independent of the choice of substance.

19-5 Entropy. In general, processes like that illustrated in Fig. 19-3, which are represented in a P-V diagram by closed paths of different shapes, etc., have different work outputs and different heat exchanges with the surroundings. The net heat inflow, $\int dQ$, varies from one process to another. However, despite this difference, in an exchange of heat there is one interesting property which is shared by all the closed-path processes. This characteristic property can be expressed in the following way. Consider the elementary heat influxes dQ (positive or negative) during the process. When we then divide each individual dQ by the corresponding temperature, we find that the sum $(dQ/T)_1 + (dQ/T)_2 + (dQ/T)_3 + \cdots$ is always zero, regardless of the shape of the closed path in the P-V diagram. This can be expressed in integral form as

$$\oint \frac{dQ}{T} = 0, \tag{19-5}$$

where $\oint$ signifies integration around a closed path. It is evident that more heat is drawn in at high temperatures than at low temperatures (leaving a net influx of heat), but when large dQ's are divided by large T's, the heat contributions dQ/T per degree add to zero.

To prove this result, we start with a Carnot cycle, where there are heat transfers only along the isotherms. If the heat transfer to the system is Q_1 at the temperature T_1 and Q_2 at T_2, we have $\int dQ/T = Q_1/T_1$ for the upper isotherm and $\int dQ/T = Q_2/T_2$ for the lower isotherm. The sum of these two contributions, $\oint dQ/T_1 = Q_1/T_1 + Q_2/T_2$, is zero, as in Eq. (19-3a).

To extend this proof so that it applies to other than Carnot processes, we proceed as follows. The process under consideration can be approximated as closely as we please by a succession of elementary isotherms and adiabatic lines, as shown in Fig. 19-3. An arbitrary isothermal element at a high temperature always has a corresponding element at a low temperature. These elements can be thought of as part of an elementary Carnot cycle, shown shaded in Fig. 19-3. If the heat influxes at the highest temperature and at the lowest temperature are dQ_1 and dQ_2, respectively, we have $dQ/T_1 + dQ_2/T_2 = 0$. The same result applies to any arbitrary elementary process, and we again find that $\int dQ/T = 0$, as indicated in Eq. (19-5).

In Eq. (19-5), if we set

$$dS = \frac{dQ}{T}, \tag{19-6}$$

we have $\int dS = 0$. The quantity S then has the property that when we go from one state of the system (gas) back to the initial state by an arbitrary path, the changes of S during the process are always such that the

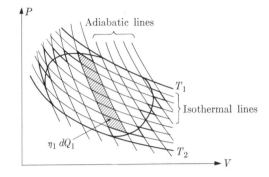

FIG. 19–3. An arbitrary cycle can be composed of a large number of small isothermal and adiabatic changes.

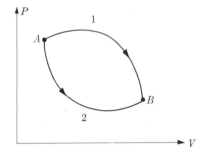

FIG. 19–4. The change of entropy is independent of the path and depends only on the initial and final states of the system.

total change of S is zero, regardless of the choice of the path. In this respect, S is quite analogous to the internal energy U. It follows that the change of S from one state to another is independent of the path chosen; it depends only on the initial and the final states, as illustrated in Fig. 19–4. Here we have shown two different paths, labeled 1 and 2, that go from A to B. The integral along the closed path from A to B via path 1 and back to A via path 2 is zero, according to Eq. (19–5), and can be expressed as

$$\left(\int_A^B dS\right)_1 + \left(\int_B^A dS\right)_2 = 0.$$

Since we have considered *reversible* processes, we can set

$$\int_B^A dS = -\int_A^B dS.$$

Therefore, we obtain

$$\left(\int_A^B dS\right)_1 = \left(\int_A^B dS\right)_2,$$

which shows that there is a change of S from state A to state B which is independent of the path between the states.

The quantity S has been given a special name, *entropy*. We have seen that this quantity is a function of state, but we have not yet examined the physical significance of this quantity. We shall find, however, that entropy can be used for the specification of the directionality of events in nature and for the classification of the relative probabilities of the occurrence of processes. This discussion follows in Sec. 19–6.

The formal calculation of the change of entropy when an ideal gas goes from one state to another can be carried out directly by means of the definition

$$S_2 - S_1 = \int_1^2 \frac{dQ}{T}, \tag{19-7}$$

used in conjunction with the first law of thermodynamics and the gas law. We obtain $dQ = C_v\, dT + P\, dV = C_v\, dT + RT\, (dV/V)$. For the entropy change of one mole of a gas, we then get

$$S_2 - S_1 = C_v \ln\left(\frac{T_2}{T_1}\right) + R \ln\left(\frac{V_2}{V_1}\right), \tag{19-8}$$

which is dependent only upon the initial and the final states, (V_1, T_1) and (V_2, T_2), and not upon the path chosen.

This result applies, of course, only to an ideal gas. When other substances are involved in the thermal interactions, we must calculate the entropy change of each body from the definition $S_2 - S_1 = \int_1^2 dQ/T$. Remember that this formula implies a *reversible* process. The importance of this statement will become apparent shortly, when we discuss the entropy changes in an irreversible process.

Certain important general properties of the entropy of a system can be found directly from the definition of entropy, and thus we do not have to evaluate the integral $\int dQ/T$ in terms of the volume and temperature, etc., of the initial and final states, as we did in the case of an ideal gas. The first important property is: *the entropy of the universe remains constant in a reversible process*. This result is apparent when we recall that in a reversible process interacting bodies are always in thermal equilibrium with each other throughout the interaction. In other words, if body A interacts with body B, both A and B have equal temperatures. Consequently, when a small amount dQ of heat is transferred from A to B, the entropy change of B is $dS_b = dQ/T_b$ and the corresponding change of

A is $dS_a = -dQ/T_a = -dS_b$. The total entropy change of the system (universe) is then zero; that is, $dS_a + dS_b = 0$. Consider the isothermal expansion of a gas. The thermally interacting bodies in this case are the gas and its surrounding heat reservoir. In the expansion, the heat absorbed by the gas is the same as that which leaves the reservoir. The temperatures of the gas and the reservoir are the same, and therefore dQ/T, the gain of entropy of the gas, is of the same magnitude as the loss of entropy of the heat reservoir. The total entropy change of the system (gas plus heat reservoir) is zero.

The second important property of entropy is: *the entropy of the universe increases in an irreversible process.* A reversible process is an idealization. All processes in nature are to some extent irreversible. In an irreversible process the interacting bodies are not in equilibrium; the temperature, or perhaps some other quantity such as density, varies from one point to another in the system. When the system is left undisturbed, it follows a definite pattern; that is, heat flows from bodies of high temperatures to bodies of lower temperatures, and mass flows in the direction of decreasing density, etc.

Whether a process is reversible or not, energy is always conserved, and in a heat transfer between two bodies, the amount of heat that leaves one body is always equal to the heat received by the other. The basic difference, then, between reversible and irreversible processes can be stated as follows. In a reversible process, the thermally interacting bodies, for example the gas and the heat reservoir in a Carnot engine, are always at the same temperature, so that heat flows from one body to the other without a change in temperature. In an irreversible transfer of heat, however, the interacting bodies are at different temperatures, so that the heat will be "degraded" in the interaction. We shall demonstrate by means of examples that when there is an irreversible change of state, the total entropy of the system of interacting bodies (universe) increases.

We have concluded previously that the entropy change in a process is uniquely specified by the initial and final states, and not by the behavior of the system during a process. When these end states are known, we can calculate the entropy change by evaluating the integral $\int dQ/T$ for a *reversible* process which takes the system from the initial to the final state.

Free expansion. A typical example that illustrates the entropy increase in an irreversible process is the free expansion of an ideal gas. Consider one mole of an ideal gas in a thermally insulated container which is divided into halves by a wall. Initially, the gas is in one half of the container, the other half being evacuated. A hole is made in the wall, and the gas flows through it (free expansion) until the pressure is the same throughout the entire container. The process is irreversible. It is not a succession of equilibrium states; during the process the density and pressure are not uniform throughout the entire gas, and we cannot specify a *state* of the gas, since P, V, and T are not well-defined quantities. If the gas is ideal, there will be no temperature change as a result of the free expansion (Chapter 18), and the final state differs from the initial state only in volume and pressure. To determine the entropy change in the process, we must determine the value of $\int dQ/T$ in a reversible process which takes the gas from the initial to the final state. The simplest reversible process in this case would be an isothermal expansion of the gas. In Eq. (19–8), the corresponding calculation of $\int dQ/T$ has been made for an ideal gas, and we found that the entropy difference between two states of a gas is given by $S_2 - S_1 = C_v \ln (T_2/T_1) + R \ln (V_2/V_1)$. In the present case, we have $T_2 = T_1$ and $V_2 = 2V_1$. The entropy change is therefore

$$S_2 - S_1 = R \ln 2.$$

If we do not keep in mind that the relation $\int_1^2 dQ/T$ refers to a *reversible* process which takes the system from the initial to the final state, we might be tempted to ask the following question. Since the gas is thermally insulated from its surroundings, why is not the integral $\int dQ/T$ equal to zero? The answer is simply that the dQ that enters into the integral is *not* the heat flow involved in the irreversible process, but is that of the reversible process used for the measurement of the entropy difference between the end states.

Heat flow between two bodies. Now consider the heat flow between two bodies A and B of equal masses and specific heats, but with different temperatures, T_a and T_b. They are brought into contact with each other, and the system $A + B$ is thermally insulated from its surroundings. If T_a is larger than T_b, heat will flow from A to B and the temperatures will eventually equalize.

Let us determine the entropy change which results when a small amount of heat dQ flows from A to B. This is accomplished by removing the heat dQ from A in a reversible process (for example, by letting A serve as the heat reservoir in a Carnot engine), and then adding dQ to B reversibly (for example, by letting B serve as the low-temperature reservoir in another Carnot engine). The entropy change of A is then $dS_a = -dQ/T_a$, and the entropy change of B is $dS_b = dQ/T_b$. The total entropy change in this process is then

$$dS = dS_a + dS_b = dQ \left(\frac{1}{T_b} - \frac{1}{T_a} \right).$$

Since T_b is smaller than T_a, we see that the total entropy change in the process is positive; the total entropy of the system increases as a result of the heat transfer from A to B.

The temperatures of the two bodies eventually will reach the equilibrium value $T_f = (T_a + T_b)/2$. The total entropy change of A is then

$$\Delta S_a = \int_{T_a}^{T_f} \frac{dQ}{T} = mc \int_{T_a}^{T_f} \frac{dT}{T} = mc \ln \frac{T_f}{T_a},$$

where m is the mass of A, and c is the specific heat. The entropy change of B is obtained from the above formula by substituting T_b for T_a. The total entropy change of $A + B$ is then

$$\Delta S = \Delta S_a + \Delta S_b = mc \ln \frac{T_f^2}{T_a T_b} = mc \ln \frac{(T_a + T_b)^2}{4 T_a T_b} > 0.$$

This quantity is positive, since

$$\frac{(T_a + T_b)^2}{4 T_a T_b} = 1 + \frac{(T_a - T_b)^2}{4 T_a T_b}$$

is greater than unity; the total entropy increases in the process. (T_f is the arithmetic mean of T_a and T_b, and $\sqrt{T_a T_b}$ is the geometric mean.)

Again, this process has taken place in a system $A + B$ which has been thermally insulated from its surroundings. By itself, it has changed its state from one value of entropy to another state of higher entropy. It is important to note that the system is thermally insulated, and so there is no heat influx to the system $A + B$ in the process. This does not mean that $\int dQ/T$ is zero in the process, because the dQ that enters into the calculation of the entropy change refers to *reversible* processes in which the members of the system are taken from the initial to the final state.

Mixing of two gases. As another example, let us consider a thermally insulated container filled with equal amounts of two gases, say oxygen and nitrogen, separated by a wall such that each occupies half the container. As the wall is removed, the two gases will mix until they are spread uniformly throughout the volume. Each gas then has expanded to twice its initial volume. If we have one mole of each gas, the entropy increase of each gas will be $R \ln (V_2/V_1) = R \ln 2$ (the temperature remains constant), and the total entropy change is $2R \ln 2$. Again we see that in an irreversible process the entropy of the system increases.

These examples—free expansion, heat flow, and the mixing of gases—all demonstrate the important fact that the entropy of the universe always increases in irreversible processes. Since all processes in nature are irreversible (at least to some extent), it follows that the universe continuously runs toward higher and higher entropy, that heat is degraded as it is transferred from regions of high temperature to regions of low temperature, and that entropy is a measure of this degradation. There may be local decreases of entropy as bodies interact with each other, but every decrease is more than balanced by an increase of the entropy elsewhere, so that the total entropy of the system increases. Only in idealized processes, which we have called reversible, is the total change of entropy equal to zero.

19–6 Entropy and probability. When a system of interacting bodies undergoes a change of state, it approaches a state of higher entropy. So far as the first law of thermodynamics is concerned, there are an infinite number of possible changes of state; some represent a decrease in the total entropy, some an increase. Nature itself singles out processes which lead to increased entropy, and rejects all changes which lead to a decrease. It then seems reasonable to expect that entropy can be used in some way for the classification of states, or changes of state, by their relative probabilities of occurrence.

This point of view is basic in Boltzmann's molecular interpretation of entropy and in the second law of thermodynamics. According to Boltzmann's interpretation, the state of a system can be described, at least in principle, in terms of the arrangements and speeds of the molecules. Molecules can be arranged in a large number of ways; some arrangements are more probable than others. The molecules seek their most probable arrangement according to the same laws of probability which predict, for example, the most probable arrangement of a large number of flipped coins. The Boltzmann theory indicates how the probability of the molecular arrangements can be calculated in terms of the macroscopic states, and how such a probability is related to the entropy. It is the purpose of this section to discuss these ideas briefly and to illustrate them by some simple examples.

An illustration of the calculation of the probability of states. To illustrate the idea involved in the calculation of the probability of various molecular arrangements in terms of the macroscopic states of a substance, we shall discuss the distribution of an ideal gas in a container. As we have already indicated, we shall assume that the laws of probability can be applied to molecules in the same way that they are applied to everyday events.

To review the elementary ideas of the laws of probability, let us consider the flipping of a coin. There are two possible outcomes of the flip, "heads" and "tails," and there is no *a priori* reason why one result should be more likely than the other. We say that heads and tails are equally probable results, and the probability of obtaining, say, heads, is then $\frac{1}{2}$. From an experimental point of view, the probability of heads is determined as the ratio between the number of successful flips (heads) and the total number of flips, when this total is very large.

When we flip two coins at the same time, there are four equally probable results: heads-heads, tails-tails, tails-heads, heads-tails. The probability of obtaining the result heads-heads, for example, is then $\frac{1}{4}$. Since there are two possible ways of obtaining a heads-tails combination of the coins, the probability of obtaining such a "mixed state," with no regard to which coin is heads, is clearly $2 \cdot \frac{1}{4} = \frac{1}{2}$. Similarly, we can readily be convinced that the number of possibilities of n_1 coins landing heads and n_2 coins landing tails when we flip $n_1 + n_2 = n$ coins is

$$\frac{1 \cdot 2 \cdot 3 \cdots n}{(1 \cdot 2 \cdot 3 \cdots n_1)(1 \cdot 2 \cdot 3 \cdots n_2)}. \tag{19-9}$$

Let us now return to the molecules of gas in the container. The container is divided into two identical parts, A and B. If we have only one gas molecule in the container, there are two possible arrangements of equal probability $\frac{1}{2}$: the molecule can be in A or it can be in B. Each of these arrangements is equally probable. When we have two molecules, a and b, in the container, there are four possible arrangements: a and b can be in A, a and b in B, a in A and b in B, or a in B and b in A. The probability of each is $\frac{1}{4}$. Of these four possible combinations, two give a uniform distribution and two a nonuniform distribution. The probability of having a uniform distribution is then $2 \cdot \frac{1}{4} = \frac{1}{2}$. As we increase the number of molecules, the probability of obtaining a uniform distribution increases rapidly, and the probability of a nonuniform distribution decreases.

In the case of three molecules, there will be $2^3 = 8$ possible combinations, and for n molecules there will be 2^n combinations, each with a probability $1/2^n$. With $n = 10$, we have $2^{10} = 1024$ combinations. Of these, only *one* will have all ten molecules in A. If we consider the arrangement of one molecule in A and nine in B, we find ten possibilities, which correspond to placing molecule number 1 in A and the others in B, placing molecule number 2 in A and the others in B, etc. If we proceed to consider the arrangement with two molecules in A and eight in B, we find that there are 45 possibilities. We can readily continue this count of the number of ways in which a state can be attained, and the result is as shown in Table 19–1. By a *state* we shall then mean an arrangement with specified *numbers* of molecules in A and in B. Which molecules are in A and which are in B is immaterial. Thus several combinations can give rise to the same state. The larger the number of combinations, the higher the probability of the existence of that state.

In this particular case, we find that about 70% of all the possible combinations are concentrated on the three central states in the table. These states represent an almost uniform distribution of the molecules in the box. As the number of molecules is increased further, uniformity will be favored more and more. With the enormously large numbers of molecules involved in gases at ordinary pressures, the probability of a uniform (or

Table 19-1

Number of molecules in A	10	9	8	7	6	5	4	3	2	1	0
Number of molecules in B	0	1	2	3	4	5	6	7	8	9	10
Number of possibilities	1	10	45	120	210	252	210	120	45	10	1

nearly uniform) distribution, for all practical purposes, is equal to unity. In one mole of a gas, the probability that all the molecules will be in A is $(1/2)^{N_0} = (1/2)^{6 \cdot 10^{23}}$, an extremely small number. The probability that there will be approximately equal numbers of molecules in A and B is unity, for all practical purposes.

Thus, using the laws of probability on a system of molecules that are assumed to be completely independent of one another, we can readily understand the behavior of a gas as it expands and spreads uniformly throughout a container. This basic idea of counting the combinations which correspond to different states of a system of molecules can be used equally well in other situations for the determination of the relative probabilities of various states. It is postulated that the particular system settles into the state which has the highest probability. This, then, is the essence of the *second law of thermodynamics in its molecular interpretation.*

In the example above, it was tacitly assumed that the particles in the various states moved with equal speeds, so that it was possible to assign equal probabilities to the various combinations of particles. In other words, we considered all the states to have the same temperature. It is possible to extend this analysis to include states of different temperatures, but we shall limit ourselves to the simple case treated above.

We shall now consider the possibility of comparing the probabilities of various states in terms of the *macroscopic* properties of the states, such as volume, temperature, density, etc. That this possibility exists is immediately apparent from the simple example of the distribution of gas molecules in a container. If there are two possible and different volumes of the gas, it seeks the larger volume. In fact, it is simple to calculate the relative probabilities of two macroscopic states which have the same temperature but different volumes. In the discussion above, we found that the probability of all the particles of a mole of a gas being in one half of a container is $(1/2)^{N_0}$, where $N_0 = 6 \cdot 10^{23}$. In complete analogy, we find that the probability of all the particles being in a volume V_1 is $(V_1/V)^{N_0}$, where

V is the total available volume. Similarly, the probability of all the particles being in a volume V_2 is $(V_2/V)^{N_0}$. The ratio X_2/X_1 between the probabilities of the particles being in V_2 and in V_1, respectively, is then

$$\frac{X_2}{X_1} = \left(\frac{V_2}{V_1}\right)^{N_0}$$

or

$$\ln \frac{X_2}{X_1} = N_0 \ln \frac{V_2}{V_1}. \tag{19–10}$$

In other words, in this simple case the relative probabilities of the two states of one mole of gas at a constant temperature can be expressed directly in terms of the ratio between the volumes of the two states.

The relation between probability and entropy. In the previous section [see Eq. (19–8)], we found that between two different states of one mole of an ideal gas at constant temperature, the entropy difference is $S_2 - S_1 = R \ln (V_2/V_1)$, and we have now seen that the probability ratio between the same states is $\ln (X_2/X_1) = N_0 \ln (V_2/V_1)$ [see Eq. (19–10)]. By comparing these two results, we can see that the entropy and the probability of a state are related to each other (at least in this particular case) as follows:

$$\Delta S = S_2 - S_1 = \frac{R}{N_0} \ln \frac{X_2}{X_1} = k \ln \frac{X_2}{X_1}, \tag{19–11}$$

where k is Boltzmann's constant. This relation between entropy and probability applies not only for states of the same temperature, but can be shown to be generally valid.

Once the entropy difference between two states has been determined, we can determine the ratio of the probabilities of the states from the Boltzmann relation

$$\frac{X_2}{X_1} = e^{(S_2 - S_1)/k}. \tag{19–12}$$

EXAMPLE. A 1001-gm water bath is at 0°C. What is the probability that state 1, in which one gram of water is ice (the latent heat being transferred to the remaining liquid), will exist, rather than state 2, in which this gram of water remains at 0°C water?

Here we are dealing with a transition between two states which are' specified as follows. The first state is: 1 gm of water at 0°C and 1000 gm of water at 0°C. The second state is: 1 gm of ice at 0°C and 1000 gm of water at $\Delta T_0°$C. Let us bring this system reversibly from one state to the other and calculate the corresponding values of $\int_1^2 dQ/T$ for the two interacting parts which comprise the system (1 gm of water and 1000 gm of water).

Let us start with the gram of water. In the extraction of heat (say, with a Carnot engine) required to form the ice, the temperature $T = T_0 = 273°$

remains constant, and the latent heat of the water, $Q_1 \simeq 80$ cal/gm, is removed. The corresponding entropy change is

$$(S_2 - S_1)_A = \int_1^2 \frac{dQ}{T} = -\frac{Q_1}{T_0}.$$

The remaining water in the bath can be heated reversibly in a similar fashion, and we obtain

$$(S_2 - S_1)_B = \frac{dQ}{T} = mc \int_1^2 \frac{dT}{T} = mc \ln \frac{T_0 + \Delta T}{T_0},$$

where $mc\, \Delta T = Q_1$.

For small values of ΔT, we can set

$$\ln \left(1 + \frac{\Delta T}{T_0}\right) = \frac{\Delta T}{T_0} - \frac{1}{2}\left(\frac{\Delta T}{T_0}\right)^2.$$

Thus the total change of entropy in such an imaginary change would be

$$S_2 - S_1 = -\frac{Q_1}{T_0} + mc \frac{\Delta T}{T_0} - mc \frac{1}{2}\left(\frac{\Delta T}{T_0}\right)^2.$$

Since $Q_1 = mc\, \Delta T$, we get

$$S_2 - S_1 = -\frac{mc}{2}\left(\frac{\Delta T}{T_0}\right)^2.$$

With $Q_1 \simeq 80$ cal, we obtain $\Delta T = 80/1000 \cdot 1 = 0.08°C$ and

$$S_2 - S_1 = -\frac{1000}{2}\left(\frac{0.08}{273}\right)^2 \simeq -4.3 \cdot 10^{-5} \text{ cal/°C}.$$

The probability ratio between state 2 and state 1 is then

$$\frac{X_2}{X_1} = \exp\left(\frac{S_2 - S_1}{k}\right) = \exp\left(-\frac{4.3 \cdot 10^{-5}}{0.33 \cdot 10^{-23}}\right) \simeq \exp\left(-1.3 \cdot 10^{19}\right).$$

The probability of this spontaneous crystallization with no external heat exchange is then extremely small indeed.

In the light of what we have now learned about the probability of states, it is interesting to discuss in more detail some of the questions mentioned in Sec. 19–1. Consider, for example, the motion of a pendulum in a gas. As the pendulum collides with the gas molecules, the organized mechanical energy of the pendulum is transferred to random motion of the molecules (heat) and the pendulum eventually stops. This kind of phenomenon is common; the probability that mechanical work will be transformed into heat, for all practical purposes, is unity. On the other hand, we have pointed out that the reverse transformation of energy from heat into mechanical organized energy does not happen; the probability of this event, for all practical purposes, is zero. How are experimental facts of this kind explained in terms of the theory of entropy and the probability of states as expressed by Eq. (19–12)? How probable is the transformation of mechanical energy into heat, and how improbable is the reverse process?

To answer these questions, we start from Eq. (19–7). Let us compute the probability that the pendulum receives mechanical energy E from the air, which then loses the same amount of heat. If we consider the heat reservoir, i.e., the atmosphere, to have an infinitely large heat capacity, the temperature of the system will remain unchanged. Then, the two states of the system with which we are concerned are:

State 1: The temperature is T and the energy of the pendulum is zero.

State 2: The temperature is T, the pendulum has a mechanical energy E, and the heat reservoir (the atmosphere) has lost an equal amount of heat; that is, $\int dQ = -E$.

The entropy change that results when the system goes from one state to the other is then the same as the entropy change of the heat reservoir, $\int dQ/T = -E/T$. The relative probability of the two states is then

$$\frac{X_2}{X_1} = e^{-E/kT}. \qquad (19\text{–}13)$$

In the motion of its center of mass, the pendulum reaches a maximum height h above ground such that $mgh = E$, where m is the mass of the pendulum. As an example, take $h = 1$ cm and $m = 1$ gm. Then, with $kT \simeq 10^{-14}$ erg (temperature $T \simeq 300°K$), we obtain

$$\frac{X_2}{X_1} \simeq \exp\left(-1 \cdot 981 \cdot 1/10^{-14}\right) \simeq \exp\left(-10^{17}\right),$$

which is such an extremely small number that the probability that heat is transformed into work can, for all practical purposes, be set equal to zero.

To find the probability that the mechanical energy of the pendulum is transformed into heat, we merely change the sign of the entropy change, since heat is now received by the heat reservoir. The ratio between the probability that the pendulum will be damped and the probability that it will remain swinging is then $\exp\left(10^{17}\right)$, i.e., such an overwhelmingly large number that the transfer of mechanical energy into heat, for all practical purposes, is a certainty.

The result in Eq. (19–13), of course, can be applied to any arbitrary mass; in particular, it can be used to compute the relative probability of finding a molecule at the ground surface and at a height h, as illustrated in the following discussion.

Density distribution in an isothermal atmosphere (the law of atmospheres).
What is the probability of finding a molecule of mass m at a distance y
above ground in comparison with the probability that it will be found at
ground level ($y = 0$)?

To determine the relative probability of these two molecular positions,
using the above concepts, we introduce $E = mgy$ into Eq. (19–13) and
obtain

$$\frac{X_2}{X_1} = e^{-E/kT} = e^{-mgy/kT}. \tag{19–14}$$

The ratio X_2/X_1 is exceedingly small for ordinary masses (say 1 gm), but
it can be seen that when we deal with molecular masses (of the order of
10^{-23} gm), the ratio can be quite close to unity even for large values of y.
That is, $(X_2/X_1) \simeq \exp(-10^{-6}\, y)$, where y is in centimeters.

The probability ratio X_2/X_1 should be the same as the density ratio
of the air above the earth at y and at $y = 0$. If we denote the molecular
weight by M, and if we set $X_2/X_1 = \rho/\rho_0$, Eq. (19–14) can then be
written as

$$\rho = \rho_0 e^{-Mgy/RT}, \tag{19–15}$$

where ρ is the density at height y and ρ_0 is the density at the ground.

It is interesting to see that this expression is indeed the same as that
obtained directly from the conditions for equilibrium in an isothermal
atmosphere. The temperature T in the atmosphere is assumed constant.
The pressure and the density vary with the height y above the ground
(see Fig. 19–5). The equilibrium of a gas element of thickness dy then
requires that the force $p - (p + dp) = -dp$ in the upward direction
must equal the force $\rho g\, dy$ in the downward direction. That is,

$$dp = -\rho g\, dy,$$

since, according to the gas law, $p = r\rho T$, where r is the gas constant per
unit mass, $r = R/M$ (M = molecular mass). Thus, inserting $dp = rT\, d\rho$,
we get

$$\frac{d\rho}{\rho} = -\frac{g}{rT}\, dy = -\frac{Mg}{RT}\, dy.$$

Direct integration then gives

$$\rho = \rho_0 e^{-Mgy/RT} = \rho_0 e^{-mgy/kT},$$

where ρ_0 is the density at $y = 0$ and
m is the mass of one gas particle
($M = N_0 m$, $k = R/N_0$). This result is identical with that obtained
above in our considerations of probability.

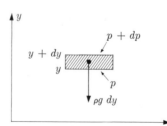

FIG. 19–5. The equilibrium of a gas
element in the earth's gravitational
field requires that $dp = -\rho g\, dy$.

EXAMPLE. The generality of the relations which we have discussed above will be illustrated by the following example, which is somewhat different in nature from those given above. The internal energy of a sodium atom in its normal state can be set equal to zero. The atom can also exist in a so-called excited state which has an extra energy of $3.32 \cdot 10^{-12}$ erg, caused by an internal displacement of the electric charges. The atoms in this state spontaneously emit a yellow sodium light, and as a result the charge displacement reverts to its original state. A certain amount of sodium vapor is now enclosed in a tube and is found to emit light of intensity I_1, when the vapor is kept at a temperature of 727°C. Suppose we wish to increase the intensity 100 times by increasing the temperature. What temperature increase can be expected to produce this intensity increase?

When we denote the number of atoms in the normal state by n_0, it is expected, on the basis of the Boltzmann relation, that the number of excited atoms at a temperature T will be

$$n = n_0 e^{-E/kT},$$

where in this case $E = 3.32 \cdot 10^{-12}$ erg is the energy required to excite an atom.

If we assume that the intensity of radiation is proportional to the number of excited atoms, we have

$$I = \text{const } n_0 e^{-E/kT}.$$

Consequently, the ratio between the intensities at two different temperatures T_1 and T_2 will be

$$\frac{I_2}{I_1} = \frac{e^{-E/kT_2}}{e^{-E/kT_1}} = \exp\left[+\left(\frac{E}{kT_1}\right)\left(1 - \frac{T_1}{T_2}\right)\right].$$

With $I_2/I_1 = 100$, we get

$$\ln 100 = \frac{E}{kT_1}\left(1 - \frac{T_1}{T_2}\right)$$

or

$$1 - \frac{T_1}{T_2} = \frac{kT_1}{E}\ln 100,$$

$$\frac{T_1}{T_2} = 1 - \frac{kT_1}{E} - \ln 100 = 1 - \frac{1.38 \cdot 10^{-16} \cdot 1000}{3.32 \cdot 10^{-12}} \cdot 4.6 \simeq 0.83,$$

$$T_2 \simeq 1200°\text{K}.$$

Entropy, irreversibility, and disorder. We have indicated repeatedly that when a change takes place in an isolated system, the system seeks its state of highest probability. Consequently, the entropy of the system increases. If a system A is in equilibrium, it does not change and its entropy remains constant. In order to bring about a change of state, A must interact with another system B. In this interaction, it is quite possible that the entropy of A will decrease, but it is always found that this decrease is more than balanced by an *increase* of the entropy of B, so that the *total* entropy of the system $A + B$ increases in the process. From observations of this kind, we can conclude that whenever a change takes place in nature the total entropy of the universe will increase, even if local decreases in entropy may occur. This statement is one form of the second law of thermodynamics.

The very idealized change of state in a *reversible* process is a succession of equilibrium states, and has *no* preferred direction. Therefore for reversible changes of the states of the *total* system the probabilities are equal. When we deal with reversible changes of the state of a system A, we attribute such changes to interactions of A with another system B. Again, in such a reversible change it is clear that the entropy of one of the systems might decrease, but it is then always compensated by an equal increase in the other, so that the total entropy change in a reversible process is zero. Although a reversible process is an idealization, and although the total entropy change in such a process is zero, it is nevertheless a very important tool for calculating the entropy difference between two states of system A, for example. In fact, this is indeed the technique by which we can calculate the probability ratios between two states of A.

Since the entropy change is zero in a reversible process and is larger than zero in an irreversible process, the entropy change can be used to measure the irreversibility of a process. The larger the irreversibility, the higher is the probability that the process will take place.

Entropy can also be considered to be a measure of "disorder"; nature seems to go from ordered states (for example, organized mechanical energy) into disordered ones (for example, random heat motion). From the same point of view, two unmixed gases represent an ordered state. When they diffuse into a common chamber, they mix with each other to form a disordered state. This interpretation, of course, is nothing more than a definition of the word *disorder* in terms of probability; it is simply another way to express the fact that nature tends toward the most probable states. Thus a disordered state is one which can be produced by a large number of different combinations of the elements (molecules) in a system. This statistical meaning of disorder is not inconsistent with the everyday usage of the word. The reason the papers on some desks most frequently seem to be in a disordered state is simply that there are so many combinations of the papers which are disordered, and so few which are ordered.

PROBLEMS

19-1. Describe some processes in nature which do not violate the first law of thermodynamics, but which, nevertheless, do not happen.

19-2. Consider the following three unidirectional processes of one mole of an ideal monatomic gas: (a) isobaric expansion at the pressure P_1 from the volume V_1 to the volume $2V_1$, (b) isothermal expansion from the state (P_1, V_1) to the volume $2V_1$, and (c) heating of the gas from P_1 to $2P_1$ at constant volume V_1. What are the mechanical efficiencies of these processes (i.e., the ratio between the work done by the gas and the heat transferred to the gas)?

19-3. Explain in detail the reason why the work done by a substance in a cyclic process can be represented by the enclosed area in the $P-V$ diagram of a cycle.

19-4. Equations (19-2) and (19-3a, b) show, for a Carnot heat engine, that

$$\frac{W}{Q_1} = \frac{Q_1 + Q_2}{Q_1} = 1 - \frac{T_2}{T_1}.$$

Explain carefully the meanings of the quantities involved in this equation, and indicate the changes, if any, that should be made so that this relation is applicable also to a refrigeration cycle.

19-5. In an isothermal expansion of an ideal gas, all heat absorbed by the gas is converted into work. What is the basic reason that heat cannot be converted into work with the same high efficiency in a periodically operating machine?

19-6. Figure 19-6 illustrates a closed-path process. We shall consider this process to consist of two Carnot cycles operating between different temperatures. Using the values of the temperatures and volumes shown in the figure, determine the efficiency of the cycle, and show that it is less efficient than a Carnot engine that runs between the highest and the lowest temperatures involved in the process. (The same result can be extended to an arbitrary closed cycle by splitting it into elementary Carnot cycles.)

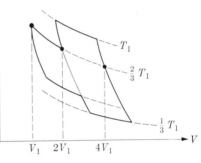

FIGURE 19-6

19-7. In the discussion of Fig. 19-2 it was shown that all reversible engines operating between the same temperatures have the same efficiency, regardless of the working substance. What can be said about the efficiency of irreversible engines? (Eff. = work/ heat absorbed.)

19-8. Explain how, in principle, temperature can be defined such that it is independent of the thermometric substance involved. Show that this definition is plausible and that it results in the same temperature scale as that obtained by means of the ideal-gas thermometer.

19-9. Show that in a Carnot engine $Q_1/T_1 + Q_2/T_2 = 0$. Is $Q_1 + Q_2$ also equal to zero? Prove that for an arbitrary closed-path reversible cycle we have $\int dQ/T = 0$. What is $\int dQ$?

19-10. An ideal gas (n moles, gas constant R) is taken from state 1 to state 3 through a constant-volume, constant-pressure process, as indicated in Fig. 19-7. (a) What is the total work done by the gas along the indicated path? (b) What is the total change in internal energy along this path? (c) What is the total heat added to the gas along this path? (d) What is the change of entropy along this path?

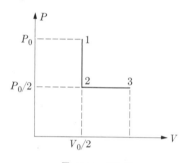

FIGURE 19-7

19-11. Derive the relation given by Eq. (19-7) which expresses the change of entropy of an ideal gas that goes from a state $V_1 T_1$ to a state $V_2 T_2$.

19-12. Show that the equation of state of an ideal gas can be expressed as $P/P_0 = (\rho/\rho_0)^\gamma e^{(S-S_0)/C_v}$, where $\gamma = C_p/C_v$.

19-13. Describe a Carnot process in both a P-V and a T-S diagram. What do the enclosed areas in these diagrams represent?

19-14. One mole of a real gas can be taken from state A (P_1, V_1, T_1) to state B (P_2, V_2, T_2) by many different processes. Which of the following pairs change by amounts which are the same for all processes? (a) Q, W, (b) S, Q, (c) U, Q, (d) U, W, (e) U, S, (f) S, W.

19-15. Show that when n coins are flipped, the number of possibilities, as given by Eq. (19-9), of getting n_1 heads and $n - n_1$ tails is the same as the coefficient of $a^{n_1} b^{n-n_1}$ in the binomial expansion of $(a + b)^n$.

19-16. Two heat reservoirs, each containing m kgm of water, have the temperatures T_1 and $3T_1$. (a) The reservoirs are brought in contact with each other, and the temperatures eventually reach the equilibrium value $2T_1$. What is the change of entropy of the system? (The two reservoirs comprise the system.) (b) In the irreversible equalization of temperature in (a), no work was obtained. Let us now use the reservoirs to run a reversible heat engine that consists of a succession of Carnot cycles, in which the hot reservoir is cooled and the cold one is heated until the temperatures of both reservoirs are the same. What is this final temperature? (c) What is the over-all thermodynamic efficiency of this machine?

19-17. A thermally insulated container is divided by a heat-conducting wall into two compartments of equal volume. Each compartment contains $6 \cdot 10^{10}$ molecules ($= 10^{-13}$ mole) of a monatomic gas at the temperature $T = 300°$K. The possibility exists that the temperature in one compartment may drop by an amount $\Delta T = 0.001°$K, and this released heat is conducted through the wall and used to raise the temperature in the other compartment by 10^{-3}K°, while the volumes of the compartments remain unchanged.

(a) What is the entropy change of the gas whose temperature decreases by ΔT? (b) Derive an equation that expresses the entropy change of the gas in the other compartment. (c) Compute the *numerical* value of the entropy change of the *system* (in ergs/°K). (d) How many times more probable is it that the temperatures in the two compartments are identical than that they differ by 0.002°K?

19–18. How high does one have to go above ground level to note a 1% change in the ratio between the number densities of nitrogen and oxygen molecules in the air? Assume isothermal atmosphere $T = 300°$.

19–19. Jupiter's atmosphere is probably composed of hydrogen, helium, ammonia, and methane. The mean molecular weight is about 3.3, and the temperature is −138°C. (a) Find the value of g near the surface of Jupiter. (b) Find the heights at which the densities of ammonia (NH_3) and helium would be reduced by an amount e from their values at the surface.

19–20. A hot spring bubbles 10 kgm/min of 85°C-water from the earth. Nearby is a large lake with water at 25°C. If a Carnot engine were run between these two reservoirs, what would be the thermodynamic efficiency? How much power (in kilowatts) could the engine produce? Assume that the 85°C-water is lowered to 25°C.

19–21. One mole of 0.5-gm ping-pong balls is spread out on a flat surface. The temperature of the ping-pong balls and their surroundings is 300°K. (a) If a snapshot were taken of all the ping-pong balls, approxi-mately how many would be 1 cm or more above the flat surface? (b) Do you see how your answer for part (a) can be expressed in terms of the length of time you would have to watch *one* ping-pong ball before it rose to 1 cm or more?

19–22. Explain why it is that the entropy of the universe increases in the free expansion of an ideal gas, even though no heat crosses the boundary of the system during the expansion.

19–23. Imagine a motion-picture camera that is capable of photographing macroscopic and microscopic phenomena together. The following are photographed: the isothermal expansion of an ideal gas, the adiabatic compression of an ideal gas, a lump of mud as it falls on a flat surface from a height h, and an ice cube as it melts in a beaker of hot water. (a) Which of these processes would look perfectly reasonable if the projector were run backward? (b) In which processes does the entropy increase? In which does it decrease? (c) What is the connection between entropy and the directionality of time?

19–24. Assume a waterfall to be h meters high. What is the entropy change per second in the universe as a result of water at temperature T falling at a rate of q kgm/sec?

CHAPTER 20

MECHANICS OF FLUIDS

Summary. We start with a discussion of the pressure distribution necessary to keep a fluid in equilibrium under the influence of both interaction and inertial forces. Examples are given that demonstrate the equilibrium of the fluid in an accelerating and in a rotating coordinate system. Then follows a brief survey of the various types of fluid motion and a description of laminar motion by means of flow lines and a velocity field. The flow field cannot be arbitrary but must satisfy the conditions imposed by the general laws of motion. These conditions lead to Gauss' law and Bernoulli's theorem.

In our previous studies of fluids (both liquids and gases), we have for the most part disregarded the influence of external forces and net motion on the pressure distribution in the fluid. In this chapter, we shall study some of the elementary aspects of the problems that arise because of such forces and motion.

20–1 Equilibrium of a fluid. The net force is zero on all parts of a fluid which is in equilibrium. When the external force is gravity, a volume element of the fluid is in equilibrium under the influence of its weight and the pressure from the surrounding liquid, as illustrated in Fig. 20–1. (For a discussion of the pressure concept, see Sec. 13–3.) The net force produced by the pressure from the surrounding liquid is then equal to the weight of the liquid element. The line of action of the force passes through

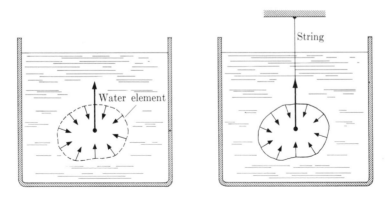

Fig. 20–1. The pressure and net force exerted by the surrounding fluid remain the same if a fluid element is replaced by another object of the same shape and in the same position as the fluid element.

the center of mass of the fluid element, since this element is in rotational equilibrium also. The pressure from the fluid element on the surrounding liquid, of course, exerts an equal but oppositely directed force which keeps the surrounding liquid in equilibrium.

If the fluid element is replaced in the same position by another body of the same shape, the equilibrium of the surrounding liquid is not disturbed and the pressure exerted on the body by the surrounding liquid is the same as it was on the displaced fluid element. Consequently, the force on the fluid element and the force on the body replacing the fluid element are the same in magnitude, direction, and line of action (Archimedes' principle). Thus, when the external force is gravity, the force on the submerged body is equal in magnitude but opposite in direction to the weight of the displaced liquid element. The upward force on the submerged body is often called the *buoyant* force.

EXAMPLE. A straight uniform bar of length L, cross-sectional area A, and density ρ is free to rotate about a fixed horizontal axis P, which is located a distance $d = L/2$ below a water surface, as shown in Fig. 20–2. The downward force of gravity is $F_1 = A\rho Lg$, and it has a lever arm $d_1 = L/2 \sin \theta$ with respect to the axis P. The buoyant force has the magnitude $F_2 = A\rho_0 g(L/2 \cos \theta)$ and has a lever arm $d_2 = (L/4 \cos \theta) \sin \theta$ (ρ_0 = density of the water). Equilibrium requires that the resultant torque be zero, and so we have $F_1 d_1 = F_2 d_2$. When we insert the values for the force and the lever arms, we obtain the equation

$$\frac{\rho_0}{4} \frac{\sin \theta}{\cos^2 \theta} = \rho \sin \theta.$$

This equation has the solutions $\theta = 0$ and $\cos^2 \theta = \rho_0/4\rho$. Note that an equilibrium position other than $\theta = 0$ is possible only if $\rho > \rho_0/4$. On the other hand, the geometry of the problem requires the angles under consideration to be less than 60°, so ρ must be less than ρ_0; i.e., an equilibrium of the type pictured in Fig. 20–2 is possible only if $\rho_0/4 < \rho < \rho_0$. If $\rho = \rho_0/2$, we obtain $\cos \theta = \frac{1}{2}$, thus $\theta = 45°$.

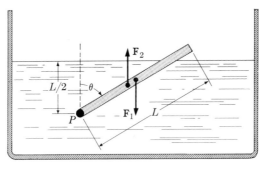

FIGURE 20–2

Clearly, the pressure in a fluid increases with depth, a fact which we used in our discussion of the gas law and in the example concerning density distribution in the atmosphere. The pressure in the fluid will depend on y in such a way that the pressure change in a distance dy is equal to the weight $\rho g\, dy$ of the fluid element of unit area and thickness dy (ρ = density). Then, if y is the vertical coordinate increasing upward, we have

$$dP = -\rho g\, dy \tag{20-1}$$

(see Fig. 20–3). When we deal with liquids rather than gases, the density can be taken as constant, and the pressure then depends linearly on y, $P = -\rho g y + \text{const}$, or

$$P + \rho g y = \text{const.} \tag{20-2}$$

In the particular example shown in Fig. 20–3, we measure y from the bottom of a container which is filled to a height H with a liquid. The pressure at $y = H$ is then equal to the atmospheric pressure P_0, the constant in Eq. (20–2) is $P_0 + \rho g H$, and the pressure distribution in the container is given by

$$P + \rho g y = P_0 + \rho g H.$$

If the density varies with y, the pressure distribution is not so simply obtained, as mentioned previously in our discussion of the density distribution in an isothermal atmosphere.

It is important to note that the pressure in the liquid adjusts itself in such a way that the surfaces of constant pressure are perpendicular to the external force, regardless of the shape of the container. (If there were a pressure variation along such a surface, there would be a net force, parallel with the surface, on each fluid element, and a corresponding motion along the surface.) The maximum pressure variation in the fluid is found in the

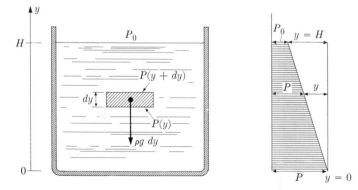

Fig. 20–3. The pressure distribution in a liquid at rest (constant ρ). $P + \rho g y = \text{const.}$

direction perpendicular to the surfaces of constant pressure. The change
of pressure per unit length in this direction is called the *pressure gradient*
in the fluid. The pressure gradient is a vector of the same magnitude as
the external force per unit volume, but oppositely directed. When the
external force is gravity, we have $dP/dy = -\rho g$ in the vertical direction.
The pressure variation per unit length in a direction $\mathbf{s}$ which makes an
angle θ with the vertical is then $dP/ds = -\rho g \cos \theta$.

If, in addition to gravity, there are other forces acting on the fluid, it
is clear that the surfaces of equal pressure need not be horizontal planes.
As examples, we shall consider a fluid in a container as a system, first with
constant acceleration, and then rotating with constant angular velocity.

Fluid in a container—system with constant acceleration. In Fig. 20–4,
the system comprised of the water and its container has a constant acceleration $\mathbf{a}_0$. In a coordinate system attached to the container, the
fluid is at rest (after oscillations have died out) under the influence of
gravity and the inertial force (Chapter 11) resulting from the acceleration.
In this coordinate system a mass element dm of the liquid is acted on by
the gravitational force $\mathbf{g}\, dm$ and the inertial force $-\mathbf{a}_0\, dm$. Here, we have
treated $\mathbf{g}$ as a vector in order to incorporate the direction of the force of
gravity. The pressure in the liquid varies in such a way that each fluid
element is in equilibrium under the influence of the force $dm(\mathbf{g} - \mathbf{a}_0)$ and
the force that corresponds to the pressure gradient in the fluid. The surfaces of equal pressure then will be perpendicular to the force $dm(\mathbf{g} - \mathbf{a}_0)$.
The surface of the water in the container is one of these planes of equal
pressure, and it will be inclined at an angle θ, determined by $\tan \theta = a_0/g$,
as illustrated in Fig. 20–4. The magnitude of the pressure variation per
unit length, perpendicular to the planes of constant pressure, is then
$dP/ds = \rho g\sqrt{1 + (a_0/g)^2}$.

If the container is accelerated upward or downward, the magnitude of
the pressure gradient becomes $\rho(g + a_0)$ or $\rho(g - a_0)$, respectively. In
the particular case of free fall, when $a_0 = g$, the pressure gradient in the
liquid is zero.

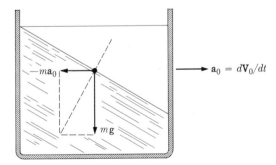

FIG. 20–4. An accelerated container of water.

It is interesting to study the effect of an accelerated fluid on the buoyant force on a submerged body. The accelerated fluid that surrounds the submerged body produces a net force on the body. If the entire fluid has an acceleration $\mathbf{a}_0$, the force (gravity plus inertial force) on a fluid element of volume dV is $\rho(\mathbf{g} - \mathbf{a}_0)\, dV$ *in an accelerated coordinate system that follows the fluid.* The surrounding fluid then acts on the element with an equal force but in the opposite direction, i.e., with the force $\rho(-\mathbf{g} + \mathbf{a}_0)\, dV$, where ρ is the density of the fluid. (The force $-\rho\mathbf{g}\, dV$ is the ordinary buoyant force, and $\rho\mathbf{a}_0\, dV$ can be called the inertial buoyant force.) This net force produced by the surrounding fluid does not change when the fluid element is replaced by the submerged body. If the density of the body is ρ_1, the external force on it (gravity plus inertial force) is $\rho_1(\mathbf{g} - \mathbf{a}_0)\, dV$, and the surrounding fluid acts on the body with the net buoyant force $\rho(-\mathbf{g} + \mathbf{a}_0)\, dV$. The total force $\mathbf{F}'$ on the body as measured in the accelerating coordinate system (Fig. 20–5) is then

$$\mathbf{F}' = (\rho_1 - \rho)(\mathbf{g} - \mathbf{a}_0)\, dV. \qquad (20\text{–}3)$$

Clearly, the direction of the total force is dependent upon the difference between the densities of the submerged body and the fluid.

An illuminating demonstration of this result is shown in Fig. 20–6. A ping-pong ball is fastened at the end of a string and hung from the cork inside a bottle. The ping-pong ball has an average density which is larger than the displaced air ($\rho_1 > \rho$), and when the bottle is moved to the right with an acceleration $\mathbf{a}_0$, there is a net (inertial) force on the ball toward the left, and the ball swings to the left. According to Eq. (20–3),

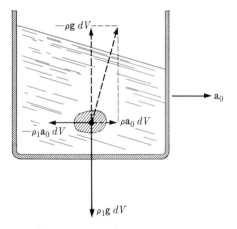

FIG. 20–5. The forces on a submerged body in an accelerated fluid, as measured from the coordinate system of the fluid. The broken lines represent buoyant forces produced by the pressure of the surrounding fluid.

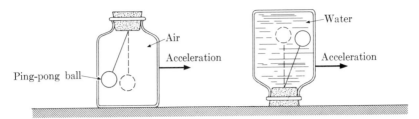

FIG. 20–6. Example demonstrating inertial and buoyancy forces in an accelerating fluid. In air the ping-pong ball is deflected in a direction opposite to that of the acceleration, but in water it is deflected in the *same* direction as the acceleration.

the net force on the ball in the horizontal direction is $-(\rho_1 - \rho)a_0\,dV$, and is in the same direction as $-a_0$, since $(\rho_1 - \rho) > 0$.

Next, let us repeat the experiment with the bottle filled with water. The bottle is turned upside down to keep the ping-pong ball submerged. When the bottle is given an acceleration a_0 to the right, the ball does not swing back, but *moves forward in the direction of the acceleration*. The inertial buoyant force from the liquid is now larger than the inertial force on the body, since the density of water is larger than the average density of the ping-pong ball. In other words, $(\rho_1 - \rho)$ is now negative and the net force $-(\rho_1 - \rho)a_0\,dV$ on the body has the same direction as a_0.

If the acceleration of the bottle is downward and equal to g, i.e., when the bottle is in free fall, the net force on the body becomes zero in the coordinate system of the bottle, and the body does not accelerate with respect to the fluid. Any element, regardless of its mass, acquires the free-fall acceleration g.

Fluid in a container—system rotating with constant angular velocity. Suppose now that the system of water and container in Fig. 20–4 is set into rotation with a constant angular velocity ω about the z-axis, as indicated in Fig. 20–7. In a coordinate system that rotates with the glass, the

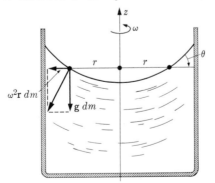

FIG. 20–7. Fluid rotating with a constant angular velocity.

fluid is at rest, and a fluid element a distance r from the axis of rotation is in equilibrium under the influence of the gravitational force $\mathbf{g}\,dm$, the inertial (centrifugal) force $\omega^2\mathbf{r}\,dm$, and the force resulting from the pressure in the fluid. Again, the surfaces of equal pressure must be perpendicular to the resultant force $dm(\mathbf{g}+\omega^2\mathbf{r})$, and the angle between the fluid surface and the horizontal plane is then given by $\tan\theta = \omega^2 r/g$; that is, the slope of the surface increases with the distance from the axis. If the equation of the surface is expressed as $z = z(r)$, we have $\tan\theta = dz/dr$, and an expression for the surface of equal pressure is obtained from the equation

$$\frac{dz}{dr} = \frac{\omega^2}{g}r,$$

which has the solution

$$z = z_0 + \frac{\omega^2}{2g}r^2.$$

The free water surface is one of the surfaces of constant pressure, and it forms a parabolic surface described by the equation above, where z_0 is the height of the water surface at $r = 0$.

20–2 Description of fluid motion. *Velocity field and flow lines.* When we observe fluids in motion, we note several obvious types of motion that seem basically distinct. Consider, for example, the highly irregular and apparently unpredictable motion of water in a rapidly moving, turbulent stream and compare this with the regular smooth flow in a large river. In the irregular or *turbulent* flow, a fluid element moves in a seemingly random path, not unlike the motion of a molecule in a gas. However, in the regular or *laminar* flow, each fluid element follows a well-defined path. Still another type of motion is the flow from a faucet or from a hose in which a water jet breaks up into droplets which move as individual mass points. Many of the problems involving turbulent flow and jet flow are complicated; we shall limit our discussion here to laminar flow.

A fluid element in a laminar flow follows a well-defined line, called a *flow line*. We shall consider here only the time-independent flow, in which all fluid elements that pass through a given point in space follow the *same* flow line with the same flow speeds. That is, the properties of the fluid, i.e., the density, the pressure, and the flow velocity at a fixed point in space, do not vary with time. It is important to note that even if the flow velocity at a given point does not vary with time, it can vary from one point to another, as in the case of water flow through a pipe of varying cross section.

Under these conditions, we can map out the motion of a fluid, once and for all, by means of flow lines which describe the paths of the fluid elements. The velocity at each point is in the direction of the flow lines; thus by drawing the velocity vector at each point of the fluid, we have specified its state of motion completely. When each point in space defines a velocity vector in this way, we say that the motion is specified by a *velocity vector field*. In many branches of physics, a description of the properties of space in terms of vector fields is quite common and useful. In previous chapters, we have described the gravitational force in terms of a force field, and similar descriptions were used for electric and magnetic forces.

It is clear that the flow-velocity field and the corresponding pressure field cannot be arbitrary but must be consistent with the basic laws of motion, i.e., the conservation of mass, momentum, and energy, all of which impose certain conditions that the velocity field must satisfy. The condition imposed by the conservation of mass is particularly simple and valuable, and we shall discuss it before we give specific examples of flow fields.

Conservation of mass. Consider the flow of a fluid through a tube of varying cross section, as shown in Fig. 20–8. If the density of the fluid at every point in the tube is time-independent, the mass per unit length of the tube is also time-independent. Therefore the mass that flows through the tube per unit time must be the same everywhere, and therefore the flow velocity along the tube must change when the cross-sectional area changes. To study this change, consider the volume between the two fixed planes of areas A_1 and A_2 across the tube shown in Fig. 20–8. When the fluid is displaced a distance ds_1 across the plane A_1, a mass $A_1\rho_1\,ds_1$ moves across the plane and enters the region between A_1 and A_2. The mass influx per unit time is then $A_1\rho_1(ds_1/dt) = A_1\rho_1u_1$, since $u_1 = ds_1/dt$. Since the total mass between A_1 and A_2 is constant, the amount of mass that leaves the tube at A_2 must be equal to the mass influx. If the velocity at A_2 is u_2 and the density is ρ_2, the corresponding mass flow per unit time is $A_2\rho_2u_2$, and conservation of mass requires that

$$A_1\rho_1u_1 = A_2\rho_2u_2 = \text{const.} \qquad (20\text{--}4)$$

If the density of the fluid is constant (as is the case with most liquids, since they are practically *incompressible*) it follows that conservation of mass requires the flow velocity to be inversely proportional to the tube area.

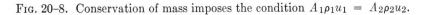

FIG. 20–8. Conservation of mass imposes the condition $A_1\rho_1u_1 = A_2\rho_2u_2$.

In this discussion we have considered the flow in an actual tube or pipe. However, the result obtained can be applied to an arbitrary time-independent flow field as follows. Imagine that the flow lines of neighboring fluid elements are drawn such that we obtain a bundle of flow lines which form a flow tube, as shown in Fig. 20–9. Since there is no velocity component perpendicular to the "wall" of the flow tube, the mass flow through the tube must be the same at all points, and we obtain the relation in Eq. (20–4) for the variation of the velocity along the flow tube.

For an incompressible fluid, the cross-sectional area of a flow tube is a direct measure of the velocity in the fluid, and this fact can be used to describe a flow field graphically. If we let the number of flow lines per unit area equal the magnitude of the velocity, we have a quantitative graphical description of the velocity field, since both the magnitude and the direction of the velocity vector are described by the flow lines. The magnitude of the velocity is proportional to the density of the flow lines.

We find that this method may be employed to give analogous descriptions of electric and magnetic fields, and the procedure should be borne in mind.

Gauss' law. We shall now consider the flow field which is produced by a spherically symmetrical source that ejects Q gm/sec of fluid into the surrounding region. The flow lines will then be straight lines that emanate radially from the source, as shown in Fig. 20–10. A flow distribution of this type is approximated by a flow of water from a hose which is submerged in water and provided with some kind of a spherical "distributor" (for example, a spherical nozzle). A radial flow distribution like that shown in the figure can also be obtained from a submerged spherical surface (a balloon) that expands radially with a radial velocity which is inversely proportional to the radius of the sphere. A spherically symmetrical

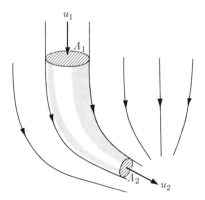

FIG. 20–9. A bundle of flow lines that form a flow tube.

field can also be obtained when a flow passes through a small hole in a plate. The flow field on the far side of the plate will be approximately the same as that from a point source located at the hole (laminar flow conditions are assumed, of course). The fluid velocity u will be constant over a spherical surface of radius r with the source at the center, and this velocity can be obtained directly from the law of conservation of mass. The area of the sphere is $4\pi r^2$, and if the density of the fluid is ρ, we obtain

$$4\pi r^2 \rho u = Q \qquad \text{or} \qquad u = \frac{Q}{4\pi\rho}\frac{1}{r^2}.$$

The velocity decreases as the inverse square of the distance from the center of the source. Incidentally, it can be noted that if the number of flow lines per unit area is chosen to equal the magnitude of the velocity, the total number of flow lines emitted from the source is $4\pi r^2 u = Q/\rho$. This same number of flow lines must cross any arbitrary closed surface that surrounds the source. Therefore, if the flow velocity component $u_n = u \cos\theta$ is normal to the surface (Fig. 20-11) we have

$$\int u\,(dS\cos\theta) = \int u_n\,dS = \frac{Q}{\rho}. \qquad (20\text{-}5)$$

This relation, which concerns the number of flow or field lines, is known as *Gauss' law*. Completely analogous considerations apply to gravitational and electric fields. For example, the electric field corresponds to the flow velocity, and the flow strength Q corresponds to the electric charge.

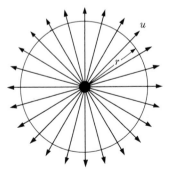

FIG. 20-10. Flow lines from a spherically symmetrical source.

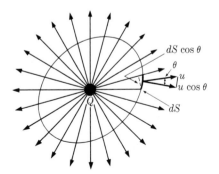

FIG. 20-11. The total mass flow from an arbitrary surface that surrounds a source can be written as $\rho\int u_n\,dS$ (Gauss' law).

20–3 The relation between flow velocity and pressure distribution.
Bernoulli's theorem. Since we now know the conditions imposed on the
velocity field by the law of conservation of mass, we can go on to study the
corresponding conditions that result from momentum and energy considerations. From this study we shall obtain the relation which must
exist between the pressure and the velocity fields in order for the general
laws of motion to be satisfied. It is instructive to start with the following
qualitative observations.

When a fluid is at rest under the influence of gravity, the pressure
gradient in the fluid is $dP/dy = -\rho g$, as shown in Sec. 20–1. If the
density is constant, this gradient corresponds to a pressure distribution
given by $P + \rho g y = $ const. This is the situation shown in Fig. 20–12(a).
The pressure inside the liquid is everywhere larger than the outside pressure P_0. If now we remove the bottom of the container, the liquid will
acquire the acceleration of free fall, as in part (b) of the figure. The excess
pressure in the liquid then vanishes; the pressure throughout the liquid
equalizes to the outside pressure P_0. Finally, in Fig. 20–12(c), the situation is intermediate between those of (a) and (b), and is more representative, in general, of problems that involve fluid motion. In (c), only a small
portion of the fluid in the neighborhood of the exit hole acquires the free-
fall acceleration demanded by the external force of gravity, and only in
this region will the pressure drop to P_0 as a result of the motion. The pressure distribution set up in the remainder of the fluid accounts for the difference between the free-fall acceleration and the actual acceleration of the
fluid. To determine this pressure distribution, it is necessary to employ
the laws of motion which relate the forces, the changes of momenta, and
the kinetic energies of a fluid element.

Consider first Fig. 20–13, which shows an incompressible fluid that
moves along a horizontal tube of varying cross section. Since the fluid is
incompressible, the volume of a fluid element does not change as it flows
through the tube. Consequently, when the fluid element is displaced to
the right from the position shown in (a) to that shown in (b), the volume
displacement dV at the left boundary is the same as the volume displacement dV at the right boundary of the fluid element. The fluid velocities
at the left and right boundaries are u_1 and u_2, respectively. The net effect
of the displacement is then completely equivalent to the removal of a
volume element dV, with a kinetic energy $\rho \, dV(u_1^2/2)$, at the left boundary,
and an addition of a volume element dV, with a kinetic energy $\rho \, dV(u_2^2/2)$,
at the right. The net gain of energy resulting from the displacement is then
$(\rho u_2^2/2 - \rho u_1^2/2) \, dV$. The work done by the pressure on the left boundary
is $P_1 \, dV$, and the work done on the right boundary is $-P_2 \, dV$. The net
work is then $(P_1 - P_2) \, dV$. When we equate the net work done on the

volume element and the corresponding gain in kinetic energy, we obtain $P_1 - P_2 = \rho u_2^2/2 - \rho u_1^2/2$, which can also be written as

$$P_1 + \rho \frac{u_1^2}{2} = P_2 + \rho \frac{u_2^2}{2} \qquad \text{(horizontal flow)}.$$

Since this relation applies to fluid motion along a horizontal tube, the effect of gravity does not enter. If the tube in Fig. 20–13 is inclined with the left-hand side at y_1 and the right-hand side at y_2, the effect of the displacement is not only to increase the kinetic energy by the amount given

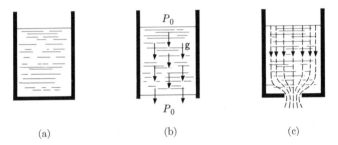

Fig. 20–12. (a) The fluid is at rest. The pressure in the fluid is larger than P_0. (b) The excess pressure in the liquid disappears as it accelerates in free fall. (c) The fluid accelerates, but not uniformly. The pressure is not as large as in (a) but is larger than in (b).

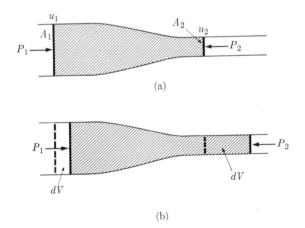

Fig. 20–13. When an incompressible fluid is displaced from the position shown in (a) to that shown in (b), it gains a kinetic energy $dV(\rho u_2^2/2 - \rho u_1^2/2)$, where dV is the displaced volume. The corresponding work done by the pressure is $(P_1 - P_2)\,dV$; that is, $P_1 + \rho u_1^2/2 = P_2 + \rho u_2^2/2$.

above, but also to increase the potential energy. When this effect is included, we obtain

$$P_1 + \rho g y_1 + \rho \frac{u_1^2}{2} = P_2 + \rho g y_2 + \rho \frac{u_2^2}{2}. \qquad (20\text{-}6)$$

This relation between the pressure distribution and the velocity distribution is called *Bernoulli's theorem.*

Although flow in an actual pipe was implied in the derivation, the result (20–6) applies equally well to any flow tube in an arbitrary flow. In other words, when a fluid element moves along its flow line, the sum of its pressure P, its potential energy $\rho g y$, and its kinetic energy $\rho u^2/2$, remains constant. We see that the pressure is high where the velocity is low, and vice versa.

It is important to remember that the Bernoulli equation (20–6) is valid only for an *incompressible, nonviscous, laminar flow.*

EXAMPLE 1. To illustrate the use of the Bernoulli equation, let us refer to Fig. 20–12(c) and calculate the speed of the water as it flows outward from the hole in the bottom of the container. Let the area of the hole be A_2 and the cross-sectional area of the entire container be A_1. If the velocity at A_2 is u_2, the water surface of the container will move downward with a velocity $u_1 = (A_2/A_1)u_2$, in accordance with the law of conservation of mass. The pressure P_1 at the surface is the same as the outside atmospheric pressure P_0, and the pressure P_2 at the outlet is also equal to P_0. If the container is filled to a height H, we have $y_2 - y_1 = H$ in the Bernoulli equation, and we obtain

$$P_1 + \rho g H + \rho \left(\frac{A_2}{A_1}\right)^2 \frac{u_2^2}{2} = P_2 + \rho \frac{u_2^2}{2},$$

and since $P_1 = P_2$, the velocity at A_2 is then

$$u_2 = \sqrt{\frac{2gH}{1 - A_2^2/A_1^2}}.$$

In many practical situations, we have $A_2/A_1 \ll 1$, and the velocity reduces to $u_2 \simeq \sqrt{2gH}$.

EXAMPLE 2. As another illustration of the use of Bernoulli's theorem, let us determine the so-called stagnation pressure on an obstacle placed in a moving fluid, as shown in Fig. 20–14. The incident fluid has a uniform velocity U. The obstacle disturbs the uniform flow as shown in the figure. At point A the flow velocity will be zero, and the pressure P_s at that point will be larger than the pressure P_0 in the

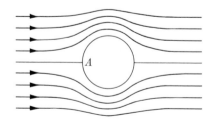

FIGURE 20–14

undisturbed fluid. Since the incident flow has the uniform velocity U, we obtain, from Bernoulli's theorem,

$$P_0 + \rho \frac{U^2}{2} = P_s.$$

In other words, the excess pressure at point A is $P_s - P_0 = \rho U^2/2$.

20–4 Extension of Bernoulli's theorem to a compressible fluid. We shall supplement the studies of the previous section with a derivation of the Bernoulli relation for a compressible fluid. We start with a given velocity field of the fluid, and assume that it is time-independent. The velocity u of a fluid element is then known as a function of its position coordinate s along the tube. Since this velocity $u(s)$ of a fluid element usually varies from point to point, the fluid has a certain acceleration at every point along the path. This acceleration can be expressed in terms of the given velocity function $u(s)$.

The change of velocity when the fluid element moves a distance ds is then $(du/ds)\,ds$, and the instantaneous change per unit time is

$$a = \frac{ds}{dt}\frac{du}{ds} = u\frac{du}{ds} = \frac{d(u^2/2)}{ds}. \qquad (20\text{–}7)$$

The forces acting on a fluid element of length ds, at s, are gravity and the force produced by the variation in pressure along s. This latter force is $-A\,dP$, where dP is the change of pressure in the length ds (A = cross-sectional area of the tube), as indicated in Fig. 20–15. The component of the force of gravity in the s-direction is $-A\rho g\,ds\cos\theta = -A\rho g\,dy$, since $ds\cos\theta = -dy$ (θ is the angle between the direction of s and the vertical). Equating the net force in the s-direction and the product of

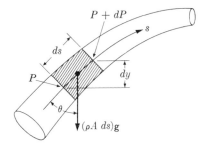

FIG. 20–15. The acceleration of the fluid element at a position s is $u(du/ds) = [d(u^2/2)]/ds$, and we obtain $\rho\{[d(u^2/2)]/ds\} = -\rho g\cos\theta - (dP/ds)$.

mass and acceleration, we obtain $-A\,dP - A\rho g\,dy = (\rho A\,ds)a$. Introducing the expression for a from Eq. (20–7), we then get

$$d\left(\frac{u^2}{2}\right) + \frac{dP}{\rho} + g\,dy = 0,$$

which integrates to

$$\frac{u^2}{2} + gy + \int \frac{dP}{\rho} = \text{const.} \qquad (20\text{–}8)$$

If the fluid is incompressible, so that the density ρ is constant, Eq (20–8) reduces to the relation given by (20–6).

If we assume that an adiabatic change of state takes place as the fluid element moves along the flow tube, we have $P/P_0 = (\rho/\rho_0)^\gamma$, where γ is the ratio between the specific heats at constant pressure and constant volume. We leave it as an exercise to show that Eq. (20–8) becomes

$$\frac{\gamma - 1}{\gamma} P + \rho gy + \rho \frac{u^2}{2} = \text{const.} \qquad (20\text{–}9)$$

(See Problem 20–13.)

20–5 Illustrations of Bernoulli's theorem. There are numerous familiar flow phenomena which we can understand on the basis of Bernoulli's theorem. As a first example, consider an airfoil in a fluid stream, as illustrated in Fig. 20–16. The flow lines about the airfoil are also shown, and we note that they are compressed above the airfoil and substantially unchanged below the foil. The flow velocity is then larger above the airfoil than below. In the undisturbed fluid, the velocity and the pressure in

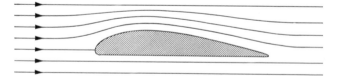

FIG. 20–16. Airfoil in a fluid flow.

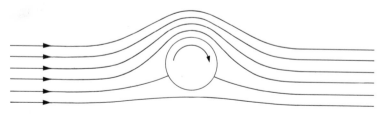

FIG. 20–17. Rotating cylinder in a fluid flow.

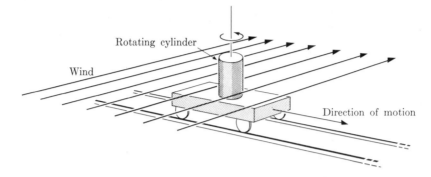

FIG. 20–18. Rotating cylinder on a car makes the car move in the direction shown when the wind blows.

the fluid are uniform, and the constant in Bernoulli's theorem is the same for all flow tubes. Therefore the higher velocity above the foil means a lower pressure above the foil than below, and as a result the flow produces a lift force on the foil.

A similar effect is produced on a rotating cylinder or sphere, as shown in Fig. 20–17. The cylinder rotates clockwise, and as a result produces a similarly directed, circulatory motion of the surrounding fluid. The fluid is set in steady motion from left to right, and the resulting flow velocity will be larger on the upper side of the cylinder than on the lower side. The corresponding Bernoulli pressure difference produces a net upward force on the cylinder.

This effect can be demonstrated as shown in Fig. 20–18. A rotating cylinder is mounted on a car on a level track. When the wind blows on the cylinder in the direction shown, i.e., perpendicular to the track, the car starts to move as a result of the Bernoulli force that is developed on the cylinder.

When a tennis ball is given a top spin, the flow velocity below the ball, relative to the ball, will be higher than that above the ball, and this combined motion produces a net Bernoulli force on the ball, directed downward. The effect is in the opposite direction, of course, when the ball is given a backward spin, in which case the Bernoulli force can be as large as the gravitational force over a certain distance, and can make the ball "float" almost along a straight line.

PROBLEMS

20–1. A wooden bar of length L and density ρ is free to rotate about a fixed horizontal axis through the lower end of the bar. The bar is submerged in a water bath, as shown in Fig. 20–19. (a) Which are the stable and which the unstable equilibrium positions of the bar? (b) The bar is displaced a small angle from its stable equilibrium, and then released. What is the frequency of the ensuing oscillation if we assume that the only effect of the liquid is the buoyant force?

20–2. A device for measuring small forces in water consists of an aluminum cylinder with a very thin pin extending from its lower surface, as shown in Fig. 20–20. The size of the air cavity in the cylinder is adjusted so that the cylinder will come to rest just below the surface of the water when the entire unit is submerged. It is prevented from sinking and held in equilibrium by letting the pin dip down into carbon tetrachloride, as shown. If the diameter of the pin is $d = 2$ mm, what vertical force on the cylinder will produce a new equilibrium position 1 cm deeper than before? The density of carbon tetrachloride is $\rho = 1.595$ gm/cm^3.

20–3. A pail of water slides down a frictionless plane of inclination angle θ. What angle does the surface of the water make with the plane?

20–4. An accelerometer consists of a liquid-filled container in which a bar with a density less than that of the

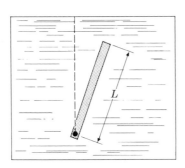

FIGURE 20–19

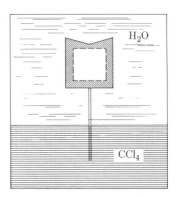

FIGURE 20–20

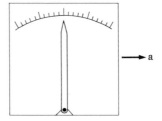

FIGURE 20–21

liquid is free to move about an axis at the bottom of the container (Fig. 20–21). The density of the liquid is ρ_1 and the density of the bar is ρ_2 ($\rho_2 < \rho_1$). The length of the bar is L. (a) In what direction does the bar move when the container is accelerated? (b) Assign numerical values to the scale above the bar, from which the acceleration can be read directly. (c) Suggest methods for increasing the sensitivity of the instrument.

20–5. A child in a car holds a balloon filled with helium. When the car is set in motion, in what direction does the balloon move if it is held at the end of a string? (Assume a closed car.)

20–6. A ping-pong ball is placed inside a water-filled tube, which can rotate about an axis as shown in Fig. 20–22. In what direction does the ball move when the tube is rotated about the axis? What would happen if instead of a ping-pong ball we have a steel ball? Explain.

20–7. Water is being discharged radially from a long cylinder at a rate of Q gm/sec per centimeter of length of the cylinder. What is the radial flow speed at a distance r from the center of the cylinder?

20–8. Indicate the flow field which is obtained when two spherically symmetrical flow sources (point sources), separated by a distance d, discharge equal amounts of water per second. The resulting flow velocity is obtained by superposition of the velocity fields of the individual sources. What is the total number of flow lines that cross an area which encloses the two sources, if the number of flow lines per unit area (perpendicular to the flow lines) is equal to the magnitude of the flow velocity?

20–9. Water is flowing through a circular tube of varying cross section, as shown in Fig. 20–23. The area at A_1 is 100 cm², and at A_2 it is $A_1/4$. The flow rate is 1 liter/sec. Plot the flow velocity as a function of the pressure distribution along the tube. The pressure at A_1 is 10 atm. Assume that the flow is laminar.

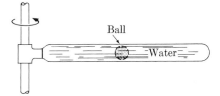

Ball

Water

FIGURE 20–22

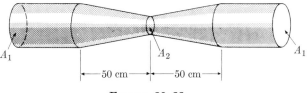

A_1 A_2 A_1

←——50 cm——→←——50 cm——→

FIGURE 20–23

20–10. Water is siphoned from a container, as illustrated in Fig. 20–24. (a) What is the velocity of the water at the outlet, which has an area much smaller than that of the container? (b) What is the pressure of the water at the highest point of the flow tube? (c) What is the value of the height h, beyond which siphoning is no longer possible?

20–11. The pitot tube shown in Fig. 20–25 is a pressure-measuring device from which flow speed can be determined. This is accomplished by a comparison of the pressure on surfaces perpendicular to and parallel with the flow, corresponding to the measuring points A_1 and A_2 in the figure. If the pressure difference is measured in terms of the height h

of a water column, what then is the flow velocity in the stream?

20–12. Prove Eq. (20–9) for the relation between the velocity and pressure in a gas, when the change of state of the gas along a flow line is adiabatic.

20–13. A container of water is mounted on a car which can move on a horizontal track (neglect friction). A hole is made in the side of the container, as shown in Fig. 20–26, and water starts to flow outward, parallel to the track. The initial height of the water is H, and the area of the hole is A (this area is much smaller than that of the container). The initial mass of the water is M_0, and the mass of the car and the container is m_0. What is the initial acceleration of the car?

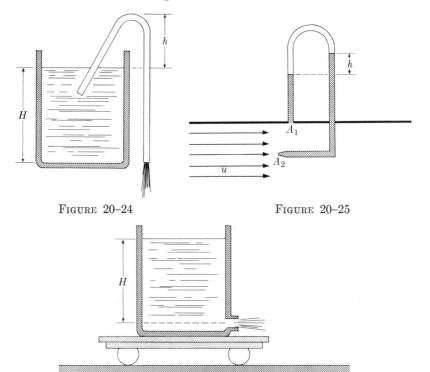

FIGURE 20–24   FIGURE 20–25

FIGURE 20–26

CHAPTER 21

TRANSVERSE AND LONGITUDINAL WAVE PULSES

Summary. We introduce the mechanics of deformable bodies and wave motion with an analysis of what happens when a deformable body is given an impulse by an external force. This problem illustrates the basic aspects of the dynamics of waves and leads to the determination of wavespeed and the relation between forces and particle velocities in a wave pulse. The analysis is applied to the study of wave pulses on springs, solid bars, and gas columns.

21-1 Introduction. Our previous work has been concerned, on the one hand, with gross motion—the motion of particles and of rigid bodies—and, on the other hand, with heat, atoms, and molecules—some of the internal properties and constituents of matter. Throughout our study of rigid bodies, we have assumed that the various parts of a body remained fixed distances apart. That is, we ignored the compressible nature of matter. We are now in a better position to drop the rigid-body approximation, and to ask how a compressible (nonrigid) body responds to externally applied forces. We shall see that this leads directly to the study of waves. Wave phenomena are important not only in this connection, but also because these phenomena are particularly descriptive of many events in nature. Light, sound, radio, and water-surface phenomena are familiar examples. Less familiar, perhaps, is the fact that atoms, electrons, and nuclear and subnuclear particles have wavelike, as well as particlelike, properties.

Generally speaking, wave motion implies the transmission of a *state*. If we stand dominoes on end in a long line and then knock over the first one, we start a train of events which leads eventually to all the dominoes being knocked down. There was no net mass transport along the line of dominoes, rather, it was their *state* of falling that traveled, and in this very simple case, the speed at which the state of falling traveled is called the *wavespeed*.

To illustrate our problem and to establish some of the ideas involved, let us consider a very special deformable body that consists of a tubular car which contains a number of balls of equal mass. The balls are free to move and are spaced equal distances apart, as illustrated in Fig. 21–1. Consider now a collision in which a body B approaches and collides with the first ball in car A. If the mass of body B is equal to the mass of the

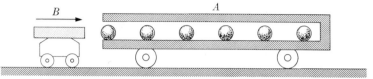

FIG. 21–1. An example of a collision in which it is evident that for the momentum to be conserved at all times, both the momentum of the car and the momentum associated with internal motion must be taken into account.

ball, B will come to rest and the first ball will move forward with a momentum equal to the initial momentum of B. This first ball will deliver its momentum to the second, the second will deliver its momentum to the third, etc., so that eventually the last ball in the row is hit. In a sense, the original momentum of B was carried down the length of A in a wave. If there were no friction between the balls and the floor of the car (the balls would then slide, not roll), A itself would not start to move until the last ball hit the end wall of the car. Of course, if we did not look inside the car, we would note an apparent violation of the law of conservation of momentum, for while the wave was traveling down A, both B and A would apparently be at rest. The law of conservation of momentum thus implies that not only the gross motion of a body but also the wave motion in the body must be considered.

Alternatively, imagine a long iron pipe at rest on a frictionless surface with a ball at rest against its far end. When one end of the pipe is given a sudden blow with a hammer, the initial motion of the ball is delayed by a definite measureable amount (about 1/100 sec for a 150-ft length of pipe). To be sure, the impulse delivered by the hammer imparted momentum to the pipe. But the pipe does not move like a rigid body. Rather, the

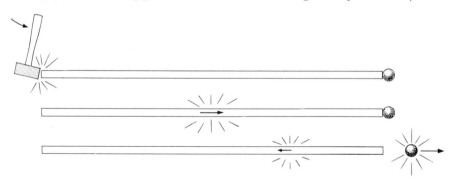

FIG. 21–2. When the long iron pipe is hit with a hammer, the momentum travels down the pipe, and the ball at the far end moves only after a time lag. Usually a wave is reflected from the far end of the pipe.

momentum is carried along the length of the pipe in a compressional wave, the iron atoms transferring their momenta from one to another until, finally, the atoms at the end transfer momentum to the ball. There usually is a wave reflected back from the end of the pipe, and this may travel back and forth along the length of the pipe, until after all the wave phenomena in the pipe have ceased, the momentum of the pipe (considered now to be a rigid body) plus the momentum of the ball is equal to the impulse supplied by the hammer. Clearly, phenomena much like this must have occurred in the pucks and cars of the collision experiments we discussed earlier, but there the travel time of the wave disturbances was very short, and by the time we made the necessary velocity measurements the bodies once again could be regarded as rigid.

Our example of the balls in the car (Fig. 21–1), incidentally, is not the best model for the transmission of a wave in matter. In our model, a somewhat weaker disturbance would make the balls move more slowly and so produce a smaller wavespeed. We shall see that in matter, over a wide range, all weak disturbances travel at the same wavespeed. We shall start our quantitative discussion of wave motion by conducting some experiments with a stretched coil-spring that permits large amplitudes and relatively slow-moving waves to be easily produced and observed.

A coil-spring is stretched out on the floor or some other relatively smooth surface. If one end of the spring is held in the hand and the hand is moved, waves will be seen to move along the spring. If the spring is given a sudden side push, a transverse wave is generated, while if the spring is suddenly stretched or compressed a little, a compressional (longitudinal) wave is generated. The names *transverse* and *longitudinal* indicate the direction of motion of the particles of which the spring is comprised. Because the transverse wave is somewhat easier to see than the longitudinal wave, we shall investigate this first.

21–2 Transverse wave pulses on a spring. A particularly simple transverse wave results when we suddenly displace the end of the spring through the distance Δy in a time Δt at a constant velocity $u = \Delta y/\Delta t$. If we displaced the end of a (really) rigid body in this manner, the whole body would move. In the spring, however, only a portion of the body participates in the motion, and this portion increases continuously during the time Δt. We say that the disturbance *propagates* along the string. The wavefront P (Fig. 20–3), as well as other points on the wave, evidently travels along the spring with a constant speed c_t, which we call the *wavespeed* or the *speed of propagation*. The subscript t indicates that we are dealing with a transverse wave. Furthermore, since the displacement is seen to increase linearly from the front P to the end Q of the pulse, it must be that all mass elements of the spring in the pulse region from

P to Q have the same transverse velocity u. From Fig. 21–3, which should be regarded as an experimental result, note carefully that *all* mass elements of the spring are at rest except those from P to Q, and that no element of mass has a velocity in the x-direction. It is the disturbance, or the state of motion, only that moves to the right, not the mass. In Fig. 21–4 is shown the transverse velocity of the mass elements of the spring which corresponds to the transverse displacement shown in Fig. 21–3.

Since we have examined some of the properties of transverse wave pulses on a spring, we now are led naturally to ask what it is that determines the wavespeed. Let us, therefore, refer to some of our first principles, and investigate the forces and mass motion.

What is the momentum in the wave pulse shown in Figs. 21–3 and 21–4? At $t = t_2$ and thereafter, there is a length of spring $\Delta x = c_t\,\Delta t$, all of which has a velocity u in the y-direction. If we denote the mass per unit length of the spring by ϵ, a length Δx has a mass $\epsilon\,\Delta x$. The momentum in the wave pulse is therefore $\epsilon\,\Delta x u$, or, with $\Delta x = c_t\,\Delta t$,

$$\Delta p_y = \epsilon c_t u\,\Delta t. \tag{21–1}$$

During the time that this momentum was being applied to the stretched spring, the only external force that had a y-component acting on the

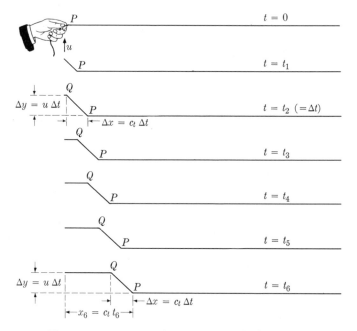

FIG. 21–3. Transverse wave motion on a stretched spring. At $t = 0$, the end of the spring is moved upward with a constant velocity u.

spring was the force of the person's hand. The impulse $F \, \Delta t$ of this force must therefore have been equal to Δp_y, that is,

$$F_y = \frac{\Delta p_y}{\Delta t} = \epsilon c_t u. \tag{21–2}$$

It is interesting to note that the driving force is proportional to the velocity u and not to du/dt as in the case of a single particle. The reason, of course, is that in a deformable body the mass participating in the motion during the time Δt of the external impulse does not remain constant, but increases at a rate $dm/dt = \epsilon c_t$. Then, from $dp/dt = m \, du/dt + u \, dm/dt$ we obtain, as before, $dp/dt = \epsilon c_t u$, since in this case of constant particle velocity we have $du/dt = 0$.

The disturbance continues to move along the spring, even after the person's hand has stopped moving the end of the spring. Let us examine the forces at an imaginary "break" somewhere *in* the moving portion of the spring. The portion to the right of the break undergoes a rate of momentum change which is $\epsilon c_t u$, as before. The force that *produces* the momentum change, however, is no longer the person's hand, but the tension in the spring. If the spring were horizontal, the portion to the left of the break would exert no transverse force on the portion to the right.

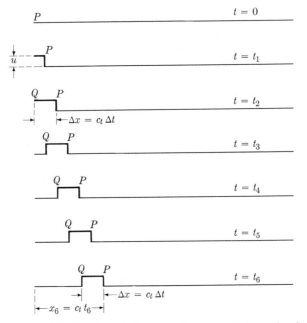

Fig. 21–4. Velocity distribution of the mass elements of the spring in Fig. 21–3.

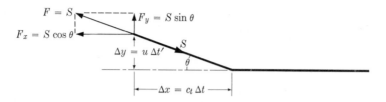

FIG. 21-5. The tension in the spring is maintained by the force F. Wave motion is produced on the spring if the direction of F is changed. When θ is small, F_y is approximately $S(u/c_t)$, and F_x is approximately S.

But because the spring is inclined, there is a force $F_y = S \sin \theta$ that produces the momentum change. Clearly, the angle θ is given by $\tan \theta = u/c_t$. Similarly, during the initial displacement of the end of the spring the driving force can be expressed both as $F_y = \epsilon c_t u$ and as $F_y = S \sin \theta$.

To carry our considerations still further, we shall now assume that the angle θ is small or, equivalently, that the transverse (particle) velocity u is small compared with the wavespeed c_t. Then, for $u \ll c_t$, we have

$$\sin \theta \approx \frac{u}{c_t} \tag{21-3}$$

and consequently

$$F_y = S \sin \theta = S \frac{u}{c_t}. \tag{21-4}$$

By combining this result with $F_y = \epsilon c_t u$, we obtain

$$S \frac{u}{c_t} = \epsilon u c_t,$$

from which the wavespeed c_t is found:

$$c_t = \sqrt{\frac{S}{\epsilon}}. \tag{21-5}$$

Under the assumption made, that is, that $\theta \ll 1$ or $u \ll c_t$, the wavespeed is then *independent of the amplitude of the disturbance* and depends only on the characteristic properties of the spring, i.e., the tension and the mass per unit length. It should be borne in mind, however, that the propagation of large transverse disturbances, i.e., disturbances in which u is comparable to c_t, is more complicated, and that in this case the wavespeed does indeed depend upon u. [The angle θ in Fig. 21-3 was taken to be 45° to simplify the drawing, but with such a large angle, we find that Eq. (21-2) is only a rough approximation.]

Note that $\sqrt{S/\epsilon}$ is the only combination of S and ϵ that has the dimensions of velocity. The tension S has the dimensions of force, $[M][L][T]^{-2}$, and the mass per unit length, ϵ, has the dimensions $[M][L]^{-1}$. Therefore $\sqrt{S/\epsilon}$ has the dimensions of velocity, $[L][T]^{-1}$.

Energy carried by a transverse wave pulse. In our study of wave motion, we have seen that momentum is carried along a moving spring, and it is important that we inquire also about the energy involved in such motion. Let us first find the energy put into the wave by the force applied when the spring is moved, and then ask what becomes of it.

The y-component of this force on the end of the spring is $F_y = Su/c_t$, and since it is applied through a distance $\Delta y = u \, \Delta t$, the work done is

$$W = F_y \, \Delta y = S \frac{u^2}{c_t} \Delta t = \epsilon c_t u^2 \, \Delta t. \qquad (21\text{–}6)$$

The kinetic energy in the wave pulse is half the product of the mass of the moving portion of the spring, $\epsilon c_t \, \Delta t$, and the squared velocity, u^2. Therefore we have

$$E = \frac{\epsilon c_t u^2 \, \Delta t}{2},$$

which accounts for just half the work done. What has become of the other half? Quite apart from the kinetic energy in the wave, there exists in the distorted spring a form of potential energy that has resulted from the work W' required to distort it. We can calculate this deformation work W' if we can imagine the spring fastened to the x-axis at Δx, and the other end moved up to $y = \Delta y$ from $y = 0$. The force F_y then depends on y,

$$F_y = S \frac{y}{\Delta x},$$

and, for the work, we have

$$W' = \int_0^{\Delta y} \frac{S}{\Delta x} y \, dy = \frac{S \, \Delta y^2}{2 \, \Delta x}.$$

Since $\Delta y = u \, \Delta t$ and $\Delta x = c_t \, \Delta t$, we find that

$$W' = \frac{\epsilon c_t u^2 \, \Delta t}{2}.$$

This amount of energy is stored in the distorted spring. Thus we have accounted for the total energy $\epsilon c_t u^2 \, \Delta t$ supplied by the external force and carried by the wave pulse along the spring.

EXAMPLE. A long spring of mass 20 gm/cm is stretched to a tension of 200 newtons. One end of the spring is given a transverse impulse by means of a constant force of 10 newtons acting for 0.2 sec. What is the wavespeed, and how much energy is carried by the wave pulse produced on the spring?

We have $S = 200$ n and $\epsilon = 2$ kgm/m, and consequently $c_t = \sqrt{S/\epsilon} = 10$ m/sec. The transverse particle velocity of the spring is obtained from the relation $F_y = \epsilon c_t u$, so that $u = F_y/\epsilon c_t = 10/2 \cdot 10 = 0.5$ m/sec. The total energy in the wave pulse is $W = \epsilon c_t u^2 \, \Delta t = 2 \cdot 10 \cdot 0.5^2 \cdot 0.2 = 1.0$ joule.

21-3 Longitudinal wave pulses on a stretched spring. If, rather than moving the end of a coil-spring to one side, we push the end forward in the direction of the spring, a longitudinal (compressional) wave is generated. Such a longitudinal wave is shown in Fig. 21–6. At time $t = 0$, a force F is applied to the end of the spring at $x = 0$ during a time Δt, so that the spring is given an impulse $F \, \Delta t$. If the spring were rigid the entire body would move as a result of the impulse, and the velocity of the spring after the impulse would be inversely proportional to the total mass of the spring. Thus if the spring were infinitely long and rigid the velocity produced by a finite impulse would be zero. However, because of the compressibility of the spring, only part of the spring will be set in motion during the time Δt of the impulse, and this part of the spring then will be given a velocity different from zero regardless of the total length of the spring. As in the case of a transverse wave, the mass participating in the motion *during* the impulse grows in proportion to the time.

The force on the spring shown in Fig. 21–6 is applied in such a way that the end of the spring moves forward with a velocity u for a time Δt. Thus the displacement of the end of the spring at $x = 0$ during Δt is $z = u \, \Delta t$, as shown. During the same time Δt, the front of the disturbance has moved forward a distance $c_l \, \Delta t$, where c_l is the wavespeed. Therefore the mass of spring participating in the motion after the impulse is $\epsilon_1(c_l - u) \, \Delta t = \epsilon c_l \, \Delta t$, where ϵ_1 is the mass per unit length of the compressed portion of the spring and ϵ is the initial mass per unit length. In the figure the length $c_l \, \Delta t$ covers seven turns of the spring. It can be seen that each of the coil turns in the wave pulse is moving with a velocity u. The momentum in the wave pulse is then

$$\Delta p_x = \epsilon c_l u \, \Delta t. \qquad (21\text{–}7)$$

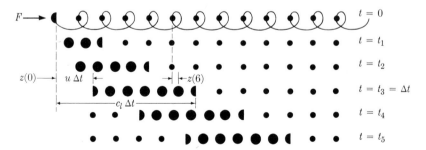

Fig. 21–6. A longitudinal (compressional) wave on a coil-spring. The small dots indicate the positions of the coil turns, and the large dots indicate the turns that are in motion. The half-round dots indicate turns that are in the process of starting, ❲, or stopping, ❳.

This momentum was imparted to the spring in a time Δt by the impulse $F \Delta t$. Thus the force that must have been exerted is $\Delta p_x / \Delta t$ or

$$F = \epsilon c_l u. \tag{21-8}$$

Although the expressions (21-7) and (21-8) are similar to expressions (21-1) and (21-2), it should be carefully noted that in a longitudinal wave pulse the momentum and force are directed along the x-axis, instead of along the y-axis as in a transverse wave pulse. In a longitudinal wave, just as in a transverse wave, the wave pulse continues to travel along the length of the spring after termination of the impulse. The force $\epsilon c u$ is now provided by the spring force itself.

The amount z by which the length of a spring changes from its equilibrium length is proportional to the force that compresses the spring. In previous discussions of the spring force (Chapter 4) this relation was expressed as $F = -Kx$, where K is the spring constant. The spring constant depends not only on the material of the spring, but also on the total length of the spring. In the present discussion the total length of the spring is of little consequence, and we need to express the elastic properties of the spring in terms of a quantity which depends only on the material and not on the length of the spring. For a given spring material we note that the change of length of a spring is proportional to both the applied force and to the length of the spring. The constant of proportionality we shall call the *linear compressibility* k of the spring. Thus if the total length of a spring is l and the change of length is Δl (positive when l is increased) we have, by definition of k,

$$\Delta l = -kFl \qquad \text{or} \qquad \frac{\Delta l}{l} = -kF. \tag{21-9}$$

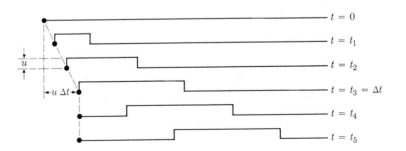

Fig. 21-7. Velocity of the coil turns (particle velocity) in a compressional wave on a coil-spring.

The minus sign arises because it will be convenient to count the force F as positive when it compresses the spring. Clearly, we can express the linear compressibility k in terms of the spring constant K by the relation

$$k = \frac{1}{Kl}. \tag{21-10}$$

(See the example at the end of this section.)

From an examination of Fig. 21–6 we see that a length $c_l \, \Delta t$ of the spring is foreshortened by an amount $u \, \Delta t$, so that we have $-\Delta l/l = u/c_l$. To produce this compression, the spring force F, according to Eq. (21–9), must be $F = -\Delta l/kl = u/kc_l$. Then, since the force also must fulfill the condition $F = \epsilon c_l u$, according to Eq. (21–8), we obtain

$$\frac{u}{kc_l} = \epsilon c_l u.$$

The wavespeed c_l can be determined from this relation:

$$c_l = \sqrt{\frac{1}{k\epsilon}}, \tag{21-11}$$

and we see that c_l is independent of the particle velocity u. In the case of a transverse wave, we made the approximation that the angle θ, or the (transverse) particle velocity u, was small compared with the wavespeed c_t. Here, a similar approximation is involved, for we have assumed that the foreshortening Δl of a length of spring is proportional to the length l of the spring and the force F. This assumption is valid only when Δl is small compared with l, for we have assumed that l in $F = \Delta l/kl$, as well as the linear compressibility, is constant. Clearly, this assumption is inappropriate if l changes significantly. The restriction $\Delta l \ll l$ is equivalent to $u \ll c_l$, and we shall see that this restriction is a usual one in the study of wave motion. The important principle of superposition, which we shall discuss later, holds only for waves in which the particle velocity u is much less than the wave velocity c.

Energy carried by a longitudinal wave pulse. As in the transverse wave case, there is energy as well as momentum in the wave pulse. When an external force is applied on the spring, the work done by this force is

$$W = Fu \, \Delta t = \frac{1}{k} \frac{u^2}{c_l} \Delta t = \epsilon c_l u^2 \, \Delta t, \tag{21-12}$$

The kinetic energy in the wave pulse is $(\epsilon c_l \, \Delta t)u^2/2$. The other half of the work done by the external force appears as the potential energy arising from the (static) deformation of the spring. *During the pulse*, the power

$W/\Delta t$ that passes a point on the spring per unit time then can be expressed as

$$R = \epsilon c u^2, \qquad (21\text{--}13)$$

for both longitudinal and transverse waves.

EXAMPLE. A spring with an unstretched length of 2 m and a mass of 4 kgm is lying on a horizontal table. One end of the spring is held fixed, and when a steady force of 20 n is applied to the other end, the spring is stretched a distance of 10 cm. (a) Determine the time required for a compressional pulse to travel from one end of the spring to the other.

The linear compressibility of the spring is $k = \Delta l/lF = 0.1/2 \cdot 20 = \frac{1}{400}\,\text{n}^{-1}$. The mass per unit length is $\epsilon = 4/2 = 2$ kgm/m. The wavespeed is therefore

$$c_l = \sqrt{\frac{1}{k\epsilon}} = \sqrt{\frac{400}{2}} = 10\sqrt{2}\ \text{m/sec},$$

and the time required for a compressional pulse to travel from one end of the spring to the other is

$$t = \frac{l}{c_l} = \frac{2}{10\sqrt{2}} = 0.141\ \text{sec}.$$

(b) Suppose now that the spring is stretched to an arbitrary length l. Determine, as a function of l, the time required for a pulse to travel from one end of the spring to the other.

When the spring is stretched, both the linear compressibility and the mass per unit length will change. The spring constant K, however, remains the same (see Problem 21–4). The linear compressibility is $k = 1/Kl$ and the mass per unit length, ϵ, is $\epsilon = m/l$, where m is the mass of the spring. The wavespeed is therefore

$$c_l = \sqrt{\frac{1}{k\epsilon}} = l\sqrt{\frac{K}{m}},$$

and the time for a compressional wave to travel the length of the spring is

$$t = \frac{l}{c_l} = \sqrt{\frac{m}{K}},$$

which is independent of the length to which the spring is stretched.

(c) Determine the speed of a transverse wave on the spring when it is stretched to a length of 4 m. How does the wavespeed depend on the length of the spring? Can the wavespeed for the transverse wave ever be equal to that for the longitudinal wave?

In order to stretch the spring to a length of 4 m, a force $F = K\,\Delta l = 200 \cdot 2 = 400$ n is required. The tension S is therefore 400 n. The mass per unit length is now $\epsilon = 4/4 = 1$ kgm/m, and the wavespeed is

$$c_t = \sqrt{\frac{S}{\epsilon}} = 20\ \text{m/sec}.$$

When the spring is stretched to an arbitrary length l, the tension is $S = K(l - l_0)$, where l_0 is the unstretched (relaxed) length. The mass per unit length is $\epsilon = m/l$, as before, thus for the transverse wavespeed we have

$$c_t = \sqrt{\frac{K(l - l_0)}{m/l}} = c_l\sqrt{1 - \frac{l_0}{l}}.$$

In other words, the transverse wavespeed on a spring is always *less* than the longitudinal or compressional wavespeed, but the speeds tend to the same value as the spring is stretched so that l is much larger than l_0. (For elastic waves in solids, in general, the longitudinal wavespeed is larger than the transverse wavespeed.)

21–4 Longitudinal wave pulses in a solid bar. Longitudinal waves in a long, thin solid bar are inherently no different from the longitudinal waves on a coil-spring. We ordinarily do not speak of the compressibility of a solid. This property is referred to as the elastic modulus, or Young's modulus, Y. If a force F (compression) is applied to a bar of area A and length l, by definition of Y we have (see Chapter 18) $F/A = -Y(\Delta l/l)$. The linear compressibility of the bar is then

$$k = -\frac{\Delta l}{lF} = \frac{A}{Y}$$

and the mass per unit length is $\epsilon = A\rho$, where ρ is the density of the solid. Then from Eq. (21–11), for the longitudinal wavespeed in the bar, we obtain

$$c_l = \sqrt{\frac{Y}{\rho}}. \tag{21–14}$$

It should be mentioned that this expression for the longitudinal wavespeed in a solid applies only if no stresses are developed transverse to the bar as a result of the wave. Such stresses can occur as a result of the transverse (Poisson) contraction and expansions that occur in a solid, as mentioned in Chapter 18. The definition of Y from the relation $\Delta l/l = -F/AY$ assumes that there are no transverse stresses in the bar.

For most metals Y is about 10^{12} dynes/cm^2, and a typical value for the density ρ is 8 gm/cm^3 (see Table 18–2). A typical longitudinal wavespeed is therefore $c_l \approx \sqrt{10^{12}/8} \approx 3 \cdot 10^5$ cm/sec (Table 20–1).

What is the molecular picture of a compressional wave? In a previous chapter, we pointed out that the atoms in a solid continuously vibrate. These frequencies of vibration are of the order of 10^{13} per second, so that the characteristic period of oscillation is of the order of 10^{-13} sec. The time it takes to transfer momentum from one atomic layer to the next, then, is of the order of 10^{-13} sec. Since the distance between adjacent layers of atoms is about 10^{-8} cm, it is clear that a disturbance at one end of a metal bar will be transmitted from atomic layer to atomic layer with a speed of the order of $10^{-8} \cdot 10^{13} = 10^5$ cm/sec.

Table 21–1. Velocity of sound in various solids

Material	Velocity, m/sec
Aluminum	5104
Iron	5100
Glass	5000
Wood (oak)	3850
Copper	3560
Lead	1227
Cork	500
Rubber	54

EXAMPLE. A hammer head of mass m and velocity v strikes the end of a *long* steel rod of area 10 cm². What must be the mass of the hammer head so that it will come to rest after it strikes the rod? Assume that the force exerted by the hammer head on the rod rises instantaneously from zero to a constant value F_0, then, after a time $\Delta t \approx 10^{-4}$ sec, drops instantaneously to zero again.

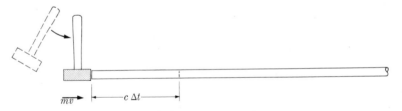

FIGURE 21–8

It is assumed that in this collision, all the initial kinetic energy of the hammer is transmitted to the compressional wave on the rod. Conservation of momentum requires that the initial momentum of the hammer now be transmitted to the wave on the rod. The momentum of the hammer was mv, and since the force on the end of the rod was constant for a time Δt, the particle velocity u is the same over the entire length $c\,\Delta t$ of the wave pulse. Then the momentum in the wave is $\rho A c u\,\Delta t$, and we have, from the law of conservation of momentum,

$$mv = \rho A c u\,\Delta t.$$

The energy in the wave pulse is $\rho Ac\,\Delta t u^2$ and we have, from the law of conservation of energy,

$$\tfrac{1}{2}mv^2 \;=\; \rho Ac\,\Delta t u^2.$$

Combining these two relations, we find that

$$u \;=\; \frac{v}{2}\,;$$

that is, the particle velocity is just half the initial velocity of the hammer. When this value for the particle velocity is inserted in the momentum equation, we obtain

$$mv \;=\; \rho Ac\,\Delta t\,\frac{v}{2} \qquad \text{or} \qquad m \;=\; \frac{\rho Ac\,\Delta t}{2}.$$

The mass of the hammer must be equal to half the mass involved in the wave pulse.

For steel the density is $7.8\ \text{gm/cm}^3$ and Young's modulus is $2\cdot 10^{12}\ \text{dynes/cm}^2$. The wavespeed is therefore

$$c \;=\; \sqrt{\frac{Y}{\rho}} \;=\; \sqrt{\frac{2\cdot 10^{12}}{7.8}} \;\approx\; 5\cdot 10^{5}\ \text{cm/sec}.$$

Since we have taken Δt to be 10^{-4} sec, the length of rod which is moving at any instant is $c\cdot\Delta t = 50$ cm. This length of rod has a mass of $\rho Ac\,\Delta t = 7.8\cdot 10\cdot 50 = 3900\ \text{gm} = 3.9$ kgm. The mass of the hammer must therefore be 1.95 kgm (weight $\simeq 4.3$ lb).

A hammer of this weight might be given a velocity of 300 cm/sec. The particle velocity of the steel in the wave pulse would therefore be 150 cm/sec, and during the time Δt the end of the rod would move a distance $u\,\Delta t = 150\cdot 10^{-4} = 0.015$ cm to the right.

The entire momentum $mv = 1950\cdot 300 = 585{,}000\ \text{gm·cm/sec}$ of the hammer was transferred to the rod in a time $\Delta t = 10^{-4}$ sec, so the force F_0 must have been $F_0 = mv/\Delta t = 5.85\cdot 10^{9}$ dynes or about 12,000 lb.

21–5 Wave pulses in a gas column. Waves generated by a piston at the end of a long column of gas are analogous to the longitudinal or compressional waves generated at the end of a long spring. The gas, like the coil-spring, is compressible and has a certain mass per unit length. Of course, when gas is confined, it exerts a pressure over the entire area of the walls of its enclosure, and so a static force $F_0 = PA$, where P is the gas pressure and A is the area of the column, is necessary to keep the gas in the column. This force does not produce a wave. But when the force is changed so that the piston moves forward, for example, a wave is produced (Fig. 21–9).

The wavespeed. In the study of waves on a spring and on a solid bar we

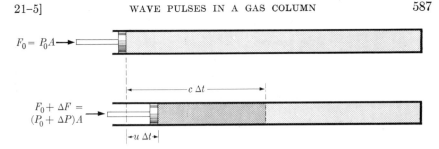

FIG. 21-9. Wave pulse produced by a moving piston in a long gas column
in a tube.

have seen that the wavespeed of a compressional or longitudinal wave
can be expressed as

$$c = \sqrt{\frac{1}{k\epsilon}}, \tag{21-15}$$

where k is the linear compressibility defined by the relation $\Delta l/l = -kF$,
where F is the compressional force that is required to produce the fractional change of length $(-\Delta l/l)$ of the column under consideration, and
ϵ is the mass per unit length. Clearly, we can apply this relation directly
for the calculation of the wavespeed in a gas column once we have determined the linear compressibility k and the mass per unit length of the
column. The latter obviously is $\epsilon = A\rho_0$, where A is the cross-sectional
area of the gas column and ρ_0 is the density of the gas (Fig. 21-9). To
determine the linear compressibility, we note that for a gas confined in a
column of uniform cross section, the fractional decrease in length, $-\Delta l/l$,
can be expressed as the fractional decrease in volume, $-\Delta V/V$, or as
the fractional increase in density, $\Delta\rho/\rho_0$. The force on the column is
$F = A\,\Delta P$ where ΔP is the pressure increment. The linear compressibility then can be expressed as

$$k = -\frac{1}{A}\frac{\Delta V}{V}\frac{1}{\Delta P} = \frac{1}{A\rho_0}\frac{\Delta\rho}{\Delta P} = \frac{\kappa}{A}, \tag{21-16}$$

where κ is the usual volume compressibility of the gas (see Chapter 17).
Then from Eq. (21-15) and with $\epsilon = A\rho_0$, we obtain the following expression for the wavespeed in a gas column:

$$c = \sqrt{\frac{1}{\kappa\rho_0}} = \sqrt{\frac{\Delta P}{\Delta\rho}}. \tag{21-17}$$

Thus the wave has the interesting property that the ratio between the
pressure change and the density change is simply the squared speed
of sound,

$$\frac{\Delta P}{\Delta\rho} = c^2. \tag{21-18}$$

For weak disturbances, i.e., when $\Delta\rho/\rho_0$ and $\Delta P/P_0$ are much less than unity, we can approximate $\Delta P/\Delta\rho$ by the derivative $dP/d\rho$. As we have seen in Chapter 17, the relation between the pressure and the density, and consequently the volume compressibility $-(1/V)\,dV/dP$, depend on the conditions under which the compression takes place. For example, the isothermal and adiabatic compressibilities are

$$\kappa_{is} = \frac{1}{P_0} \quad \text{and} \quad \kappa_{ad} = \frac{1}{\gamma P_0} \qquad (21\text{--}19)$$

respectively. Then, by introducing these expressions into Eq. (21–17), we obtain the following expressions for the wavespeed under isothermal and adiabatic conditions:

$$c_{is} = \sqrt{\frac{P_0}{\rho_0}} = \sqrt{\frac{RT_0}{M}}, \qquad c_{ad} = \sqrt{\frac{\gamma P_0}{\rho_0}} = \sqrt{\frac{\gamma RT_0}{M}} = \sqrt{\gamma}\,c_{is}, \qquad (21\text{--}20)$$

in which $\gamma = c_p/c_v$ is the ratio between the specific heats at constant pressure and constant volume. The expressions containing the temperature in (21–20) were obtained, of course, by using the gas law $PV = RT$ (one mole), in terms of which the density $\rho = M/V$ can be expressed as $\rho = PM/RT$.

In an overwhelming majority of cases experiments show that the measured wavespeed is in good agreement with the adiabatic value. In air at 20°C (293°K), for example, the measured speed is 344 m/sec $=$ 1129 ft/sec. The calculated value based on the isothermal assumption is $c_{is} = 292$ m/sec, whereas the adiabatic value is $c_{ad} = 344$ m/sec, using $\gamma = 7/5$, appropriate to a diatomic gas.

We shall see in the next chapter that weak waves of arbitrary shape, such as ordinary sound waves, can be built up by linear superposition of weak wave pulses of the type discussed here, and that the adiabatic wavespeed $c = \sqrt{\gamma P_0/\rho_0}$ applies also to these waves. This speed is usually called the speed of sound and all (weak) wave disturbances in elastic media are usually called *sound waves*.

It is important to note that, according to our analysis, the speed of sound in a given gas depends only on the temperature of the gas. Thus if we change the pressure in a gas container by continuous pumping, the speed of sound in the gas should remain constant so long as the temperature of the gas is constant. This result has been experimentally confirmed over a wide range of pressures. However, at very low pressures, at which the gas ceases to behave like a continuum, and at very high pressures where the ideal gas assumption fails because of intermolecular attractions, the speed of sound *does* depend on the static pressure as well as on the temperature.

Table 21-2. Velocity of sound in various gases and liquids

	Temperature, °C	Velocity, m/sec
Gases		
H_2	0	1269.5
Air, 1 atm	0	331.7
Air, 50 atm	0	334.7
Cl_2	0	205.3
Liquids		
Water	20	1482
Benzene	17	1166
Carbon tetrachloride	20	938

The square of the speed of sound is inversely proportional to the molecular weight. For example, the speed of sound in hydrogen is about four times as large as the speed of sound in air (see Table 21–2). The dependence of the speed of sound on temperature and molecular weight as given by Eq. (21–20) is consistent with the molecular interpretation of the propagation of sound waves. For the gas column shown in Fig. 21–9, the molecules which collide with the moving piston will acquire a small additional velocity in the x-direction. This additional velocity is of the order of u, the piston velocity, and is much less than the thermal molecular speed. The "information" about the moving piston at the end of the column and the additional momentum acquired by the molecules then are expected to be passed along from one molecular layer to another with a velocity of the same order as the thermal molecular velocity.

Indeed, like the speed of sound, the thermal molecular speed, as obtained from the kinetic theory of gases, is proportional to $\sqrt{T}$ and inversely proportional to $\sqrt{M}$. The root-mean-square value of the molecular speed is $v = \sqrt{3RT/M}$, as compared with the value $c = \sqrt{\gamma RT/M}$ for the speed of sound.

Properties of a wave pulse. The dynamics of a wave pulse in a gas can be developed by analogy with the waves on a coil-spring and a solid bar. With reference to Fig. 21–9, we note that when the gas is in equilibrium the force on the movable piston is $F_0 = P_0 A$, where P_0 is the static pressure in the gas. If the piston is moved forward with a velocity u during the time Δt, a mass $\rho_0 A c \, \Delta t$ of the gas is set in motion with the velocity u. We see from Fig. 21–9 that a gas column initially of length $c \, \Delta t$ is compressed to length $(c - u) \, \Delta t$. Therefore if the increase of the gas density in the region of the wave pulse is $\Delta \rho$, conservation of mass requires that

$(c - u)(\rho_0 + \Delta\rho) = c\rho_0$, from which is obtained $\Delta\rho = \rho_0 u/(c - u)$. If the velocity u is much less than the wavespeed c, this expression reduces to

$$\Delta\rho = \delta = \frac{u}{c}\rho_0, \qquad (21\text{--}21)$$

where, for convenience in further discussion, we have introduced the notation δ for $\Delta\rho$.

As in the case of the coil-spring or the bar, the particle velocity u clearly is not the total velocity of the individual molecules, since the major part of the molecular velocity arises from thermal random motion. Rather, the particle velocity u is the additional average velocity which the molecules acquire as a result of the external impulse or force on the medium.

We have now obtained the increase in the density in the region of the wave pulse, and the corresponding increase in pressure follows directly from Eq. (21–18), which states that the ratio $\Delta P/\Delta\rho$ between the pressure change and the density change is simply c^2. Just as we introduced a special symbol for the density increase it will be convenient to denote the pressure increase ΔP by p, and we shall call p the sound pressure. Then, from Eqs. (21–18) and (21–21), we get

$$p = c^2\delta = \rho_0 cu. \qquad (21\text{--}22)$$

As we have seen in the foregoing, the compression of the gas is adiabatic, and consequently the changes of the density and the pressure in the gas will be accompanied by a change of temperature. We leave it as an exercise (Problem 21–10) to show that the temperature increase in the wave pulse is

$$\Delta T = \theta = (\gamma - 1)\frac{u}{c}T_0. \qquad (21\text{--}23)$$

The relation (21–22) between the sound pressure and the particle velocity also could have been obtained from the impulse-momentum relation. Only the excess force pA on the piston contributes to the momentum transfer to the gas column, and as this force acts during the time Δt, a mass $\rho_0 Ac\,\Delta t$ of the gas is given a velocity u. Then, from the impulse-momentum relation, we obtain $pA\,\Delta t = \rho_0 Ac\,\Delta tu$, or $p = \rho_0 cu$, as before.

In calculating the work done on the gas column by the piston as it is moved forward the distance $u\,\Delta t$, we must consider the total force $(P_0 + p)A$ on the piston. The work per unit area is

$$(P_0 + p)u\,\Delta t = P_0 u\,\Delta t + pu\,\Delta t = P_0 u\,\Delta t + \rho_0 cu^2\,\Delta t,$$

which is the energy transferred to the wave pulse. As we shall see in the following, the average displacement of the piston in the generation of a wave usually is zero, and under these conditions the first term, $P_0 u\,\Delta t$, averages to zero. Then only the remaining second term represents the wave energy. We shall continue this discussion in the next chapter.

PROBLEMS

21–1. A coil-spring fixed at one end has a relaxed length $L = 3$ m, a spring constant $K = 4.5$ n/m, and a total mass $M = 1$ kgm. The spring is stretched to a length of 6 m. A transverse wave pulse is generated on the spring by moving the end transversely with a constant velocity $u = 2$ m/sec during the time $t = 0$ to $t = 0.2$ sec. (a) What is the wavespeed on the spring? (b) Sketch the shape of the spring at the times $t = 0.1$, 0.2, and 0.3 sec. (c) What time is required for the pulse to travel the entire length of the spring? (d) If the spring is stretched to a length of 12 m, what then is the time required for the pulse to reach the end?

21–2. Refer to the previous problem. (a) What impulse is delivered to the spring? (b) Sketch the transverse particle velocity of the spring at $t = 0.1$, 0.2, and 0.3 sec. (c) At $t = 0.3$ sec, what portion or portions of the spring are not in equilibrium?

21–3. Two springs A and B of equal lengths l and equal masses m, but with different spring constants, $K_a = 2K_b$, are joined at point C and stretched to a total length of $4l$, as shown in Fig. 21–10. The other ends of A and B are held fixed. (a) Determine the length of each of the springs when stretched. (b) A transverse impulse is applied at the junction C, so that each spring receives a transverse wave pulse. If this impulse is delivered at $t = 0$, determine the ratio t_a/t_b, where t_a and t_b are the arrival times of these pulses at the fixed ends of the springs, A and B, respectively.

21–4. Refer to Problems 21–1 and 21–2. (a) How much work was done to produce the wave pulse on the spring? (b) By direct calculation, find the kinetic energy in the pulse, and also the energy required to statically deform the spring into the shape of the wave.

21–5. Consider the coil-spring described in Problem 21–1. This spring is given a longitudinal impulse by moving the end forward with a constant velocity $u = 2$ m/sec during the time $t = 0$ to $t = 0.2$ sec. The spring is stretched to $L = 6$ m. (a) What is the wavespeed? (b) Sketch the particle-velocity distribution on the spring at the times $t = 0.1$, 0.2, and 0.3 sec. (c) What is the total impulse delivered to the spring? (d) When does the pulse reach the end of the spring? Show that the length of the spring, provided it is longer than the relaxed length, does not affect this time. Is the same statement true for the transverse wave?

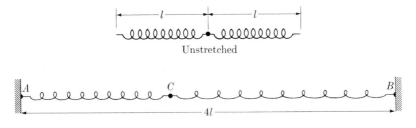

Unstretched

FIGURE 21–10

21-6. Refer to Problem 21-3. Suppose that an impulse is delivered *along* the spring at the junction C, so that longitudinal waves are generated. What are the times of arrival of the wave pulses at A and B?

21-7. From the data given in Table 18-3 determine the longitudinal wave-speed in aluminum, iron, lead, and copper.

21-8. A long steel bar is given an impulse at one end. The duration of the impulse is 10^{-3} sec, during which time the driving force is constant, $F = 10^5$ n. The area of the bar is $A = 10$ cm^2 and the force is uniformly distributed over this area. Determine the energy density of the wave pulse generated by the impulse. What would be the energy density, under similar conditions, in a bar of copper? aluminum?

21-9. A long straight iron bar of cross-sectional area 10 cm^2 is at rest on a frictionless table. A small body of mass $m = 2$ kgm, with an initial speed of $v = 10$ m/sec, collides head-on with the end of the bar and is observed to bounce back with a speed of 2 m/sec after the collision. (a) Estimate the collision time and the con-

tact force in the collision. Assume that the collision is such that the total mechanical energy (including the wave energy) is conserved, and that the contact force is constant during the interaction. (b) For your analysis in (a) to be valid the length of the bar must exceed a certain value. Determine this length. (c) Using the length determined in (b), what then is the center-of-mass velocity of the bar after the oscillations in the bar have died out?

21-10. Calculate the speed of sound in H$_2$, He, and CS$_2$ at 0°C.

21-11. Refer to Eq. (21-23) in the text and derive this expression for the temperature increase in a wave pulse in a gas.

21-12. The temperature of a jet at the nozzle of a jet engine is about 1000°F. What is the speed of sound in the jet?

21-13. The first portion of a "sonic boom" can be approximated by a wave pulse of the type discussed in the text. Suppose the excess pressure in the pulse is 0.1 atm in air of 20°C. What then are (a) the particle velocity in the wave pulse, (b) the excess density, and (c) the excess temperature?

CHAPTER 22

SUPERPOSITION OF WAVE PULSES; HARMONIC WAVES

Summary. The principle of superposition of forces, when applied to small-amplitude waves on deformable bodies, leads to the principle of linear superposition of particle velocities and displacements in wave pulses. The familiar properties of elementary wave pulses, discussed in the previous chapter, then are found to be directly applicable to small-amplitude waves of arbitrary time dependence. Thus the force-velocity relation and the calculation of power and total energy in waves are still valid, as we shall illustrate by examples. The meaning of retarded time is discussed and the mathematical description of a one-dimensional wave follows and is applied to the study of harmonic waves. Finally, a brief analysis of the one-dimensional wave equation is given.

22–1 Linear superposition of waves. Early in our study of mechanics we discussed the principle of superposition of forces, which, in essence, expresses the experimental fact that the rate of momentum transferred by a number of forces acting on a body is the same as the rate of momentum transferred by a single force which is the vector sum of the individual forces. This principle, as we have seen, applies to any arbitrary number of particles and consequently also to a deformable body. In the case of weak wave disturbances on a deformable body, we saw in Chapter 21 that the rate of momentum transferred to a body is proportional to the particle velocity in the wave. In this case, then, the superposition principle can be expressed in terms of a linear superposition of particle velocities.

To investigate this matter experimentally, we shall, as before, use transverse waves because they are easily observed. The first experiment involves two external impulses, delivered in succession, one directed *upward*, followed by one directed *downward*. If these two impulses are applied separately to an initially undisturbed spring, the displacement wave pulses y_1 and y_2 and the particle velocity impulses u_1 and u_2 would be as shown in Fig. 22–1. When *both* impulses are applied to the same spring, the spring clearly is somewhat deformed by the time the second impulse is applied, but if the deformation is sufficiently small we find indeed that the spring responds to the second impulse in the same way as if it had not been disturbed by the first impulse. Thus the total wave pulse is found to be the sum or linear superposition of y_1 and y_2. The relation $F = \epsilon c u$ in Eq. (21–8) then applies at all times during the generation of the wave, if u is the total particle velocity in the wave and F is the total driving force.

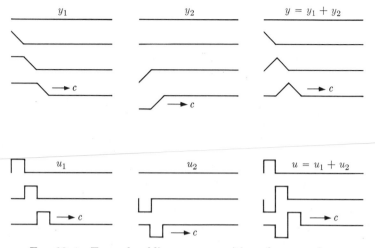

FIG. 22–1. Example of linear superposition of wave pulses.

EXAMPLE. A spring is stretched such that it has a tension $S = 12.8$ n and a mass of 0.2 kgm/m. It is acted on by a transverse force at one end, $x = 0$, such that the transverse displacement of the spring depends upon time, as shown in Fig. 22–2. (a) Determine the transverse particle velocity as a function of time at $x = 0$. (b) Determine the transverse force as a function of time at $x = 0$. (c) What is the shape of the spring as seen in a multiflash photograph of the spring taken at time $t = 0.7$ sec?

The particle velocity at $x = 0$ is merely the time derivative of the displacement, so that during the interval from 0 to 0.4 sec the particle velocity is 50 cm/sec, and during the next 0.1 sec the velocity is -200 cm/sec.

The transverse force on the spring at $x = 0$ is $F_y = \epsilon c u$. The wavespeed is $c = \sqrt{S/\epsilon} = 8$ m/sec, and so the force is 0.8 n during the interval from 0 to 0.4 sec, and is -3.2 n in the interval from 0.4 to 0.5 sec.

The displacement of the spring *as a function of* x at a given time is what we would obtain in a flash picture of the spring at that time. It should be noted that the part of the pulse that has traveled farthest is the part which was generated first, namely, that labeled A in the figure. Since this part is generated at $t = 0$ sec, we find that during the time $t = 0.7$ sec, it has traveled at a speed $c = 8$ m/sec and therefore has reached the point $0.7 \cdot 8 = 5.6$ m from the origin. Point B, the peak of the pulse, is generated at $t = 0.4$ sec and at $t = 0.7$ sec it has traveled for only 0.3 sec and therefore has reached the point $x = 0.3 \cdot 8 = 2.4$ m. Similarly, the final part C of the pulse has traveled for 0.2 sec and at $t = 0.7$ sec is located $0.2 \cdot 8 = 1.6$ m from the origin. The total length of the pulse along the spring is $c \, \Delta t = 8 \cdot 0.5 = 4$ m, where the duration $\Delta t = 0.5$ sec.

As a further and perhaps more interesting experiment, consider two similar impulses that are applied on opposite ends of a long spring. One impulse travels to the right and one to the left. From Fig. 22–3, which

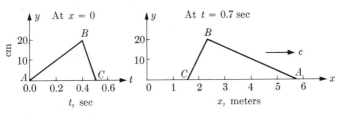

FIGURE 22–2

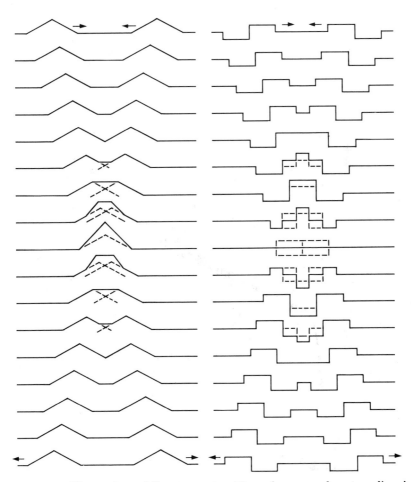

FIG. 22–3. Illustration of linear superposition of wave pulses traveling in opposite directions.

should be regarded as an experimental result, we see that the two wave impulses cross over each other and emerge looking just as they did before. Further, the particle displacement y on the spring is just the sum of the particle displacements in the individual wave pulses. Similarly, the particle velocity u is obtained by linear superposition.

EXAMPLE 1. Consider two similar wave pulses traveling in opposite directions on a spring. The displacement pulses are equal but opposite and at one moment they will cancel each other, so that the string is completely straight, as shown in Fig. 22–4. How can the energy of these wave pulses be accounted for at that moment?

There is an amount of energy, say E_1, in each of the wave pulses. Half the energy in each pulse is kinetic and half is potential. When the pulses overlap, there is no potential energy. But note the particle velocity u. The initial kinetic energy of each pulse is $E_1/2$ so that E_1 is the total initial kinetic energy. However, at the instant of overlap the particle velocity pulses add, so that the total particle velocity is twice what it was before and the kinetic energy is $4 \cdot E_1/2 = 2E_1$. Since there is no potential energy, $2E_1$ is the total energy, and this accounts for the total energy $E_1 + E_1$ before the pulses met.

EXAMPLE 2. A spring is distorted initially in the shape shown in Fig. 22–5, and then released. What is the subsequent motion of the spring?

The initial displacement can be considered as the superposition of two wave pulses, one traveling to the left and one to the right (see Fig. 22–3), because such superposition entirely reproduces the initial state of the spring. Then, as the spring is released, half the initial displacement pulse will travel to the left and the other half to the right. Initially the energy is purely potential but after the release the energy in the traveling pulses is half kinetic and half potential.

The superposition principle permits us to regard a wave pulse of arbitrary shape as the linear superposition of many small elementary wave pulses (Fig. 22–6). Of course, with an arbitrarily large number of elementary wave pulses we can approximate the shape of a given wave as closely as we choose. Since each of the individual pulses travels with the same wavespeed c and their shapes and sizes do not change, we can similarly conclude that any *arbitrary* wave pulse will travel with wavespeed c and without change of shape and size if friction and other losses are neglected. This is a very important consequence of the superposition principle and is, of course, subject to the restriction that it is valid only when the particle velocity is much less than the wave velocity.

Since, as we have seen in Chapter 21, for each elementary wave pulse the relation between the driving force and the particle velocity can be expressed in the form

$$F = \epsilon c u, \tag{22–1}$$

it follows from the superposition principle that this relation applies not

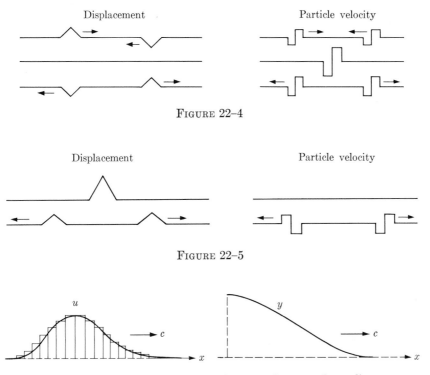

Figure 22-4

Figure 22-5

Fig 22-6. A (weak) wave of arbitrary shape can be treated as a linear super-position of elementary wave pulses.

only to wave pulses but to all weak waves of arbitrary shape produced by continuously varying driving forces. Before we use this relation in the study of continuous waves on springs, bars, and air columns we wish to make some remarks about what determines the choice of sign of the quantities u and F in this relation.

Let us start with the case of a transverse wave on a spring. As in the previous chapter, the transverse driving force is applied at the left end, $x = 0$, of the spring. The force, particle velocity, and particle displacement are all counted positive when directed in the positive y-direction, and under these conditions we have $F = \epsilon c u$. The wave that is produced travels in the positive x-direction, and in an imaginary cut of the spring in the region of the wave we have a transverse force F_1 which is related to the particle velocity at that point by $F_1 = \epsilon c u_1$. The force F_1 is then the force that acts on the portion of the spring which is to the right of the cut. The transverse force that acts on the left portion, of course is $-F_1$. (See Fig. 21–5.)

Consider now a transverse wave that travels in the negative x-direction. The relation between the transverse force and the particle velocity is, of course, the same as before if we use the force which acts on the portion of the spring to the left of an imaginary cut of the spring. However, if we consistently express the relation between particle velocity and transverse force in terms of the force acting on the portion to the right of the cut, we have $F_2 = -\epsilon c u_2$ for a wave traveling to the left.

It is easy to convince oneself that a similar result is obtained also for longitudinal waves on springs, bars, and air columns. In the case of a sound wave in a gas, for example, we produced a wave pulse by displacing a piston in the positive x-direction (see Fig. 21–9). The piston then generated a compressional wave which traveled in the positive x-direction and the relation between the pressure and the particle velocity in the wave was $p_1 = \rho c u_1$. If the piston is displaced in the negative x-direction a rarefaction wave traveling in the positive x-direction is produced and the particle velocity in this wave is negative. However, in this wave also the sound pressure p is negative and again we have $p_1 = \rho c u_1$. If, on the other hand, we have a wave traveling in the negative x-direction the sound pressure is positive in a compression but the particle velocity is in the negative x-direction and we have $p_2 = -\rho c u_2$. Similar relations apply also to the longitudinal waves on a spring and on a bar if in these cases F is counted positive when the body is compressed. These relations follow directly if we take the wavespeed as $+c$ for waves moving to the right and $-c$ for waves moving to the left.

As mentioned before, only weak waves, in which $u \ll c$, can be linearly superimposed. We can easily understand this limitation if we consider a large-amplitude wave on a spring. In the region of a large deformation of the spring the tension and the mass per unit length (and consequently the product ϵc) no longer can be considered to be the same as on the rest of the spring. Then, if an additional wave pulse were added on the spring the wavespeed and particle velocity of this pulse would depend on the existing deformation of the spring. In regions of large displacement the wavespeed is larger than in regions of small displacement, and a distortion of wave shape results.

Energy in a wave. If the force producing a wave on a spring or a solid bar is F and if u is the particle velocity in the wave at the point of application of the force, the power delivered to the wave by the force is $R = Fu$. When the particle velocity is related to the driving force by the relation $u = F/\epsilon c$ for any arbitrary time dependence of F, we see that the expression

$$R = Fu = \epsilon c u^2 \qquad (22\text{--}2)$$

is generally valid. This power is transferred to the wave and is carried by the wave in the direction of propagation. The total energy transferred to a wave then is obtained from the integral

$$H = \int R \, dt = \epsilon c \int u^2 \, dt, \qquad (22\text{–}3)$$

where the integration extends over the time of application of the force. When this relation is applied to waves on a solid bar or a gas column we have $\epsilon = A\rho$, where A is the cross-sectional area and ρ is the density.

In the case of sound generation by a piston in a gas column, as in Fig. 21–9, the power delivered by the piston is contributed not only by the sound pressure p but also by the static pressure P_0, so that

$$(P_0 + p)u = P_0 u + \rho_0 c u^2,$$

where $p = \rho_0 c u$ has been introduced. Similarly, the total energy delivered by a piston of unit area is

$$H = P_0 \int u \, dt + \rho_0 c \int u^2 \, dt. \qquad (22\text{–}4)$$

In most cases the net displacement $\int u \, dt$ of the piston (and the gas) is zero, and therefore the first term in (22–4) is zero.

EXAMPLE. We wish to find the total energy in the wave described in Fig. 22–2. The wave is generated by a transverse displacement in which the end of the spring is moved out to $y = 0.2$ m and back again. The outward displacement takes place in the time interval between $t = 0$ and $t_1 = 0.4$ sec and the return displacement in the time interval between $t_1 = 0.4$ sec and $t_2 = 0.5$ sec. The velocities in these displacements were constant and equal to $u_1 = 0.2/0.4 = 0.5$ m/sec and $u_2 = -0.2/0.1 = -2$ m/sec respectively. We have $\epsilon = 0.2$ kgm/m and the tension in the spring is $S = 12.8$ n, so that $c = \sqrt{64} = 8$ m/sec. Thus we have $\epsilon c = 1.6$ kgm/sec. The total energy in the wave is then

$$H = \epsilon c \left[\int_0^{t_1} u_1^2 \, dt + \int_{t_1}^{t_2} u_2^2 \, dt \right] = \epsilon c [u_1^2 t_1 + u_2^2 (t_2 - t_1)]$$

$$= 1.6[0.5^2 \cdot 0.4 + 4 \cdot 0.1] = 0.8 \text{ joule}.$$

22–2 **Mathematical description of a wave.** In this section we shall discuss briefly the elements of the mathematical description of the properties of a one-dimensional wave. We start by considering the basic property that the wave travels with constant speed and without change of shape. For example, if a wave generated at $x = 0$ travels in the positive x-direction, it is clear that the displacement in the wave at position x and time t originated at the source point, $x = 0$, at the earlier time $t - (x/c)$. This time is often called the *retarded time*. Consequently, if a wave traveling in the positive x-direction is generated at $x = 0$ by a displacement which varies with time as the function $y(t)$, the displacement at the point x at the time t is given by

$$y(x, t) = y\left(t - \frac{x}{c}\right),\qquad (22\text{--}5)$$

which is the value of y evaluated at the retarded time $t - (x/c)$. Note that this description applies to a wave traveling in the *positive* x-direction. A wave traveling in the negative x-direction is described in a similar manner by the function $y[t + (x/c)]$ if, as before, the displacement at $x = 0$ is given by $y(t)$.

The displacement is described by a function of two variables, location x and time t. When we observe the motion at a fixed point in space only t varies, and x is fixed. On the other hand, a flash picture of the displacement at a certain time t gives the variation of y with x with t held constant. The particle velocity at a certain fixed point x, of course, is the time derivative of the displacement. To indicate that x is kept constant in this differentiation it is customary to use the partial differentiation symbol $\partial/\partial t$, and the particle velocity then can be expressed by the partial time derivative

$$u(t, x) = \frac{\partial y}{\partial t}.\qquad (22\text{--}6)$$

If we are dealing with transverse waves on a spring, the slope of the spring can be expressed in a similar manner as $\partial y/\partial x$, the partial derivative of y with respect to x. There exists a simple relationship between the t- and x-derivatives of the wave function $y[t - (x/c)]$. If we set $z = t - (x/c)$, we have

$$\frac{\partial y}{\partial t} = \left(\frac{\partial y}{\partial z}\right)\left(\frac{\partial z}{\partial t}\right) = \frac{\partial y}{\partial z}$$

and

$$\frac{\partial y}{\partial x} = \left(\frac{\partial y}{\partial z}\right)\left(\frac{\partial z}{\partial x}\right) = -\left(\frac{1}{c}\right)\left(\frac{\partial y}{\partial z}\right),$$

and therefore $c(\partial y/\partial x) = -\partial y/\partial t$. Similarly, for a wave $y[t + (x/c)]$ traveling in the negative x-direction, $c(\partial y/\partial x) = \partial y/\partial t$. Thus for waves traveling in the positive and in the negative x-directions, we have

$$\frac{\partial y}{\partial x} = \mp \frac{1}{c}\frac{\partial y}{\partial t}\qquad (22\text{--}7)$$

respectively.

For transverse waves on a spring, we can determine the transverse force on the spring at an imagined cut of the spring at the point x, as indicated in Fig. 22–7. The total force on the length of the spring to the right of the

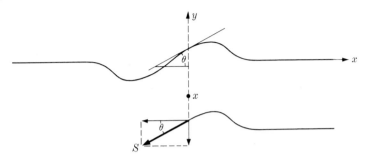

FIG. 22–7. The transverse force is $-S \sin \theta \approx -S \, (\partial y / \partial x)$.

point x is, of course, the tension S directed as shown, and if the slope of the spring at this point is positive, the y-component of this force is negative, so that

$$F_y = -S \frac{\partial y}{\partial x}. \qquad (22\text{–}8)$$

Then, using the results in Eqs. (22–3) and (22–4) and $c^2 = S/\epsilon$, we obtain, as before,

$$F_y = \pm \epsilon c u$$

for waves in the positive and negative x-directions respectively.

22–3 Harmonic waves. In this section we shall study the very important special case when the driving force varies harmonically with time. Then, at the driving point $x = 0$ we can set $F = F_0 \cos \omega t$, where $f = \omega / 2\pi = 1/T$ is the frequency and T is the period. This driving force may generate a wave on a spring, on a bar, or on a gas column. In any case, the particle velocity produced at $x = 0$ can be expressed as $u(0, t) = (F_0/\epsilon c) \cos \omega t = u_0 \cos \omega t$, and the particle displacement can be written as $y(0, t) = (u_0/\omega) \sin \omega t$ or

$$y(0, t) = y_0 \sin \omega t. \qquad (22\text{–}9)$$

The displacement $y(x, t)$ at a position x at time t is equal to the displacement which was generated at $x = 0$ at the earlier or retarded time $t - (x/c)$, so that we have

$$y(x, t) = y_0 \sin \omega \left(t - \frac{x}{c} \right). \qquad (22\text{–}10)$$

The continuous harmonic displacement at the driven end of a spring, for example, may be thought of as a series of pulses which travel along the spring, all with the same wavespeed c. The distance that such a pulse

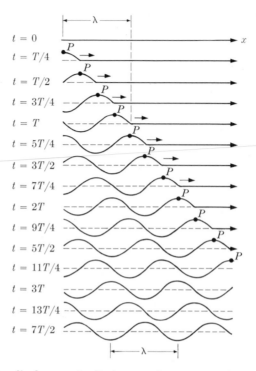

FIG. 22-8. The displacement $y(0, t) = y_0 \sin \omega t$ at $x = 0$ generates the wave $y(x, t) = y_0 \sin \omega[t - (x/c)]$.

travels in a time equal to the period T is called a *wavelength*, λ, which then can be expressed as

$$\lambda = cT = \frac{c}{f}. \qquad (22\text{--}11)$$

The wavelength λ is then the distance along the spring between two similar pulses, or the repetition distance of the periodic wave as it appears in flash photographs of the spring, as illustrated in Fig. 22–8. A wave of this kind is called a *traveling harmonic wave*, in contrast to a so-called standing wave, which we shall discuss later. When the wave reaches the far end of the elastic medium, the spring in this case, the wave usually will be reflected, and the wave pattern in Fig. 22–8 will be altered. Presently we are concerned only with the traveling wave, and for convenience we shall consider the elastic medium to be infinitely long.

The mathematical expression for a traveling harmonic wave can be written in several different ways. For example, by introducing T and λ into Eq. (22–10) we obtain

$$y(x, t) = y_0 \sin 2\pi \left(\frac{t}{T} - \frac{x}{\lambda} \right). \qquad (22\text{--}12)$$

From (22–12), we see that at a given value of x, the argument of the sine function will change by 2π when t is increased by T, and that at a given time t, the argument of the sine function changes by 2π when the point of observation is changed from x to $x + \lambda$.

Equation (22–11) is the wave resulting from a displacement $y(0, t) = y_0 \sin \omega t$ at $x = 0$. We can also say that it is the wave which at $t = 0$ has a displacement given by $y(x, 0) = -y_0 \sin (2\pi x/\lambda)$. Accordingly, a wave which travels in the positive x-direction and which has the displacement $y(x, 0) = y_0 \sin (2\pi x/\lambda)$ at $t = 0$ is given by

$$y(x, t) = -y_0 \sin \left[2\pi \left(\frac{t}{T} - \frac{x}{\lambda} \right) \right].$$

If the time dependence of the displacement at $x = 0$ is of the more general form $y(0, t) = y_0 \sin (\omega t + \phi)$, where ϕ is a phase angle, the resulting wave traveling in the positive x-direction will have the general form

$$y(x, t) = y_0 \sin \left[\omega \left(t - \frac{x}{c} + \phi \right) \right]. \tag{22–13}$$

EXAMPLE. Figure 22–9 is a representation of three flash pictures of a traveling wave on a spring of mass per unit length $\epsilon = 0.2$ kgm/m. The first flash picture is labeled $t = 0$, although the motion was initiated earlier. However, the clock or whatever timing mechanism was used on the camera started at this time. We wish to determine (a) the wavespeed, (b) the wavelength and frequency, (c) the transverse driving force, (d) the tension, and (e) the mathematical expression for the wave.

The wave clearly travels in the positive x-direction and the wavespeed is $1/0.1 = 10$ m/sec because the point P, for example, travels a distance of 1 m in 0.1 sec.

The wavelength is 3 m because at $t = 0$ the spring shape goes through a complete cycle in 3 m. The frequency f is therefore $c/\lambda = 10/3$ cycles/sec, and the period T is $1/f = 0.3$ sec.

The displacement amplitude y_0 is 0.1 m, and so the maximum transverse velocity is $u_0 = \omega y_0 = 2\pi \cdot (10/3) \cdot 0.1 = 2.1$ m/sec. The amplitude of the driving force is therefore $F_0 = \epsilon c u_0 = 0.2 \cdot 10 \cdot 2.1 = 4.2$ n.

The tension is $S = c^2 \epsilon = 10^2 \cdot 0.2 = 20$ n.

The shape of the spring at $t = 0$ is given by $y = y_0 \sin (2\pi x/\lambda)$.

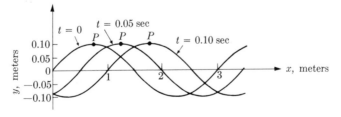

FIGURE 22–9

The general expression for a wave traveling in the positive x-direction is of the form $y(x, t) = y_0 \sin [2\pi(t/T - x/\lambda + \phi)]$, and if this wave is to have the shape $y_0 \sin (2\pi x/\lambda)$ at $t = 0$, the phase angle must be such that $\sin (-2\pi x/\lambda + \phi) = \sin (2\pi x/\lambda)$; that is, $\phi = \pi$. The wave then can be written simply as $y(x, t) = -y_0 \sin [2\pi(t/T - x/\lambda)]$.

Energy transmission in a traveling harmonic wave. Let us now apply the general expression $R = Fu$ (see Eq. 22–2) for the power carried by a wave. In the case of a harmonic driving force $F = F_0 \cos \omega t$, the particle velocity at $x = 0$ is $u = (F_0/\epsilon c) \cos \omega t = u_0 \cos \omega t$, and the power becomes

$$R(t) = \frac{F_0^2}{\epsilon c} \cos^2 \omega t = \epsilon c u_0^2 \cos^2 \omega t. \tag{22–14}$$

This power must be transferred to the harmonic wave, and it is transmitted by the wave as it travels in the positive x-direction. The power varies with time between the value 0 and the maximum value $\epsilon c u_0^2$. Since $\cos^2 \omega t = (1 - \cos 2\omega t)/2$, we see that the power fluctuates with the frequency 2ω about the average value

$$\overline{R} = \tfrac{1}{2}\epsilon c u_0^2. \tag{22–15}$$

In most cases it is this average power, rather than the instantaneous power, that is of interest.

This expression for the power applies to all the waves we have studied. For solid bars and gas columns we have $\epsilon = A\rho_0$, where A is the cross-sectional area and ρ_0 the density. The average power transmitted per unit area is called the *intensity* I of the harmonic wave. Thus for waves on solid bars and gas columns we have

$$I = \tfrac{1}{2}\rho_0 c u_0^2 \tag{22–16}$$

and the corresponding average energy density in the wave is

$$h = \frac{I}{c} = \tfrac{1}{2}\rho_0 u_0^2. \tag{22–17}$$

EXAMPLE 1. Refer to the harmonic wave on a spring illustrated in Fig. 22–9. What is the average power transmitted by the spring? The maximum particle displacement of the wave is 0.1 m and since the frequency of oscillation is $f = 10/3 \text{ sec}^{-1}$, the maximum particle velocity is

$$u_0 = \omega y_0 = 2\pi \cdot \tfrac{10}{3} \cdot 0.1 \simeq 2.1 \text{ m/sec.}$$

The mass per unit length of the spring is $\epsilon = 0.2 \text{ kgm/m}$ and the wavespeed is $c = 10 \text{ m/sec}$, so that $\epsilon c = 2 \text{ kgm/sec}$. The average power then becomes

$$R = \tfrac{1}{2}\epsilon c u_0^2 = 4.4 \text{ joules/sec} = 4.4 \text{ watts.}$$

EXAMPLE 2. The threshold of hearing in the human ear at 1000 cycles/sec is known to correspond to an average wave intensity of about 10^{-16} watt/cm². Assume that a sound wave of this intensity is generated by a moving piston at the end of a uniform straight tube. (a) What is the velocity amplitude? (b) What is the displacement amplitude of the piston? (c) What is the wavelength and the energy density in the wave?

An intensity of 10^{-16} watt/cm² corresponds to an intensity of 10^{-9} erg·sec^{-1}/cm². The density of air at 20°C and 76 cm Hg pressure is $\rho_0 \simeq 0.0014$ gm/cm³ and the speed of sound is $c \simeq 340$ m/sec. Thus the quantity $\rho_0 c$ is approximately equal to 42 gm/cm²·sec and the particle velocity obtained from $I = \rho c u_0^2/2$ then is $u_0 \simeq \sqrt{2 \cdot 10^{-9}/42} \simeq 7 \cdot 10^{-6}$ cm/sec. The particle displacement amplitude is $z_0 = u_0/\omega$, and with $\omega = 2\pi \cdot 1000$ sec^{-1}, we get $z_0 \simeq 10^{-9}$ cm, which is somewhat less than a typical atomic dimension. Finally, the wavelength of the 1000 cycle/sec sound wave is $\lambda = c/f = 34.4$ cm, and the average energy density in the wave is $h = I/c \simeq 3 \cdot 10^{-14}$ erg/cm³.

22–4 The wave equation. As we have seen in the foregoing, the particle displacement in a wave traveling in the positive x-direction can be expressed as $y(t - x/c)$ and, similarly, we have for a wave traveling in the negative x-direction the expression $y(t + x/c)$. The particle velocity in the wave is then $\partial y/\partial t$ and, as shown in Eq. (22–7), it is related in a simple way to the rate of change of y with respect to x:

$$\frac{\partial y}{\partial t} = \mp c \frac{\partial y}{\partial x}. \qquad (22\text{–}18)$$

Here the minus and plus signs refer to waves traveling in the positive and negative x-directions respectively. Therefore a characteristic property of a one-dimensional wave is that the time rate of change of a quantity is ($\mp c$) times the spatial rate of change. Consequently, if we differentiate Eq. (22–18) to obtain the acceleration $\partial^2 y/\partial t^2$, we obtain

$$\frac{\partial^2 y}{\partial t^2} = c^2 \frac{\partial^2 y}{\partial x^2}. \qquad (22\text{–}19)$$

This equation, which is satisfied by waves traveling with the speed c in the positive as well as in the negative direction, applies to all the different types of one-dimensional waves we have studied, and it is called the one-dimensional *wave equation*.

In obtaining this equation we started from the expression for a traveling wave and showed that the derivatives of the wave function are related in this simple way. Conversely, if it is known in advance that the second time derivative of a quantity y is proportional to the second spatial derivative of the same quantity, so that $\partial^2 y/\partial t^2 = $ (const) $\partial^2 y/\partial x^2$, then $y(x, t)$ is a wave or a superposition of waves and the squared wave speed must equal the constant ratio between $\partial^2 y/\partial t^2$ and $\partial^2 y/\partial x^2$. The wavespeed, of course, depends on the elastic properties of the medium under consideration.

Let us illustrate now, by a specific example, that the analysis of the motion of a mass element on a string does indeed lead to a wave equation for the particle displacement of the string. The particle of the string is the element between x and $x + \Delta x$ in Fig. 22–10. The mass of this element is $\epsilon \, \Delta x$, and it is acted on by two forces, the tension forces at the ends of the element. The magnitude of these forces are the same and are equal to the tension S, but since the slope of the string changes, the forces do not completely cancel each other but leave a net component in the transverse direction. According to Eq. (22–8), the transverse force acting on the portion of the string to the right of a cut is $-S(\partial y/\partial x)$, and the force on the string to the left of a cut then is $S(\partial y/\partial x)$. Thus the net force on the element in the positive y-direction is $-S(\partial y/\partial x)_x + S(\partial y/\partial x)_{x+\Delta x}$, which can be expressed as $S(\partial^2 y/\partial x^2)\,\Delta x$. The equation of motion of the mass element then is $\epsilon\,\Delta x(\partial^2 y/\partial t^2) = S(\partial^2 y/\partial x^2)\,\Delta x$, or

$$\frac{\partial^2 y}{\partial t^2} = \left(\frac{S}{\epsilon}\right)\frac{\partial^2 y}{\partial x^2} = c^2\,\frac{\partial^2 y}{\partial x^2}, \qquad (22\text{–}20)$$

and we see that $\partial^2 y/\partial t^2$ is indeed proportional to $\partial^2 y/\partial x^2$, as in the wave equation. The constant of proportionality is S/ϵ, and the wavespeed then is

$$c = \sqrt{\frac{S}{\epsilon}}.$$

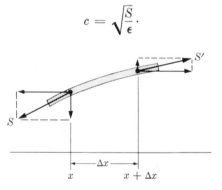

FIG. 22–10. The net transverse force on the mass element $\epsilon\,\Delta x$ is $S(\partial y/\partial x)_{x+\Delta x} - S(\partial y/\partial x)_x$.

Problems

22–1. At the instant $t = 1.2$ sec a transverse wave on a spring of mass density $\epsilon = 0.3$ kgm/m has the shape shown in Fig. 22–11. The wavespeed on the spring is 10 m/sec. Plot (a) the particle displacement, (b) the particle velocity, and (c) the transverse force, as functions of time at $x = 0$ and at $x = 20$ cm.

22–2. The transverse wavespeed on a stretched string is $c = 10$ m/sec. The transverse displacement at $x = 0$, the beginning of the string, is $y(t, 0) = 0.1(t^2 - t^3)$ m, when $0 < t < 1.0$ sec, and $y = 0$ for all other values of t.

(a) Plot the transverse displacement as a function of time at $x = 0$. (b) Plot the transverse displacement as a function of x at $t = 1.0$ sec. (c) What is the mathematical expression for the displacement as a function of time at $x = 10$ m? What are the displacements at this point at $t = 1.0$, 1.5, and 3.0 sec? (d) What is the transverse particle velocity at $x = 10$ m and $t = 1.5$ sec? (e) What is the slope of the string at $x = 10$ m and $t = 1.5$ sec? (f) If the mass per unit length of the string is $\epsilon = 2$ gm/cm, what is the transverse force at the beginning of the string? (g) What is the total transverse momentum of the wave pulse as it travels along the string?

22–3. It is observed that a pulse requires 0.1 sec to travel from one end to the other of a long string. The tension in the string is provided by passing the string over a pulley to a weight which has 100 times the mass of the string. (Use $g = 10$ m/sec^2.) (a) What is the length of the string? (b) The ends of the string are given simultaneous impulses such that each wave pulse, in the shape of an isosceles triangle, travels toward the center from each end of the string. The triangles have bases of 1 m and heights of 20 cm. What are the transverse velocities of the string on the leading and lagging sides of the triangles? (c) Plot the particle displacement, particle velocity, and the transverse force as functions of time at each end of the string. (d) What is the shape and what is the particle velocity of the string when the pulses are superimposed at the center?

22–4. What is the total energy carried by the wave pulse (a) in Problem 22–1, and (b) in Problem 22–2?

22–5. Consider a long string along an x-axis. The transverse wavespeed is 10 m/sec and the mass per unit length is 0.1 kgm/m. At points A and B, located at $x_a = 5$ m and $x_b = -5$ m, the string is given the trans-

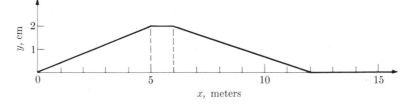

x, meters

Figure 22–11

verse displacements shown as functions of time in Fig. 22–12. (a) Sketch the shape of the string at $t = 0.3, 0.5,$ and 1 sec. (b) Which point between A and B is always at rest? (c) Sketch the corresponding transverse force distributions. (d) What is the total energy on the string between A and B at $t = 0.5$ sec and at $t = 1.5$ sec?

22–6. A spring one meter long and made of a certain material has a spring constant $K = 100$ n/m and a mass of 0.25 kgm. The end $x = 0$ of a long spring of this material is driven by a longitudinal displacement $z(0, t) =$ $0.02[(t/t_0) — (t/t_0)^2]$ m during the time between $t = 0$ and $t = t_0 = 0.2$ sec. The displacement is zero at all other times. (a) What are the particle velocity and the driving force as functions of time at $x = 0$? (b) During what time interval is the wave pulse passing the point $x = 10$ m? (c) What region of the spring is occupied by the wave pulse at the time $t = 2$ sec? (d) What is the total energy in the pulse?

22–7. Refer to Problem 22–6. The displacement

$$z(0, t) = z_0[(t/t_0) — (t/t_0)^2]$$

for $0 < t < t_0,$ $z(0, t) = 0$ for $0 > t > t_0,$ where $t_0 = 0.2$ sec, now is applied first to the end of a steel bar and then to the end of an air column. (a) What should be the value of z_0 in these two cases in order that the maximum power per cm^2 be 1 watt/cm^2? The static pressure in the air column is 1 atm $\simeq 10^6$ dynes/cm^2. (b) What is the total energy in the wave pulse in the two cases if the cross-sectional area of both the bar and the air column is $A = 2\ cm^2$? (c) Is the result in (a) consistent with the small-amplitude assumption?

22–8. Consider the string in Problem 22–2. The end of the string is driven in transverse harmonic motion, $y = y_0 \sin \omega t,$ with a frequency $f = 10$ sec^{-1} and an amplitude $y_0 = 0.2$ m. (a) What is the displacement, as a function of time, at a distance $x = 1$ m? (b) Sketch the shape of the string at the time $t = 0.5$ sec. What is the wavelength? (c) What are the transverse velocity, acceleration, and force, as functions of time, at $x = 1$ m? Determine the amplitudes of these quantities. (d) What is the phase difference between the harmonic oscillation of the spring at $x = 0$ and at $x = 0.2$ m?

22–9. Three consecutive flash photographs of a traveling wave on a string are reproduced in Fig. 22–13. With reference to the figure, determine the displacement amplitude of the wave,

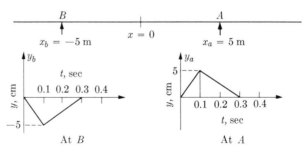

FIGURE 22–12

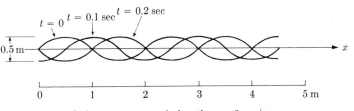

String: mass per unit length, $\epsilon = 3$ gm/cm

FIGURE 22–13

the wavelength, the wavespeed, the frequency of the driving force, and the amplitude of the driving force. What is the power in the wave, and what is the energy density on the string?

22–10. It is desired to generate a traveling sound wave in a pipe of cross-sectional area $2\ m^2$, at a frequency of 20 cycles/sec and a pressure amplitude equal to 0.01 atm. If this sound wave is to be generated at the beginning of the pipe by a plane piston with the same area as the pipe, what should be the displacement amplitude of the piston and the driving force on the piston? What is the total power carried by the sound wave along the pipe?

22–11. What intensity of a sound wave corresponds to a velocity amplitude of one-tenth of the speed of sound?

22–12. A harmonic sound pressure wave $p = p_0 \sin(\omega t - 2\pi x/\lambda)$ has a pressure amplitude $p_0 = 1$ dyne/cm^2 and a frequency of 1000 cycles/sec. What are the mathematical expressions for the particle displacement, particle velocity, density, and temperature waves associated with the sound wave? For each wave, determine the amplitude. Which of these waves are in phase with the pressure wave?

22–13. What particle displacement amplitude is required at the end of a

steel bar to generate a harmonic sound with a frequency of 10^6 cycles/ sec and an intensity of 10 watts/cm^2?

22–14. A vibrating piston is first applied to the air column in a long tube and then to the end of a long steel bar with the same area as the tube. What is the ratio between the sound intensities generated by the piston in the air and in the steel bar, (a) if the driving force on the piston is the same in the two cases, and (b) if the displacement amplitude is the same in the two cases?

22–15. A mass-spring oscillator ($m = 2$ kgm, spring constant $K = 32$ n/cm) is connected to a long, stretched string, as shown in Fig. 22–14. The mass is sliding on a horizontal frictionless guide bar in the y-direction, and the string extends in the x-direction. The string is stretched to a tension of $S = 100$ n,

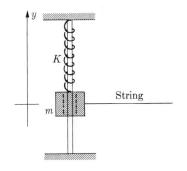

FIGURE 22–14

and its mass per unit length is $\epsilon = 0.25$ kgm/m. Disregard reflections from the far end of the string. (a) What is the frequency of free oscillations of the oscillator, disregarding the effect of the string? (b) What is the nature of the effect of the string on the motion of the oscillator? Does the string act like an additional mass, stiffness, or like a friction force?

(c) What is the Q-value (see Chapter 8) of the oscillator, considering the effect of the string? (d) Suppose that the oscillator is released from $y = y_0 = 5$ cm. Indicate the shape and length of the wavetrain on the string at the time when the amplitude of the oscillations has decreased to the value $1/e$ of the initial value. What will be the shape of the string after a long time?

CHAPTER 23

REFLECTION OF WAVES AND
CHARACTERISTIC OSCILLATIONS

Summary. Waves are usually reflected at a boundary between two elastic media. The mechanics of the reflection and transmission of a wave pulse with rectangular velocity distribution is investigated, and by application of conservation of momentum and energy we determine the reflected and transmitted wave pulses. The analysis is compared with the familiar and somewhat analogous problem of the one-dimensional perfectly elastic collision between two particles, one of which is initially at rest. The wave field resulting from the superposition of an incident and a reflected wave and the properties of a standing wave are then studied. The analysis of the successive reflections at the ends of an elastic body leads to the concepts of characteristic times and frequencies and to the study of characteristic or normal modes of oscillation. The decomposition of an arbitrary oscillation into normal modes is mentioned briefly, and finally the forced harmonic motion of a finite elastic body is illustrated in terms of the motion of a string.

In our previous study of waves we mentioned only the possibility of reflection of waves at boundaries but did not attempt an analysis of this phenomenon. Wave reflection is sufficiently important to warrant a special study, and in this chapter we shall investigate not only the mechanics of the reflection process but also the properties of the wave which result when an incident and a reflected wave are superimposed.

23–1 Reflection of waves. Qualitatively, the reflection of waves is, of course, familiar from such events as the echo of a sound wave or the reflection of a wave ripple on a water surface or on a rope. The latter is particularly illuminating and simple to study experimentally. If one end of a long, stretched rope or tightly wound coil-spring is fastened to a wall and the other end is given a transverse impulse, the resulting wave pulse, when it arrives at the wall, is reflected without noticeable change of amplitude. The direction of the particle displacement and the particle velocity in the reflected pulse, however, are reversed. Experiments of this kind show that a reflection will occur also at the junction with another spring of different mass per unit length. As the mass of the second spring is continuously decreased from a very large initial value, we find that the strength of the reflected pulse decreases, until it vanishes altogether when the masses per unit length of the two springs are identical. If the mass of the second spring is decreased even further, a reflected wave is again obtained, which now has a particle displacement and particle velocity in the same direction as in the initial wave. In all cases a portion of the incident wave will be transmitted across the junction to the second spring.

In the quantitative analysis of the reflection problem we shall make use of the principle of superposition, according to which a wave of arbitrary shape can be built up by linear superposition of elementary wave pulses with rectangular velocity distribution (see Fig. 22–6). Consequently, it is sufficient to study the behavior of such an elementary wave pulse as it reaches the interface between two media. To be specific, we shall consider a transverse wave pulse on a spring but, as in the previous study of waves, we find that the arguments and equations used, and the results obtained in the analysis, are directly applicable to longitudinal waves on springs, solid bars, and gas columns.

As indicated in Fig. 23–1, the initial wave pulse has a particle velocity u_i and a duration Δt. It travels with a speed c_1 on a spring which has a mass ϵ_1 per unit length. This spring is joined to a second spring with a mass ϵ_2 per unit length and a wavespeed c_2. After having reached the junction, the incident wave pulse divides into a reflected and a transmitted pulse with particle velocities u_r and u_t respectively. The object of the analysis is to determine the values of u_r and u_t in terms of the incident particle velocity u_i and the properties of the two springs. The conditions before and after the reflection are those shown in Fig. 23–1. As we have seen in the experiments discussed above, under certain conditions the reflected and the incident particle velocities have different signs, and this fact, of course, must be predicted by the analysis.

As we have seen in Chapter 21, the momentum (in the transverse direction) of the incident wave pulse is $\epsilon_1 c_1 u_i \, \Delta t$, and the total energy is $\epsilon_1 c_1 u_i^2 \, \Delta t$. Similar expressions apply to the reflected and transmitted wave pulses. Then, conservation of momentum and energy require that

$$\epsilon_1 c_1 u_i = \epsilon_1 c_1 u_r + \epsilon_2 c_2 u_t,$$
$$\epsilon_1 c_1 u_i^2 = \epsilon_1 c_1 u_r^2 + \epsilon_2 c_2 u_t^2. \tag{23-1}$$

These two equations are sufficient for the determination of the two unknown velocities u_r and u_t. We obtain

$$\epsilon_1 c_1 (u_i - u_r) = \epsilon_2 c_2 u_t, \qquad u_i + u_r = u_t \tag{23-2}$$

and

$$u_r = \frac{1 - (\epsilon_2 c_2/\epsilon_1 c_1)}{1 + (\epsilon_2 c_2/\epsilon_1 c_1)} u_i; \qquad u_t = \frac{2}{1 + (\epsilon_2 c_2/\epsilon_1 c_1)} u_i. \tag{23-3}$$

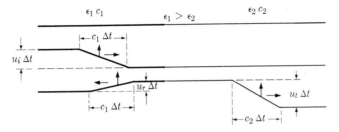

$\epsilon_1 c_1$ $\quad\quad\quad\epsilon_1 > \epsilon_2\quad\quad\quad$ $\epsilon_2 c_2$

FIG. 23–1. Reflection and transmission of an elementary wave pulse.

Before we proceed to discuss these results it is interesting and illuminating to note that the problem of wave reflection is somewhat analogous to the one-dimensional perfectly elastic collision between two balls, one of which is originally at rest. (See Chapter 7.) If the colliding balls A and B have the masses m_a and m_b and if B is initially at rest, we have, from conservation of momentum and energy,

$$m_a v_a = m_a v_a' + m_b v_b',$$
$$m_a v_a^2 = m_a v_a'^2 + m_b v_b'^2,$$

(23–4)

where the primed quantities are the velocities after the collision. From these equations we obtain

$$v_a' = \frac{1 - (m_b/m_a)}{1 + (m_b/m_a)}\, v_a, \qquad v_b' = \frac{2}{1 + (m_b/m_a)}\, v_a.$$

(23–5)

The initial velocity of A corresponds to the particle velocity in the incident wave pulse and, similarly, the velocities of A and B after the collision correspond to the particle velocities in the reflected and transmitted pulses respectively. Only when the masses of the balls are equal, $m_b = m_a$, is the entire initial momentum and energy of A delivered to B, so that the final velocity of A is zero. Similarly, for springs, only when the springs are identical, or rather when $\epsilon_2 c_2 = \epsilon_1 c_1$, is the reflected wave zero and the entire momentum and energy transferred across the junction to the adjacent spring. Furthermore, we note that when $m_b > m_a$ and, analogously, when $\epsilon_2 c_2 > \epsilon_1 c_1$, the velocities v_a' and u_r are negative; that is, their directions are opposite those of v_a and u_i respectively. This result is consistent with the experimental observation, discussed earlier, that the particle velocity in a wave pulse on a spring is reversed when reflected from a wall (Fig. 23–3).

Once the reflected and transmitted velocity waves have been determined it is simple to obtain the corresponding reflected and transmitted displacement waves. For a wave traveling in the positive x-direction we have $\partial y_1/\partial x = (1/c)\,\partial y_1/\partial t = -u_1/c$, and for a wave traveling in the negative x-direction the relationship is $\partial y_2/\partial x = (1/c)\,\partial y_2/\partial t = u_2/c$. (See Eq. 22–7.) Figure 23–2 shows the transverse velocity and displacement wave pulses in the case when $\epsilon_1 c_1 < \epsilon_2 c_2$.

The ratios u_r/u_i and u_t/u_i are called the *velocity reflection coefficient* and the *velocity transmission coefficient*, respectively. These coefficients, which depend only on the ratio $\epsilon_2 c_2/\epsilon_1 c_1$, are plotted as functions of this ratio in Fig. 23–3. The quantity ϵc is often called the *characteristic wave im-*

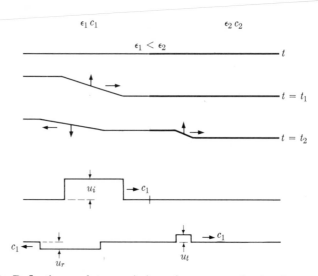

FIG. 23–2. Reflection and transmission of a wave pulse in the case where $\epsilon_2 c_2 > \epsilon_1 c_1$. The spring on the left has a smaller mass per unit length than the spring on the right. The incident pulse is partially transmitted and partially reflected. The *particle* velocity in the reflected pulse is *downward*, while the *particle* velocity in the incident and transmitted pulses is *upward*.

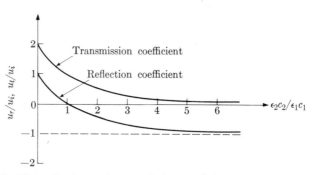

FIG. 23–3. The reflection and transmission coefficients for a velocity wave that is transmitted from medium 1 to medium 2.

pedance of the medium. If $\epsilon_1 c_1$ is larger than $\epsilon_2 c_2$, as is the case illustrated in Fig. 23–1, the transmitted pulse is larger and the reflected pulse is smaller than the incident pulse. In the limit, when $\epsilon_1 c_1$ is very much larger than $\epsilon_2 c_2$, the transmitted pulse is twice as large as the incident pulse and the reflected pulse is equal to the incident pulse. We might wonder about the conservation of energy in this case, since clearly there is as much energy in the reflected as in the incident pulse, which leaves nothing for the transmitted portion. The saving feature is that when we have $\epsilon_2/\epsilon_1 = 0$, we have $\epsilon_2 = 0$ for any finite ϵ_1, thus no energy is carried in the transmitted wave. Actually, the *energy transmission coefficient* $\epsilon_2 c_2 u_t^2/\epsilon_1 c_1 u_i^2$ becomes

$$\frac{\epsilon_2 c_2 u_t^2}{\epsilon_1 c_1 u_i^2} = \frac{4r}{(1 + r)^2}, \qquad \text{where} \qquad r = \frac{\epsilon_2 c_2}{\epsilon_1 c_1}. \qquad (23\text{–}6)$$

If $\epsilon_2 c_2$ is greater than $\epsilon_1 c_1$, as in Fig. 23–2, the transmitted pulse will always be smaller than the incident pulse. Further, the reflected pulse is always changed in sign; that is, if in the incident pulse the particles moved *upward* as the wave approached, the particles would move *downward* as the reflected wave approached. In the limit $\epsilon_2 = \infty$ (for example, a spring connected to a stone wall), there is no transmitted pulse and the reflected pulse has the same amplitude as the incident pulse, but a particle velocity in a direction opposite to that of the incident particle velocity. Figure 23–4 illustrates the reflection of a transverse wave pulse on a spring in the two limiting cases $\epsilon_2 c_2/\epsilon_1 c_1 = \infty$ and $\epsilon_2 c_2/\epsilon_1 c_1 = 0$.

The analysis we have carried through and the results we have obtained for the reflection and transmission coefficients are directly applicable to waves of arbitrary time dependence and to both transverse waves and longitudinal waves on springs, solid bars, and gas columns. Of course in

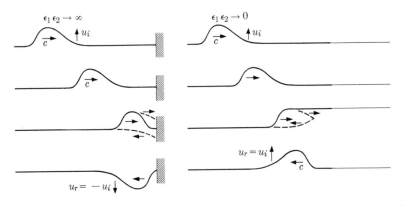

FIG. 23–4. Reflected transverse wave pulses for a spring connected to a wall and to a very much lighter string.

the case of longitudinal waves, the longitudinal wavespeed must be used in the expression for the characteristic wave impedance ϵc. Furthermore, when dealing with waves on solid bars and gas columns it is customary to use the characteristic impedance ρc per unit area.

EXAMPLE. An iron bar carrying a longitudinal wave is joined at one end to (a) an air column, (b) a water column, and (c) a copper bar. The cross-sectional areas in all cases are the same as that of the iron bar. What fraction of the incident wave energy is transmitted to the various media?

Using the data in, for example, Table 17–3, we obtain for the characteristic wave impedance of iron $\rho_1 c_1 \simeq 4 \cdot 10^6$ gm/sec·cm^2. Similarly, for air, water, and copper we have $(\rho c)_a \simeq 42$, $(\rho c)_w \simeq 1.5 \cdot 10^6$, and $(\rho c)_C \simeq 3.2 \cdot 10^6$ gm/sec·cm^2. Then, from Eq. (23–6), we find the following energy transmission coefficients (a) $4 \cdot 10^{-5}$, (b) 0.79, and (c) 0.98. Clearly, the energy transmitted from the iron bar to air is extremely small, whereas in the case of transmission to water and, in particular, to copper, the energy transfer is considerable. When the characteristic impedances of two wave media are the same, there are no reflected waves generated when an incident wave crosses their boundary. The "matching" or "making equal" of the impedances of two joined wave media is a familiar and important problem in many engineering applications of wave phenomena.

Associated with the reflected and transmitted displacement and particle velocity waves, we also find reflected and transmitted force waves or, in the case of a gas column, pressure waves. The relation between the force and the particle velocity, as discussed in connection with Eq. (22–1), is $F_1 = \epsilon c u_1$ for a wave traveling in the positive x-direction and $F_2 = -\epsilon c u_2$ for a wave traveling in the negative x-direction. Similarly, for a wave in a gas we have $p_1 = \rho c u_1$ and $p_2 = -\rho c u_2$ for waves in the positive and negative directions respectively. It follows, then, that the *force (and pressure) transmission coefficient* F_t/F_i is the same as the velocity transmission coefficient, whereas the *force (and pressure) reflection coefficient* F_r/F_i is the *negative* of the velocity reflection coefficient.

For all wave types that we have studied the reflection and transmission coefficients are determined uniquely by the ratio $\epsilon_2 c_2/\epsilon_1 c_1$ (or $\rho_2 c_2/\rho_1 c_1$) of the characteristic wave impedances of the two media involved. When dealing with the reflection of transverse waves at the junction between two strings, we note that the ratio $\epsilon_2 c_2/\epsilon_1 c_1$ can be expressed simply in terms of the masses ϵ_2 and ϵ_1 because the tension $S = c^2 \epsilon$ in the two strings must be the same. Therefore *in this case* (transverse waves on a string) we get

$$\frac{\epsilon_2 c_2}{\epsilon_1 c_1} = \frac{c_1}{c_2} = \sqrt{\frac{\epsilon_2}{\epsilon_1}}.$$

Boundary conditions. While we have deduced the properties of the waves reflected and transmitted at the junction of two springs from momentum

and energy considerations, we could equally well have deduced these properties from necessary conditions on the waves *at* the junction or the boundary
between the two springs. Since the springs are joined, the total displacement of one spring must be the same as the total displacement of the other
spring at the junction. The spring on the far side of the junction carries
only the transmitted wave, and the total displacement of this spring then
is y_t. The other spring, on the other hand, carries both the incident and
the reflected waves, and its total displacement is then $y_i + y_r$. The condition of continuity of displacement at the junction then is

$$y_i + y_r = y_t \quad \text{(at junction)}.$$

It is obvious that not only the displacements but also the particle velocities of the two springs must be the same at the junction (otherwise the
springs would not hang together), and we have

$$u_i + u_r = u_t \quad \text{(at junction)}. \tag{23–7}$$

For convenience of description and calculation, we have quite regularly
assumed the existence of rectangular velocity pulses and displacement
pulses which have sharp bends. This assumption is not realistic because
the mass elements at sharp bends would have infinite accelerations. (If
the bends were not smooth, the infinitesimal element of mass at the bend
would be under the influence of a finite force component in the transverse
direction, and so have infinite acceleration.) In practice, therefore, the
velocity pulses always have a finite slope and the bends in the coil-spring
are always rounded off or smooth, as shown in Fig. 23–4. Thus, in order
to prevent infinite acceleration, the transverse force component on both
sides of an imaginary cut of the spring and on both sides of the junction
between two springs must be the same. We recall that the transverse force
can be expressed as $F_1 = \epsilon c u_1$ for a wave traveling in the positive x-
direction, and as $F_2 = -\epsilon c u_2$ for a wave in the negative x-direction. The
total transverse force in the transmitted wave is then $F_t = \epsilon_2 c_2 u_t$, and
the total transverse force corresponding to the superimposed incident and
reflected waves is $F_i + F_r = \epsilon_1 c_1 u_i - \epsilon_1 c_1 u_r$. The continuity of the
transverse force at the junction then can be expressed as

$$F_i + F_r = F_t \quad \text{or} \quad \epsilon_1 c_1 (u_i - u_r) = \epsilon_2 c_2 u_t \quad \text{(at junction)}. \tag{23–8}$$

In the case of a sound wave in a gas column this boundary condition simply expresses continuity of pressure. The conditions obtained from the
continuity of particle velocity and force as expressed by Eqs. (23–7) and
(23–8) are equivalent to the conditions (23–2) obtained from the conservation of momentum and energy. The condition of the continuity of the
transverse force was a result of the continuity of the slope of the spring,

and it is clear that we could have expressed this condition directly in terms of the slopes:

$$\frac{\partial y_i}{\partial x} + \frac{\partial y_r}{\partial x} = \frac{\partial y_t}{\partial x} \quad \text{(at junction)}.$$

EXAMPLE 1. Two strings with $\epsilon_1 = 0.1$ kgm/m and $\epsilon_2 = 0.4$ kgm/m are joined and are kept under a tension $S = 10$ n, as shown in Fig. 23–5. The end of the light string is given two transverse impulses, one immediately following the other, so that a displacement wave on the light string results, as shown in the figure.

The wavespeed on the light string is $c_1 = \sqrt{S/\epsilon_1} = \sqrt{10/0.1} = 10$ m/sec, while the wavespeed on the heavy string is $c_2 = \sqrt{10/0.4} = 5$ m/sec. The amplitude and transverse particle velocity at corresponding parts of the pulses are related by

$$u_t = \frac{2}{1 + \sqrt{\epsilon_2/\epsilon_1}} u_i = \frac{2}{1 + \sqrt{0.4/0.1}} u_i = \tfrac{2}{3} u_i$$

and

$$u_r = \frac{1 - \sqrt{\epsilon_2/\epsilon_1}}{1 + \sqrt{\epsilon_2/\epsilon_1}} u_i = -\tfrac{1}{3} u_i.$$

The reflected wave pulse is therefore "turned upside down" and reduced to one-third of the incident amplitude. The transmitted wave pulse is of the same sign

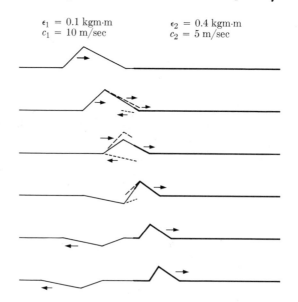

FIG. 23–5. Reflection of a wave from a junction. Note that the slope of the strings is continuous at the junction.

as the incident pulse, but is reduced to two-thirds of the incident amplitude. Note carefully that the two strings are joined smoothly. The ratio between the transmitted and incident wave energies, i.e., the energy transmission coefficient, is $\epsilon_2 c_2 u_t^2 / \epsilon_1 c_1 u_i^2 = 8/9$.

EXAMPLE 2. Refer to the example at the end of Sec. 21-4, where a compressional wave was produced in a steel rod by the blow of a hammer. We assumed that the hammer exerted a constant force on the rod during its period of contact, $\Delta t = 10^{-4}$ sec. This force turned out to be $5.85 \cdot 10^9$ dynes, and we found that the wave velocity in the rod was $c = \sqrt{Y/\rho} = 5 \cdot 10^5$ cm/sec and the particle velocity in the compressional wave was $u = v/2$ or half the initial velocity of the hammer.

Suppose now that the rod had a *finite* length. Since the wave traveled a distance of $c\,\Delta t = 50$ cm during the collision time, it is clear that for a rod length exceeding 25 cm, the reflected wave from the far end of the rod could not have returned to influence the collision between the hammer and the rod. Suppose, therefore, that the length of the rod was 100 cm. By the time the reflected wave returned to the driven end, the hammer would no longer be in contact with the rod, and the wave would be reflected again and would travel the length of the rod $5 \cdot 10^5/100 = 5000$ times a second. These wave traversals do not continue indefinitely, of course. In each traversal, some of the ordered kinetic energy in the wave is converted into the random thermal kinetic energy of the iron atoms, and when the wave motion finally ceases, the rod once again is an undeformed body, with a velocity V such that momentum is conserved. For a 100-cm rod, the mass M would be 7800 gm, and the velocity V would be $mv/M = 60$ cm/sec. The kinetic energy of the rod is now $MV^2/2 = 1.4 \cdot 10^6$ ergs, whereas the original kinetic energy of the hammer and of the wave was $mv^2/2 = 87.8 \cdot 10^6$ ergs. The difference, $mv^2/2 - MV^2/2 = 86.4 \cdot 10^6$ ergs, served eventually to heat the rod.

To a casual observer, all this activity within the rod is not apparent and, in any case, is all over in a very short time. The collision is inelastic and some kinetic energy of gross motion is lost. The longer the rod (over 25 cm), the more inelastic will be the collision, for the velocity V must change as $1/M$ in order to keep the momentum fixed, and the kinetic energy varies as $MV^2/2$. If the rod is exactly 25 cm long, it will have a mass of 1950 gm, the same as that of the hammer. Then, based on the assumption that the hammer comes to rest after the collision, the final kinetic energy of the rod will be equal to the initial kinetic energy of the hammer. This result also can be understood by considering the waves in the rod, as follows.

As the compressional wave travels along the rod, the particle velocity acquired by the iron atoms in the rod is $u_i = v/2$. At the end of the rod, this wave will be reflected and the particle velocity in the reflected wave is $u_r = u_i = v/2$, because the reflection coefficient at the end of the rod is unity. The net particle velocity is therefore $u = u_i + u_r = v/2 + v/2 = v$. Since the rod is 25 cm long, the reflected wave reaches the end of the rod where the hammer hit just as the hammer leaves the rod, and also just as the original incident wave is terminating. The reflected wave is re-reflected such that it directly follows the original wave, and the whole rod has a particle velocity of v. Since this is true, there is no kinetic energy of vibration, and the center of mass also moves with a velocity v. Hence we have an elastic collision between the hammer and the rod.

The phenomena we have just described is indicative of the wave nature of any perfectly elastic collision between extended bodies. When collisions are inelastic, some of the energy of the incident body is transformed into vibrational kinetic energy and the associated energy in the waves is eventually dissipated into heat, sound, or some other form of energy not associated with gross mechanical motion.

23–2 Standing waves. After having studied the mechanics of wave reflection we are prepared to determine the waves that result when we superimpose incident and reflected waves. Of particular interest are the waves obtained in this manner when the waves involved are harmonic and the amplitudes of the reflected and incident waves are the same. This is the case, for example, when a harmonic wave is reflected from the fixed end of a spring, when a sound wave in a tube is reflected from a rigid wall, or when a wave is reflected from the free end of a solid bar. In the first two cases the velocity reflection coefficient is -1, and in the last case it is $+1$.

In all these examples, then, the resulting wave is the sum of two harmonic waves of equal amplitudes and frequencies, traveling in opposite directions. The addition of these waves, of course, can be shown graphically, and it is easy to convince oneself in this manner that the resulting wave has the interesting characteristic that at certain points the amplitude of oscillation is always zero. The distance between these points, the *nodal points*, or *nodes*, is half a wavelength. In the region between the nodes the wave amplitude varies from zero (at the nodes) to a maximum value midway between the nodes. A wave of this type is called a *standing wave*, since there is no direction of travel associated with the wave motion. Figure 23–6 shows the transverse displacement in a standing wave on a spring. The period of oscillation in this particular case is 8 sec and the displacement of the spring is shown at different times during the course of one-half a period. Note that in the region between two nodes the oscillations at all points are in phase. In a traveling wave, also shown in Fig. 23–6 for comparison, the amplitude of oscillation is the same at all points and the phase varies continuously along the spring.

The mathematical description of a standing wave simply is the sum of a wave $y_1 = y_0 \sin \omega(t - x/c)$ traveling in the positive x-direction and a wave $y_2 = y_0 \sin \omega(t + x/c)$ traveling in the negative x-direction. When these waves represent an incident and a reflected wave respectively, they should contain phase angles ϕ_1 and ϕ_2 which depend on where and how the wave is generated and reflected and upon the choice of the origin of t and x. However, these phase angles can be eliminated by proper

Period $T = 8$ sec

$t = 0,\ 1,\ 2,\ 3,\ 4$ sec

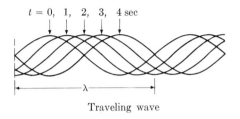

Traveling wave

$t = 0,1,2,3,4$ sec

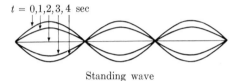

Standing wave

Fig. 23–6. A traveling harmonic wave and a standing transverse wave on a spring. In both cases the frequency and period ($T = 8$ sec) are the same. The spring assumes the shapes indicated at $t = 0, 1, 2, 3$ and 4 sec.

choice of the origin of t and x, and if we set $\phi_1 = \phi_2 = 0$ the standing wave is given by

$$y = y_0 \sin \omega \left(t - \frac{x}{c} \right) + y_0 \sin \omega \left(t + \frac{x}{c} \right) = \left(2y_0 \cos \frac{2\pi x}{\lambda} \right) \sin \omega t.$$

This expression was obtained by expanding the two sine functions, using $\sin (a \pm b) = \sin a \cos b \pm \cos a \sin b$. If, on the other hand, we use $y_1 = y_0 \sin \omega(t - x/c + \pi) = -y_0 \sin \omega(t - x/c)$ for the incident wave, corresponding to $\phi_1 = \pi$, we obtain

$$y = -y_0 \sin \omega \left(t - \frac{x}{c} \right) + y_0 \sin \omega \left(t + \frac{x}{c} \right) = \left(2y_0 \sin \frac{2\pi x}{\lambda} \right) \cos \omega t.$$
$$(23\text{–}9)$$

This latter form we shall find somewhat more convenient to use later in this chapter in the discussion of characteristic oscillations and forced motion of standing waves.

We now see that at each point x we have a harmonic motion expressed by the time-dependent factor $\cos \omega t$. However, the amplitude of the motion varies from one point to another, as expressed by the x-dependent factor $2y_0 \sin (2\pi x/\lambda)$. The minimum amplitude clearly is zero and the maximum amplitude is $2y_0$. The points of zero amplitude, the nodes, are determined by $\sin (2\pi x/\lambda) = 0$, and it follows that the distance d between two nodal points is given by $2\pi \, d/\lambda = \pi$; that is, $d = \lambda/2$.

Standing waves are most commonly produced as a result of reflections, as will be further discussed in the next section. However, they can also be produced by two independent sources of disturbance, one of which produces a wave that travels to the right and the other a wave that travels to the left. These two independent sources must have exactly the same frequency, for if they do not, the standing wave will drift either to the right or left at a speed which depends on the frequency difference. Of course, when reflections are used to produce one of the traveling waves, the frequencies of the two waves are necessarily the same.

When a harmonic wave on a spring is reflected at the fixed end of the spring or when a sound wave in a tube is reflected from a rigid wall in the tube, it is clear that the particle displacement and the particle velocity at the termination are zero. (The velocity reflection coefficient is -1.) The resulting standing wave then has a node at the fixed end and the other nodes are located at the distances $\lambda/2$, λ, $3\lambda/2$, and so on, from the end. If, on the other hand, a wave is reflected from the free end of a spring or a solid bar (velocity reflection coefficient $+1$), the particle displacement and the particle velocity have maxima at the end and the nodes in the standing wave in this case are located at the distances $\lambda/4$, $3\lambda/4$, $5\lambda/4$, and so on, from the end. As a wave reflected from the fixed end of a spring returns to the driven end of the spring, it will usually be reflected again, and one might think that the steady-state motion of a continuously driven spring must be regarded as the sum of an infinite number of waves traveling back and forth on the spring. However, it is not difficult to show (Problem 23–10), that an arbitrary number of harmonic waves of the same frequency traveling in the same direction can be replaced by a single harmonic traveling wave. Therefore the harmonic steady-state motion of a spring can always be considered as a superposition of two harmonic waves traveling in opposite directions.

In terms of energy, the difference between a traveling and a standing wave is that in the traveling wave there is a net energy flow; whereas in a standing wave there is none. The energy is "trapped" in the standing wave and the energy density then varies from point to point as $\sin^2(2\pi x/\lambda)$. In the traveling wave the energy density is independent of x. If the maximum particle velocity amplitude in the standing wave is u_m and the mass per unit length is ϵ_1 the energy density in the standing wave, averaged over t and x, is easily shown to be (Problem 23–11)

$$h = \frac{\epsilon u_m^2}{4}. \tag{23–10}$$

EXAMPLE. The distance between two successive nodes in a standing wave on a spring is 20 cm, and the maximum displacement amplitude is $y_m = 2$ cm. The frequency of oscillation is 100 cycles/sec, and the mass per unit length of the spring is $\epsilon = 0.2$ kgm/m. (a) What is the tension in the spring? (b) What is the energy contained on the spring between two nodes?

(a) The distance between two nodes is $\lambda/2$, and consequently the wavelength of the waves making up the standing wave is $\lambda = 40$ cm $= 0.4$ m. From $c = \lambda f$ we obtain, with $f = 100$ cycles/sec, $c = 0.4 \cdot 100 = 40$ m/sec. From $c = \sqrt{S/\epsilon}$ we find $S = \epsilon c^2 = 0.2 \cdot 1600 = 320$ n.

(b) The maximum particle velocity amplitude of the spring (midway between two nodes) is $u_m = 2\pi f y_m = 2\pi \cdot 100 \cdot 0.02 = 4\pi$ m/sec, and the particle velocity at other points between the nodes is then given by $u_m \cos(2\pi x/\lambda) \sin \omega t$. Since a mass element $\epsilon \, dx$ of the spring performs harmonic motion, the total energy of oscillation of this mass element is equal to the maximum kinetic energy $\epsilon[u_m \cos(2\pi x/\lambda)]^2/2$, and the total energy contained between two nodes is then

$$H = \int_0^{\lambda/2} \frac{\epsilon}{2} u_m^2 \cos^2\left(\frac{2\pi x}{\lambda}\right) dx = \frac{\lambda}{8} \epsilon u_m^2 = 0.04\pi \text{ joule.}$$

23–3 Characteristic frequencies and times. Characteristic frequencies were treated in our study of the harmonic oscillator and therefore are familiar. It may be recalled that a mass m which moves under the influence of a spring force $F = -Kx$ has a characteristic frequency $f = 2\pi\sqrt{K/m}$. An oscillator which is started from an initial state returns to that state f times per second, or every $T = 1/f$ sec. The harmonic oscillator has only *one* characteristic frequency. It is a matter of everyday experience that other bodies, for example the strings and air columns of musical instruments, also have characteristic frequencies. However, in contrast to the mass-spring oscillator, a finite string has *many* characteristic frequencies. As a matter of fact, all deformable bodies which have continuous mass distribution and a finite size (ropes, strings, wires, air columns, etc.) have an infinite number of characteristic frequencies. In this section we shall study the nature of these characteristic frequencies and their relationships to the geometric and physical natures of the media.

Consider a string under tension, with both ends tied to rigid supports. As shown in Fig. 23–7, the string is distorted at an arbitrary point, say C, and then at time $t = 0$ is released. The original deformation P splits into two parts, P' and P'', each with half the displacement amplitude of the original deformation. Parts P' and P'' travel with the wavespeed c to the right and to the left, respectively. In a time $t_1 = x/c$, P'' reaches the left-hand end of the string, and at this point it is reflected, after which its displacement is downward rather than upward. In a time $t_2 = L/c$, P'' reaches the right-hand end of the string, and at this point is reflected, and again has an upward displacement. In a time $t_3 = (L - x)/c$, P'' is again at point C, the elapsed time being $T_1 = t_1 + t_2 + t_3 = 2L/c$. An entirely similar sequence of reflections takes place for the other pulse

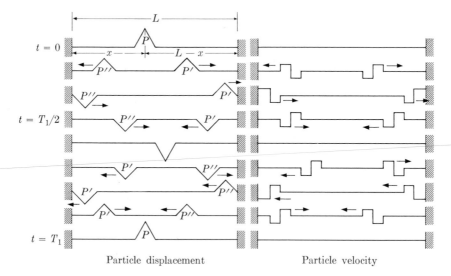

Particle displacement   Particle velocity

FIG. 23–7. A string of length L is distorted in the shape P and at $t = 0$ is released. Two pulses P' and P'' result, one traveling to the right and one to the left. The string comes back to its original shape in the time $T_1 = 2L/c$. At $t = 0$, there is no kinetic energy in the wave pulses, since all mass elements of the string have zero velocity.

P', and at $t = T_1 = 2L/c$, both pulses arrive back at point C and combine to form the original deformation P. The time T_1, called the *characteristic time* for the string, and its reciprocal, the *characteristic frequency*, are then

$$T_1 = \frac{2L}{c}, \qquad f_1 = \frac{1}{T_1} = \frac{c}{2L}. \tag{23–11}$$

An initial distortion of a string with both ends fixed will reappear in the characteristic time T_1, or will repeat with a frequency f_1. Expressions of the form of (23–10) will always result for the characteristic time and frequency, because the string itself is characterized by its length L and the wavespeed c. Only L/c has the dimensions of time. Note that only bodies with *finite* dimensions can have characteristic times and frequencies.

Since the pulse considered in Fig. 23–7 is arbitrary, it follows from the principle of superposition that any number of pulses on the string or any arbitrary continuous displacement will reappear in the characteristic time T_1.

Some special types of deformation will reappear more often than once in the time T_1. Consider again Fig. 23–7. In a time $T_1/2$, a deformation very much like the original deformation has appeared, but it is downward rather than upward and is a distance x from the right end of the string rather than a distance x from the left end. If the original deformation of the string had consisted of two parts, one a distance x from the left and one a distance x from the right, and if one of the deformations had been upward and the other downward, the original shape of the string would reappear in a time $T_1/2$. The two original deformations would, in effect, simply have changed places. A further example of a deformation which repeats in the characteristic time $T_2 = T_1/2 = L/c$ sec and another which repeats every $T_3 = T_1/3 = 2L/3c$ sec are shown in Fig. 23–8. The corresponding characteristic frequencies are $f_2 = 2f_1$ and $f_3 = 3f_1$. Note that the deformation which has the characteristic frequency $f_2 = 2f_1$ is composed of *two* parts which are antisymmetrical with respect to the center of the springs. Similarly, the deformation with the frequency $f_3 = 3f_1$ divides the string into *three* antisymmetrical parts. Analogously, a deformation which divides the spring into n antisymmetrical parts has a characteristic frequency,

$$f_n = nf_1 = \frac{nc}{2L}. \tag{23–12}$$

This can be interpreted as the fundamental or first characteristic frequency of a string of length L/n. An example of a deformation which repeats $15f_1 = 15c/2L$ times per second is shown in Fig. 23–9.

In summary, then, a string of finite length (and the same general arguments hold for such other media as columns of gas, springs, etc.) possesses an infinite number of characteristic frequencies. These characteristic frequencies depend not only upon the wavespeed, but also upon the length of the medium. Similar sets of characteristic frequencies exist for a string with both ends free, and for a string with one end fixed and the other free.

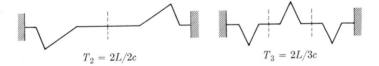

$$T_2 = 2L/2c \qquad\qquad T_3 = 2L/3c$$

Fig. 23–8. (a) A string deformation which reappears $f_2 = c/L = 2f_1$ times per second, and (b) another which reappears $f_3 = 3c/2L = 3f_1$ times per second. Note the symmetry about the dotted lines.

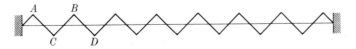

Fig. 23–9. A deformation which reappears $15c/2L$ times per second. In a time $2L/15c$, half of B moves to the left to form half of a new A, while half of C moves to the left, is reflected, and then moves to the right to form the other half of the new A. In the meantime, A has divided into two halves, one of which forms part of the new B, and the other of which forms part of the new C.

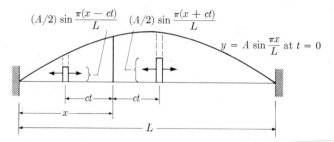

FIG. 23–10. The displacement x at time t is comprised of the sums of half the elementary displacements which are located at $x - ct$ and at $x + ct$ at $t = 0$.

Normal modes of motion. A sinusoidal initial shape or deformation of a string is of special importance, because it turns out that the time dependence of the resulting motion of the string is harmonic. This phenomenon has already been encountered in our discussion of standing waves. Consider now a string with an initial displacement $y(0, t) = A \sin \pi x/L$, as shown in Fig. 23–10. We wish to determine the displacement $y(t, x)$ at an arbitrary x at a later time t. As discussed in the previous section, each elementary displacement will divide into halves, one-half traveling to the right and one to the left. The displacement of the string at x at time t will therefore be comprised of two parts, the sums of half the elementary displacements which were at $x - ct$ and $x + ct$ at $t = 0$. The total displacement x at time t will therefore be

$$y_1(x, t) = \frac{A}{2} \sin \frac{\pi}{L} (x - ct) + \frac{A}{2} \sin \frac{\pi}{L} (x + ct)$$

$$= A \sin \frac{\pi x}{L} \cos \frac{\pi ct}{L} \tag{23–13}$$

or

$$y_1 = A \sin \frac{\pi x}{L} \cos 2\pi f_1 t = A \sin \frac{\pi x}{L} \cos \frac{2\pi t}{T_1},$$

where

$$f_1 = \frac{1}{T_1} = \frac{c}{2L}.$$

In a completely analogous manner we find that if the initial displacement of the string is $y(x, 0) = A \sin (n\pi x/L)$, the subsequent displacement is given by

$$y_n(x, t) = A \sin \frac{n\pi x}{L} \cos 2\pi f_n t, \tag{23–14}$$

where

$$f_n = nf_1 = \frac{nc}{2L}.$$

It is clear, by comparison with Eq. (23-9), that the motions y_1 and y_n can be regarded as standing waves resulting from the superposition of traveling waves with the wavelengths λ_1 and λ_n given by $\lambda_1/2 = L$, $n\lambda_n/2 = L$ respectively. The wavelength of the first oscillation y_1 then is such that the length of the string is equal to the distance between two nodes in the standing wave, and the nth oscillation in effect divides the string into n parts, each equal to the distance $\lambda_n/2$ between two nodes. The ends of the string, of course, always must coincide with two nodes, since the ends are held fixed. Thus if we introduce the wavelength $\lambda_n = 2L/n$ and the period $T_n = 1/f_n = 2L/cn$ into Eq. (23-13), we obtain

$$y_n(x,\, t) \;=\; A \sin \frac{n\pi x}{L} \cos 2\pi f_n t \;=\; A \sin \frac{2\pi x}{\lambda_n} \cos \frac{2\pi t}{T_n}. \qquad (23\text{-}15)$$

It is implied that x is measured from one end of the string, so that at $x = 0$ and $x = L$ the displacement is zero. Oscillations of this type, which are harmonic both in t and x, are called the *characteristic oscillations* or the *normal modes* of the string.

EXAMPLE. A string of mass 0.2 kgm/m and length $L = 0.6$ m is fixed at both ends and stretched such that it has a tension $S = 80$ n. Initially, the string, deformed to conform to the shape of its third normal mode, has an amplitude of $A = 0.5$ cm. (a) What is the frequency of the oscillation? (b) What is the maximum transverse velocity amplitude? (c) What is the total energy of the oscillation?

The wavespeed is $c = \sqrt{S/\epsilon} = \sqrt{80/0.2} = 20$ m/sec. In the third normal mode, the string is 3/2 wavelengths long, and so $3\lambda/2 = L = 0.6$ m and

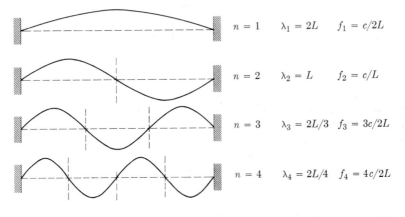

$$n = 1 \qquad \lambda_1 = 2L \qquad f_1 = c/2L$$
$$n = 2 \qquad \lambda_2 = L \qquad f_2 = c/L$$
$$n = 3 \qquad \lambda_3 = 2L/3 \quad f_3 = 3c/2L$$
$$n = 4 \qquad \lambda_4 = 2L/4 \quad f_4 = 4c/2L$$
$$n \qquad\quad \lambda_n = 2L/n \quad f_n = nc/2L$$

FIG. 23-11. Normal modes of a string which is fixed at both ends. Note that the nth mode divides the string into n (anti)symmetrical parts.

$\lambda_3 = 0.4$ m. The frequency is therefore $f_3 = c/\lambda_3 = 20/0.4 = 50$ cycles/sec, and $T_3 = 0.02$ sec.

The displacement of the string is

$$y(x, t) = A \sin \frac{3\pi x}{L} \cos \omega_3 t$$

and the transverse particle velocity is

$$u(x, t) = -\left(\omega_3 A \sin \frac{3\pi x}{L}\right) \sin \omega_3 t.$$

The maximum amplitude of the velocity is therefore

$$u_m = \omega_3 A = 2\pi \cdot 50 \cdot 0.5 = 50\pi \text{ cm/sec.}$$

Only the elements of string at $x = \lambda/4$, $3\lambda/4$, and $5\lambda/4$ ($x = 0.1$ m, 0.3 m, and 0.5 m) have this maximum velocity amplitude.

Each element of mass of the string moves as a simple harmonic oscillator, and so the total energy in the oscillation must be the same as the maximum kinetic energy. (When the kinetic energy is maximum, the displacement y is zero.) At x, a length dx of string then has the energy of oscillation

$$dH = \tfrac{1}{2}\epsilon \, dx u_m^2 \sin^2 \frac{2\pi x}{\lambda}.$$

Integrating from $x = 0$ to $x = L = 3\lambda/2$, we obtain

$$E = \frac{\epsilon u_m^2}{2} \int_0^L \sin^2 \frac{3\pi x}{L} \, dx = \frac{L\epsilon u_m^2}{4} \simeq 0.075 \text{ joule.}$$

Note that $L\epsilon u_m^2/4$ is just half the kinetic energy that a length L of string would have if the entire length were harmonically oscillating with an amplitude A and angular frequency ω.

If one end of a string is held fixed and the other end is free, which is approximately the case at the junction to a string of much smaller mass per unit length, a new but related set of normal modes results. At the fixed end the displacement, of course, is zero and at the free end, the transverse force and hence the slope of the string must be zero. Thus the free end has maximum displacement and particle velocity. The first four normal modes for this case are illustrated in Fig. 23–12.

EXAMPLE. A spring with one fixed and one free end lies on a frictionless horizontal table. The spring oscillates in longitudinal motion in its fundamental harmonic mode. The length of the unstretched spring is L, the mass is M, and the spring constant is K. Determine the frequency of oscillation.

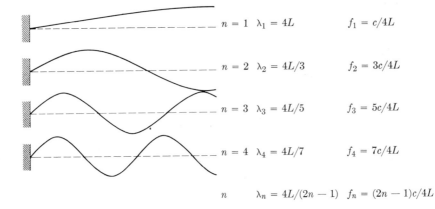

$n = 1$ $\lambda_1 = 4L$ $f_1 = c/4L$

$n = 2$ $\lambda_2 = 4L/3$ $f_2 = 3c/4L$

$n = 3$ $\lambda_3 = 4L/5$ $f_3 = 5c/4L$

$n = 4$ $\lambda_4 = 4L/7$ $f_4 = 7c/4L$

n $\lambda_n = 4L/(2n - 1)$ $f_n = (2n - 1)c/4L$

Fig. 23–12. Normal modes of a string that has one fixed end and one free end.

The speed of propagation of a longitudinal wave is $c = \sqrt{1/\kappa\epsilon}$ where $\kappa = 1/KL$ and $\epsilon = M/L$. We get $c = L\sqrt{K/M}$, and the fundamental frequency is

$$f_1 = \frac{c}{4L} = \frac{1}{4}\sqrt{\frac{K}{M}}.$$

In other words, the frequency of oscillation is the same as that of an ideal mass-spring oscillator that consists of a mass $M_1 = 4M/\pi^2$ at the end of a massless spring of spring constant K.

Characteristic oscillations in two and three dimensions. Each character-istic frequency of the one-dimensional motion of a spring, gas column, solid bar, or any other similar elastic system, corresponds to a certain char-acteristic mode of oscillation. Such a mode is described in terms of a *wave function.* In the case of a spring clamped at both ends, the wave function for the nth mode is $y_n = A \sin (n\pi x/L) \cos (2\pi t/T_n)$, where n may be thought of as the number of sections into which the spring is divided by the nodes in the standing-wave displacement.

Similar characteristic frequencies and modes of oscillation are found also under the more general conditions of wave motion in a plane or in space. It is particularly simple to demonstrate such modes of oscillation on a thin membrane such as a soap film. Figure 23–13 shows a few such oscillations obtained by means of a soap film which is excited by a sound wave of the proper frequency. Parts (a) and (b) of the figure illustrate series of characteristic oscillations of a circular and of a square mem-brane, respectively. The white lines in the photographs indicate dis-placement maxima, not nodes.

The characteristic wave functions which describe the modes of a square membrane are quite similar to those which describe a string. In fact, the

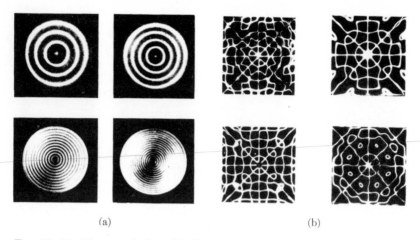

(a)   (b)

FIG. 23–13. Characteristic oscillations of a circular and a square membrane of soap film. Courtesy of Ludwig Bergmann.

displacement of the square membrane is given by

$$y_{mn}(x, z, t) = A \sin \frac{m\pi x}{L_x} \sin \frac{n\pi z}{L_z} \cos 2\pi f_{mn} t, \qquad (23\text{--}16)$$

where m and n can take on any integral value. It follows that there is a "double infinity" of possible modes with characteristic frequencies which can be expressed as

$$f_{mn} = \frac{c}{2} \sqrt{\left(\frac{m}{L_x}\right)^2 + \left(\frac{n}{L_z}\right)^2}, \qquad (23\text{--}17)$$

where $m, n = 1, 2, 3, \ldots$ and L_x, L_z are the lengths of the sides of the membrane.

An important difference exists between characteristic modes in the one- and two- (or three-) dimensional cases. In one dimension, there is a one-to-one correspondence between the characteristic frequencies and the characteristic modes of oscillation. In the two- or three-dimensional case, however, there may be several modes of oscillation which have the *same* frequency. For example, if L_x/L_z is an integer equal to q, the modes described by the number pair ($m = 0, n = q$) have the same frequency as the mode described by the number pair ($m = q, n = 0$). Modes of this kind are called *degenerate*.

Similarly, a closed volume like an ordinary rectangular room has a "triple infinity" of possible characteristic modes of oscillation, with characteristic frequencies given by

$$f_{klm} = \frac{c}{2} \sqrt{\left(\frac{k}{L_x}\right)^2 + \left(\frac{l}{L_y}\right)^2 + \left(\frac{m}{L_z}\right)^2}, \qquad (23\text{--}18)$$

where $k, l, m = 0, 1, 2, \ldots$. An even greater probability for the occurrence of degenerate modes exists, and the higher the symmetry of the room, the higher is the degeneracy. In the design of rooms for sound reproduction, it is important to avoid degeneracies. With a high degree of degeneracy, the modes "bunch" and frequencies or frequency regions in the spectrum are then undesirably enhanced.

Fourier decomposition. When the initial displacement of a string is a combination of fundamental modes (a simple example is shown in Fig. 23–14) the individual modes will oscillate independently of each other. This further illustrates the superposition principle. The initial displacement shown in Fig. 23–14 is $y(x, 0) = y_1(x, 0) + y_2(x, 0)$, or

$$y(x, 0) = A \sin \frac{\pi x}{L} + A \sin \frac{2\pi x}{L}. \tag{23-19}$$

If the initial displacement were specified by either $y_1(x, 0)$ or $y_2(x, 0)$, we would have

$$y_1(x, t) = A \sin \frac{\pi x}{L} \cos \frac{2\pi t}{T_1}$$

or

$$y_2(x, t) = A \sin \frac{2\pi x}{L} \cos \frac{2\pi t}{T_2},$$

respectively, where $T_1 = 2L/c$ and $T_2 = L/c$. When the initial displacement is the sum $(y_1 + y_2)$, the eventual time-dependence of the displacement is

$$y(t, x) = A \sin \frac{\pi x}{L} \cos \frac{2\pi t}{T_1} + A \sin \frac{2\pi x}{L} \cos \frac{2\pi t}{T_2}, \tag{23-20}$$

as determined from the principle of superposition.

The French mathematician J. B. Fourier (1768–1830) showed that, conversely, any arbitrary initial displacement can be decomposed into

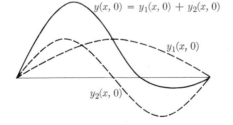

FIG. 23–14. If the initial displacement of the string is $y(x, 0) = y_1(x, 0) + y_2(x, 0)$, the string displacement will change with time as $y(x, t) = y_1(x, t) + y_2(x, t)$.

sine functions of properly chosen amplitudes. Each of these displacements will produce a normal mode of oscillation. If $f(x)$ is the initial shape of a string, the so-called Fourier decomposition or representation of this function is*

$$f(x) = \sum_{n=1}^{\infty} A_n \sin \frac{n\pi x}{L}, \qquad (23\text{-}21)$$

where the values of A_n are given by

$$A_n = \frac{2}{L} \int_0^L f(x) \sin\left(\frac{n\pi x}{L}\right) dx. \qquad (23\text{-}22)$$

The subsequent motion is then a superposition of normal modes

$$y(x, t) = \sum_{n=1}^{\infty} A_n \sin \frac{n\pi x}{L} \cos \frac{2\pi t}{T_n}, \qquad (23\text{-}23)$$

where $T_n = 2L/nc$.

23–4 Forced motion and resonance. The characteristic modes of motion of finite springs or finite columns of gas are analogous to the free motion of a mass-spring oscillator. Just as we studied both the forced and free motion of the mass-spring oscillator, we shall now briefly study the forced motion of a string.

In the forced motion of a mass-spring oscillator, the amplitude of oscillation at resonance is limited only by the damping in the system. The response of a finite string or a gas column to a driving force is quite similar. The basic difference is that the latter systems have an infinite number of characteristic frequencies, instead of only one. At any of these characteristic frequencies, the system can be driven to a very large amplitude with a very small (in fact with zero) driving force.

As in most of our previous discussions, we shall limit our quantitative considerations to the case of transverse waves on a string or spring. Consider, as in Fig. 23–15, a string of length L, with a fixed left-hand end and with its right-hand end at $x = L$ driven as $y_m \cos \omega t$, where $\omega = 2\pi f$ is the angular frequency, which can be varied. As a result of this periodic displacement of one end of the string, a standing wave of the form (compare Eq. 23–9)

$$y(x, t) = A \sin \frac{2\pi x}{\lambda} \cos \omega t \qquad (23\text{-}24)$$

---

* See, for example, Thomas, *loc. cit.*, p. 821.

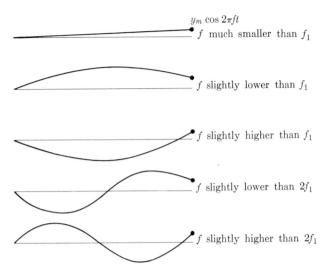

Fig. 23-15. The string is driven at the right-hand end as $y = y_m \cos 2\pi ft$. The string is in resonance at the frequencies $f = nf_1 = n2L/c$.

will be produced on the string. At the point $x = L$ we must have

$$y(L, t) = y_m \cos \omega t = A \sin \frac{2\pi L}{\lambda} \cos \omega t, \qquad (23\text{-}25)$$

and this determines A in terms of y_m:

$$A = \frac{y_m}{\sin (2\pi L/\lambda)}. \qquad (23\text{-}26)$$

Here $\lambda = c/f = 2\pi c/\omega$ and f is the driving frequency. We then have

$$y(x, t) = y_m \frac{\sin (2\pi x/\lambda)}{\sin (2\pi L/\lambda)} \cos \omega t = y_m \frac{\sin (2\pi x/\lambda)}{\sin (\pi f/f_1)} \cos 2\pi ft, \quad (23\text{-}27)$$

where $f_1 = c/2L$ is the first characteristic frequency for a string fixed at both ends. When the driven frequency is very small, say one per day, the wavelength λ is very large. Then (23-27) reduces to

$$y(x, t) \simeq y_m(x/L) \cos \omega t \qquad (f \ll f_1).$$

The string stretches straight from the fixed end at $x = 0$, $y = 0$, to the driven point at $x = L$, $y = y_m \cos \omega t$. As the frequency f is increased, the amplitude of the standing waves on the string approaches infinity as f approaches f_1, and the string is in resonance with the driving frequency. Similarly, each time f coincides with a characteristic frequency, so that $f = f_n = nf_1$, the value of $\sin (\pi f/f_1)$ in the denominator of (23-27) is zero and the amplitude is infinite.

It must be emphasized that these considerations have referred only to the steady-state motion of the string. If a string, initially at rest, is suddenly subjected to an oscillating displacement at one of its ends, a traveling wave will result. This traveling wave will reflect from the fixed end, and then for a while there will be a very complicated motion, followed finally by the steady-state motion we have discussed. When the steady-state standing-wave motion is attained, no energy is propagated along the string and, on the average, no energy is supplied from the driven end. During the time that the steady-state condition is being established, however, energy is supplied from the driven end.

Our analysis indicates that at any one characteristic frequency, the amplitude would become infinite in the steady-state condition of the wave motion. In practice, however, several factors limit the wave amplitude. For example, there are always dissipative forces present. The air absorbs energy as it is driven by the string, and some energy is required to overcome internal friction in the string. The energy lost to these dissipative effects always increases with the amplitude of the wave motion, and a point is eventually reached at which the energy lost equals the energy transferred to the string. Furthermore, we must remember that our entire analysis is valid only when the particle velocity is much less than the wavespeed or, equivalently, when the displacement amplitude is much less than one wavelength.

In the above analysis we have expressed the displacement of the spring in terms of the displacement $y = y_m \cos \omega t$ at the driving point $x = L$ of the spring (see Fig. 23–15). If y_m is held constant as the driving frequency is varied, the driving force at this point must vary with frequency. (In order to sustain a constant value of y_m at the resonance frequencies the driving force would have to be infinite, under our assumption of no damping.)

PROBLEMS

23-1. The speed of transverse waves on a spring A, 2 m long, is 10 m/sec and on spring B is 20 m/sec. Springs A and B are joined and the tension is 50 n. A wave pulse with a constant particle velocity of 2 m/sec is generated on A. (a) What are the masses per unit length of springs A and B? (b) What are the velocity amplitudes of the transmitted and reflected pulses? (c) Sketch the entire spring shape (A and B) at $t = 0.05$, 0.2, 0.225, 0.25, and 0.3 sec. (d) What fraction of the incident energy is transmitted, and what fraction is reflected?

23-2. A container is filled with helium and air. Assume that there is a well-defined boundary between the two gases. A sound wave is incident on this boundary from the air. Determine the pressure reflection and transmission coefficients at normal incidence. If the sound pressure amplitude of the incident wave is p_0, what then is the sound pressure amplitude at the boundary?

23-3. What fraction of the sound energy is transmitted into the water when a sound wave strikes the surface of a lake at normal incidence?

23-4. How does the characteristic wave impedance of air vary with temperature if the static pressure is constant? Suppose that the temperature in an air column is 20°C in the region between 0 and $x = x_0$ and 100°C in the region $x > x_0$. A sound wave originating at $x = 0$ strikes the boundary at $x = x_0$. If the incident pressure amplitude is 1 dyne, what are the amplitudes of the reflected and the transmitted waves?

23-5. One end of a copper bar is joined to the end of an aluminum bar. The cross-sectional areas of the bars are the same. A wave pulse with a total energy of 100 joules is generated in the copper bar and travels toward the aluminum bar. (a) How much energy is transmitted into the aluminum bar? (b) Suppose, instead, that the wave pulse travels from the aluminum bar to the copper bar. The shape and the total energy of the pulse is the same as before. What energy is transmitted into the copper bar? (c) In which of the two cases (a) and (b) is the particle velocity at the interface largest?

23-6. A coil-spring with mass ϵ per unit length and tension S is driven at one end in transverse motion, and the other end is attached to a (massless) ring which can slide on a horizontal bar which is normal to the direction of the spring, as shown in Fig. 23-16. (a) What is the reflection coefficient for the transverse displacement wave at the end of the spring if the bar is frictionless? (b) Suppose instead that a bar with friction is used, such that the friction force on the ring has the magnitude ru, where u is the velocity of the ring. What should be the value

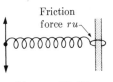

Friction force ru

FIGURE 23-16

of r to eliminate wave reflection from the end of the spring?

23–7. A spring of mass per unit length $\epsilon = 4$ kgm/m lies on a frictionless surface and is held in tension, $S = 64$ n, by two long lengths of light string, each of $\epsilon' = 1$ gm/m. (a) In a pulse traveling along the spring, what fraction of the energy is reflected and what fraction transmitted? (b) If the length of stretched spring is 4 m, what time Δt is required for a pulse to travel this length? (c) A constant transverse force F_0 is applied to an end of the spring for a time $\Delta t/2$. Sketch the spring displacement and velocity waves at $t_1 = 0$, $t_2 = 0.8\,\Delta t$, $t_3 = \Delta t$, $t_4 = 1.20\,\Delta t$, $t_5 = 1.6\,\Delta t$, where t is measured from the instant of application of the force F_0. (d) Repeat part (c) for a force F_0 applied for a time Δt and for a time $2\,\Delta t$.

23–8. A steel bar 100 m long and 10 cm in diameter is initially at rest. It is given an impulse at one end. The particle velocity is 2 m/sec. Assume that the impulse consists of a constant force F_0 applied for a time Δt. (a) What is the time Δt_1 required for the compressional wave to reach the far end of the rod? (b) What is the particle velocity of the various parts of the rod at this instant? (c) How long should Δt be, in order that all parts of the rod have the same particle velocity at all times? Is there more than one possible value for Δt? (d) What should F_0 be? (e) What work was done by F_0?

23–9. Consider two harmonic waves, A and B, of equal amplitude and equal wavelength, traveling in opposite directions. At time $t = 0$ let the two waves be in a position such that the displacements in the two waves are in phase. Indicate graphically the individual displacements of A and B at the times $t = 0$, $T/4$, $T/2$, $3T/4$, and $t = T$, where T is the period. Add the individual displacements of A and B graphically and discuss properties of the resulting standing wave.

23–10. With reference to the discussion in the text, show that the sum of an arbitrary number of harmonic waves traveling in the same direction with the same wavespeed, and all of the same wavelength, can be described by a single harmonic wave. [Clearly, it is sufficient to carry through the analysis for only two waves:

$$y_1 = A \sin (\omega t - 2\pi x/\lambda)$$

and

$$y_2 = B \sin (\omega t - 2\pi x/\lambda + \phi).]$$

23–11. Show that in a standing wave the energy per unit length, averaged over space and time, is $h = \epsilon u_m^2/4$ [see Eq. (23–10) in the text], where u_m is the maximum particle velocity amplitude in the wave and ϵ is the mass per unit length.

23–12. Show that the sum of the two waves $A \sin (\omega t + \phi_1 - 2\pi x/\lambda)$ and $A \sin (\omega t + \phi_2 + 2\pi x/\lambda)$ is a standing wave.

23–13. Sound is introduced into a pipe from two thin tubes A and B, separated by a distance d, as shown in Fig. 23–17. The sound in these tubes is generated by identical loudspeakers which, in turn, are driven by a single oscillator. Each tube generates a sound wave in the pipe in each direction from the tube. The tubes are so small that the waves generated by one are not disturbed by the presence of the other tube. The tubes are the same length and the loudspeakers operate in

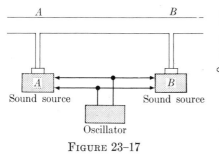

FIGURE 23–17

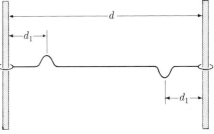

FIGURE 23–18

phase. (a) Describe the nature of the sound-pressure waves in the region to the right of B, to the left of A, and between A and B. (b) If each tube generates a wave in each direction with an amplitude p_m, what then is the pressure amplitude in the wave to the right of B, expressed in terms of d and the wavelength λ of the sound produced? What is the total power generated by the speakers? (c) What is the maximum pressure amplitude in the region between A and B? Sketch the amplitude distribution between A and B. (d) In particular, what are the pressure amplitudes in (b) and (c) if $d = 2\lambda$, $d = 2.25\lambda$, and $d = 2.5\lambda$? (e) What happens to the amplitudes in (b), (c), and (d) if the leads to one of the loudspeakers are reversed such that the sound sources operate out of phase?

23–14. A string is held stretched between two parallel bars, as shown in Fig. 23–18. Each end of the string is attached to a small ring which can slide without friction on the bars. The string is released from an initial displacement, as shown. The length of the string is d and the wavespeed is c. What time elapses before the string returns to the initial displacement, if (a) the rings are free to move on the bars? (b) one ring is fixed? (c) both rings are fixed?

23–15. A bird lands on a telephone wire stretched between poles 100 ft apart. The impulse the bird produces on the wire results in transverse wave pulses which travel 200 ft/sec. When and in what direction (up or down) will the transverse waves return to the bird to remind him of his landing, if the bird (a) lands in the center of the span? (b) lands $33\frac{1}{3}$ ft from one end? (c) lands 25 ft from one end?

23–16. A wire of mass per unit length $\epsilon = 0.2$ gm/m is fixed at both ends and vibrates in its lowest characteristic mode at 200 cycles/sec. The length of the wire is 1 m. (a) What is the tension? (b) What are the frequencies of modes 2, 3, 4, and 5? (c) If the tension were constant, how should the length of the string be altered such that the lowest mode would vibrate at the frequencies found in part (b)?

23–17. A cord A of mass 200 gm and length 2 m is fastened to a cord B of mass 50 gm and length 1 m. The cords are joined, stretched to a tension of $S = 490$ n, and clamped at the free ends. Thus the combined length is 3 m. (a) Find the ratio between the wavelengths on A and B for vibrations of the same frequency. (b) Find the lowest frequency of a standing wave of the system which would have a node at the junction M.

23–18. What is the total energy of oscillation of the nth characteristic mode of oscillation of a string of length L with a maximum amplitude A? The tension in the string is S.

23–19. A string of length L, which is clamped at both ends and has a tension S, is displaced a distance h at its center and released. (a) What is the energy of the subsequent oscilla-tion? (b) How often will the shape reappear? See Fig. 23–19.

23–20. The initial displacement of a string is

$$y = 10 \sin (\pi x/d) + 5 \sin (3\pi x/d).$$

The lowest characteristic frequency of the string is 25 cycles/sec, and its length is $L = 100$ cm. What is the displacement of the string at $t = 0.01$, 0.02, 0.03, and 0.04 sec?

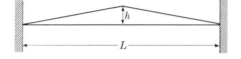

FIGURE 23–19

APPENDICES

APPENDIX A

APPROXIMATE VALUES OF
SOME PHYSICAL CONSTANTS

G, in Newton's gravitational law	$6.67 \cdot 10^{-11}$ n·m^2/kgm^2 or
	$6.67 \cdot 10^{-8}$ dyne·cm^2/gm^2
g, gravitational acceleration (nominal)	9.8 m/sec^2 or
	980 cm/sec^2 or
	32 ft/sec^2
c, velocity of light in vacuum	$3 \cdot 10^8$ m/sec
N_0, Avogadro's number	$6.02 \cdot 10^{23}$ molecules/mole
k, Boltzmann's constant	$1.38 \cdot 10^{-16}$ erg/°K or
	$1.38 \cdot 10^{-23}$ joule/°K
R, gas constant	$8.31 \cdot 10^7$ ergs/mole·°K or
	0.082 liter·atm/mole·°K or
	1.99 cal/mole·°K
M, mass of proton	$1.67 \cdot 10^{-24}$ gm
m, mass of electron	$9.1 \cdot 10^{-28}$ gm
h, Planck's constant	$6.62 \cdot 10^{-27}$ erg·sec
e, electric charge of electron	$1.6 \cdot 10^{-19}$ coul
1 cal, mechanical equivalent of heat	4.1855 joules
1 atm, atmospheric pressure	14.7 lb/in^2 or
	$1.013 \cdot 10^6$ dynes/cm^2

CONVERSION FACTORS

1 inch $= 2.54$ cm
1 foot $= 30.48$ cm
1 angstrom $= 10^{-8}$ cm
1 mile $= 5280$ ft
1 joule $= 10^7$ ergs
1 newton $= 10^5$ ergs $\simeq 0.224$ lb
1 horsepower $= 746$ watts $= 550$ ft·lb/sec

APPENDIX B

SOME APPROXIMATE DATA
REGARDING THE SOLAR SYSTEM

Planet	Mass (earth = 1)	Diameter (earth = 1)	Period (T)	Eccentricity of orbit	Mean distance to sun (earth = 1)
Mercury	0.54	0.38	87.97 da	0.206	0.39
Venus	0.814	0.97	224.7 da	0.007	0.72
Earth	1.0	1.0	365.3 da	0.017	1.0
Mars	0.107	0.52	1.88 yr	0.093	1.52
Jupiter	318.35	10.97	11.86 yr	0.048	5.2
Saturn	95.3	9.03	29.46 yr	0.056	9.54
Uranus	14.58	3.72	84.02 yr	0.047	19.19
Neptune	17.26	3.38	164.79 yr	0.009	30.07
Pluto	0.1	0.45	247.7 yr	0.249	39.51

CONSTANTS OF THE SOLAR SYSTEM

Earth
> Mass $6 \cdot 10^{24}$ kgm
>
> Equatorial radius $6.4 \cdot 10^{6}$ m
>
> Mean distance from sun $1.49 \cdot 10^{11}$ m

Moon
> Mass $7.3 \cdot 10^{22}$ kgm
>
> Radius $1.7 \cdot 10^{6}$ m
>
> Mean distance from earth $3.84 \cdot 10^{8}$ m

Sun
> Mass $2 \cdot 10^{30}$ kgm
>
> Radius $7 \cdot 10^{8}$ m

APPENDIX C

GRAVITATIONAL FORCE OF A SPHERE

We wish to show that the force on a small body outside a uniform sphere of mass M is $F = -G(mM/r^2)$, where r is the distance to the center of the sphere. This can be done if we show that the potential energy of such a mass is $V = -G(mM/r)$. Then the force follows directly from the potential energy, since $F = -\partial V/\partial r$. Recall now our discussion in Chapter 7, where we emphasized that the potential energy which results from many individual forces acting on a body may be obtained simply by adding all the separate potential-energy contributions. Let us, therefore, find the potential energy of a thin spherical shell of radius a. The potential energy from many such shells may then be added. In this development, we shall assume that the density of the matter which makes up any one spherical shell is constant. Consider a ring of width $a\,d\theta$, where a is the radius of the shell. The area of this ring is $2\pi a^2 \sin\theta\,d\theta$, and if the mass per unit area of the shell is ϵ, the mass of the ring is $2\pi a^2 \epsilon \sin\theta\,d\theta$. The potential energy of a mass m located a distance r from the center of the shell is

$$dV = -G\frac{2\pi a^2 \epsilon \sin\theta\,d\theta}{z}m$$

(see Fig. C–1). The distance z is given by the law of cosines:

$$z^2 = r^2 + a^2 - 2ar\cos\theta. \tag{C–1}$$

We shall now integrate over all the thin rings which make up the thin shell and this integration is best done over z rather than θ. From (C–1), we have

$$z\,dz = ar\sin\theta\,d\theta,$$

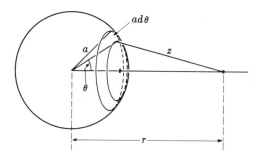

FIGURE C–1

and so for dV, we have

$$dV = -G \frac{2\pi a \epsilon}{r} m \, dz. \tag{C-2}$$

The integration over z must be from $z = r - a$ to $z = r + a$. Thus we have

$$V = -G \frac{2\pi a m}{r} \int_{r-a}^{r+a} dz = -G \frac{4\pi a^2 \epsilon m}{r} = -G \frac{m m_s}{r}, \tag{C-3}$$

where m_s is the mass of the thin shell. Clearly, when we add the effects of all the concentric thin shells which comprise the sphere, we get

$$V = -G \frac{M m}{r}.$$

Note that we have assumed here that the density of the sphere, if it varies at all, varies only with the distance from the center. Our result would not be true if the density were not constant over a given thin shell.

APPENDIX D

TRAJECTORIES IN THE GRAVITATIONAL FIELD

We start with the expression (10–8a) in the text for the force. Next, we insert the known value $F = -FMm/r^2 = -K/r^2 = -Ku^2$, so that $(l^2/m)u^2(u + d^2u/d\theta^2) = Ku^2$. The equation for the trajectory is then

$$\frac{d^2u}{d\theta^2} + u = \frac{Km}{l^2},$$

which, with $w = u - Km/l^2$, reduces to

$$\frac{d^2w}{d\theta^2} = -w. \tag{D–1}$$

(This equation is an old acquaintance. In the study of harmonic motion of Chapter 8, we met this type of equation, except that there, different symbols were used.) We can immediately write the solution as

$$w = A \cos (\theta + \phi),$$

or, introducing u, as

$$u = \frac{1}{r} = A \cos (\theta + \phi) + \frac{Km}{l^2}. \tag{D–2}$$

Equation (D–2) may now be rewritten as

$$r = \frac{b^2/a}{1 + e \cos (\theta + \phi)} = \frac{a(1 - e^2)}{1 + e \cos (\theta + \phi)}, \tag{D–3}$$

where

$$\frac{b^2}{a} = \frac{l^2}{Km} \tag{D–4}$$

and

$$e = \frac{Al^2}{Km}.$$

From analytic geometry we know that Eq. (D–3) represents an ellipse when $e < 1$, a hyperbola when $e > 1$, and a parabola when $e = 1$. So far, we have considered only the elliptic orbits. From our earlier discussion, we conclude that the parabolic and hyperbolic trajectories then should correspond to the escape trajectories and to $H \geq 0$, whereas trapped orbits are only elliptic and circular and correspond to $H < 0$.

Indeed, we can convincingly establish this result by expressing e (and therefore the constant A) in terms of the total energy of the body at the point where the velocity is perpendicular to the minor axis, i.e., at the point where $r = a$. The velocity v_1 at that point can be expressed in terms of the constant angular momentum l as $l = mv_1b$, and thus the kinetic energy is $E_1 = l^2/2mb^2$. Clearly, the potential energy is $V_1 = -K/a$, and the total energy is then $H = l^2/2mb^2 - K/a$. Using Eq. (D–4), we see that this expression for H reduces to $H = -K/2a$, or

$$a = -\frac{K}{2H} = -\frac{GMm}{2H}. \tag{D–5}$$

The value of b then follows from Eq. (D–4):

$$b = l\sqrt{\frac{a}{mK}} = l\sqrt{-\frac{1}{2mH}}. \tag{D–6}$$

The corresponding value of e derived from $e^2 = 1 - b^2/a^2$ becomes

$$e = \sqrt{1 + \frac{2l^2H}{K^2m}}. \tag{D–7}$$

In other words, it is only when $H < 0$ that we have $e < 1$, indicating an elliptic orbit. When $H = 0$, we have $e = 1$ and a parabolic orbit; and when $H > 0$, we have $e > 1$ and a hyperbolic orbit.

It is interesting to observe, from Eq. (D–5), that in the case of an elliptic orbit, the major axis of the elliptic orbit of a given particle is determined *solely by the total energy of the particle*. Also note from Eq. (D–4) that, for a given energy, the minor axis is proportional to the angular momentum l, as we expected.

APPENDIX E

ALPHABETIC LIST OF THE ELEMENTS

Element	Symbol	Atomic number Z	Element	Symbol	Atomic number Z
Actinium	Ac	89	Holmium	Ho	67
Aluminum	Al	13	Hydrogen	H	1
Americium	Am	95	Indium	In	49
Antimony	Sb	51	Iodine	I	53
Argon	A	18	Iridium	Ir	77
Arsenic	As	33	Iron	Fe	26
Astatine	At	85	Krypton	Kr	36
Barium	Ba	56	Lanthanum	La	57
Berkelium	Bk	97	Lead	Pb	82
Beryllium	Be	4	Lithium	Li	3
Bismuth	Bi	83	Lutetium	Lu	71
Boron	B	5	Magnesium	Mg	12
Bromine	Br	35	Manganese	Mn	25
Cadmium	Cd	48	Mendelevium	Md	101
Calcium	Ca	20	Mercury	Hg	80
Californium	Cf	98	Molybdenum	Mo	42
Carbon	C	6	Neodymium	Nd	60
Cerium	Ce	58	Neon	Ne	10
Cesium	Cs	55	Neptunium	Np	93
Chlorine	Cl	17	Nickel	Ni	28
Chromium	Cr	24	Niobium	Nb	41
Cobalt	Co	27	Nitrogen	N	7
Copper	Cu	29	Nobelium	No	102
Curium	Cm	96	Osmium	Os	76
Dysprosium	Dy	66	Oxygen	O	8
Einsteinium	E	99	Palladium	Pd	46
Erbium	Er	68	Phosphorus	P	15
Europium	Eu	63	Platinum	Pt	78
Fermium	Fm	100	Plutonium	Pu	94
Fluorine	F	9	Polonium	Po	84
Francium	Fr	87	Potassium	K	19
Gadolinium	Gd	64	Praseodymium	Pr	59
Gallium	Ga	31	Promethium	Pm	61
Germanium	Ge	32	Protactinium	Pa	91
Gold	Au	79	Radium	Ra	88
Hafnium	Hf	72	Radon	Rn	86
Helium	He	2	Rhenium	Re	75

APPENDIX F

NATURAL TRIGONOMETRIC FUNCTIONS

Angle					Angle				
Degree	Radian	Sine	Cosine	Tan-gent	Degree	Radian	Sine	Cosine	Tan-gent
0°	.000	0.000	1.000	0.000					
1°	.018	.018	1.000	.018	46°	0.803	0.719	0.695	1.036
2°	.035	.035	0.999	.035	47°	.820	.731	.682	1.072
3°	.052	.052	.999	.052	48°	.838	.743	.669	1.111
4°	.070	.070	.998	.070	49°	.855	.755	.656	1.150
5°	.087	.087	.996	.088	50°	.873	.766	.643	1.192
6°	.105	.105	.995	.105	51°	.890	.777	.629	1.235
7°	.122	.122	.993	.123	52°	.908	.788	.616	1.280
8°	.140	.139	.990	.141	53°	.925	.799	.602	1.327
9°	.157	.156	.988	.158	54°	.942	.809	.588	1.376
10°	.175	.174	.985	.176	55°	.960	.819	.574	1.428
11°	.192	.191	.982	.194	56°	.977	.829	.559	1.483
12°	.209	.208	.978	.213	57°	.995	.839	.545	1.540
13°	.227	.225	.974	.231	58°	1.012	.848	.530	1.600
14°	.244	.242	.970	.249	59°	1.030	.857	.515	1.664
15°	.262	.259	.966	.268	60°	1.047	.866	.500	1.732
16°	.279	.276	.961	.287	61°	1.065	.875	.485	1.804
17°	.297	.292	.956	.306	62°	1.082	.883	.470	1.881
18°	.314	.309	.951	.325	63°	1.100	.891	.454	1.963
19°	.332	.326	.946	.344	64°	1.117	.899	.438	2.050
20°	.349	.342	.940	.364	65°	1.134	.906	.423	2.145
21°	.367	.358	.934	.384	66°	1.152	.914	.407	2.246
22°	.384	.375	.927	.404	67°	1.169	.921	.391	2.356
23°	.401	.391	.921	.425	68°	1.187	.927	.375	2.475
24°	.419	.407	.914	.445	69°	1.204	.934	.358	2.605
25°	.436	.423	.906	.466	70°	1.222	.940	.342	2.747
26°	.454	.438	.899	.488	71°	1.239	.946	.326	2.904
27°	.471	.454	.891	.510	72°	1.257	.951	.309	3.078
28°	.489	.470	.883	.532	73°	1.274	.956	.292	3.271
29°	.506	.485	.875	.554	74°	1.292	.961	.276	3.487
30°	.524	.500	.866	.577	75°	1.309	.966	.259	3.732
31°	.541	.515	.857	.601	76°	1.326	.970	.242	4.011
32°	.559	.530	.848	.625	77°	1.344	.974	.225	4.331
33°	.576	.545	.839	.649	78°	1.361	.978	.208	4.705
34°	.593	.559	.829	.675	79°	1.379	.982	.191	5.145
35°	.611	.574	.819	.700	80°	1.396	.985	.174	5.671
36°	.628	.588	.809	.727	81°	1.414	.988	.156	6.314
37°	.646	.602	.799	.754	82°	1.431	.990	.139	7.115
38°	.663	.616	.788	.781	83°	1.449	.993	.122	8.144
39°	.681	.629	.777	.810	84°	1.466	.995	.105	9.514
40°	.698	.643	.766	.839	85°	1.484	.996	.087	11.43
41°	.716	.656	.755	.869	86°	1.501	.998	.070	14.30
42°	.733	.669	.743	.900	87°	1.518	.999	.052	19.08
43°	.751	.682	.731	.933	88°	1.536	.999	.035	28.64
44°	.768	.695	.719	.966	89°	1.553	1.000	.018	57.29
45°	.785	.707	.707	1.000	90°	1.571	1.000	.000	∞

ANSWERS TO
ODD-NUMBERED PROBLEMS

ANSWERS TO ODD-NUMBERED PROBLEMS

CHAPTER 1

1–1. (b) $\bar{v}_{1-2} = -48$ ft/sec, $\bar{v}_{1-1.5} = -40$ ft/sec,
$\bar{v}_{1-1.1} = -33.6$ ft/sec, $\bar{v}_{1-1.01} = -32.16$ ft/sec.
(c) $v_1 = -32$ ft/sec.

1–3. (b) 7 cm. (c) $\bar{v}_{1-2} = 7$ cm/sec, $v_1 = 3$ cm/sec, $v_{1.5} = 6.75$ cm/sec, $v_2 = 12$ cm/sec.

1–5. 32.15 ft/sec^2, 9.754 m/sec^2.

1–7. $|\mathbf{X}| = \sqrt{153}$ mi. Direction 21.8° west of south.

1–9. (a) $\mathbf{A}$, $\mathbf{B}$, and $\mathbf{C}$ are parallel. (b) $\mathbf{B} = 0$. (c) $\mathbf{A}$ perpendicular to $\mathbf{B}$. (d) $\mathbf{A}$ and $\mathbf{B}$ point in opposite directions.

1–11. (a) Straight across, so as to land 3 mi downstream. Time $\frac{1}{5}$ hr. (b) Against the stream at an angle of $\theta = \cos^{-1}(\frac{3}{5}) = 53.2°$ with the bank. Time $\frac{1}{4}$ hr.

1–13. $v_b = \dfrac{93}{1 + 4.4 \cdot 10^{-16}} \simeq 93$ ft/sec.

1–15. $v_{ab} = 0.996c$, $v_{ba} = -0.996c$.

1–17. $\cos \theta = \dfrac{24}{\sqrt{17 \cdot 41}}$; $\theta \simeq 25°$.

CHAPTER 2

2–1. (a) 2 kgm. (b) 2.44 kgm.

CHAPTER 3

3–1. $v_b' = 2$ m/sec opposite to B's initial direction.

3–3. 2370 m/sec.

3–5. $2.72 \cdot 10^7$ cm/sec.

3–7. Cannot happen unless $V_2 = 0$. Then the velocity of the second ball will be zero after the collision for any initial velocity.

3–9. (a) 4 m/sec. (b) 4 m/sec. (c) 8 m/sec and 0 m/sec.

3–11. (a) $\dfrac{2m_a}{m_a + m_b}$. (b) $\dfrac{m_a}{m_a + m_b}$. (c) Upper limit is $v_a' = 2v_b$ when $m_a/m_b = 0$.

3–13. $|v_a'| = \frac{11}{13}v_0$.

3–15. $d = \frac{60}{83}R \simeq 0.72R$ from the earth's center.

3–17. $L/4$.

3–19. (a) 800 dynes. (b) −200 dynes. (c) 0.

3–21. (a) $m_b = 4$ kgm.

3–23. $t_1 = v_0/3g \simeq 0.34$ sec. Separation $2v_0t_1 \simeq 6.8$ m. $t_2 = 3v_0/g \simeq 3.06$ sec. Separation $2v_0t_2 \simeq 61.2$ m. (Note two answers.)

3–25. $\frac{1}{3}$ ft.

3–27. $v = \frac{2}{9}\dfrac{r^2}{\eta}\rho g \simeq 3020$ cm/sec.

3–29. (a) 30 cm from the left wall. (b) 150 m/sec².

3–31. F.

3–33. $T = \dfrac{2m_1m_2}{m_1 + m_2}g$.

3–35. 12.5 lb.

3–37. $v = \sqrt{\dfrac{F}{A\rho}} \simeq 1400$ ft/sec.

3–39. (a) $V = \dfrac{mvN}{Nm + M}$.

CHAPTER 4

4–1. $v_a = 5$ m/sec, $v_b = \sqrt{10}$ m/sec, 34.5°.

4–5. $p = 1.27$ kgm·m/sec, $m = 2.5$ gm.

4–7. (a) $X = 1$, $Y = 3$ m. (b) $V_x = 40$ ft/sec, $V_y = 0$.

4–9. Center of mass is a distance $\pi L/(64 - 4\pi)$ to the left of the center of the plate.

4–15. $K = 37$ n/m; $F_x = 0$, $F_y = -0.327$ n.

4–17. $q = 2.5 \cdot 10^{-6}$ coul.

4–21. (b) $a = g/2$, directed tangentially toward the bottom of the hoop; $F = \omega(3 - \sqrt{3}/2)$ directed radially outward.

4–23. (a) $w_1 \sin\phi_1 = w_2 \sin\phi_2$. (b) $S = w_1 \sin\phi_1 = w_2 \sin\phi_2$, $F_1 = w_1 \cos\phi_1$, $F_2 = w_2 \cos\phi_2$, both directed toward center of cylinder.

4–25. m_1 will be 10 cm from P.

4–27. (a) $(a_A)_x = 2.5$ m/sec²; $(a_B)_x = -\frac{5}{3}$ m/sec²; $(a_B)_y = -\frac{5}{2}$ m/sec²; $(a_C)_y = \frac{15}{8}$ m/sec².
(b) $(a_{AB})_y = -\frac{3}{2}$ m/sec². (c) 0.

4–29. (b) $\tan\theta = \mu$.

4–31. (b) $S = g\cos\theta(\mu_b - \mu_a)m_am_b/(m_a + m_b) = 0.57$ n.

4–33. $a = g\sin\theta - \rho v_0/(m_0 - \rho t)$ until $t = (m_0 - M)/\rho$, then $a = g\sin\theta$ thereafter.

CHAPTER 5

5-1. $t = \sqrt{2h/g}$ in both cases.

5-3. $\tan\theta = 4h/l$, $v_0^2 = \dfrac{gl^2}{8h}\left[1 + \left(\dfrac{4h}{l}\right)^2\right]$.

5-5. $\tan\theta_1 = 1$ and $\tan\theta_2 = 3$ $\quad(\theta_1 = 45°, \theta_2 \simeq 71.6°)$.

5-7. $T = 2\pi\sqrt{(R+h)/g} \simeq 1.44$ hr. From a point on the earth in the plane of the orbit, the satellite should be visible for a time $t = T\theta/\pi$, where $\theta = \cos^{-1}(R/R+h)$.

5-9. $\dfrac{1}{2\pi}\sqrt{10g/R} \simeq 0.735$ cycle/sec $\simeq 44$ rev/min.

5-11. $v = \sqrt{rg/\mu} \simeq 14$ m/sec.

5-13. (a) $v = \sqrt{\mu gr}$. (b) $\tan\theta = v^2/rg$.

5-15. About $1.6 \cdot 10^8$ cm/sec.

5-17. $v'_x = v$, $v'_y = Eqx_0/mv$; $v'^2 = v^2 + (Eqx_0/mv)^2$.

5-19. Same as in 5-18 except that the pitch increases with time, since the particle has an acceleration (Eq/m) in the direction of the field.

5-21. Particle turns when $t = t_0[1 + (\frac{3}{2})^{1/3}]$ at the position

$$x = \frac{F_0 t_0^2}{2m}[1 + \tfrac{1}{2}(\tfrac{3}{2})^{1/3}].$$

5-23. $F = (2\pi)^2 mR/T^2 \simeq 3.5 \cdot 10^{21}$, $n \simeq 0.76 \cdot 10^{21}$ lb $(\simeq 3.8 \cdot 10^{16}$ ropes$)$.

CHAPTER 6

6-1. (a) $J = mg\,\Delta t = 19.6$ n·sec in both first and second second. After t sec $J = 19.6\,t$ n·sec.

(b) 19.6 kgm·m/sec, $t = 1$ sec.
39.2 kgm·m/sec, $t = 2$ sec.
$J = mgt = 19.6t$ kgm·m/sec.

(c) $J = m\sqrt{2gh} = 88.4$ n·sec.

$\bar{F} = \dfrac{J}{\Delta t} = 442$ n.

6-3. (a) $J \simeq 6.18$ n·sec at an angle of $-\tan^{-1}\frac{1}{4}$ from x-axis.

(b) $v \simeq 6.94$ m/sec at an angle of $+\tan^{-1}\frac{17}{12}$ from x-axis.

6-5. (a) $p = (5/\pi)(1 - \cos 4\pi t)$ n·sec.

(b) $J = 20/\pi$ n·sec.

(c) $J = 0$.

6-7. $J = 0.435$ lb·sec, $\bar{F} = 43.5$ lb.

6-9. $\Delta p = 50$ gm·cm/sec in each case.

Final velocities are: sand, $V = 5 \cdot 10^6$ cm/sec,
ice, $V = 50$ cm/sec,
auto, $V = 5 \cdot 10^{-5}$ cm/sec. $\quad$ (cont.)

Kinetic energy acquired: sand $= 1.25 \cdot 10^8$ ergs,
$$\text{ice} \quad = 1250 \text{ ergs},$$
$$\text{auto} = 1.25 \cdot 10^{-3} \text{ erg}.$$

6–11. (a) Small. (b) 3.21 m/sec. No. (c) No.

6–13. $F = 4000$ n, $P = 1.6 \cdot 10^6 \sqrt{x}$ joules/sec.

6–15. (a) $E = 2mgr = 1.96 \cdot 10^5$ ergs.
 (b) The normal force is always perpendicular to v.
 (c) No. Note that *net* work by components is zero.

6.17. $\Delta E = 3x_0(4F_0 + mg)$,
$$\bar{P} = \frac{\Delta E}{\Delta t} = \frac{3x_0}{t_0}(4F_0 + mg).$$

6–19. When calculated nonrelativistically, $v' = 3.95c$, where $c = 3 \cdot 10^{10}$ cm/sec is the speed of light. The correct speed, relativistically calculated, is $v = 0.9935c$.

6–23. $v_A = J/m$ toward B,
$$E = \frac{J^2}{2m},$$
$$V_0 = \frac{J}{2m}.$$

6–25. $V_i = \dfrac{m_1 + m_2}{m_1}\left[2\mu gx + \dfrac{Kx^2}{m_1 + m_2}\right]^{1/2}.$

6–27. (a) $dp/dt = 20$ dynes. (b) $F_b = \sqrt{500}$ dynes. (c) 39 cm.
 (d) 780 ergs.

6–29. $E = 2K^2/mv_0^2 \, d^2$

6–31. (a) $F = 10$ n. (b) $t = \frac{3}{20}$ sec.

6–33. (a) $v = 600$ cm/sec. (b) 0.98.

6–35. $T = \sqrt{h/g}\left(\sqrt{2} - 2 + \dfrac{2}{1 - \sqrt{1 - e}}\right).$

6–37. $x = Ft^2/2m.$ $x = 2\sqrt{2P/m}\, t^{3/2}/3.$

6–39. $\Delta E = 33$ joules.

CHAPTER 7

7–1. (a) $K = mv^2/x^2 = 200$ n/m. (c) $J = 2mv = 2$ n·sec.

7–3. If $y = 0$ and $V = 0$ at the water surface and if two surfaces of the cube are always horizontal, we get

$$V_1 = d^3\rho g y \qquad\qquad\qquad (y > d/2),$$
$$V_2 = d^3 gy(\rho - \rho_0/2) + d^2\rho_0 gy^2/4 \qquad (-d/2 < y < d/2),$$
$$V_3 = d^3 gy(\rho - \rho_0) \qquad\qquad (y < -d/2),$$

where d is the side length of the cube and ρ_0 is the density of water.

7–5. $E_a = 8$, $E_b = 12$, $E_c = 6$ ergs.

7–7. $S = mg \cos \theta + mv^2/l = (2H/l) + mg(3 \cos \theta - 2)$, where H is the total mechanical energy and l the length of the pendulum. The tension can be zero only when $mgl < H < \frac{5}{2}mgl$ and the angle is given by $\cos \theta = -\frac{2}{3}[(H/mgl) - 1]$.

7–9. (a) $F_x = -Kx + \dfrac{C}{L - x}$.   (b) $V = \dfrac{Kx^2}{2} + C \ln \left(\dfrac{L - x}{L} \right)$.

(c) $x = \dfrac{L}{2} \left(1 \pm \dfrac{\sqrt{5}}{3} \right)$.   (d) $H = V_{\max} = \frac{5}{36}KL^2(\frac{5}{2} - \ln 6)$.

7–11. (a) $E_1 = \dfrac{GM_e}{R} \left(1 - \dfrac{R}{r_e} \right) - \dfrac{GM_m}{r_e} \left(1 - \dfrac{r_e}{D - r_e} \right)$.

(b) $E_2 = \dfrac{GM_e}{R} \left(1 - \dfrac{R}{r_e} \right) + \dfrac{GM_m}{D + R} \left(1 - \dfrac{D + R}{D + r_e} \right)$,

where R = earth radius. (Other notations, see Problem 7–10.)

7–13. $v = 2\pi D/T \simeq 10^3$ m/sec,
$r_2 = 2D \simeq 7.68 \cdot 10^8$ m (D = earth-moon distance).

7–15. (a) $18 \cdot 10^4$ ft·lb.   (b) 900 lb.

7–17. (a) 7 lb.   (b) 350 ft·lb.   (c) 50 ft/sec.

7–19. (a) $F_x = -12x + 9x^2$.   (b) $\frac{32}{9}$ joules.

(c) $t = \displaystyle\int_0^{x_1} \sqrt{\dfrac{m}{2(H - V)}} \, dx$.

7–21. (a) $V = -mgR(1 - \cos \theta) + \frac{1}{8}KR^2[\sqrt{1 + 4(1 - \cos \theta)} - 1]^2$.

(b) $(mv^2/2)_{\min} = \dfrac{KR^2}{2} - 2mgR$.

(c) $N_1 = 5mg - KR$, $N_2 = KR - mg$.

Problem possible only if $4mg/R < K < 5mg/R$.

7–27. (a) $m_b = m_a$.   (b) $m_a > m_b$.   (c) $m_a < m_b$.

7–29. (a) $V = 10$ cm/sec.   (b) $P = 20$ gm·cm/sec.   (c) $10(1 + \sqrt{2})$ and $10(1 - \sqrt{2})$ cm/sec.

7–31. Motion in same direction, $\Delta E = 2.5 \cdot 10^3$ ergs.
Motion in opposite direction, $\Delta E = -0.5 \cdot 10^3$ ergs.

CHAPTER 8

8–5. $K = 4 \cdot 10^5$ dynes/cm.

8–7. $K \simeq 600$ lb/ft.

8–9. (a) $x = L(2K_2 + K_1)/(K_2 + K_1)$, where x is measured from left wall.
(b) $\omega = \sqrt{(K_1 + K_2)/m}$.

8–11. No. Period would become shorter for larger amplitudes.

8–15. $x = 10 \cos \pi/4 = 7.07$ cm, $v = -v_0 \sin \pi/4 = -890$ cm/sec, $K = 1.6 \cdot 10^5$ dynes/cm.

8–17. $J = 1$ n·sec, $J = 0.41$ n·sec.

8–19. (a) $x_1/x_2 = 4$, (b) $\omega_1/\omega_2 = \frac{1}{2}$, (c) $E_1/E_2 = \frac{1}{4}$.

8–21. (a) $v = 2$ ft/sec. (b) $a = 4$ ft/sec^2, directed along the tangent to the circular path. (c) $T = 4\pi$ sec.

8–23. $\omega_p/\omega_e = 2\sqrt{2}$.

8–25. (a) The period increases.

(b) $$T = 4 \int_0^{\theta_0} \frac{d\theta}{\sqrt{(2g/l)(\cos \theta - \cos \theta_0)}}.$$

(c) $$T = 4 \int_0^{x_0} \sqrt{\frac{m}{2[H - V(x)]}}\, dx, \text{ where } V(x) = \frac{K}{2}(\sqrt{l^2 + x^2} - l)^2,$$

$H = V(x_0)$, and l, the relaxed length of the spring, is the distance from the spring pivot to the origin.

8–27. (a) Body 1 moves d to the right. (b) $V_0 = \sqrt{K/m}\, d/2$, $x_0 = d/2$.

8–29. (a) $\omega_0 = 10$ sec^{-1}. (b) $Q = 30\pi$, $\tau = 6\pi$ sec. (c) $R = \frac{1}{3}\pi$ n·sec/cm. (d) $F_f = Rv \simeq \frac{1}{3}\pi$ n when the mass crosses the equilibrium position the first time.

8–33. (a) $F_1 = Kx_0 \cos \omega t$. (b) $F_2 = -m\omega^2 x_0 \cos \omega t$.
(c) $F_3 = m(\omega_0^2 - \omega^2)x_0 \cos \omega t$. (d) 0. (e) System behaves as in (b).

8–35. $x_0 = 0.00405, 0.021, 0.0405, 0.00134$ ft;
$F_0 = Kx_0$, where $K = 1.23 \cdot 10^4$ lb/ft.

8–37. (a) $T = 2\pi\sqrt{l/g} \simeq 3.45$ sec.
(b) $\theta_0 = 0.0185$ rad.
(e) Bullet should be fired when pendulum is at $\theta = 0$, moving in same direction as bullet.

8–39. (a) $x = \dfrac{x_0}{1 - (\omega^2/\omega_0^2)} \sin \omega t$. (b) $4x_0/3$. (c) $f = 1.32f_0$.

(d) $F_s = -\dfrac{m\omega^2 x_0}{1 - (\omega^2/\omega_0^2)} \sin \omega t$.

CHAPTER 9

9–1. (a) $p_\theta \simeq 20, 14.1, 1.67, 0.1$ kgm·m/sec. (b) $p_\theta r = 10$ kgm·m^2/sec.

9–3. All impulses are directed toward 0 and have the following magnitudes in kgm·m/sec:

$$J_a = \sqrt{116}, \ J_b = \sqrt{\tfrac{89}{2}}, \ p_c = p_b, \ p_d = p_a.$$

9–5. $R = l^2/mA$.

9–7. (a) $\omega = (r_0/r)^2\omega_0$.   (b) $3m(r_0\omega_0)^2/2$.

9–9. (a) 500 cm²/sec.   (b) 3000 gm·cm²/sec.
     (c) 0.05, 0.735, 0.10, 0.0735 sec⁻¹.

9–15. (a) Center of mass velocity $m_2v_0/(m_1 + m_2)$.   Rotation about the center of mass with an angular velocity $\omega = v_0/d$.   (b) $S = \mu v_0^2/d$, where μ is the reduced mass: $\mu = m_1m_2/(m_1 + m_2)$.

9–17. (a) $(\frac{35}{36})(ML^2/3)$.   (b) $ML^2/3$.

9–19. $R/\sqrt{2}, \; L/\sqrt{3}, \; L/\sqrt{12}$.

9–21. (a) 28 kgm·m²/sec.   (b) 0.

9–23. (a) $p_x = 50\sqrt{3}, \; p_y = 50$ kgm·m/sec.
     (b) $l = -50(4\sqrt{3} - 3)$ kgm·m²/sec.

9–25. (a) $l_x = -21, \; l_y = -9, \; l_z = 13, \; l = \sqrt{691}$.
     (b) $d = \sqrt{691}/\sqrt{14}$.
     (c) Angular momentum is zero about any point on the line of motion.

9–33. (a) $L_x = 6, \; L_z = -4, \; L = \sqrt{52}$ kgm·m²/sec. (b) No.

9–35. No. Yes.

9–37. $\tau_x = -13, \; \tau_y = 14, \; \tau_z = 4, \; \tau = 19.5$ n·m, $\cos\theta_x = -0.665$, $\cos\theta_y = 0.72, \; \cos\theta_z = 0.0205$.

9–41. No.

9–43. Yes.

CHAPTER 10

10–1. $\rho = 3g/4\pi RG = 5450$ kgm/m³ $= 5.45$ gm/cm³.

10–5. (a) $F = Gm^2/4r^2 = 0.04$ n $\simeq 0.0088$ lb.
     (b) $V = 0.0752$ joule.
     (c) $v = 1.26 \cdot 10^{-3}$ m/sec.

10–7. $v = \sqrt{GM/R} = 7900$ m/sec, $T = 2\pi R/v = 5080$ sec, $t = 255$ sec.

10–9. (a) $a = 4850$ mi.   (b) $e = 0.134$.
     (c) $H = -GMm/2a = -mgR^2/2a = -2.61 \cdot 10^8$ ft·lb.
     (d) $v_a = 2.06 \cdot 10^4$ ft/sec.   (e) $v_p = 2.7 \cdot 10^4$ ft/sec.
     (f) $l = 5.58 \cdot 10^{11}$ slug·ft²/sec.

10–11. $v = \sqrt{GM/R}$.

10–13. (a) $H_A/H_B = 4$, but note that A has the larger total mechanical energy.   (b) $T_A/T_B = \frac{1}{8}$.

10–17. $H = -GMm/2R, \; l = m\sqrt{GMR}\sin\phi, \; a = R, \; b = \sqrt{2}\,R\sin\phi$, $\cos\theta_1 = -\cos 2\phi$.

10–19. $r \leq 5.7 \cdot 10^{-12}$ cm.

10–21. (a) $a = 2.55 \cdot 10^{-12}$ cm. (b) $n = 3.9 \cdot 10^{18}$. (c) $t = 2.65 \cdot 10^{-3}$ cm.

CHAPTER 11

11–1. 2.5 and −2.5.

11–3. (a) $E' = 13.5$ ft·lb, $E = 67.5$ ft·lb.
(b) $E' = 13.5$, $E = 121.5$.
(c) $E' = 13.5$, $E = 13.5$.
(d) Toward the rear, with a speed $v' = 6$ ft/sec.

11–5. $\tan \theta' = \dfrac{v \sin \theta}{v \cos \theta - V} = \dfrac{1}{\sqrt{3} - 1}$, $\theta' \simeq 54°$.

11–7. (a) $V = \dfrac{m_a}{m_a + m_b} v_a.$

(b) $v_a^* = \dfrac{m_b}{m_a + m_b} v_a,$ $v_b^* = -\dfrac{m_a}{m_a + m_b} v_a.$

(c) $v_a^{*\prime} = -\dfrac{m_b}{m_a + m_b},$ $v_b^{*\prime} = \dfrac{m_a}{m_a + m_b} v_a.$

(d) $v_a' = \dfrac{m_a - m_b}{m_a + m_b} v_a,$ $v_b' = \dfrac{2m_a}{m_a + m_b} v_a.$

(e) $E_a^{*\prime} = \left(\dfrac{m_a m_b}{m_a + m_b}\right)^2 \dfrac{v_a^2}{2m_b},$ $E_b^{*\prime} = \left(\dfrac{m_a m_b}{m_a + m_b}\right)^2 \dfrac{v_a^2}{2m_b};$

$E_a' = \left(\dfrac{m_a - m_b}{m_a + m_b}\right)^2 \dfrac{m_a v_a^2}{2},$ $E_b' = \dfrac{4 m_a m_b}{(m_a + m_b)^2} \dfrac{m_a v_a^2}{2}.$

11–9. Energy lost is E^* (see Problem 8).

11–15. (a) Toward the rear of the train. (b) $t = \sqrt{2h/g} \simeq 0.43$ sec.
(c) 0.93 ft toward rear.

11–17. (a) Interaction force in the direction of motion is the spring force $F_x = -Kx$. Inertial force $- m\mathbf{a}$, opposite to the acceleration. (b) $x_{\max} = 2ma/K$. (c) Harmonic motion. Amplitude $x_0 = ma/K$. (d) $2ma - ma \cos \omega t$.

11–19. (a) Interaction forces: gravity and tension in the string. Inertial force: $mg \sin \theta$ directed opposite the acceleration of car. (b) $mg \sin \theta$, $s \sin \alpha$, $-mg \sin \theta$. (c) $\alpha = 0$. (d) $mg \cos \theta$. (e) Oscillatory. (f) $T = 2\pi\sqrt{l/g \cos \theta}$, amplitude θ.

11–21. $T = 2\pi\sqrt{R^3/GM} = T_0$, where T_0 is the orbital period.

11–25. (a) $F_r = -GmM/R^2 = -m\omega^2 R$. (b) $m\omega_r^2$, where R and r are the distances from the center of the earth to the object and to the origin of the satellite coordinate system respectively. (c) No. Only when the object is at the center of the coordinate system.

11–29. $f = (1/2\pi)\sqrt{g/R} \simeq 0.2$ rev/sec $= 12$ rev/min.

11–31. $v' = g/2\omega \simeq 6.75 \cdot 10^4$ m/sec.

11–33. $v' \simeq \omega R/2$.

11–35. $2m\omega v' \sin \lambda \simeq 45$ lb.

11–37. $x = (\omega g/3)(2h/g)^{3/2}$.

11–39. (a) $F_r = -[(GmM/R^3) - m\omega^2]r$.
(b) $T = \pi\sqrt{R^3/(GM - R^3\omega^2)}$.
(c) $|F_c| = 2m\omega R\sqrt{(GM/R^3) - \omega^2}$.

CHAPTER 12

12–1. 6, 5.

12–3. Circular, with $v = 12.3$ m/sec.

12–5. (a) $V_x = 3$ m/sec, $V_y = 0, \omega = 0$.
(b) $V_x = 1.5$ m/sec, $V_y = 0, \omega = -1.5$ sec^{-1}.
(c) $V_x = 2$ m/sec, $V_y = 0, \omega = -1$ sec^{-1}.
(d) $V_x = 3$ m/sec, $V_y = 3$ m/sec, $\omega = -1$ sec^{-1}.

12–9. (a) $a_x = a_y = 6F/m$.   (b) $a_x = 5F/m, a_y = 2F/m$.
(c) $a_x = 2F/m, a_y = 2F/m$.   (d) $a_x = 25F/m, a_y = 24F/m$.

12–13. A point $L/6$ from the center, measured toward the free end.

12–15. 4:1.

12–17. (a) $V = A \Delta t = F \Delta t/[M + (4mk^2/r^2)]$, where M is mass of car including wheels. $M_{\text{eff}} = M + 4mk^2/r^2$.

(b) $V^2 = 2F \Delta x/[M + (4mk^2/r^2)]$. M_{eff} as in part (a).

12–19. (a) $a = -4g/5$. (b) $T = mg/5$. (c) $v = 4\sqrt{gR}$.

12–21. $h = \pi^2 R^2 g/8V^2$.

12–23. $x = L/2\sqrt{3} = 0.866$ m from the center of mass.

12–25. Yes.

12–27. (a) $V = v/2$. (b) $L = mvr/2$. (c) $\omega = v/3r$. (d) $mv^2/6$.

12–29. (a) $\omega = mv_0/MR = \frac{4}{3}$ sec^{-1}.   (b) 0.   (c) Eventually wheel will come to rest, and locomotive will have speed v_0.

12–31. (b) $a = 2F(1 - \mu)/3M$.

12–33. $\omega^2 = 16g/3R$. Center of mass reaches $5R/12$ rather than $R/2$.

12–35. (a) $T = 2\pi\sqrt{2R/g}$. (b) $T = 2\pi\sqrt{3R/2g}$.
(c) $\omega^2 = 2g/R, \omega^2 = 8g/3R$.

12–37. (a) $F_x = 0, F_y = Mg/4$.

(b) $F_y = Mg + \dfrac{3Mg}{2}\left[\cos^2\theta - \dfrac{\sin^2\theta}{2}\right], F_x = -\dfrac{9Mg}{4}\cos\theta\sin\theta$.

12–39. (a) $MVL/2$. (b) $\omega = 3V/2L$. (c) $\frac{1}{4}$.

12–41. $240/9\pi$ ft·lb.

12–43. (a) $\omega_a = \dfrac{\sqrt{g/R}}{\sqrt{1+(r^2/2r^2)}}$.　(b) $\omega_b = \sqrt{g/R}$.　(c) $\omega_c = \sqrt{2g/3R}$.

12–45. From wall, $F_x = 2300\sqrt{3}$ lb, $F_y = -1000$;
　　　　from cable, $F_x = -2300\sqrt{3}$, $F_y = 2300$ lb.

12–47. $S = 1150$ lb.

12–49. $\tau = MgR \sin\theta$.

12–51. (a) $\mu \geq \frac{3}{20}$.　(b) $F_x = 72/5$ lb, $F_y = 121/5$ lb.

CHAPTER 13

13–1. (a) $l_1 = l_z = m_1\omega\, d^2$, $l_2 = l_x = m_2\omega\, d^2/2$.
　　　　Total $|1| = \sqrt{l_x^2 + l_z^2}$.
　　(b) $\Delta l_{1x} = m\omega\, d^2(4 - \sqrt{2})/8$, $\Delta l_{1z} = -m\omega\, d^2/4\sqrt{2}$, $\Delta l_2 = -\Delta l_1$.
　　(c) Same.
　　(d) $\tan\theta = (4 - \sqrt{2})/(8 - \sqrt{2})$ where θ is the angle between l_1' and
the z-axis in the xz-plane.

13–3. (a) $l_z = mR^2\omega/2$, $l_x = mR^2\omega/2$.　(b) $\Delta l_x = mR^2\omega$.
　　(c) $|1| = \sqrt{5}\, mR^2\omega/2$.

13–5. $\Omega = 2gd/R^2\omega \simeq 0.1$ sec^{-1}.

13–7. Angular deviation $\Delta\theta = \tau\,\Delta t/l \simeq 0.13$ (7.6°).

13–9. $|1| = \sqrt{(I_0\omega)^2 + (mv\, d)^2}$, where $I_0 = mR^2/2$ and $v = \sqrt{2g\, d}$.

13–11. $\omega_2 < gd/2k^2\omega_1$.

13–13. (a) $mR^2/2$, $m[(R^2/4) + (d^2/12)]$; $4mr^2/5$, $2mR^2 + (4mr^2/5)$,　where
$2R$ is the distance between the spheres of radius r and mass m.
　　(b) $d = \sqrt{3}\, R$.

13–15. (a) $-y = \frac{4}{3}$ ft.
　　(b) $L_x = 170/6$, $L_y = 5$ slug·ft^2/sec at the instant shown.
　　(c) $x = 1.5$ ft.

13–17. (a) Vertical direction.
　　(b) $\omega \sin\theta$ and $\omega \cos\theta$.
　　(c) $l = (Md^2/3)\omega \sin\theta$ in the vertical plane perpendicular to the bar.
　　(d) $(Md^2/3)\omega^2 \sin\theta \cos\theta$.

CHAPTER 14

14–1. (a) Low in the 0 to 100°C region, high in the 100 to 500°C region.
　　(b) 0°and 100°C.

14–5. $m(T - 100) = 113,000$, where m is mass of copper in grams and T
is its temperature. A kilogram of copper would have to be at 213°C.

14–9. 200 sec.

14–11. (a) $T = 83°C$. (b) $0.115 \, \text{gm/min}$.

14–13. (a) $dT/dr = -31.3 \, \text{deg/cm}$. (b) $q = 0.0395 \, \text{cal/cm·sec}$.

14–17. $\Delta T = (T_1 - T_2)e^{-t/\tau}$, $\tau = Lmc/2KA$.

14–19. $363 \, \text{watts/m}^2$.

CHAPTER 15

15–1. $m_m/m_0 = 1.52 \, n_0/n_m$, where n_0 and n_m are integers.

15–3. $d = (M/N_0\rho)^{1/3}$. With $\rho = 1.43 \cdot 10^{-3} \, \text{gm/cm}^3$ we get $d \simeq 3 \cdot 10^{-7}$, 10^{-7}, $8 \cdot 10^{-6}$, $3.5 \cdot 10^{-7}$ cm.

15–5. $2N_0$; $6N_0$; $N_0/238$, where $N_0 = 6 \cdot 10^{23}$.

15–7. $M/\rho \simeq 7.2 \, \text{cm}^3$.

CHAPTER 16

16–1. (a) $2mv$.
   (b) $Nv/6l$ molecular collisions with each wall per second.
   (c) $Nmv^2/3l$, $Nmv^2/3l$, $Nmv^2/3l^3$.
   (d) $P = Nmv^2/3V$.
   (e) $mv^2/2 = 3kT/2$.

16–3 (a) $2nmv^2 \cos^2 \phi$. (b) $(\sin \phi \, d\phi)/2$.

16–5. (a) 1. (b) 4.

16–7. $4.7 \cdot 10^4$, $9.95 \cdot 10^4$, $3.66 \cdot 10^4$ cm/sec.

16–9. $E \simeq 10^{-46}$ erg, $kT \simeq 4 \cdot 10^{-14}$ erg.

16–11. $1.5 \cdot 10^9$ sec or about 50 yr.

16–13. $l = 1/4\pi\sqrt{2}(r_1 + r_2)^2 n$.

16–17. 0.085, independent of temperature.

16–21. $2 \cdot 10^{-6}$ dyne.

16–23. (a) $1.06 \cdot 10^{-27}$ erg·sec, $2.12 \cdot 10^{-27}$ sec^{-1}.
   (b) $n = 2.95 \cdot 10^{27}$.
   (c) $1 + 0.34 \cdot 10^{-27}$ rev/sec.

16–29. $r = 3\bar{v} \, \Delta t/4$, where $\Delta t = 1$ sec.

16–31. (a) $3.1 \cdot 10^{-15} \, \text{cm}^2$. (b) $1.1 \cdot 10^{-9}$ gm.

CHAPTER 17

17–3. Net work = net heat absorbed.

17–7. $\Delta T \simeq 0.12°C$.

17-9. (a) New volume $V_1 = V[1 + (mg/AP)]^{-1/\gamma}$.

(b) $V_2 = V[1 - (mg/AP)]^{-1/\gamma}$.

(c) Work by gravity $(mg/A)(V - V_1)$ and $(mg/A)(V_2 - V)$;

$T_1 = T[1 + (mg/AP)]^{(\gamma-1)/\gamma}$,

$T_2 = T[1 - (mg/AP)]^{(\gamma-1)/\gamma}$,

where $\gamma = \frac{7}{5}$ and $P = RT/V$.

17-11. $P_2 = 5^{1/\gamma} = 5^{3/5} \simeq 2.62$ atm.

17-13. $\Delta Q = \mu C_p \Delta T = \frac{5}{2}(P_1 V_1/T_1)\Delta T \simeq 1.9$ cal (He) and $\frac{7}{2}(P_1 V_1/T_1)\Delta T \simeq 2.65$ cal (O_2).

17-15. $\omega_0 = \sqrt{(A^2/Vm)(\gamma_0 + \gamma_H)P}$ $(\gamma_0 = \frac{7}{5}; \gamma_H = \frac{5}{3})$.

CHAPTER 18

18-5. (a) $T = 107°C$. (b) $T = 130.4°C$.

18-7. The second day.

18-11. (a) $\sigma = L\rho a_0/2$. (b) $\Delta L = L^2 \rho a_0/2Y$.

(c) $\sigma = 3.9 \cdot 10^6$ dynes/cm^2, $\Delta L = 3.9 \cdot 10^{-4}$ cm.

18-13. $\sigma = \dfrac{\rho \omega^2}{3r}(R^3 - r^3)$.

18-15. (a) $d \simeq 2.3 \cdot 10^{-8}$ cm.

(b) $K \simeq 4.6 \cdot 10^4$ dynes/cm, $f_0 \simeq 3.34 \cdot 10^{12}$ sec^{-1}.

(c) $1.35 \cdot 10^{-9}$ cm.

(d) $597°C$.

18-17. $\kappa = 3(1 - 2\mu)/Y$.

18-19. $1.5 \cdot 10^{-3}K$ cal.

18-23. $\Delta L = 1.3 \cdot 10^{-2}$ cm, $\sigma = 3.1 \cdot 10^8$ dynes.

CHAPTER 19

19-13. $\oint P\, dV$ = net work output and $\oint T\, dS = \oint dQ$ = net heat input.

19-17. (a) $\Delta S_1 = \mu C_v \ln [1 - (\Delta T/T)]$.

(b) $\Delta S_2 = \mu C_v \ln [1 + (\Delta T/T)]$, where μ = number of moles.

(c) $\Delta S = -\mu C_v (\Delta T/T)^2 \simeq -1.4 \cdot 10^{-16}$ erg/°K.

(d) $X_1/X_2 \simeq e \simeq 2.73$.

19-19. (a) $g \simeq 2650$ cm·sec^{-2}.

(b) $h_A \simeq 2.5 \cdot 10^5$ cm (1.55 mi), $h_{He} \simeq 1.06 \cdot 10^6$ cm (6.6 mi).

19-21. (a) $6 \cdot 10^{23} \exp(-1.2 \cdot 10^{16})$.

CHAPTER 20

20-1. (a) Bar vertical and above the pivot is stable if $\rho < \rho_0$, where ρ is the density of wood and ρ_0 is the density of water. Bar vertical and below the pivot is unstable.

(b) $\omega_0 = \sqrt{3g(\rho_0 - \rho)/2L\rho}$.

20–3. 0°.

20–5. (b) Balloon moves in the direction of acceleration.

20–7. $u = Q/2\pi\rho r$.

20–11. $u = \sqrt{2gh}$

20–13. $a = 2A\rho gH/(m_0 + M_0)$.

CHAPTER 21

21–1. (a) 9 m/sec. (c) $\frac{2}{3}$ sec. (d) $2\sqrt{6}/9 \simeq 0.54$ sec.

21–3. (a) $l_a = \frac{5}{3}l$, $l_b = \frac{7}{3}l$. (b)$\sqrt{\frac{5}{7}}$.

21–5. (a) $6\sqrt{4.5} \simeq 12.7$ m/sec. (c) $0.4\sqrt{4.5} \simeq 0.85$ n·sec.
      (d) $\sqrt{m/K} = 1/\sqrt{27}$ sec.

21–7. $4.7 \cdot 10^3$, $5 \cdot 10^3$, $1.1 \cdot 10^3$, $3.7 \cdot 10^3$ m/sec.

21–9. (a) $\Delta t = \dfrac{2m(v_1 - v_2)}{A\rho c(v_1 + v_2)} \simeq 0.8 \cdot 10^{-4}$ sec

      $(v_1 = 10, v_2 = -2$ m/sec$)$.

   (b) $l > \dfrac{c\,\Delta t}{2} = \dfrac{m(v_1 - v_2)}{A\rho(v_1 + v_2)} \simeq 0.2$ m.

   (c) $V = v_1 + v_2 = 8$ m/sec.

21–13. (a) $2.4 \cdot 10^3$ cm/sec. (b) $\delta \simeq 0.7\rho_0$, $\theta \simeq 0.28 \cdot T_0$.

CHAPTER 22

22–3. (a) $l = 10$ m. (b) $u = +40$ m/sec on the leading sides, -40 m/sec on the lagging sides. (d) Triangle of height 40 cm, base 1 m. Particle velocity is everywhere instantaneously zero.

22–5. (d) $\frac{3}{40}$ joule, 0.

22–7. (a) $z_0 = 0.32$ cm for steel, $z_0 = 47$ cm for air.
      (b) $H = A\rho c z_0^2/3t_0$, $H = 1.3 \cdot 10^7 z_0^2$ ergs for steel,
      $H = 1.5 \cdot 10^2 z_0^2$ ergs for air.
      (c) Yes.

22–9. $y_0 = 0.25$ m, $\lambda = 2$ m, $c = 5$ m/sec, $f = 0.4$ sec^{-1},
      $F_0 = 0.3\pi$, $\overline{R} = 0.3\pi^2$ watts, $h = 0.06\pi^2$ joules/m.

22–11. $I \simeq 27.3 \cdot 10^7$ ergs·cm^{-2}·sec^{-1} $= 27.3$ watts·cm^{-2}.

22–13. $z_0 = 1.1 \cdot 10^{-7}$ cm.

22–15. (a) $\omega_0 = \sqrt{K/m} = 40$ sec^{-1}.
      (b) The string has the effect of a friction or drag force, $F = -Ru = -5u$, where u is the velocity.
      (c) $Q = \omega_0 m/R = 16$.

CHAPTER 23

23–1. (a) $\epsilon_a = \frac{1}{2}$, $\epsilon_b = \frac{1}{8}$ kgm/m.
  (b) $u_t = \frac{8}{3}$ m/sec, $u_r = \frac{2}{3}$ m/sec.
  (d) $\frac{8}{9}$ and $\frac{1}{9}$.

23–3. $E_t/E_i \simeq 4/r \simeq 1.2 \cdot 10^{-3}$.

23–5. (a) 82 joules. (b) 82 joules. (c) In (a).

23–7. (a) $\frac{15}{16}$, $\frac{1}{16}$. (b) 1 sec.

23–13. (a) Traveling waves to the left of A and to the right of B. Standing wave between A and B.
  (b) $2p_m \cos \pi d/\lambda$, $4A/\rho cp_m^2 \cos(2\pi d/\lambda)$, where A = area.
  (c) $2p_m$.
  (e) $2p_m \sin \pi d/\lambda$, $2p_m$.

23–15. (a) $\frac{1}{2}$ sec (up), 1 sec (down), etc.
  (b) $\frac{2}{3}$ sec (up), $\frac{4}{3}$ sec (up), 1 sec (down), etc.
  (c) $\frac{1}{4}$ sec (up), $\frac{3}{4}$ sec (up), 1 sec (down), etc.

23–17. (a) $\lambda_a/\lambda_b = 1/2\sqrt{2}$. (b) $f = 70/\sqrt{2}$ cycles/sec.

23–19. (a) $(2S/L)h^2$. (b) $c/2L$ times per sec.

INDEX